Formula 1
FACTS & TRIVIA

THOUSANDS OF FASCINATING FACTS AND QUESTIONS FOR EVERY FORMULA 1 FAN

WRITTEN AND COMPILED BY
ANNA O'BRIEN

SIENA

This edition published and distributed by Siena

This edition published 1999
Siena is an imprint of Parragon

Parragon
Queen Street House
4-5 Queen Street
Bath BA1 1HE

Printed and bound in the UK

Compiled by Anna O'Brien

Design by Moo Design

© Western Media Publishing Limited

ISBN 0 75252 973 0

CONTENTS

1950s

QUIZ & FACT

QUIZ 1

Answers on page 10

1 **Who won the very first World Drivers' Championship in 1950?**
   a. Juan Manuel Fangio   *b. Luigi Fagioli*   *c. Guiseppe Farina*

2 **For which team did he drive?**
   a. Vanwall   *b. Alfa Romeo*   *c. Mercedes*

3 **How many times did the great Juan Manuel Fangio win the Drivers' Championship in the fifties?**
   a. Three   *b. Five*   *c. Six*

4 **What was Fangio's nationality?**
   a. Brazilian   *b. Argentinian*   *c. Peruvian*

5 **On which circuit did he win his first Grand Prix in 1950?**
   a. Casablanca   *b. Silverstone*   *c. Monaco*

6 **What was the nickname of the burly Argentinian driver Froilan Gonzalez?**
   a. The Matador   *b. The Stevedore*   *c. The Pampas Bull*

7 **How many times did he win the Drivers' title in the fifties?**
   a. One   *b. Two*   *c. None*

8 **Which great British driver made his debut in the 1951 Swiss Grand Prix?**
   a. Mike Hawthorn   *b. Jim Clark*   *c. Stirling Moss*

9 **Which unique American race was included in the World Championship series from 1950 to 1960?**
   a. Riverside   *b. Indianapolis*   *c. Watkins Glen*

10 **What is its nickname?**
   a. The Schoolyard   *b. The Courtyard*   *c. The Brickyard*

Answers to page 10
1 *c.* Mike Hawthorn   2 *c.* A bow tie   3 *a.* Three   4 *b.* Argentina   5 *c.* Mercedes
6 *b.* Froilan Gonzalez   7 *b.* 21   8 *c.* Aintree   9 *b.* Alfonso de Portago   10 *a.* Mercedes

QUIZ 2

Answers on page 11

1 In 1951, Luigi Fagioli became the oldest man ever to win a World Championship Grand Prix in a shared car (with Fangio). A record which exists to this day. How old was he?
a. 43 *b.* 53 *c.* 63

2 How old was Fangio when he competed in his first World Championship Grand Prix at Silverstone in 1950?
a. 29 *b.* 39 *c.* 49

3 Who won the 1951 World Drivers' Championship?
a. Alberto Ascari *b.* Reg Parnell *c.* Juan Manuel Fangio

4 The 1951 German Grand Prix took place on a circuit over 14 miles in length. What was it called?
a. The Osterreichring *b.* The Rhinering *c.* The Nurburgring

5 Which extrovert driver became the first Englishman to win a World Championship round at Reims in France in 1953?
a. James Hunt *b.* Graham Hill *c.* Mike Hawthorn

6 What is the famous logo of Ferrari?
a. A dancing bear *b.* A prancing horse *c.* A flying elephant

7 Who won the Drivers' title for Ferrari in both 1952 and 1953?
a. Stirling Moss *b.* Jack Fairman *c.* Alberto Ascar

8 In 1955, Ascari crashed into the sea. At which race?
a. Riverside *b.* Long Beach *c.* Monaco

9 Which car was he driving?
a. Bugatti *b.* Lancia *c.* Alfa Romeo

10 The fifties saw a Siamese Prince competing in the Championship. What was his name?
a. Prince Juha *b.* Prince Bira *c.* Prince Chula

Answers to page 11
1 *a.*one 2 *c.*none 3 *c.*Mike Hawthorn 4 *b.*Jack Brabham 5 *c.*Sir Alfred Owen
6 *a.*British Racing Motors 7 *b.*Tony Vandervell 8 *c.*Green 9 *c.*Silver 10 *c.*The Silver Arrows

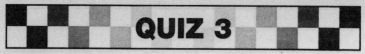

QUIZ 3

Answers on page 8

1 **Which British driver was known as the Farnham Flier?**
   a. Peter Collins   *b. Innes Ireland*   *c. Mike Hawthorn*

2 **What distinctive item of clothing did Mike Hawthorn always wear when driving?**
   a. A peaked cap   *b. Red socks*   *c. A bow tie*

3 **How many Grands Prix did Hawthorn win during his career?**
   a. Three   *b. 13*   *c. 23*

4 **Which South American country hosted a Grand Prix for the first time in 1953?**
   a. Uruguay   *b. Argentina*   *c. Venezuela*

5 **Which great German team returned to the fray in 1954?**
   a. Volkswagen   *b. Audi*   *c. Mercedes*

6 **Which Argentinian driver scored his second British Grand Prix victory in 1954?**
   a. Juan Manuel Fangio   *b. Froilan Gonzalez*   *c. Onofre Marimon*

7 **How old was Stirling Moss when he made his Grand Prix debut?**
   a. 19   *b. 21*   *c. 25*

8 **Moss won his first Grand Prix in Britain in 1955. At which venue, now better known for a different form of horsepower?**
   a. Donington   *b. Silverstone*   *c. Aintree*

9 **Which Spanish Ferrari driver twice rode in the Grand National?**
   a. Andrea de Cesaris   *b. Alfonso de Portago*   *c. Ricardo Rodriguez*

10 **Which leading team withdrew from Formula 1 at the end of 1955 in the wake of the accident at the Le Mans race in which 83 spectators were killed?**
   a. Mercedes   *b. BRM*   *c. Ferrari*

Answers to page 8
1 *c.* Guiseppe Farina   **2** *b.* Alfa Romeo   **3** *b.* Five   **4** *b.* Argentinian   **5** *c.* Monaco
6 *c.* The Pampas Bull   **7** *c.* None   **8** *c.* Stirling Moss   **9** *b.* Indianapolis   **10** *c.* The Brickyard

---

QUIZ 4

Answers on page 9

1 **How many Argentinian drivers won the World title in the fifties?**
   a. one   b. two   c. three

2 **How many Argentinian drivers have won the title since?**
   a. two   b. one   c. none

3 **Who became the first British driver to win the title in 1958?**
   a. Stirling Moss   b. Mike Hailwood   c. Mike Hawthorn

4 **Who became the first Australian to win the title in 1959?**
   a. Denny Hulme   b. Jack Brabham   c. Stan Jones

5 **Name the British millionaire who owned the BRM team in the fifties.**
   a. Lord Hesketh   b. Lord March   c. Sir Alfred Owen

6 **What do the initials BRM stand for?**
   a. British Racing Motors   b. British Racing Men   c. British Racing Magic

7 **Which millionaire industrialist owned the Vanwall team?**
   a. Colin Vanwall   b. Tony Vandervell   c. Colin Chapman

8 **In which colours were the Vanwalls painted?**
   a. Red white and blue   b. Yellow   c. Green

9 **What colours did Mercedes cars carry in the fifties?**
   a. Black   b. Red   c. Silver

10 **And what was the team's nickname?**

   a. The Red Arrows   b. The Shooting Stars   c. The Silver Arrows

Answers to page 9

1 *b.* 53 2 *b.* 39 3 *c.* Juan Manuel Fangio 4 *c.* Nurburgring 5 *c.* Mike Hawthorn
6 *b.* A Prancing Horse 7 *c.* Alberto Ascari 8 *c.* Monaco 9 *c.* Paul Hawkins
10 *b.* Prince Bira

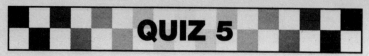

QUIZ 5

Answers on page 14

1 **There were two Grands Prix in Italy in 1957, one at Pescara. Where was the other?**
   a. San Marino   *b. San Remo*   *c. Monza*

2 **A British car won a World Championship round for the first time ever in 1957 - on British soil at Aintree. Which car?**
   a. Vauxhall   *b. Vanwall*   *c. Vandervell*

3 **Which two British drivers shared the victory?**
   a. Moss/Brooks   *b. Moss/Hill*   *c. Moss/Clark*

4 **What was Tony Brooks' by profession?**
   a. Schoolteacher   *b. Lawyer*   *c. Dentist*

5 **Stirling Moss took the Vanwall to victory in both Italian Grands Prix in 1957. Who finished second on both occasions?**
   a. Brooks   *b. Bira*   *c. Fangio*

6 **Fangio won his last World Championship title in 1957 In which car?**
   a. Vanwall   *b. Bugatti*   *c. Ferrari*

7 **How many Grands Prix did Fangio win during his career?**
   a. 24   *b. 34*   *c. 44*

8 **Which future World Champion made his Formula 1 debut at Monaco driving a Lotus in 1958?**
   a. Colin Chapman   *b. Graham Hill*   *c. Jackie Stewart*

9 **Which future Formula 1 tycoon tried to qualify a Connaught for the same race?**
   a. Tom Walkinshaw   *b. Max Moseley*   *c. Bernie Ecclestone*

10 **What nationality is Roy Salvadori?**
   a. Italian   *b. British*   *c. Brazilian*

Answers to page 13
1 *c.*Maria Teresa de Filipis   **2 *c.***Italian   **3 *b.***10th   **4 *b.***Fangio   **5 *b.***Spun into banking
6 *b.*Avgas   **7 *b.***Peter Collins   **8 *b.***Mon ami mate   **9 *b.***Vanwall
10 *b.*Maurice Trintignant

QUIZ 6

Answers on page 12

1 Who was the first woman to take part in a World
   Championship Grand Prix?
   a. Michele Mouton *b. Bette Hill* *c. Maria Teresa de Filippis*

2 What was her nationality?
   a. British *b. Belgian* *c. Italian*

3 Where did she finish in her first race in the 1958 Belgian
   Grand Prix?
   a. First *b. 10th* *c. Did not finish*

4 Which motor racing legend retired from Grand Prix racing
   after the 1958 French Grand Prix?
   a. Gonzalez *b. Fangio* *c. Moss*

5 What happened to him on the very last lap of his career?
   a. Ran out of fuel *b. Spun into the banking* *c. Puncture*

6 What was the control fuel introduced for the 1958 season?
   a. Diesel *b. Avgas* *c. Pump fuel*

7 Which British driver proudly won his home Grand Prix at
   Silverstone in 1958 only to die tragically at the Nurburgring
   two weeks later?
   a. Innes Ireland *b. Peter Collins* *c. Graham Hill*

8 What was the nickname given to him by his great friend and
   team-mate, Mike Hawthorn?
   a. Boy Wonder *b. Mon ami mate* *c. Buddy*

9 Which team won the first official Formula 1 Constructors'
   title in 1958 then pulled out of racing due to the owner's ill
   health?
   a. Ferrari *b. Vanwall* *c. BRM*

10 Which 40-year-old French driver took his second Monaco
   Grand Prix win of the fifties in 1958?
   a. Louis Chiron *b. Maurice Trintignant* *c.Jean-Christophe Boullion*

Answers to page 14

1 *b.*Morocco 2 *c.*Stuart Lewis-Evans 3 *c.*Jo Bonnier 4 *b.*Zandvoort 5 *c.*Sebring
6 *c.*Bruce McLaren 7 *c.*22 8.*b.*Cooper-Climax 9 *b.*New Zealander 10 *c.*Cooper-
Climax

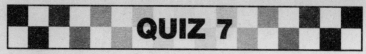

QUIZ 7

Answers on page 13

1 **Which North African country hosted a Grand Prix for the first and, to date, only time in history in 1958?**
   a. Ethiopia   *b.* Morocco   *c.* Tunisia

2 **Stirling Moss won the race but his Vanwall team-mate was fatally burnt during the race. Who was he?**
   a. Tony Brooks   *b.* Mike Hawthorn   *c.* Stuart Lewis-Evans.

3 **Who scored BRM's first ever Grand Prix victory in 1959?**
   a. Stirling Moss   *b.* Jack Brabham   *c.* Jo Bonnier

4 **On which European seaside circuit?**
   a. Monte Carlo   *b.* Zandvoort   *c.* Spa

5 **The very first official US Grand Prix was the last round of the 1959 calendar. Where was it held?**
   a. Watkins Glen   *b.* Indianapolis   *c.* Sebring

6 **Who became the youngest driver ever to win a Grand Prix at this race?**
   a. Graham Hill   *b.* Denny Hulme   *c.* Bruce McLaren

7 **How old was he?**
   a. 18   *b.* 22   *c.* 24

8 **Which car was he driving?**
   a. McLaren   *b.* Cooper-Climax   *c.* Brabham

9 **What nationality was he?**
   a. British   *b.* New Zealander   *c.* American

10 **Who won the 1959 Constructors' title?**
   a. BRM   *b.* Lotus-Climax   *c.* Cooper-Climax

Answers to page 12
1 *c.*Monza **2** *b.*Vanwall **3** *a.*Moss/Brooks **4** *c.*Dentist **5** *c.*Fangio **6** *c.*Ferrari
7 *a.*24 **8** *b.*Graham Hill **9** *c.*Bernie Ecclestone **10** *b.*British

FACT FILE 1

The inaugural round of the Formula 1 World Championship was held on the Silverstone circuit in Northamptonshire on 13th May 1950.

Silverstone was originally a military airfield and the British Racing Drivers' Club organised the first post-war British Grand Prix there in 1948 after pre-war circuits such as Brooklands and Donington Park had fallen into disuse.

The introduction of the 'official' World Championship in 1950 was the butt of much criticism from the 'die-hard purists' in the sport and was virtually ignored by much of the media.

But it was a right royal occasion. King George VI, Queen Elizabeth and Princess Margaret watched the race from a precarious perch on a step ladder at Stowe corner!

Alfa Romeo dominated the race and filled the first three places.

Reg Parnell was the top-placed British driver finishing in third place, despite hitting a hare.

Italy's Guiseppe Farina took pole position, set fastest lap and won the 70-lap race by 2.6 seconds.

The very first multiple first lap pile-up in the World Championship took place in the next race in Monaco. Waves crashing over the harbour front caught out Farina who skidded, stalled, and helplessly took out eight other cars.

Juan Manuel Fangio picked his way through the wreckage to win the race by two miles!

The first World Championship pit stop fire occured in the 1950 Swiss Grand Prix. Felice Bonetto's Maserati pressure system exploded and the whole pit was demolished. Happily no-one was injured - and Bonetto was classified fifth overall!

Britain's Peter Whitehead finished a brave third for Ferrari in the 1950 French Grand Prix. Sadly, he would later lose his life in the 1958 Tour de France.

Alfa won all six races of the Championship.

'Team orders' were much in evidence throughout the year, with lead drivers allowed to take over their team-mates' cars during races. Nothing is new in motorsport!

FACT FILE 2

Today's teams take, on average, eight seconds to refuel and change all four wheels.

In the 1951 Belgian Grand Prix, Fangio's pit crew took 14 minutes 18 seconds to put him back into the race!

His Alfa had been fitted with special - very expensive - concave wheels. One jammed!

His team-mate Farina's stop took just 39 seconds. He won the race.

Alfa Romeo won all nine rounds of the fledgling World Championship in 1950 and 1951.

Ferrari broke their stranglehold when Froilan Gonzalez won the 1951 British Grand Prix at Silverstone.

The Pedralbes circuit in Barcelona used part of the main road to Madrid!

Alfa Romeo retired from Grand Prix racing at the end of 1951. The next time an Alfa-powered car appeared was in South Africa in 1962.

Alberto Ascari took the 1952 World title. He won six of the year's seven Grands Prix.

However, he failed to score at Indianapolis (which counted for World Championship points). He retired his Ferrari after just 40 of the 200 laps.

Fangio did not contest any rounds of the 1952 title chase. He broke his neck early in the year in a race at Monza.

Connaught made their Championship debut at Silverstone in 1952. Two of their cars, driven by British drivers, finished fourth and fifth at their first attempt.

The fourth-placed car was driven by Denis Poore, later to gain fame as boss of Norton motorcycles.

FACT FILE 3

Guiseppe Farina became the oldest man to win a Championship Grand Prix driving by himself when he took his Ferrari to victory at the Nurburgring in 1953 - he was 46.

It was the last Grand Prix victory of his career.

Fangio described him as a 'mad driver'.

Farina was killed in a road accident in 1966, when his Lotus Cortina hit a tree en route to the French Grand Prix.

Mike Hawthorn's Ferrari beat Fangio's Maserati by just one second after two and three quarter hours of racing at the 1953 French Grand Prix at Reims.

His was the first victory for a British driver in the World Championship.

The mighty Mercedes team joined the Grand Prix arena at the 1954 French Grand Prix at Reims for the first time since 1939.

Their cars finished first and second, with Fangio (who else?) finishing half a length in front of his team-mate Karl Kling.

The Vanwall Special made its World Championship debut at the 1954 British Grand Prix at Silverstone in the hands of Britain's Peter Collins. He finished a magnificent seventh in the Italian Grand Prix later in the year, beating the might of Maserati home.

This success persuaded team boss, Tony Vandervell, to go racing properly!

In January 1955, he signed Mike Hawthorn to spearhead his attack.

Hawthorn resigned from the team after his team boss wrecked the Vanwall's clutch whilst driving the car to the circuit in Belgium! Ron Denis and Eddie Jordan please note!

FACT FILE 4

Double World Champion Alberto Ascari died whilst testing a Ferrari sports car at Monza in 1955. He was 36, the same age as his famous father Antonio who was killed whilst leading the French Grand Prix in 1925. He, too, died on the 26th of the month.

The Monza circuit, home of the Italian Grand Prix, spent half a million pounds inserting two high-speed bankings into the autodrome for the 1955 race.

Britain's Peter Collins won his first ever World Championship round at Spa in 1955.

His Ferrari finished ahead of that of Paul Frere - a Belgian journalist!

A third Vanwall was entered in the 1956 French Grand Prix at Reims for a man who would later gain fame as a World Championship winning constructor - Colin Chapman.

Unfortunately, Chapman wrote the car off in practice and failed to start the race.

Peter Collins won his second successive race, at Reims, by just 0.3 seconds from his Ferrari team mate Eugenio Castellotti.

So, for the very first time in history, a British driver led the World Championship!

Not for long! The maestro, Fangio, won the next two rounds in Britain and Germany.

Fangio seemed to have lost his Championship chances in the final round at Monza when his Ferrari suffered terminal engine and suspension failure.

Collins, in a supremely selfless gesture, gave his car to his teammate. Fangio finished second and clinched his fourth World title just three points ahead of Stirling Moss.

Moss was destined never to win the crown. He finished runner-up four times in a row from 1955 to 1958.

18

FACT FILE 5

There was plenty for British fans to shout about in the 1957 season. A British team, with three British drivers!

Tony Vandervell signed up Stirling Moss, Tony Brooks and Stuart Lewis-Evans to drive his Vanwalls.

Fangio, unable to reconcile his differences with Enzo Ferrari, joined Maserati in search of his fifth World title.

Ferrari signed Hawthorn to join Collins, Musso and Castellotti in an awesome line-up.

There was mayhem on lap four of the Monaco Grand Prix. Moss crashed coming out of the tunnel; Collins took avoiding action and hit the barriers and Hawthorn slithered into his Ferrari team-mate after ripping off a front wheel (which splashed into harbour) after an altercation with Brooks' Vanwall.

Britain's three leading drivers were left to watch and wonder as Fangio (who else?) cruised to victory!

Australia's Jack Brabham pushed his Cooper-Climax over the line to finish sixth.

After 52 World Championship Grands Prix a British car won a title round - in Britain!

Moss steered the Vanwall to victory at Silverstone, after taking over from Tony Brooks.

It was the first major Grand Prix win for a British car since Henry Segrave won the French Grand Prix in 1923 in a Sunbeam.

Italy hosted two title rounds in 1957. One was at the Adriatic coastal town of Pescara, where none other than Ferrari supremo Enzo Ferrari won the Grand Prix in 1924!

FACT FILE 6

The smallest number of cars ever to start a World Championship Grand Prix is 10 - at the 1958 season-opener in Argentina.

There were three Ferraris, six Maseratis and a lone, privately - entered Cooper-Climax.

The Cooper won! The driver? Stirling Moss! The reason? He did not make a tyre stop.

Moss won a total of four rounds of the 1958 Championship, three for Vanwall, but Mike Hawthorn pipped him to the Drivers' title by just one point.

Tony Brooks won three rounds, at Spa, Nurburgring and Monza. His brave drives clinched the inaugural Constructors' Championship for Vanwall, the first in what was to prove a long line of success for British Constructors in the World Championship.

The winner of the 1952 Indianapolis 500 made his debut in the 1958 French Grand Prix.

America's Troy Ruttman was classified 10th in his Maserati.

The man who would be America's first Formula One World Champion also made his debut in the same race. Phil Hill brought his Maserati home in seventh place.

The French Grand Prix was the final race in the illustrious career of Juan Manuel Fangio.

Phil Hill joined Ferrari for the remainder of 1958 and helped his team-mate Hawthorn to win the title, waving him through in the closing stages of the Moroccan Grand Prix.

Hawthorn finished second to claim the coveted crown - and promptly retired.

He was tragically killed in a road accident just three months later when his Jaguar crashed into a tree on the Guilford By-Pass.

He was 29.

FACT FILE 7

The death of Hawthorn and the withdrawal of Vanwall left a huge void at the start of the 1959 season.

Most people's money was on Ferrari, who had added Britain's Tony Brooks to their line-up, to take the honours. But there were surprises in store...

Jack Brabham became the first Australian to win a Championship round when he took his Cooper-Climax to victory in the first race of the year, in Monaco.

And Jo Bonnier became the first Swedish driver ever to taste the victory champagne when he gave BRM their very first Championship win in the very next round, in Holland.

The sun was so hot at the 1959 French Grand Prix - some estimates put it as high as 110 degrees Farenheit - that the track surface began to melt! Brooks mastered the conditions to give Ferrari their first Championship victory in 12 months. But his French team-mate, Jean Behra, was fired - for punching the team manager!

There were no Ferraris at the 1959 British Grand Prix because of a strike at the factory.

Brabham won the race for Cooper but a new Antipodean star was born. The 22-year-old New Zealander, Bruce McLaren, battled for second place with Moss all the way to the line, finishing just one fifth of a second behind!

Jack Brabham won the 1959 World Drivers' title, whilst Cooper Climax clinched the Constructors' Championship. Brabham ran out of fuel in the final race of the season, the US Grand Prix at Sebring, and had to push his works Cooper half a mile home to fourth place!

Moss's ambitions were frustrated yet again, third overall, despite winning two races in the Cooper-Climax of privateer Rob Walker, in Monza and Portugal, where he lapped the entire field.

1950s

RESULTS

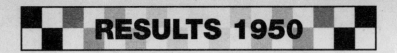

RESULTS 1950

1950 The birth of the official World Drivers' Championship.
Seven rounds including Indianapolis. Points were 8-6-4-3-2 for the first
five places. Plus one point for the fastest lap. The best four results
counted for the title.

ROUND 1/EUROPEAN GRAND PRIX
SILVERSTONE, GREAT BRITAIN, 13 MAY

1. FARINA (ITA)	ALFA ROMEO	2HR 13MIN 23.6SEC
2. FAGIOLI (ITA)	ALFA ROMEO	2HR 13MIN 26.2SEC
3. REG PARNELL (GB)	ALFA ROMEO	2HR 14MIN 15.6SEC
4. GIRAUD-CABANTOUS (FRA)	TALBOT	68 LAPS
5. ROSIER (FRA	TALBOT	68 LAPS
6. GERARD (GB)	ERA	67 LAPS

Race: 70 laps of 2.9mile/4.7km (204.4miles/329kms)
Fastest lap: Farina 1min 50.6sec 94.04mph/ 151.3kph
Pole position: Farina 1min 50.8sec 21 starters, 12 classified finishers

ROUND 2/MONACO GRAND PRIX
MONTE-CARLO, 21 MAY

1. FANGIO (ARG)	ALFA ROMEO	3HR 13MIN 18.7SEC
2. ASCARI (ITA)	FERRARI	99 LAPS
3. CHIRON (FRA)	MASERATI	98 LAPS
4. SOMMER (FRA)	FERRARI	97 LAPS
5. BIRA (THAI)	MASERATI	95 LAPS
6. GERARD (GB)	ERA	94 LAPS

Race: 100 laps of 1.98mile/3.18 km (198miles/318kms)
Fastest lap: Fangio 1min 51sec 64.09mph/103.14kph
Pole position: Fangio 1m 50.2sec 19 starters, 7 classified finishers

ROUND 3 /INDIANAPOLIS 500
INDIANAPOLIS, 30 MAY

1. PARSONS (USA)	WYNN'S KURTIS	138 LAPS
2. HOLLAND(USA)	BLUE CROWN	137 LAPS
3. ROSE (USA)	KECK OFFENHAUSER	137 LAPS
4. GREEN (USA)	NOVI	137 LAPS
5. CHITWOOD/BETTENHAUSEN(USA)	WOLFE	136 LAPS
6. WALLARD (USA)	BLUE CROWN	136 LAPS

Race: 200 laps of 2.5mile/4.02km(race stopped after 138 laps because of rain)
Fastest lap: Holland 1min 09.8sec 129mph/207.6kph
Pole position: Faulkner(USA) Grant Piston 33 starters, 22 classified finishers

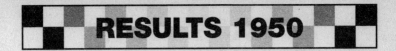
RESULTS 1950

ROUND 4/SWISS GRAND PRIX
BREMGARTEN, BERNE, 4 JUNE

1. FARINA (ITA)	ALFA ROMEO	2HR 2MIN 53.7SEC
2. FAGIOLI (ITA)	ALFA ROMEO	2HR 2MIN 54.1SEC
3. ROSIER (FRA)	TALBOT	41 LAPS
4. BIRA (THAI)	MASERATI	40 LAPS
5. BONETTO (ITA)	MASERATI	40 LAPS
6. DE GRAFFENRIED(SWISS)	MASERATI	40 LAPS

Race: 42 laps of 4.52mile/7.28km (190 miles/306kms)
Fastest lap: Farina, 2min 41.6sec, 100.8mph/162.2kph
Pole position: Fangio, Alfa Romeo, 2min 42.1sec 18 starters, 11 classified finishers

ROUND 5/BELGIAN GRAND PRIX
SPA-FRANCORCHAMPS, 18 JUNE

1. FANGIO (ARG)	ALFA ROMEO	2HR 47MIN 26SEC
2. FAGIOLI (ITA)	ALFA ROMEO	2HR 47MIN 40SEC
3. ROSIER (FRA)	TALBOT	2HR 49MIN 45SEC
4. FARINA (ITA)	ALFA ROMEO	2HR 51MIN 31SEC
5. ASCARI(ITA)	FERRARI	34 LAPS
6. LEVEGH (FRA)	TALBOT	33 LAPS

Race: 35 laps of 8.76mile/14.08km (306miles/492.8kms)
Fastest lap: Farina, 4min 34.1sec 115mph/185.2kph
Pole position: Farina, 4min 37.0sec 14 starters, 10 classified finishers

ROUND 6/ FRENCH GRAND PRIX
REIMS, 2 JULY

1. FANGIO (ARG)	ALFA ROMEO	2HR 57MIN 52.8SEC
2. FAGIOLI (ITA)	ALFA ROMEO	2HR 58MIN 18.5SEC
3. WHITEHEAD (GB)	FERRARI	2HR 59MIN 30.3SEC
4. MANZON	SIMCA-GORDINI	61 LAPS
5. CHABOUD/ETANCELIN (FRA)	TALBOT	59 LAPS
6. ROSIER/POZZI (FRA)	TALBOT	56 LAPS

Race: 64 laps of 4.86mile/7.82km (311mile/500.5km)
Fastest lap: Fangio 2min 35.6sec, 112.6mph/180.8kph
Pole position: Fangio, 2min 30.6sec 18 starters, 10 classified finishers

ROUND 7/ITALIAN GRAND PRIX
MONZA, 3 SEPTEMBER

1. FARINA	ALFA ROMEO	2HR 51MIN 17.4SEC
2. SERAFINI/ASCARI (ITA)	FERRARI	2HR 52MIN 36.0SEC
3. FAGIOLI (ITA)	ALFA ROMEO	2HR 52MIN 53.0SEC
4. ROSIER (FRA)	TALBOT	75 LAPS
5. ETANCELIN (FRA)	TALBOT	75 LAPS
6. DE GRAFFENRIED (SWISS)	MASERATI	72 LAPS

Race: 80 laps of 3.9mile/6.3km (312miles /504kms)
Fastest lap: Fangio, 2min 00sec, 117.45mph/189kph
Pole position: Fangio, 1m 58.3sec 27 starters, 7 classified finishers

RESULTS 1950/1

DRIVERS' WORLD CHAMPIONSHIP 1950

1. FARINA   30 *points*   4. ROSIER   13 *points*
2. FANGIO   27 *points*   5. ASCARI   11 *points*
3. FAGIOLI   24 *points*   6. PARSONS   8 *points*

1951 There was no Monaco Grand Prix in 1951 but two new names appeared on the calendar, the German and the Spanish Grand Prix. There were eight rounds. Points were 8-6-4-3-2 for the first five places, plus one point for the fastest lap. Best four races of the eight counted (including Indy).

ROUND 1/SWISS GRAND PRIX
BREMGARTEN, BERNE, 27 MAY

1. FANGIO (ARG)	ALFA ROMEO	2HR 7MIN 53.6SEC
2. TARUFFI (ITA)	FERRARI	2HR 8MIN 48.9SEC
3. FARINA (ITA)	ALFA ROMEO	2HR 9MIN 12.9SEC
4. SANESI (ITA)	ALFA ROMEO	41 LAPS
5. DE GRAFFENRIED (SWISS)	ALFA ROMEO	40 LAPS
6. ASCARI (ITA)	FERRARI	40 LAPS

Race: 42 laps of 4.52 mile/7.28km (190 miles/306kms)
Fastest lap: Fangio, 2min 51.1sec, 95.18mph/153.17kph
Pole position: Fangio, 21 starters, 14 classified finishers

ROUND 2/INDIANAPOLIS 500
INDIANAPOLIS, 29 MAY

1. WALLARD (USA)	BELANGER	3HR 57MIN 38.05SEC
2. NAZARUK (USA)	ROBINS	
3. MCGRATH (USA)	HINCKLE	
4. LINDEN (USA)	LEITENBERGER	
5. BALL (USA)	BLAKELY	
6. BANKS (USA)	BLUE CROWN	

Race: 200 laps of 2.5mile/4.02km
Fastest lap: Wallard, 1min 07.26sec, 133.81mph/215.35kph
Pole position: Nalon (USA) Novi 33 starters, 8 classified finishers

ROUND 3/BELGIAN GRAND PRIX
SPA-FRANCORCHAMPS, 17 JUNE

1. FARINA (ITA)	ALFA ROMEO	2HR 45MIN 46.2SEC
2. ASCARI (ITA)	FERRARI	2HR 48MIN 37.2SEC
3. VILLORESI (ITA)	FERRARI	2HR 50MIN 08.1SEC
4. ROSIER (FRA)	TALBOT	34 LAPS
5. GIRAUD-CABANTOUS (FRA)	TALBOT	34 LAPS
6. PILETTE (BEL)	TALBOT	33 LAPS

Race: 36 laps of 8.76mile/14.08km (306miles/492.8kms)
Fastest lap: Fangio, 4min 22.1sec, 120.5mph/193.9kph
Pole position: Fangio, 4min 25sec 13 starters, 9 classified finishers

RESULTS 1951

ROUND 4/EUROPEAN GRAND PRIX

REIMS, 1 JULY

1. FANGIO (ARG)	ALFA ROMEO	3HR 22MIN 11SEC
2. ASCARI (ITA)	FERRARI	3HR 23MIN 9.2SEC
3. VILLORESI (ITA)	FERRARI	74 LAPS
4. REG PARNELL (GB)	FERRARI	73 LAPS
5. FARINA (ITA)	ALFA ROMEO	73 LAPS
6. CHIRON (FRA)	TALBOT	71 LAPS

Race: 77 laps of 4.86mile/7.82km (374 miles/602kms)
Fastest lap: Fangio, 2min 27.8sec, 118.3mph/190.4kph
Pole position: Fangio, 2min 25.7sec 23 starters, 11 classified finishers

ROUND 5/BRITISH GRAND PRIX

SILVERSTONE, 14 JULY

1. GONZALEZ (ARG)	FERRARI	2HR 42MIN 18.2SEC
2. FANGIO (ARG)	ALFA ROMEO	2HR 43MIN 9.2SEC
3. VILLORESI (ITA)	FERRARI	88 LAPS
4. BONETTO (ITA)	ALFA ROMEO	87 LAPS
5. REG PARNELL (GB)	BRM	85 LAPS
6. SANESI (ITA)	ALFA ROMEO	84 LAPS

Race: 90 laps of 2.9mile/4.7km (263miles/423kms)
Fastest lap: Farina, Alfa Romeo, 1min 44sec, 99.9mph/160.9kph
Pole position: Gonzalez, 1min 44.4sec 20 starters, 13 classified finishers

ROUND 6/GERMAN GRAND PRIX

NURBURGRING, 29 JULY

1. ASCARI (ITA)	FERRARI	3HR 23MIN 3.3SEC
2. FANGIO (ARG)	ALFA ROMEO	3HR 23MIN 33.8SEC
3. GONZALEZ (ARG)	FERRARI	3HR 27MIN 42.3SEC
4. VILLORESI (ITA)	FERRARI	3HR 28MIN 53.5SEC
5. TARUFFI (ITA)	FERRARI	3HR 30MIN 52.4SEC
6. FISCHER (SWISS)	FERRARI	19 LAPS

Race: 20 laps of 14.17mile/22.81km (283miles/455kms)
Fastest lap: Fangio, 9min 55.8sec, 85.7mph/137.9kph
Pole position: Ascari, 9min 55.8sec 22 starters, 11 classified finishers

ROUND 7/ITALIAN GRAND PRIX

MONZA, 16 SEPTEMBER

1. ASCARI (ITA)	FERRARI	2HR 42MIN 39.3SEC
2. GONZALEZ (ARG)	FERRARI	2HR 43MIN 23.9SEC
3. BONETTO/FARINA (ITA)	ALFA ROMEO	79 LAPS
4. VILLORESI (ITA)	FERRARI	79 LAPS
5. TARUFFI (ITA)	FERRARI	78 LAPS
6. SIMON (FRA)	SIMCA-GORDINI	74 LAPS

Race: 80 laps of 3.91mile/6.3km (312 miles/ 504kms)
Fastest lap: Farina, 1min 56.5sec, 121.5mph/195kph
Pole position: Fangio, Alfa Romeo, 1min 52.3sec 20 starters, 9 classified finishers

RESULTS 1951/2

ROUND 8/SPANISH GRAND PRIX
PEDRALBES (BARCELONA) 28 OCTOBER

1. FANGIO (ARG)	ALFA ROMEO	2HR 46MIN 54.1SEC
2. GONZALEZ (ARG)	FERRARI	2HR 47MIN 48.4SEC
3. FARINA (ITA)	ALFA ROMEO	2HR 48MIN 39.6SEC
4. ASCARI (ITA)	FERRARI	68 LAPS
5. BONETTO (ITA)	ALFA ROMEO	68 LAPS
6. DE GRAFFENRIED (SWISS)	ALFA ROMEO	66 LAPS

Race: 70 laps of 3.92mile/6.308km (274.4miles/441.560kms)
Fastest lap: Fangio, 2min 16.93sec, 103.2mph/166.1kph
Pole position: Ascari, 2min 10.59sec, 19 starters, 10 classified finishers

 DRIVERS' WORLD CHAMPIONSHIP 1951

1.	FANGIO	31 points	4.	FARINA	119 points
2.	ASCARI	25 points	5.	VILLORESI	15 points
3.	GONZALEZ	24 points	6.	TARUFFI	10 points

1952 Alfa withdrew from racing. There were eight rounds to the Championship again. Spain was replaced on the calendar by the Dutch Grand Prix at Zandvoort. Points were 8-6-4-3-2 for the first five places, plus one point for fastest lap. Best four scores from eight races (including Indy).

ROUND 1 /SWISS GRAND PRIX
BREMGARTEN, BERNE, 18 MAY

1. TARUFFI (ITA)	FERRARI	3HR 1MIN 56.1SEC
2. FISCHER (SWISS)	FERRARI	3HR 4MIN 23.3SEC
3. BEHRA (FRA)	GORDINI	61 LAPS
4. WHARTON (GB)	FRAZER-NASH	60 LAPS
5. BROWN (GB)	COOPER-BRISTOL	59 LAPS
6. DE GRAFFENRIED (SWISS)	MASERATI-PLATÉ	58 LAPS

Race: 62 laps of 4.52mile/7.28km (280miles/451kms)
Fastest lap: Taruffi, 2min 49.1sec, 96.3mph/ 155kmh
Pole position: Farina, Ferrari, 2min 47.5sec 21 starters, 8 classified finishers

ROUND 2/INDIANAPOLIS 500
INDIANAPOLIS, 30 MAY

1. RUTTMAN (USA)	AGAJANIAN	3HR 52MIN 41.88SEC
2. JIM RATHMANN (USA)	GRANCOR-WYNN	
3. HANKS (USA)	BARDAHL	
4. CARTER (USA)	BELANGER	
5. CROSS (USA)	BOWES SEAL	
6. BRYAN (USA)	PETER SCHMIDT	

Race: 200 laps of 2.5mile/4.02km
Fastest lap: Vukovich (USA), Fuel injection, 1min 06.6sec, 135mph/217.48kph
Pole position: Agabashian (USA), Cummins 33 starters, 19 classified finishers

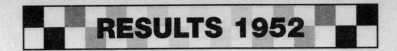

RESULTS 1952

ROUND 3/EUROPEAN GRAND PRIX
SPA-FRANCORCHAMPS, 22 JUNE

1. ASCARI (ITA)	FERRARI	3HR 3MIN 46.3SEC
2. FARINA (ITA)	FERRARI	3HR 5MIN 41.5SEC
3. MANZON (FRA)	GORDINI	3HR 8MIN 14.7SEC
4. HAWTHORN (GB)	COOPER-BRISTOL	35 LAPS
5. FRERE (BEL)	HWM	34 LAPS
6. BROWN (GB)	COOPER-BRISTOL	34 LAPS

Race: 36 laps of 8.76mile/14.12km (315miles/507kms)
Fastest lap: Ascari, 4min 54sec, 107.4mph/172.9kph
Pole position: Ascari, 4min 37sec 22 starters, 15 classified finishers

ROUND 4/FRENCH GRAND PRIX
ROUEN LES ESSARTS, 6 JULY

1. ASCARI (ITA)	FERRARI	77 LAPS
2. FARINA (ITA)	FERRARI	76 LAPS
3. TARUFFI (ITA)	FERRARI	75 LAPS
4. MANZON (FRA)	GORDINI	74 LAPS
5. TRINTIGNANT (FRA)	GORDINI	73 LAPS
6. COLLINS (GB)	HWM	72 LAPS

Race: Three hours of 3.17mile/5.1km circuit
Fastest lap: Ascari, 2min 17.3sec, 82.6mph/133kph
Pole position: Ascari, 2min 14.8 sec 20 starters, 12 classified finishers

ROUND 5/ BRITISH GRAND PRIX
SILVERSTONE, 19 JULY

1. ASCARI (ITA)	FERRARI	2HR 44MIN 11SEC
2. TARUFFI (ITA)	FERRARI	84 LAPS
3. HAWTHORN (GB)	COOPER-BRISTOL	83 LAPS
4. POORE (GB)	CONNAUGHT	83 LAPS
5. THOMPSON (GB)	CONNAUGHT	82 LAPS
6. FARINA (ITA)	FERRARI	82 LAPS

Race: 85 laps of 2.9mile/4,7km (248miles/399kms)
Fastest lap: Ascari, 1min 52sec, 94mph/151kph
Pole position: Farina, 1min 50sec 31 starters, 22 classified finishers

ROUND 6/GERMAN GRAND PRIX
NURBURGRING, 3 AUGUST

1. ASCARI (ITA)	FERRARI	3HR 6MIN 13.3SEC
2. FARINA (ITA)	FERRARI	3HR 6MIN 27.4SEC
3. FISCHER (SWISS)	FERRARI	3HR 13MIN 23.4SEC
4. TARUFFI (ITA)	FERRARI	17 LAPS
5. BEHRA (FRA)	GORDINI	17 LAPS
6. LAURENT (BEL)	FERRARI	16 LAPS

Race: 18 laps of 14.17mile/22.81km (255 miles/409kms)
Fastest lap: Ascari, 10min 5.1sec, 84.4mph/135.9kph
Pole position: Ascari 30 starters, 7 classified finishers

RESULTS 1952/3

ROUND 7/DUTCH GRAND PRIX
ZANDVOORT, 17 AUGUST

1. ASCARI (ITA)	FERRARI	2HR 53MIN 28SEC
2. FARINA (ITA)	FERRARI	2HR 54MIN 8.6SEC
3. VILLORESI (ITA)	FERRARI	2HR 55MIN 2.9SEC
4. HAWTHORN (GB)	COOPER-BRISTOL	88 LAPS
5. MANZON (FRA)	GORDINI	87 LAPS
6. TRINTIGNANT (FRA)	GORDINI	87 LAPS

Race: 90 laps of 2.6mile/4.18km (234miles/376 kms)
Fastest lap: Ascari, 1min 49.8sec, 85.4mph/137.5kph
Pole position: Ascari, lmin 46.5sec 18 starters, 9 classified finishers

ROUND 8/ ITALIAN GRAND PRIX
MONZA, 7 SEPTEMBER

1. ASCARI (ITA)	FERRARI	2HR 50MIN 45.6SEC
2. GONZALEZ (ARG)	MASERATI	2HR 51MIN 47.4SEC
3. VILLORESI (ITA)	FERRARI	2HR 52MIN 42.8SEC
4. FARINA (ITA)	FERRARI	2HR 52MIN 57SEC
5. BONETTO (ITA)	MASERATI	79 LAPS
6. SIMON (FRA)	FERRARI	79 LAPS

Race: 80 laps of 3.92mile /6.3km (312 miles/504kms)
Fastest lap: Ascari and Gonzalez, 2min 6.1sec, 117.6mph/179.86kph
Pole position: Ascari, 2min 05.7sec 24 starters, 15 classified finishers

 DRIVERS' WORLD CHAMPIONSHIP 1952

1. ASCARI	36 *points*	4. FISCHER 10 *points*
2. FARINA	24 *points*	4. HAWTHORN 10 *points*
3. TARUFFI	22 *points*	6. MANZON 9 *points*

1953 Motor sport mad Argentina hosted a World Championship round for the first time and Britain's Mike Hawthorn signed for Ferrari. There were nine rounds. Points: 8-6-4-3-2 for first five places, plus one point for fastest lap. (Fractions indicate shared fastest laps). Best FOUR placings from nine races (including Indy).

ROUND 1/ARGENTINE GRAND PRIX
BUENOS AIRES, 18 JANUARY

1. ASCARI (ITA)	FERRARI	97 LAPS
2. VILLORESI (ITA)	FERRARI	96 LAPS
3. GONZALEZ (ARG)	MASERATI	96 LAPS
4. HAWTHORN (GB)	FERRARI	96 LAPS
5. GALVEZ (ARG)	MASERATI	96 LAPS
6. BEHRA (FRA)	GORDINI	94 LAPS

Race: 3hrs of 2.43mile/3.91km
Fastest lap: Ascari, 1 min 48.4sec, 89.73mph/129.92kph
Pole position: Ascari, 1min 55.4sec 16 starters, 9 classified finishers

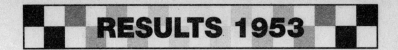

RESULTS 1953

ROUND 2/INDIANAPOLIS 500

INDIANAPOLIS, 30 MAY

1. VUKOVICH (USA)	FUEL INJECTION	3HR 53MIN 01.7SEC
2. CROSS (USA)	SPRINGFIELD WELD	
3. HANKS (USA)	BARDAHL	
4. AGABASHIAN (USA)	GRANCOR-ELGIN	
5. MCGRATH (USA)	HINKLE	
6. DAYWALT (USA)	SUMAR	

Race: 200 laps of 2.5mile/4.02km
Fastest lap: Vukovich, 1min 06.24sec, 135.87mph/218.66kph
Pole position: Vukovich 33 starters, 12 classified finishers

ROUND 3/DUTCH GRAND PRIX

ZANDVOORT, 7 JUNE

1. ASCARI (ITA)	FERRARI	2HR 53MIN 35.8SEC
2. FARINA (ITA)	FERRARI	2HR 53MIN 46.2SEC
3. GONZALEZ (ARG)/BONETTO(ITA)	MASERATI	89 LAPS
4. HAWTHORN (GB)	FERRARI	89 LAPS
5. DE GRAFFENRIED (SWISS)	MASERATI	88 LAPS
6 TRINTIGNANT (FRA)	GORDINI	87 LAPS

Race: 90 laps of 2.6mile/4.19km (234 miles/376kms)
Fastest lap: Villoresi (ITA), Ferrari. 1min 52.8sec, 83.1mph/133.8kph
Pole position: Ascari, 1min 51.1sec 19 starters, 9 classified finishers

ROUND 4/BELGIAN GRAND PRIX

SPA-FRANCORCHAMPS, 21 JUNE

1. ASCARI (ITA)	FERRARI	2HR 48MIN 30.35SEC
2. VILLORESI (ITA)	FERRARI	2HR 51MIN 18.54SEC
3. MARIMON (ARG)	MASERATI	35 LAPS
4. DE GRAFFENRIED (SWISS)	MASERATI	35 LAPS
5. TRINTIGNANT (FRA)	GORDINI	35 LAPS
6. HAWTHORN (GB)	FERRARI	35 LAPS

Race: 36 laps of 8.76mile/14.12km (315miles/506kms)
Fastest lap: Gonzalez (ARG), Maserati, 4min 34 sec, 115.3mph/185.5kph
Pole position: Fangio (ARG) Maserati, 4min 30sec 20 starters, 11 classified finishers

ROUND 5/ FRENCH GRAND PRIX

REIMS, 5 JULY

1. HAWTHORN (GB)	FERRARI	2HR 44MIN 18.6SEC
2. FANGIO (ARG)	MASERATI	2HR 44MIN 19.6SEC
3. GONZALEZ (ARG)	MASERATI	2HR 44MIN 20.0SEC
4. ASCARI (ITA)	FERRARI	2HR 44MIN 23.2SEC
5. FARINA (ITA)	FERRARI	2HR 44MIN 26.2SEC
6. VILLORESI (ITA)	FERRARI	2HR 45MIN 34.5SEC

Race: 60 laps of 5.19mile/8.35km (311 miles/500 kms)
Fastest lap: Fangio, 2min 41.1sec, 115.9mph/186.5kph
Pole position: Ascari, 2min 41.2sec 25 starters, 15 classified finishers

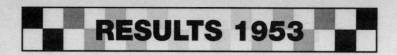

RESULTS 1953

ROUND/6 BRITISH GRAND PRIX
SILVERSTONE, 18 JULY

1. ASCARI (ITA)	FERRARI	2HR 50MIN 00SEC
2. FANGIO (ARG)	MASERATI	2HR 51MIN 00SEC
3. FARINA (ITA)	FERRARI	88 LAPS
4. GONZALEZ (ARG)	MASERATI	88 LAPS
5. HAWTHORN (GB)	FERRARI	87 LAPS
6. BONETTO (ITA)	MASERATI	82 LAPS

Race: 90 laps of 2.9mile/4.7km (263 miles/423kms)
Fastest lap: Ascari/Gonzalez, 1m 50sec, 95.79mph/154.16kph
Pole position: Ascari, 1min 48sec 28 starters, 10 classified finishers

ROUND 7/GERMAN GRAND PRIX
NURBURGRING, 2 AUGUST

1. FARINA (ITA)	FERRARI	3HR 2MIN 25SEC
2. FANGIO (ARG)	MASERATI	3HR 3MIN 29SEC
3. HAWTHORN (GB)	FERRARI	3HR 4MIN 8.6SEC
4. BONETTO (ITA)	MASERATI	3HR 11MIN 13.6SEC
5. DE GRAFFENRIED (SWISS)	MASERATI	17 LAPS
6. MOSS (GB)	COOPER-ALTA	17 LAPS

Race: 18 laps of 14.17mile/22.81km (255 miles/410kms)
Fastest lap: Ascari (ITA), Ferrari, 9min 56sec, 85.6mph/137.78kph
Pole position: Ascari, 9min 59.8sec 34 starters, 16 classified finishers

ROUND 8/SWISS GRAND PRIX
BREMGARTEN, BERNE, 23 AUGUST

1. ASCARI (ITA)	FERRARI	3HR 01MIN 34.4SEC
2. FARINA (ITA)	FERRARI	3HR 02MIN 47.3SEC
3. HAWTHORN (GB)	FERRARI	3HR 03MIN 10.4SEC
4. BONETTO(ITA)/FANGIO(ARG)	MASERATI	64 LAPS
5. LANG (GER)	MASERATI	62 LAPS
6. VILLORESI (ITA)	FERRARI	62 LAPS

Race: 65 laps of 4.52mile/7.28km (294 miles/473.2kms)
Fastest lap: Ascari, 2min 42sec, 101.1mph/162.5kph
Pole poition: Fangio, 2min 40.1sec 20 starters, 9 classified finishers

ROUND 9/ITALIAN GRAND PRIX
MONZA, 13 SEPTEMBER

1. FANGIO (ARG)	MASERATI	2HR 49MIN 45.9SEC
2. FARINA (ITA)	FERRARI	2HR 49MIN 47.3SEC
3. VILLORESI (ITA)	FERRARI	79 LAPS
4. HAWTHORN (GB)	FERRARI	79 LAPS
5. TRINTIGNANT (FRA)	GORDINI	79 LAPS
6. MIERES (ARG)	GORDINI	77 LAPS

Race: 80 laps of 3.92mile/6,3km (312 miles/ 504kms)
Fastest lap: Fangio, 2min 4.5sec, 113.2mph/182.17kph
Pole position: Ascari, 2min 02.7sec 30 starters, 16 classified finishers

RESULTS 1953/4

1954 Mercedes joined the Championship chase with Fangio in dominant mood and the name of Vanwall was added to the entry lists. The Spanish Grand Prix returned to the calendar and the Dutch round was dropped. There were nine rounds. Points: 8-6-4-3-2 for first five places. Plus one point for fastest lap. Best FIVE scores out of nine races (including Indy). Fractions represent shared fastest laps.

ROUND 1/ARGENTINE GRAND PRIX
BUENOS AIRES, 17 JANUARY

1. FANGIO(ARG)	MASERATI	87 LAPS 3HR 0MIN 55.8SEC
2. FARINA (ITA)	FERRARI	87 LAPS 3HR 2MIN 14.8SEC
3. GONZALEZ (ARG)	FERRARI	87 LAPS 3HR 2MIN 56.8SEC
4. TRINTIGNANT(FRA)	FERRARI	86 LAPS
5. BAYOL (FRA)	GORDINI	89 LAPS
6. SCHELL(USA)	MASERATI	84 LAPS

Race: 3 hours of 2.43mile/3.91km
Fastest lap: Gonzalez, 1min 48.2sec, 80.8mph/130kph
Pole position: Ascari (ITA), Ferrari, 1min 55.4sec 16 starters, 9 classified finishers

ROUND 4/INDIANAPOLIS 500
INDIANAPOLIS, 30 MAY

1. VUKOVICH (USA)	FUEL INJECTION SPECIAL	3HR 49M 17.27SEC
2. BRYAN (USA)	DEAN VAN LINES	
3. MCGRATH (USA)	HINCKLE	
4. RUTTMAN (USA)	AUTO SHIPPERS	
5. NAZARUK (USA)	MCNAMARA	
6. AGABASHIAN (USA)	MERZ ENGINEERING	

Race: 200 laps of 2.5mile/4.02km
Fastest lap: McGrath, 1min 04.04sec, 140.54mph/226.17kph
Pole position: McGrath 33 starters, 19 classified finishers

ROUND 3/BELGIAN GRAND PRIX
SPA-FRANCORCHAMPS, 20 JUNE

1. FANGIO(ARG)	MASERATI	2HR 44MIN 42.4SEC
2. TRINTIGNANT (FRA)	FERRARI	2HR 45MIN 6.6SEC
3. MOSS (GB)	MASERATI	35 LAPS
4. GONZALEZ(ARG)/HAWTHORN(GB)	FERRARI	35 LAPS
5. PILETTE (BEL)	GORDINI	35 LAPS
6. BIRA (THAI)	MASERATI	35 LAPS

Race: 36 laps of 8.76mile/14.12km (315miles/508kms)
Fastest lap: Fangio, 4min 25.5sec, 119.0mph/191.5kph
Pole position: Fangio, 4m 22.1sec 14 starters, 7 classified finishers

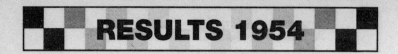

RESULTS 1954

ROUND 4/FRENCH GRAND PRIX
REIMS, 4 JULY

1. FANGIO (ARG)	MERCEDES	2HR 42MIN 47.9SEC
2. KLING (GER)	MERCEDES	2HR 42MIN 48SEC
3. MANZON (FRA)	FERRARI	60 LAPS
4. BIRA (THAI)	MASERATI	60 LAPS
5. VILLORESI (ITA)	MASERATI	58 LAPS
6. BEHRA (FRA)	GORDINI	56 LAPS

Race: 61 laps of 5.16mile/8.3km (315miles/506.3kms)
Fastest lap: Herrmann (GER), Mercedes, 2min 32.9sec, 121.4mph/195.5kph
Pole position: Fangio, 2min 29s.4sec 21 starters, 7 classified finishers

ROUND 5/BRITISH GRAND PRIX
SILVERSTONE, 17 JULY

1. GONZALEZ (ARG)	FERRARI	2HR 56MIN 14SEC
2. HAWTHORN (GB)	FERRARI	2HR 57MIN 24SEC
3. MARIMON (ARG)	MASERATI	89 LAPS
4. FANGIO (ARG)	MERCEDES	89 LAPS
5. TRINTIGNANT (FRA)	FERRARI	87 LAPS
6. MIERES (ARG)	MASERATI	87 LAPS

Race: 90 laps of 2.9mile/4.7km (263 miles/423kms)
Fastest lap: Gonzalez/Hawthorn/Moss(GB)/Ascari(ITA)/Marimon/Behra(FRA)/Fangio !!
1min 50sec, 95.79mph/154.16kph
Pole position: Fangio, 1min 50sec 29 starters, 15 classified finishers

ROUND 6/EUROPEAN GRAND PRIX
NURBURGRING, 1 AUGUST

1. FANGIO (ARG)	MERCEDES	3HR 45MIN 45.8SEC
2. GONZALEZ(ARG)/HAWTHORN(GB)	FERRARI	3HR 47MIN 22.3SEC
3. TRINTIGNANT (FRA)	FERRARI	3HR 50MIN 54.4SEC
4. KLING (GER)	MERCEDES	3HR 51MIN 52.3SEC
5. MANTOVANI (ITA)	MASERATI	3HR 54MIN 36.3SEC
6. TARUFFI (ITA)	FERRARI	21LAPS

Race: 22 laps of 14.17mile/22.81km (312miles/501kms)
Fastest lap: Kling, 9min 55.1sec, 85.7mph/137.9kph
Pole position: Fangio, 9min 50.1sec 20 starters, 10 classified finishers

ROUND 7/SWISS GRAND PRIX
BREMGARTEN, BERNE, 22 AUGUST

1. FANGIO (ARG)	MERCEDES	3HR 0MIN 34.5SEC
2. GONZALEZ (ARG)	FERRARI	3HR 1MIN 32.3SEC
3. HERRMANN (GER)	MERCEDES	65 LAPS
4. MIERES (ARG)	MASERATI	64 LAPS
5. MANTOVANI (ITA)	MASERATI	64 LAPS
6. WHARTON (GB)	MASERATI	64 LAPS

Race: 66 laps of 4.52mile/7.28km (298 miles/480.5kms)
Fastest lap: Fangio, 2min 39.7sec, 101.9mph/164kph
Pole position: Gonzalez, 2min 39.5sec 15 starters, 8 classified finishers

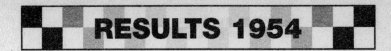

RESULTS 1954

ROUND 8/ITALIAN GRAND PRIX

MONZA, 5 SEPTEMBER

1. FANGIO (ARG)	MERCEDES	2HR 47MIN 47.9SEC
2. HAWTHORN(GB)	FERRARI	79 LAPS
3. GONZALES(ARG)/MAGLIOLI(ITA)	FERRARI	78 LAPS
4. HERRMANN (GER)	MERCEDES	77 LAPS
5. TRINTIGNANT (FRA)	FERRARI	75 LAPS
6. WACKER(USA)	GORDINI	75 LAPS

Race: 80 laps of 3.92mile/6.3km (312miles/504kms)
Fastest lap: Gonzalez, 2min 0.8sec, 116mph/187kph
Pole position: Fangio, 1min 59.0sec 20 starters, 11 classified finishers

ROUND 9/SPANISH GRAND PRIX

PEDRALBES, BARCELONA, 24 OCTOBER

1. HAWTHORN (GB)	FERRARI	3HR 13MIN 52.1SEC
2. MUSSO (ITA)	MASERATI	3HR 15MIN 05.3SEC
3. FANGIO (ARG)	MERCEDES	79 LAPS
4. MIERES (ARG)	MASERATI	79 LAPS
5. KLING (GER)	MERCEDES	79 LAPS
6. GODIA (ESP)	MASERATI	76 LAPS

Race: 80 laps of 3.92mile/6.32km (313mile/505.6kms)
Fastest lap: Ascari (ITA) Lancia, 2min 20.4sec, 100.7mph/162kph
Pole position: Ascari 2min 18.1sec 21 starters, 9 classified finishers

 DRIVERS' WORLD CHAMPIONSHIP 1954

1.	FANGIO	42 *points*	5.	KLING	12 *points*
2.	GONZALEZ	25 *points*	6.	HERMANN	8 *points*
3.	HAWTHORN	26.64	6.	VUKOVICH	8 *points*
4.	TRINTIGNANT	17 *points*			

1955 A tragic year for motorsport. Ascari died in a test crash at Monza and the horrific accident at Le Mans claimed the life of Pierre Levegh and 83 spectators. The Swiss, German and Spanish Grands Prix were immediately cancelled. Monaco returned to the calendar for the first time since 1950. The sweltering heat necessitated numerous driver changes during the Argentine race. The Championship totalled just seven races. Points: 8-6-4-3-2 for first five places, plus one point for fastest lap. Best FIVE scores from seven races (including Indy) counted.

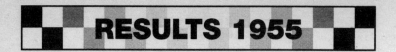

RESULTS 1955

ROUND 1/ARGENTINE GRAND PRIX
BUENOS AIRES, 16 JANUARY

1. FANGIO (ARG)	MERCEDES	3HR 0MIN 38.6SEC
2. FARINA (ITA)(ALSO GONZALEZ AND TRINTIGNANT) FERRARI		3HR 2MIN 08.2SEC
3. MAGLIOLI (ITA)(ALSO FARINA AND TRINTIGNANT) FERRARI		94 LAPS
4. KLING (GER)(ALSO MOSS AND HERRMANN)	MERCEDES	94 LAPS
5. MIERES (ARG)	MASERATI	91 LAPS
6. BEHRA (FRA)/SCHELL (USA)	MASERATI	88 LAPS

Race: 96 laps of 2.43mile/3.91km (233miles/375kms)
Fastest lap: Fangio, 1min 48.3sec, 80.8mph/130kph
Pole position: Gonzalez, 1min 43.1 sec 21 starters, 7 classified finishers

ROUND 2/MONACO GRAND PRIX
MONTE CARLO, 22 MAY

1. TRINTIGNANT (FRA)	FERRARI	2HR 58MIN 9.8SEC
2. CASTELLOTTI (ITA)	LANCIA	2HR 58MIN 30SEC
3. PERDISSA (ITA)/BEHRA(FRA)	MASERATI	99 LAPS
4. FARINA (ITA)	FERRARI	99 LAPS
5. VILLORESI (ITA)	LANCIA	99 LAPS
6. CHIRON (FRA)	LANCIA	95 LAPS

Race: 100 laps of 1.95mile/3.15km (195miles/315kms)
Fastest lap: Fangio(ARG), Mercedes, 1min 42.4sec, 68.7mph/110.57kph
Pole position: Fangio 1min 41.1sec 20 starters, 9 classified finishers

ROUND 3/INDIANAPOLIS 500
INDIANAPOLIS, 30 MAY

1. SWEIKERT(USA)	JOHN ZINK SPECIAL	3HR 53MIN 59.53SEC
2. TONY BETTENHAUSEN(USA)	CHAPMAN	
3. DAVIES (USA)	BARDAHL	
4. THOMSON (USA)	SCHMIDT SPECIAL	
5. FAULKNER (USA)	MERZ	
6. LINDEN(USA)	MASSAGLIA	

Race: 200 laps of 2.5mile/4.02km circuit
Fastest lap: Vukovitch (USA), Hopkins, 1min 03.67sec, 141.4mph/227.5kph
Pole position: Hoyt(USA) Robbins   33 starters, 14 classified finishers (Vulkovich, fatal accident lap 56)

ROUND 4/BELGIAN GRAND PRIX
SPA-FRANCORCHAMPS, 5 JUNE

1. FANGIO(ARG)	MERCEDES	2HR 39MIN 29SEC
2. MOSS (GB)	MERCEDES	2HR 39MIN 37.1SEC
3. FARINA (ITA)	FERRARI	2HR 41MIN 9.5SEC
4. FRERE (BEL)	FERRARI	2HR 42MIN 54.5SEC
5. MIERES(ARG)/BEHRA(FRA)	MASERATI	35 LAPS
6. TRINTIGNANT(FRA)	FERRARI	35 LAPS

Race: 36 laps of 8.76mile/14.12km (308miles/508kms)
Fastest lap: Fangio, 4min 20.6sec, 121.2mph/195.06kph
Pole position: Castellotti, 4min 18.1sec 13 starters, 9 classified finishers

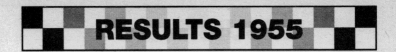

RESULTS 1955

ROUND 5/ DUTCH GRAND PRIX
ZANDVOORT, 19 JUNE

1. FANGIO (ARG)	MERCEDES	2HR 54MIN 23.8SEC
2. MOSS (GB)	MERCEDES	2HR 54MIN 24.1SEC
3. MUSSO (ITA)	MASERATI	2HR 55MIN 20.9SEC
4. MIERES (ARG)	MASERATI	99 LAPS
5. CASTELLOTTI (ITA)	FERRARI	97 LAPS
6. BEHRA (FRA)	MASERATI	97 LAPS

Race: 100 laps of 2.6mile/4.19km (260miles/419kms)
Fastest lap: Mieres, 1min 40.9sec, 92.9mph/149kph
Pole position: Fangio 1min 40sec 16 starters, 11 classified finishers

ROUND 6 /BRITISH GRAND PRIX
AINTREE, 16 JULY

1. MOSS (GB)	MASERATI	3HR 7MIN 21.2SEC
2. FANGIO (ARG)	MERCEDES	3HR 7MIN 21.4SEC
3. KLING (GER)	MERCEDES	3HR 8MIN 33SEC
4. TARUFFI (ITA)	MERCEDES	89 LAPS
5. MUSSO (ITA)	MASERATI	89 LAPS
6. HAWTHORN(GB)/CASTELLOTTI(ITA)	FERRARI	87 LAPS

Race: 90 laps of 3mile/4.83km (270miles/434.5kms)
Fastest lap: Moss, 2min 0.4sec, 89.7mph/144.36kph
Pole position: Moss, 2min 00.4sec 25 starters, 9 classified finishers

ROUND 7/ITALIAN GRAND PRIX
MONZA, 11 SEPTEMBER

1. FANGIO(ARG)	MERCEDES	2HR 25MIN 4.4SEC
2. TARUFFI (ITA)	MERCEDES	2HR 25MIN 5.1SEC
3. CASTELLOTTI (ITA)	FERRARI	2HR 25MIN 50.6SEC
4. BEHRA (FRA)	MASERATI	49 LAPS
5. MENDITEGUY(ARG)	MASERATI	49 LAPS
6. MAGLIOLI (ITA)	FERRARI	49 LAPS

Race: 50 laps of new 6.2mile/10km (310miles/500kms)
Fastest lap: Moss (GB) Mercedes, 2min 46.9sec, 134mph/215.7kph
Pole position: Fangio, 2min 46.5sec 20 starters, 9 classified finishers

---

DRIVERS' WORLD CHAMPIONSHIP 1955

1. FANGIO	40 *points*	4. TRINTIGNANT	11.33
2. MOSS	23 *points*	5. FARINA	10.33 *points*
3. CASTELLOTTI	12 *points*	6. TARUFFI	9 *points*

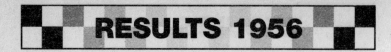

RESULTS 1956

1956 Mercedes withdrew after their all-conquering 1955 season, so Fangio joined Ferrari. The Championship was a three-way tussle between Fangio, Moss and Collins. The German Grand Prix returned to the world series. There were eight rounds. Points: 8-6-4-3-2 for the first five places, plus one point for fastest lap. Best FIVE out of eight scores (including Indy). Fractions indicate either shared fastest laps or shared drives.

ROUND 1/ARGENTINE GRAND PRIX

BUENOS AIRES, 22 JANUARY

1. FANGIO(ARG)/MUSSO(ITA)	FERRARI	3HR 0MIN 3.7SEC
2. BEHRA(FRA)	MASERATI	3HR 0MIN 28.1SEC
3. HAWTHORN (GB)	MASERATI	96 LAPS
4. LANDI(BRA)/GERINI(ITA)	MASERATI	92 LAPS
5. GENDEBIEN(BEL)	FERRARI	91 LAPS
6. URIA(URG)/O.GONZALEZ(URG)	MASERATI	88 LAPS

Race: 98 laps of 2.43mile/3.91km (233miles/ 375kms)
Fastest lap: Fangio, 1min 45.3sec, 83.1mph/133.7kph
Pole position: Fangio, 1min 42.5sec 13 starters, 6 classified finishers

ROUND 2/MONACO

MONTE CARLO, 13 MAY

1. MOSS (GB)	MASERATI	3HR 0MIN 32.9SEC
2. FANGIO(ARG)/COLLINS(GB)	FERRARI	3HR 0MIN 39SEC
3. BEHRA (FRA)	MASERATI	99 LAPS
4. CASTELLOTTI(ITA)/FANGIO(ARG)	FERRARI	94 LAPS
5. DA SILVA RAMOS(BRA)	GORDINI	93 LAPS
6. PILETTE(BEL)BAYOL(FRA)	GORDINI	88 LAPS

Race: 100 laps of 1.95mile/3.15km (195miles/315kms)
Fastest lap: Fangio, 1min 44 sec, 67.4mph/108.45kph
Pole position: Fangio, 1min 44 sec 14 starters, 8 classified finishers

ROUND 3/INDIANAPOLIS 500

INDIANAPOLIS, 30 MAY

1. FLAHERTY (USA)	ZINK SPECIAL	3HR 53MIN 28.84SEC
2. HANKS (USA)	MALEY SPECIAL	
3. FREELAND(USA)	ESTES SPECIAL	
4. PARSONS (USA)	AGAJANIAN SPECIAL	
5. D. RATHMAN (USA)	MCNAMARA SPECIAL	
6. SWEIKERT (USA)	D-A LUBRICANT SPECIAL	

Race: 200 laps of 2.5mile/4.02km
Fastest lap: P. Russo (USA) Novi Vespa, 1min 02.32sec, 144.42mph/232.42kph
Pole position: Flaherty, 33 starters, 19 classified finishers

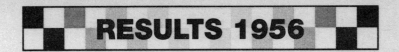

RESULTS 1956

ROUND 4/BELGIAN GRAND PRIX

SPA-FRANCORCHAMPS, 3 JUNE

1. COLLINS(GB)	FERRARI	2HR 40MIN 00.3SEC
2. FRERE (BEL)	FERRARI	2HR 41MIN 51.6SEC
3. MOSS(GB)/PERDISSA(ITA)	MASERATI	2HR 43MIN 16.9SEC
4. SCHELL (USA)	VANWALL	34 LAPS
5. VILLORESI (ITA)	MASERATI	33 LAPS
6. PILETTE (BEL)	FERRARI	33 LAPS

Race: 36 laps of 8.76mile/14.12km (308miles/508kms)
Fastest lap: Moss, 4min 14.7sec, 124.0mph/199.5kph
Pole position: Fangio(ARG), Ferrari, 4min 09.8sec 15 starters, 8 classified finishers

ROUND 5/FRENCH GRAND PRIX

REIMS, 1 JULY

1. COLLINS (GB)	FERRARI	2HR 34MIN 23.4SEC
2. CASTELLOTTI (ITA)	FERRARI	2HR 34MIN 23.7SEC
3. BEHRA(FRA)	MASERATI	2HR 35MIN 53.3SEC
4. FANGIO (ARG)	FERRARI	2HR 35MIN 58.5SEC
5. MOSS(GB)/PERDISSA (ITA)	MASERATI	59 LAPS
6. ROSIER (FRA)	MASERATI	57 LAPS

Race: 61 laps of 5.16mile/8.3km (315 miles/506kms)
Fastest lap: Fangio, 2min 25.8sec, 127.3mph/205kph
Pole position: Collins, 2min 23.3 sec 18 starters, 11 classified finishers

ROUND 6/BRITISH GRAND PRIX

SILVERSTONE, 14 JULY

1. FANGIO (ARG)	FERRARI	2HR 59MIN 47SEC
2. COLLINS(GB)/DE PORTAGO(SPA)	FERRARI	100 LAPS
3. BEHRA (FRA)	MASERATI	99 LAPS
4. FAIRMAN (GB)	CONNAUGHT	98 LAPS
5. GOULD(GB)	MASERATI	97 LAPS
6. VILLORESI(ITA)	MASERATI	96 LAPS

Race: 101 laps of 2.9mile/4.7km (295miles/475kms)
Fastest lap: Moss(GB), Maserati, 1min 43.2sec, 102.1mph/164.32kph
Pole position: Moss, 1min 41sec 28 starters, 11 classified finishers

ROUND 7/GERMAN GRAND PRIX

NURBURGRING, 5 AUGUST

1. FANGIO (ARG)	FERRARI	3HR 38MIN 43.7SEC
2. MOSS (GB)	MASERATI	3HR 39MIN 30.1SEC
3. BEHRA (FRA)	MASERATI	3HR 46MIN 22.0SEC
4. GODIA (SPA)	MASERATI	20 LAPS
5. ROSIER (FRA)	MASERATI	19 LAPS
6. VOLONTERIO(SWISS)	MASERATI	16 LAPS

Race: 22 laps of 14.17mile/22.8km (312miles/501kms)
Fastest lap: Fangio, 9 min 41.6sec, 87.7mph/141.2kpn
Pole position: Fangio, 9min 51.2sec 19 starters, 5 classified finishers

RESULTS 1956/7

ROUND 8/EUROPEAN GRAND PRIX
MONZA, 2 SEPTEMBER

1. MOSS(GB)	MASERATI	2HR 23MIN 41.3SEC
2. FANGIO(ARG)/COLLINS(GB)	FERRARI	2HR 23MIN 47.0SEC
3. FLOCKHART (GB)	CONNAUGHT	49 LAPS
4. GODIA (SPA)	MASERATI	49 LAPS
5. FAIRMAN (GB)	CONNAUGHT	47 LAPS
6. PIOTTI (ITA)	MASERATI	47 LAPS

Race: 50 laps of 6.2mile/10 km (310miles/500kms)
Fastest lap: Moss, 2min 45.5sec, 135.4mph/217.9 kph
Pole position: Fangio, 2min 42.6sec 24 starters, 11 classified finishers

 DRIVERS' WORLD CHAMPIONSHIP 1956

1.	FANGIO	30 points	4.	BEHRA	22 points
2.	MOSS	27 points	5.	FLAHERTY	8 points
3.	COLLINS	25 points	6.	CASTELLOTTI	7.5 points

1957 For the first time British drivers in a British car mounted a serious threat to the Italian teams' domination of the World Championship. The Vanwall challenge took on serious proportions. Fangio, after irreconcilable differences, left Ferarri for Maserati. Italy hosted two Grands Prix. There were eight rounds. Points: 8-6-4-3-2 for first five places, plus one point for fastest lap. Best FIVE scores from eight races (including Indy).

ROUND 1/ARGENTINE GRAND PRIX
BUENOS AIRES, 13 JANUARY

1. FANGIO (ARG)	MASERATI	3HR 00MIN 55.9SEC
2. BEHRA (FRA)	MASERATI	3HR 01MIN 14.2SEC
3. MENDITEGUY(ARG)	MASERATI	99 LAPS
4. SCHELL(USA)	MASERATI	99 LAPS
5. GONZALEZ(ARG)/DE PORTAGO(SPA) FERRARI		98 LAPS
6. PERDISA(ITA)/COLLINS(GB)/VON TRIPS (GER)FERRARI		98 LAPS

Race: 100 Laps of 2.34mile/3.91km (234 miles/ 391kms)
Fastest lap: Moss(GB), Maserati, 1min 44.7sec, 83.6mph/134.5kph
Pole position: Moss, 1min 42.6sec 14 starters, 10 classified finishers

ROUND 2/MONACO GRAND PRIX
MONTE CARLO, 19 MAY

1. FANGIO (ARG)	MASERATI	3HR 10MIN 12.8SEC
2. BROOKS(GB)	VANWALL	3HR 10MIN 38.0SEC
3. GREGORY (USA)	MASERATI	103 LAPS
4. LEWIS-EVANS (GB)	CONNAUGHT	102 LAPS
5. TRINTIGNANT (FRA)	FERRARI	100 LAPS
6. BRABHAM(AUS)	COOPER-CLIMAX	100 LAPS

Race: 105 laps of 1.95mile/3.15km (205miles/330kms)
Fastest lap: Fangio 1min 45.6sec, 66.6mph/107kph
Pole position: Fangio, Imin 42.7sec 16 starters, 6 classified finishers

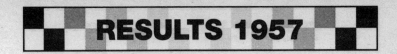

RESULTS 1957

ROUND 3/ INDIANAPOLIS 500
INDIANAPOLIS, 30 MAY

1. HANKS (USA)	BELOND EXHAUST	3HR 41MIN 14.25SEC
2. J. RATHMANN(USA)	CHIROPRACTIC	
3. BRYAN(USA)	DEAN VAN LINES	
4. P. RUSSO (USA)	NOVI AUTO AIR	
5. LINDEN (USA)	MCNAMARA	
6. BOYD (USA)	BOWES SEAL FAST	

Race: 200 laps of 2.5mile/4.02km circuit
Fastest lap: J. Rathmann, 1min 02.75sec, 143.43mph/230.8kph
Pole position: O'Connor(USA), Sumar 33 starters, 17 classified finishers

ROUND 4/FRENCH GRAND PRIX
ROUEN-LES-ESSARTS, 7 JULY

1. FANGIO (ARG)	MASERATI	3HR 7MIN 46.4SEC
2. MUSSO (ITA)	FERRARI	3HR 8MIN 32.2SEC
3. COLLINS(GB)	FERRARI	3HR 9MIN 52.4SEC
4. HAWTHORN(GB)	FERRARI	76 LAPS
5. SCHELL (USA)	MASERATI	70 LAPS
6. BEHRA (FRA)	MASERATI	70 LAPS

Race: 77 laps of 4.06mile/6.54km (312miles/504kms)
Fastest lap: Musso, 2min 22.4sec, 102.7mph/165kph
Pole position: Fangio, 2min 21.5sec 15 starters, 7 classified finishers

ROUND 5/EUROPEAN GRAND PRIX
AINTREE, 20 JULY

1. MOSS(GB)/BROOKS(GB)	VANWALL	3HR 06MIN 37.8SEC
2. MUSSO (ITA)	FERRARI	3HR 07MIN 03.4SEC
3. HAWTHORN (GB)	FERRARI	3HR 07MIN 20.6SEC
4. TRINTIGNANT(FRA)	FERRARI	88 LAPS
5. SALVADORI(GB)	COOPER-CLIMAX	85 LAPS
6. GERARD (GB)	COOPER-BRISTOL	82 LAPS

Race: 90 laps of 3mile/4.83km (270 miles/435kms)
Fastest lap: Moss, 1min 59.2sec, 90.6mph/145.8kph
Pole position: Moss, 2min 00.2sec 18 starters, 8 classified finishers

ROUND 6/GERMAN GRAND PRIX
NURBURGRING, 4 AUGUST

1. FANGIO(ARG)	MASERATI	3HR 30MIN 38.3SEC
2. HAWTHORN (GB)	FERRARI	3HR 30MIN 41.9SEC
3. COLLINS (GB)	FERRARI	3HR 31MIN 13.9SEC
4. MUSSO (ITA)	FERRARI	3HR 34MIN 15.9SEC
5. MOSS (GB)	VANWALL	3HR 35MIN 15.8SEC
6. BEHRA (FRA)	MASERATI	3HR 35MIN 16.8SEC

Race: 22 laps of 14.17mile/22.8km (312miles/501kms)
Fastest lap: Fangio, 9min 17.4sec, 91.5mph/147.3kph
Pole position: Fangio, 9min 25.6sec 24 starters, 15 classified finishers

RESULTS 1957/8

ROUND 7/ PESCARA GRAND PRIX

PESCARA, ITALY, 18 AUGUST

1. MOSS (GB)	VANWALL	2HR 59MIN 22.7SEC
2. FANGIO (ARG)	MASERATI	3HR 02MIN 36.6SEC
3. SCHELL (USA)	MASERATI	3HR 06MIN 09.5SEC
4. GREGORY(USA)	MASERATI	3HR 07MIN 27.8SEC
5. LEWIS-EVANS (GB)	VANWALL	17 LAPS
6. SCARLATTI (ITA)	MASERATI	17 LAPS

Race: 18 laps of 15.89mile/25.58km (286.02miles/460.44kms)
Fastest lap: Moss, 9min 44.6sec, 97.88mph/157.52kph
Pole position: Fangio, 9min 44.6sec 16 starters, 7 classified finishers

ROUND 8/ITALIAN GRAND PRIX

MONZA, 8 SEPTEMBER

1. MOSS(GB)	VANWALL	2HR 35MIN 03.9SEC
2. FANGIO (ARG)	MASERATI	2HR 35MIN 45.1SEC
3. VON TRIPS (GER)	FERRARI	85 LAPS
4. GREGORY(USA)	MASERATI	84 LAPS
5. SCHELL(USA)/SCARLATTI(ITA)	MASERATI	84 LAPS
6. HAWTHORN(GB)	FERRARI	83 LAPS

Race: 87 laps of 3.57mile/5.75km (311miles/500kms)
Fastest lap: Brooks(GB),Vanwall, 1min 43.7sec, 124.0mph/199kph
Pole position: Lewis-Evans(GB) Vanwall, 1min 42.4sec 18 starters, 11 classified finishers.

 DRIVERS' WORLD CHAMPIONSHIP 1957

1. FANGIO	40 *points*	4. HAWTHORN 13 *points*
2. MOSS	25 *points*	5. BROOKS 11 *points*
3. MUSSO	16 *points*	6. GREGORY 10 *points*

1958 Minimum race lengths were reduced to 300kms or two hours. The Constructors' World Title was introduced for the first time and went to a British team, Vanwall. There were two new Grand Prix venues, in Portugal and Morocco. British star Peter Collins lost his life at the Nurburgring and Stuart Lewis-Evans died from burns after an accident in Morocco. The calendar expanded to 11 races. Points: 8-6-4-3-2 for first five places, plus one point for fastest lap. Best SIX out of 11 races (including Indy).

RESULTS 1958

ROUND 1/ARGENTINE GRAND PRIX
BUENOS AIRES, 18 JANUARY

1. MOSS(GB)	COOPER-CLIMAX	2HR 19MIN 33.7SEC
2. MUSSO (ITA)	FERRARI	2HR 19MIN 36.4SEC
3. HAWTHORN (GB)	FERRARI	2HR 19MIN 46.3SEC
4. FANGIO(ARG)	MASERATI	2HR 20MIN 26.7SEC
5. BEHRA (FRA)	MASERATI	78 LAPS
6. SCHELL (USA)	MASERATI	77 LAPS

Race: 80 laps of 2.42mile/3.9km (194miles/ 312kms)
Fastest lap: Fangio, 1min 41.8sec, 85.96mph/138.34kph
Pole position: Fangio, 1min 42sec 10 starters, 9 classified finishers

ROUND 2/MONACO GRAND PRIX
MONTE CARLO, 18 MAY

1. TRINTIGNANT(FRA)	COOPER-CLIMAX	2HR 52MIN 27.9SEC
2. MUSSO (ITA)	FERRARI	2HR 52MIN 48.2SEC
3. COLLINS (GB)	FERRARI	2HR 53MIN 06.7SEC
4. BRABHAM (AUS)	COOPER-CLIMAX	97 LAPS
5. SCHELL (USA)	BRM	91 LAPS
6. ALLISON (GB)	LOTUS	90 LAPS

Race: 100 laps of 1.95mile/3.15km (195miles/ 315kms)
Fastest lap: Hawthorn(GB), Ferrari, 1min 40.6sec, 69.9mph/112.3kph
Pole position: Brooks(GB), Vanwall, 1min 39.08sec 16 starters, 6 classified finishers

ROUND 3/DUTCH GRAND PRIX
ZANDVOORT, 26 MAY

1. MOSS (GB)	VANWALL	2HR 4MIN 49.2SEC
2. SCHELL (USA)	BRM	2HR 5MIN 37.1SEC
3. BEHRA (FRA)	BRM	2HR 6MIN 31.5SEC
4. SALVADORI (GB)	COOPER-CLIMAX	74 LAPS
5. HAWTHORN (GB)	FERARRI	74 LAPS
6. ALLISON (GB)	LOTUS-CLIMAX	73 LAPS

Race: 75 laps of 2.6mile/4.19km (195miles/ 314km)
Fastest lap: Moss 1min 37.6sec, 96.1mph/154.6kph
Pole position: Lewis-Evans(GB), Vanwall, 1min 37.1sec, 17 starters, 11 class. finishers

ROUND 4/INDIANAPOLIS 500
INDIANAPOLIS, 30 MAY

1. BRYAN(USA)	BELOND	3HR 44MIN 13.8SEC
2. G. AMICK (USA)	DEMLER	
3. BOYD (USA)	BOWES SEAL FAST	
4. T.BETTENHAUSEN (USA)	JONES & MALEY	
5. J. RATHMANN(USA)	LEADER CARD	
6. REECE(USA)	JOHN ZINK SPECIAL	

Race: 200 laps of 2.5mile/4.02km
Fastest lap: Bettenhausen, 1min 02.37sec, 144.3mph/232.2kph
Pole position: D. Rathmann, McNamara 33 starters, 13 classified finishers

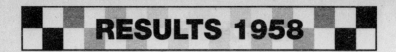

RESULTS 1958

ROUND 4/ EUROPEAN GRAND PRIX

SPA-FRANCORCHAMPS, 15 JUNE

1. BROOKS (GB)	VANWALL	1HR 37MIN 6.3SEC
2. HAWTHORN(GB)	FERRARI	1HR 37MIN 27.0SEC
3. LEWIS-EVANS (GB)	VANWALL	1HR 40MIN 7.2SEC
4. ALLISON (GB)	LOTUS-CLIMAX	1HR 41MIN 21.8SEC
5. SCHELL(USA)	BRM	23 LAPS
6. GENDEBIEN (BEL)	FERRARI	23 LAPS

Race: 24 laps of 8.76mile/14.1km (210miles/338kms)
Fastest lap: Hawthorn,3min 58.3sec, 132.36mph/213.01kph
Pole position: Hawthorn, 3min 57.1sec 19 starters, 10 classified finishers

ROUND 4 /INDIANAPOLIS 500

INDIANAPOLIS, 30 MAY

1. BRYAN (USA)	BELOND AP	3HR 4MIN 13.8SEC
2. G. AMICK (USA)	DEMLER	
3. BOYD (USA)	BOWLES SEAL FAST	
4. BETTENHAUSEN (USA)	JONES MALEY	
5. J. RATHMANN (USA)	LEADER CARD	
6. REECE (USA)	JOHN ZINK SPECIAL	

Race: 200 laps of 2.5mile/4.02km
Fastest lap: Bettenhausen, 1min 02.37sec. 144.3mph/232.2kph
Pole position: D. Rathmann, McNamara 33 starters, 13 classified finishers

ROUND 6/FRENCH GRAND PRIX

REIMS, 7 JULY

1. HAWTHORN (GB)	FERRARI	2HR 3MIN 21.3SEC
2. MOSS (GB)	VANWALL	2HR 3MIN 45.9SEC
3. VON TRIPS (GER)	FERRARI	2HR 4MIN 21.0SEC
4. FANGIO (ARG)	MASERATI	2HR 5MIN 9.0SEC
5. COLLINS (GB)	FERRARI	2HR 8MIN 46.2SEC
6. BRABHAM (AUS)	COOPER-CLIMAX	49 LAPS

Race: 50 laps of 5.16mile/8.3km (258miles/415kms)
Fastest lap: Hawthorn, 2min 24.9sec, 128.17mph/206.26kph
Pole position: Hawthorn, 2min 21.7sec 21 starters, 11 classified finishers

ROUND 7/ BRITISH GRAND PRIX

SILVERSTONE, 19 JULY

1. COLLINS (GB)	FERRARI	2HR 9MIN 4.2SEC
2. HAWTHORN (GB)	FERRARI	2HR 9MIN 28.4SEC
3. SALVADORI (GB)	COOPER-CLIMAX	2HR 9MIN 54.8SEC
4. LEWIS-EVANS (GB)	VANWALL	2HR 9MIN 55.0SEC
5. SCHELL(USA)	BRM	2HR 10MIN 19SEC
6. BRABHAM (AUS)	COOPER-CLIMAX	2HR 10MIN 27.4SEC

Race: 75 laps of 2.9mile/4.7km (258miles/352.5kms)
Fastest lap: Hawthorn, 1min 40.8sec, 104.5mph/168.2kph
Pole position: Moss (GB), Vanwall, 1min 39.4sec 20 starters, 9 classified finishers

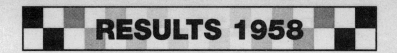

RESULTS 1958

ROUND 8/GERMAN GRAND PRIX
NURBURGRING, 3 AUGUST

1. BROOKS (GB)	VANWALL	2HR 21MIN 15.0SEC
2. SALVADORI (GB)	COOPER-CLIMAX	2HR 24MIN 44.7SEC
3. TRINTIGNANT (FRA)	COOPER-CLIMAX	2HR 26MIN 26.2SEC
4. VON TRIPS (GER)	FERRARI	2HR 27MIN 31.3SEC
5. MCLAREN (NZ)	COOPER-CLIMAX	2HR 27MIN 41.3SEC
6. BARTH(GER)	PORSCHE	2HR 27MIN 47.4SEC

Race: 15 laps of 14.17mile/22.8km (213miles/342kms)
Fastest lap: Moss(GB), Vanwall, 9min 9.2sec, 92.9mph/149.5kph
Pole position: Hawthorn (GB), Ferrari, 9min 14.0sec 25 starters, 10 classified finishers

ROUND 9/PORTUGUESE GRAND PRIX
OPORTO, 24 AUGUST

1. MOSS (GB)	VANWALL	2HR 11MIN 27.8SEC
2. HAWTHORN (GB)	FERRARI	2HR 16MIN 40.5SEC
3. LEWIS-EVANS (GB)	VANWALL	49 LAPS
4. BEHRA (FRA)	BRM	49 LAPS
5. VON TRIPS (GER)	FERRARI	49 LAPS
6. SCHELL (USA)	BRM	49 LAPS

Race: 50 laps of 4.6mile/7.41km (230miles/370kms)
Fastest lap: Hawthorn, 2min 32.37sec, 108.7mph/175kph
Pole position: Moss, 2min 34.2sec 15 starters, 9 classified finishers

ROUND 10/ITALIAN GRAND PRIX
MONZA, 7 SEPTEMBER

1. BROOKS(GB)	VANWALL	2HR 3MIN 47.8SEC
2. HAWTHORN (GB)	FERRARI	2HR 4MIN 12.0SEC
3. PHIL HILL (USA)	FERRARI	2HR 4MIN 16.1SEC
4. SHELBY(USA)/GREGORY(USA)	MASERATI	69 LAPS
5. SALVADORI (GB)	COOPER-CLIMAX	62 LAPS
6. GRAHAM HILL (GB)	LOTUS-CLIMAX	62 LAPS

Race: 70 laps of 3.57mile/5.75km (250miles/402kms)
Fastest lap: Phil Hill, 1min 42.9sec, 125.0mph/201.17kph
Pole position: Moss(GB), Vanwall, 1min 40.5sec 21 starters, 7 classified finishers

ROUND 11/ MOROCCAN GRAND PRIX
AIN-DIAB, CASABLANCA, 19 OCTOBER

1. MOSS(GB)	VANWALL	2HR 9MIN 15.1SEC
2. HAWTHORN (GB)	FERRARI	2HR 10MIN 39.8SEC
3. P. HILL (USA)	FERRARI	2HR 10MIN 40.6SEC
4. BONNIER (SWE)	BRM	2HR 11MIN 01.8SEC
5. SCHELL (USA)	BRM	2HR 11MIN 48.8SEC
6. GREGORY(USA)	MASERATI	52 LAPS

Race: 53 laps of 4.73mile/7.62km (250miles/404kms)
Fastest lap: Moss, 2min 22.5sec, 119.3mph/192kph
Pole position: Hawthorn, 2min 23.1sec 25 starters, 16 classified finishers

RESULTS 1958/9

DRIVERS' WORLD CHAMPIONSHIP 1958

1. HAWTHORN 42 *points*	4. SALVADORI	15 *points*
2. MOSS	41 *points*	5. COLLINS	14 *points*
3. BROOKS	24 *points*	5. SCHELL	14 *points*

CONSTRUCTORS' WORLD CHAMPIONSHIP 1958

1. VANWALL	48 *points*	4. BRM	18 *points*
2. FERRARI	40 *points*	5. MASERATI	17 *points*
3. COOPER/CLIMAX	31 *points*	6. LOTUS-CLIMAX	3 *points*

1959 The year started on a sombre note with the death of World Champion, Mike Hawthorn, in a road accident. Vanwall withdrew from the fray. The Antipodean challenge materialised. There were nine rounds. The USA hosted a Grand Prix for the first time in history. Points: 8-6-4-3-2 for first five places, plus one point for fastest lap. Best FIVE out of nine races including Indy.

ROUND 1/ MONACO GRAND PRIX

MONTE CARLO, 10 MAY

1. BRABHAM(AUS)	COOPER-CLIMAX	2HR 55MIN 51.3SEC
2. BROOKS (GB)	FERRARI	2HR 56MIN 11.7SEC
3. TRINTIGNANT (FRA)	COOPER-CLIMAX	98 LAPS
4. P. HILL (USA)	FERRARI	97 LAPS
5. MCLAREN (NZ)	COOPER-CLIMAX	96 LAPS
6. SALVADORI (GB)	COOPER-MASERATI	83 LAPS

Race: 100 laps of 1.95mile/3.15km (195mile/ 315kms)
Fastest lap: Brabham, 1min 40.4sec, 70.1mph/112.7kph
Pole position: Moss, Cooper-Climax, 1min 39.6sec 16 starters, 6 classified finishers

INDIANAPOLIS 500

INDIANAPOLIS, 30 MAY

1. WARD(USA)	LEADER CARD	3HR 40MIN 20SEC
2. J. RATHMANN(USA)	SIMONIZ	
3. THOMSON(USA)	RACING ASSOCIATES	
4. BETTENHAUSEN (USA)	HOOVER	
5. GOLDSMITH (USA)	DEMLER	
6. BOYD (USA)	BOWES SEAL FAST	

Race: 200 laps of 2.5mile/4.02kms
Fastest lap: Thomson, 1min 01.89sec, 145.42mph/234kph
Pole position: Thomson 33 starters, 16 classified finishers

RESULTS 1959

ROUND 3/DUTCH GRAND PRIX

ZANDVOORT, 31 MAY

1. BONNIER (SWE)	BRM	2HR 5MIN 26.8SEC
2. BRABHAM (AUS)	COOPER-CLIMAX	2HR 5MIN 41.0SEC
3. GREGORY (USA)	COOPER-CLIMAX	2HR 6MIN 49.8SEC
4. IRELAND(GB)	LOTUS	74 LAPS
5. BEHRA(FRA)	FERRARI	74 LAPS
6. P. HILL (USA)	FERRARI	73 LAPS

Race: 75 laps of 2.6mile/ 4.2km (195 miles/ 315kms)
Fastest lap: Moss(GB), Cooper-Climax, 1min 36.7mph, 96.9mph/156kph
Pole position: Bonnier, 1min 36.0sec 15 starters, 10 classified finishers

ROUND 4/ EUROPEAN GRAND PRIX

REIMS, 5 JULY

1. BROOKS(GB)	FERRARI	2HR 1MIN 26.5SEC
2. P. HILL(USA)	FERRARI	2HR 1MIN 54.0SEC
3. BRABHAM(AUS)	COOPER-CLIMAX	2HR 3MIN 04.2SEC
4. GENDEBIEN (BEL)	FERRARI	2HR 3MIN 14SEC
5. MCLAREN(NZ)	COOPER-CLIMAX	2HR 3MIN 14.2SEC
6. FLOCKHART (GB)	BRM	2HR 3MIN 32.2SEC

Race: 50 laps of 5.16mile//8.3km (258miles/415kms)
Fastest lap: Moss(GB), BRM, 2min 22.8sec, 130mph/ 209kph
Pole position: Brooks, 2min 19.4sec 21 starters, 12 classified finishers

ROUND 5/BRITISH GRAND PRIX

AINTREE, 18 JULY

1. BRABHAM (AUS)	COOPER-CLIMAX	2HR 30MIN 11.6SEC
2. MOSS (GB)	BRM	2HR 30MIN 33.8SEC
3. MCLAREN(NZ)	COOPER-CLIMAX	2HR 30MIN 34.0SEC
4. SCHELL(USA)	BRM	74 LAPS
5. TRINTIGNANT (FRA)	COOPER-CLIMAX	74 LAPS
6. SALVADORI (GB)	ASTON-MARTIN	74 LAPS

Race: 75laps of 3mile/4.83km (25miles/362kms)
Fastest lap: Moss/McLaren, 1min 57sec, 92.3mph/ 148.5kph
Pole position: Brabham, 1min 58.0sec 18 starters, 9 classified finishers

ROUND 6/GERMAN GRAND PRIX

AVUS, BERLIN, 2 AUGUST

1. BROOKS (GB)	FERRARI	2HR 9MIN 31.6SEC
2. GURNEY(USA)	FERRARI	2HR 9MIN 2.2SEC
3. P. HILL (USA)	FERRARI	2HR 10MIN 36.7SEC
4. TRINTIGNANT (FRA)	COOPER-CLIMAX	59 LAPS
5. BONNIER (SWE)	BRM	58 LAPS
6. BURGESS(GB)	COOPER-MASERATI	56 LAPS

Race: 60 laps of 5.16mile/8.3km (309miles/498kms)
Fastest lap: Brooks, 2min 4.5sec, 149.0mph/240kph
Pole position: Brooks, 2min 05.9sec 15 starters, 7 classified finishers

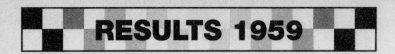

RESULTS 1959

ROUND 7/ PORTUGUESE GRAND PRIX

MONSANTO, LISBON, 23 AUGUST

1. MOSS(GB)	COOPER-CLIMAX	2HR 11MIN 55.41SEC
2. GREGORY(USA)	COOPER-CLIMAX	61 LAPS
3. GURNEY(USA)	FERRARI	61 LAPS
4. TRINTIGNANT(FRA)	COOPER-CLIMAX	60 LAPS
5. SCHELL (USA)	BRM	59 LAPS
6. SALVADORI (GB)	ASTON MARTIN	59 LAPS

Race: 62 laps os 3.38 miles/5.44kms (209miles/336.35kms)
Fastest lap: Moss, 2min 5.07sec, 97.3mph/156.58kph
Pole position: Moss, 2min 02.9sec 16 starters, 10 classified finishers

ROUND 8/ITALIAN GRAND PRIX

MONZA, 13 SEPTEMBER

1. MOSS (GB)	COOPER-CLIMAX	2HR 4MIN 5.4SEC
2. P.HILL (USA)	FERRARI	2HR 4MIN 52.1SEC
3. BRABHAM (AUS)	COOPER-CLIMAX	2HR 5MIN 17.9SEC
4. GURNEY (USA)	FERRARI	2HR 5MIN 25.0SEC
5. ALLISON (GB)	FERRARI	71 LAPS
6. GENDEBIEN (BEL)	FERRARI	71 LAPS

Race: 72 laps of 3.57mile/5.75km (257miles/414kms)
Fastest lap: P. Hill, 1min 40.4sec, 128.13mph/ 206.2kph
Pole position: Moss, 1min 39.7sec 21 starters, 15 classified finishers

US GRAND PRIX

SEBRING, FLORIDA, 12 DECEMBER

1. MCLAREN(NZ)	COOPER-CLIMAX	2HR 12MIN 35.7SEC
2. TRINTIGNANT(FRA)	COOPER-CLIMAX	2HR 12MIN 36.3SEC
3. BROOKS (GB)	FERRARI	2HR 15MIN 36.6SEC
4. BRABHAM (AUS)	COOPER-CLIMAX	2HR 17MIN 33.0SEC
5. IRELAND (GB)	LOTUS-CLIMAX	39 LAPS
6. VON TRIPS (GER)	FERRARI	38 LAPS

Race: 42 laps of 5.2mile/ 8.37km (218miles/ 351kms)
Fastest lap: Trintignant, 3min 5.0sec, 101.1mph/162.8kph
Pole position: Moss(GB), Cooper-Climax, 3min 00sec 18 starters, 7 classified finishers

 DRIVERS' WORLD CHAMPIONSHIP 1959

1. BRABHAM	31 points	4. P.HILL	20 points
2. BROOKS	27 points	5. TRINTIGNANT	19 points
3. MOSS	25.5 points	6. MCLAREN	16.5 points

CONSTRUCTORS' WORLD CHAMPIONSHIP 1959

1. COOPER/CLIMAX	40 points	3. BRM	18 points
2. FERRARI	32 points	4. LOTUS-CLIMAX	5 points

1960s

QUIZ & FACT

QUIZ 1

Answers on page 52

1 **Who won the 1960 World Drivers' Championship?**
   a. Phil Hill   *b.* Graham Hill   *c.* Jack Brabham

2 **Which youthful Antipodean driver took his second successive victory in a World Championship Grand Prix in the first round of 1960 in Argentina?**
   a. Jack Brabham   *b.* Denny Hulme   *c.* Bruce McLaren

3 **Which British driver brought his Ferrari home in a career-best second place in the same race?**
   a. Tony Brooks   *b.* Cliff Allison   *c.* Innes Ireland

4 **Who designed the trend-setting, space frame, Lotus 18 for the 1960 season?**
   a. Colin Chapman   *b.* Colin Vandervell   *c.* Frank Costin

5 **Who claimed the first ever Grand Prix win for a Lotus at Monaco in 1960?**
   a. Stirling Moss   *b.* John Surtees   *c.* Graham Hill

6 **What colour was the car?**
   a. Green   *b.* Red   *c.* Blue

7 **Which Scottish driver, who was to become a double World Champion, made his Formula One debut for Team Lotus in the Dutch Grand Prix?**
   a. Jackie Stewart   *b.* Bruce McLaren   *c.* Jim Clark

8 **What was his profession before he became a racing driver?**
   a. Farmer   *b.* Fisherman   *c.* Lorry driver

9 **Which former World Motorcycle Champion contested the 1960 British Grand Prix for Lotus?**
   a. Mike Hailwood   *b.* Geoff Duke   *c.* John Surtees

10 **Who flagged off the 1960 British Grand Prix?**
   a. The Queen   *b.* Stirling Moss   *c.* The Prime Minister

---

Answers to page 52
1 *a.*Scottish 2 *c.*Indianapolis 3 *c.*Phil Hill 4 *b.*Ferrari 5 *c.*Wolfgang von Trips
6 *b.*Giancarlo Baghetti 7 *c.*Porsche 8 *c.*Stirling Moss 9 *b.*Innes Ireland 10 *b.*Tony Brooks

QUIZ 2

Answers on page 53

1 **What was the nickname of Ferrari's great German driver Wolfgang von Trips?**
a. Hermann   *b. Taffy*   *c. Wolfie*

2 **Which British driver, later to win two World titles, emerged as BRM team-leader in 1960?**
a. Graham Hill   *b. Jim Clark*   *c. Innes Ireland*

3 **Where did he finish in the 1960 British Grand Prix?**
a. First   *b. Did not finish*   *c. Third*

4 **How many successive races did Jack Brabham win for Cooper in 1960?**
a. Two   *b. Five*   *c. Seven*

5 **What was his nickname?**
a. Jacko   *b. Black Jack*   *c. Brabs*

6 **Why was Stirling Moss disqualified from the 1960 Portuguese Grand Prix?**
a. Overtaking on the parade lap   *b. Overtaking under a yellow flag*
c. Driving in the wrong direction

7 **Who became the first American driver ever to win a Grand Prix at Monza in 1960?**
a. Dan Gurney   *b. Phil Hill*   *c. Graham Hill*

8 **Where was the 1960 United States Grand Prix held?**
a. Dockside   *b. Long Beach*   *c. Riverside*

9 **Which highly popular, fun-loving, British 'hell-raiser' finished second in the States?**
a. Innes Ireland   *b. John Surtees*   *c. Stirling Moss*

10 **Who won the Constructors' Championship for a second successive year in 1960?**
a. Cooper-Climax   *b. Ferrari*   *c. Lotus-Climax*

Answers to page 53
1 *b.*Stirling Moss **2** *c.*Goodwood **3** *b.*BRM **4** *c.*Spa **5** *b.*Dan Gurney **6** *b.*Graham
Hill **7** *a.*Jim Clark **8** *c.*Lola **9** *c.*Jack Brabham **10** *c.*South Africa

---

QUIZ 3

Answers on page 50

1 **What nationality was Innes Ireland?**
   a. Scottish   b. Irish   c. Welsh

2 **Which race, which had been part of the World Championship from the beginning, was dropped in 1961?**
   a. Monaco Grand Prix   b. Italian Grand Prix   c. Indianapolis

3 **Which American driver won the 1961 World Drivers' title?**
   a. Dan Gurney   b. Richie Ginther   c. Phil Hill

4 **And which team clinched the Constructors' Championship for the first time in 1961?**
   a. Lotus   b. Ferrari   c. Porsche

5 **Which great German driver, who was later to die in a tragic accident at Monza, won both the Dutch and the British Grands Prix in 1961?**
   a. Hans Herrmann   b. Hans Stuck   c. Wolfgang von Trips

6 **Can you name the Italian driver who won the French Grand Prix at Reims in his very first World Championship outing in 1961?**
   a. Gianni Spagheti   b. Giancarlo Baghetti   c. Roy Salvadori

7 **Which famous German manufacturer finished third overall in the 1961 Constructors' title chase?**
   a. Mercedes   b. Auto Union   c. Porsche

8 **Which great British driver won a Grand Prix, for what was to prove the last time in his illustrious career, at the Nurburgring in 1961?**
   a. Tony Brooks   b. Tim Parnell   c. Stirling Moss

9 **Which British driver took the one and only win in his Grand Prix career in the United States Grand Prix at Watkins Glen in 1961?**
   a. Tony Marsh   b. Innes Ireland   c. Henry Taylor

10 **Which British hero retired from Grand Prix racing at the end of the year?**
   a. Graham Hill   b. Tony Brooks   c. Jim Clark

Answers to page 50
1 *a.*Jack Brabham 2 *c.*Bruce McLaren 3 *b.*Cliff Allison 4 *a.*Colin Chapman
5 *a.*Stirling Moss 6 *c.*Blue 7 *c.*Jim Clark 8 *a.*Farmer 9 *c.*John Surtees
10 *b.*Stirling Moss

QUIZ 4

Answers on page 51

1 **Which British super star was seriously injured before the start of the 1962 season?**
   a. Graham Hill   *b.* Stirling Moss   *c.* Jim Clark

2 **Where did the accident happen?**
   a. On the road   *b.* Silverstone   *c.* Goodwood

3 **Graham Hill won his first World Championship race in Zandvoort, Holland in 1962. For which team was he driving?**
   a. Porsche   *b.* BRM   *c.* Lotus

4 **Jim Clark won the first race of his World Championship career in 1962. Where?**
   a. Silverstone   *b.* Monaco   *c.* Spa

5 **Which American driver claimed both his and Porsche's first ever World Championship win in the 1962 French Grand Prix at Rouen?**
   a. Phil Hill   *b.* Dan Gurney   *c.* Mario Andretti

6 **Which British driver won the 1962 Drivers' title?**
   a. Jim Clark   *b.* Graham Hill   *c.* Innes Ireland

7 **Which British driver finished second in the Championship?**
   a. Jim Clark   *b.* Graham Hill   *c.* Innes Ireland

8 **For which British team did John Surtees drive in 1962?**
   a. Lotus   *b.* Leyton House   *c.* Lola

9 **The very first Brabham Formula One car made its debut at the Nurburgring in 1962. Who drove it?**
   a. Bruce McLaren   *b.* Denny Hulme   *c.* Jack Brabham

10 **The 1962 title chase went down to the wire in the last race of the series which was held in a country which had never staged a Grand Prix before. Where was it?**
   a. Brazil   *b.* Australia   *c.* South Africa

Answers to page 51
1 *b.*Taffy   **2** *a.*Graham Hill   **3** *b.*Did not finish   **4** *b.*Five   **5** *b.*Black Jack   **6** *c.*Driving in the wrong direction   **7** *b.*Phil Hill   **8** *c.*Riverside   **9** *a.*Innes Ireland
10 *a.*Cooper-Climax

QUIZ 5

Answers on page 56

1 **Which British driver won the 1963 World Championship for Lotus?**
   a. Graham Hill *b. Jim Hall* *c. Jim Clark*

2 **How many races did he win in the season?**
   a. Five *b. Seven* *c. Nine*

3 **Which British driver joined Ferrari for the 1963 season?**
   a. Innes Ireland *b. John Surtees* *c. Graham Hill*

4 **Which New Zealand driver made his Formula One debut in 1963 at the age of 19 in a Parnell Racing Lola?**
   a. Denny Hulme *b. Chris Amon* *c. Bruce McLaren*

5 **Where did Ferrari finish in the 1963 World Constructors' Championship?**
   a. Second *b. Third* *c. Fourth*

6 **Which British driver scored his first ever victory, and Ferrari's only Grand Prix win of the year, at the Nurburgring in 1963?**
   a. John Surtees *b. Phil Hill* *c. Lorenzo Bandini*

7 **Who won the 1963 Constructors' title?**
   a. BRM *b. Brabham-Climax* *c. Lotus-Climax*

8 **Which central American country hosted a Grand Prix for the first time in 1963?**
   a. Honduras *b. Guatemala* *c. Mexico*

9 **The series returned to South Africa for the final round of the 1963 series. Who won the race to overtake Fangio's record and notch up seven wins in one season?**
   a. Graham Hill *b. Jim Clark* *c. Jack Brabham*

10 **Which American driver drove his heart out to give the Brabham-Climax its best Championship result of the year? He finished second in the 1963 South African Grand Prix at East London.**
   a. Phil Hill *b. Dan Gurney* *c. Mario Andretti*

Answers to page 56
1 *c.*Dan Gurney **2** *b.*American **3** *b.*Brands Hatch **4** *a.*Jim Clark **5** *c.*Honda
6 *a.*Did not finish **7** *a.*Zeltweg **8** *a.*Lorenzo Bandini **9** *c.*Graham Hill **10** *c.*John Surtees

---

QUIZ 6

Answers on page 57

1 **How many Grands Prix did Graham Hill and Jim Clark win between them from 1962 to 1966?**
a. 29   b. 39   c. 49

2 **Who became the first and, to date, the only man to win both two-wheel and four-wheel World Championships in 1964?**
a. Barry Sheene   b. Mike Hailwood   c. John Surtees

3 **What was his margin of victory in the Championship over second-place man, Graham Hill?**
a. half a point   b. one point   c. 10 points

4 **For which team did he drive?**
a. McLaren   b. Ferrari   c. BRM

5 **Who won the Constructors' title for the second time in Championship history?**
a. Brabham   b. BRM   c. Ferrari

6 **Which former motorcycle World Champion finished sixth in the 1964 Monaco Grand Prix in a Lotus?**
a. Giacomo Agostini   b. John Surtees   c. Mike Hailwood

7 **What was his nickname?**
a. Woodie   b. Mike the Bike   c. Mikey

8 **Which British driver led from start to finish in his Lotus in the 1964 Dutch Grand Prix?**
a. Mike Hailwood   b. Peter Arundell   c. Jim Clark

9 **Which devastatingly handsome heir to a major cosmetic company empire made his Grand Prix debut in a Lotus at Spa in 1964?**
a. Peter Lauder   b. Peter Grimaldi   c. Peter Revson

10 **What nationality was he?**
a. French   b. American   c. Italian

Answers to page 57
1 *a.*Jochen Rindt **2** *b.*Jackie Stewart **3** *c.*BRM **4** *b.*Sixth **5** *b.*Jim Clark **6** *c.*Six
7 *c.*Graham Hill **8** *c.*He was busy winning the Indy 500 **9** *c.*Denny Hulme
10 *c.*Jackie Stewart

QUIZ 7

Answers on page 54

1 **Which driver gave the Brabham its first World Championship victory in the 1964 French Grand Prix?**
   a. Jack Brabham   *b.* Jo Siffert   *c.* Dan Gurney

2 **What nationality was he?**
   a. Australian   *b.* American   *c.* Austrian

3 **Which British circuit hosted the Championship Grand Prix for the first time in 1964?**
   a. Goodwood   *b.* Brands Hatch   *c.* Brooklands

4 **Which British driver won the race?**
   a. Jim Clark   *b.* Graham Hill   *c.* John Surtees

5 **Which Japanese car made its Championship debut at the Nurburgring in 1964?**
   a. Toyota   *b.* Maki   *c.* Honda

6 **Where did it finish?**
   a. Did not finish   *b.* Eighth   *c.* Tenth

7 **Where was the first ever Austrian Grand Prix held in 1964?**
   a. Zeltweg   *b.* Zolder   *c.* Salzburg

8 **Which popular Italian driver, who was to lose his life tragically in Monaco in 1967, claimed his sole career victory for Ferrari in Austria?**
   a. Lorenzo Bandini   *b.* Vittorio Brambilla   *c.* Giancarlo Baghetti

9 **Who won the 1964 US Grand Prix at Watkins Glen for BRM to keep his Championship hopes alive?**
   a. Richie Ginther   *b.* Innes Ireland   *c.* Graham Hill

10 **Who finished second in Mexico to secure the 1964 titles for himself and his team?**
   a. Jim Clark   *b.* Graham Hill   *c.* John Surtees

Answers to page 54
1 *a.*Jim Clark **2** *b.*Seven **3** *b.*John Surtees **4** *b.*Chris Amon **5** *c.*Fourth **6** *a.*John Surtees **7** *c.*Lotus-Climax **8** *c.*Mexico **9** *b.*Jim Clark **10** *b.*Dan Gurney

---

QUIZ 8

Answers on page 55

1 **Who made his Grand Prix debut in front of his home crowd in Austria in 1964?**
   a. Jochen Rindt   *b.* Clay Regazzoni   *c.* Gerhard Mitter

2 **Which British driver, later to become a triple world title holder, made his Grand Prix debut in the first round of the 1965 season in South Africa?**
   a. Jackie Stewart   *b.* Peter Arundell   *c.* Richard (Dickie) Attwood

3 **In which car?**
   a. Lotus   *b.* Tyrrell   *c.* BRM

4 **Where did he finish?**
   a. First   *b.* Sixth   *c.* Did not finish

5 **Which British driver won the 1965 World Drivers' title for Lotus?**
   a. Jackie Stewart   *b.* Jim Clark   *c.* Graham Hill

6 **How many of the season's ten Grands Prix did he win?**
   a. Two   *b.* Four   *c.* Six

7 **Who notched up his third successive Monaco victory for BRM in 1965?**
   a. Richie Ginther   *b.* Maurice Trintignant   *c.* Graham Hill

8 **Why did Jim Clark miss the 1965 Monaco Grand Prix?**
   a. He was injured   *b.* He missed his flight
   c. He was busy winning the Indy 500

9 **Which New Zealand driver, later to become a World Champion, made his debut for Brabham in the 1965 Monaco Grand Prix?**
   a. Howden Ganley   *b.* Bruce McLaren   *c.* Denny Hulme

10 **Who beat his illustrious BRM team-mate, Graham Hill, to snatch his first Grand Prix victory at Monza in 1965?**
   a. Jochen Rindt   *b.* Masten Gregory   *c.* Jackie Stewart

---

Answers to page 55

1 *a.*29   **2** *c.*John Surtees   **3** *b.*one point   **4** *b.*Ferrari   **5** *c.*Ferrari   **6** *c.*Mike Hailwood
7 *b.*Mike the Bike   **8** *c.*Jim Clark   **9** *c.*Peter Revson   **10** *b.*American

---

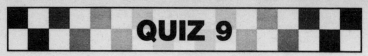

QUIZ 9

Answers on page 62

1   Who won the US Grand Prix for the third year in succession in 1965?
    a. Jack Brabham   *b.* Jim Clark   *c.* Graham Hill

2   Which American driver scored the only Grand Prix victory of his career in Mexico in 1965?
    a. Ronnie Bucknum   *b.* Richie Ginther   *c.* Al Unser

3   Which Japanese-powered car was he driving?
    a. Honda   *b.* Yamaha   *c.* Toyota

4   Which British driver, later to die tragically in practice for the 1968 Indianapolis 500, achieved a career best third-place finish for Lotus in Mexico in 1965?
    a. Dickie Attwood   *b.* Mike Spence   *c.* Bob Anderson

5   Who won the 1966 World Championship in a car bearing his own name?
    a. John Surtees   *b.* Bruce McLaren   *c.* Jack Brabham

6   Who was his New Zealand team-mate?
    a. Larry Perkins   *b.* Howden Ganley   *c.* Denny Hulme

7   What was his nickname?
    a. Big Den   *b.* Kiwi Den   *c.* The Bear

8   Which engine did Bruce McLaren use to power his car in the 1966 British Grand Prix?
    a. Ford   *b.* Serenissima   *c.* Repco

9   How many successive Grands Prix did Jack Brabham win in 1966?
    a. Three   *b.* Four   *c.* Seven

10 Which British Ferrari driver finished second in the first Grand Prix of his career at Reims in 1966?
    a. Mike Spence   *b.* Mike Parkes   *c.* Mike Hailwood

Answers to page 60
1 *c.* Graham Hill **2** *a.* Ford-Cosworth **3** *c.* Lotus **4** *c.* Jim Clark **5** *b.* Dan Gurney
6 *b.* Eagle-Weslake **7** *b.* Five **8** *c.* Toronto **9** *c.* Jacky Ickx **10** *c.* Brabham

QUIZ 10

Answers on page 61

1 **Which Italian driver claimed his first and only Grand Prix victory for Ferrari at Monza in 1966?**
   a. Consalvo Sanesi   *b.* Giorgio Scarlatti   *c.* Ludovico Scarfiotti

2 **Which British driver, sadly killed in a road accident in 1977, made the home fans delirious, finishing second and making it a Ferrari one-two?**
   a. John Surtees   *b.* Graham Hill   *c.* Mike Parkes

3 **Which brewing company heir made his Grand Prix debut in the 1966 German Grand Prix at the Nurburgring?**
   a. Phil Carling   *b.* Piers Courage   *c.* Jan Carlsberg

4 **Which ebullient, fun-loving, Scottish driver made his last Grand Prix appearance in the 1966 Mexican Grand Prix for BRM?**
   a. Jim Clark   *b.* Jackie Stewart   *c.* Innes Ireland

5 **Which British driver, a former World Champion, won the season's final round in Mexico for Cooper-Maserati?**
   a. Graham Hill   *b.* John Surtees   *c.* Jim Clark

6 **Who became the first Mexican driver ever to win a Grand Prix in the opening round of the 1967 season in South Africa?**
   a. Pedro Lamy   *b.* Pedro Rodriguez   *c.* Ricardo Rodriguez

7 **Which Southern African driver finished second?**
   a. Guy Tumner   *b.* Ian Scheckter   *c.* John Love

8 **Which New Zealand driver took his first ever Grand Prix victory at Monaco in 1967?**
   a. Bruce McLaren   *b.* Denny Hulme   *c.* Chris Amon

9 **Which car was he driving?**
   a. McLaren   *b.* Amon   *c.* Brabham

10 **Where did he finish in the 1967 World Drivers' Championship?**
   a. First   *b.* Second   *c.* Fourth

Answers to page 61

1 *b.* Jim Clark   2 *c.* 25   3 *c.* Graham Hill   4 *c.* Richard Attwood   5 *b.* Graham Hill
6 *c.* Bruce McLaren   7 *c.* Matra   8 *a.* Jacky Ickx   9 *c.* Jo Siffert   10 *c.* Mario Andretti

---

59

QUIZ 11

Answers on page 58

1   **Which British driver joined Jim Clark in the Lotus works team for 1967?**
    a. John Surtees   *b.* Mike Hailwood   *c.* Graham Hill

2   **Which legendary engine made its debut in the 1967 Dutch Grand Prix at Zandvoort?**
    a. Ford-Cosworth   *b.* Tecno   *c.* Repco

3   **Which car did it power?**
    a. Brabham   *b.* Eagle   *c.* Lotus

4   **Who won the 1967 Dutch Grand Prix first time out in the Lotus 49?**
    a. Jackie Stewart   *b.* Graham Hill   *c.* Jim Clark

5   **Which American driver won the 1967 Belgian Grand Prix at Spa in his own car?**
    a. Mario Andretti   *b.* Dan Gurney   *c.* Carol Shelby

6   **In which high-flying car?**
    a. Shelby-Cobra   *b.* Eagle-Weslake   *c.* Falcon-Ford

7   **How many British Grands Prix wins did Jim Clark score between 1962 - 1967?**
    a. Four   *b.* Five   *c.* Six

8   **Canada hosted its first ever Grand Prix in 1967 at Mosport Park, outside which major city?**
    a. Montreal   *b.* Vancouver   *c.* Toronto

9   **Which Belgian driver, later to become a Ferrari team-leader, finished sixth in the 1967 Italian Grand Prix at Monza?**
    a. Thierry Boutsen   *b.* Bruno Thiry   *c.* Jacky Ickx

10 **Which team won the 1967 World Constructors' title?**
    a. Eagle   *b.* Lotus   *c.* Brabham

Answers to page 62
1 *a.*Jackie Stewart **2** *c.*Six **3** *c.*Matra **4** *c.*Jacky Ickx **5** *c.*Vic Elford **6** *b.*Mario Andretti **7** *b.*Johnny Servoz-Gavin **8** *c.*Jochen Rindt **9** *b.*Piers Courage **10** *c.*Graham Hill

QUIZ 12

Answers on page 59

1 Which double World Champion died on April 7th 1968 in a
   Formula Two race at the Hockenheim circuit in Germany?
   a. Jack Brabham   **b.** Jim Clark   **c.** Graham Hill

2 How many Grand Prix victories did he win during his career?
   a. 21   **b.** 24   **c.** 25

3 Which British driver became the first man to win Monaco four
   times in 1968?
   a. Jackie Stewart   **b.** John Surtees   **c.** Graham Hill

4 Which British driver finished second in the race in a BRM to
   claim the best ever finish of his Grand Prix career?
   a. Piers Courage   **b.** Jackie Oliver   **c.** Richard Attwood

5 Who won the 1968 World Drivers' Championship?
   a. Jackie Stewart   **b.** Graham Hill   **c.** Denny Hulme

6 Which Antipodean driver won the 1968 Belgain Grand Prix at
   Spa in a car bearing his own name?
   a. Chris Amon   **b.** Jack Brabham   **c.** Bruce McLaren

7 Which French car savoured its first Grand Prix triumph at
   Zandvoort in 1968 in the hands of Jackie Stewart?
   a. Talbot   **b.** Ligier   **c.** Matra

8 Which Belgian driver claimed his first World Championship
   victory in the rain-soaked 1968 French Grand Prix?
   a. Jacky Ickx   **b.** Teddy Pilette   **c.** Lucien Bianchi

9 Who becme the very first Swiss driver to win a Grand Prix at
   Brands Hatch in 1968?
   a. Marc Surer   **b.** Xavier Perrot   **c.** Jo Siffert

10 Which American debutant Formula 1 driver shocked everyone
   by taking pole position in his Lotus in the 1968 US Grand Prix
   at Watkins Glen?
   a. Al Unser   **b.** Bobby Unser   **c.** Mario Andretti

Answers to page 59

1 c. Ludovico Scarfiotti **2 c.** Mike Parkes **3 b.** Piers Courage **4 c.** Innes Ireland
5 b. John Surtees **6 b.** Pedro Rodriguez **7 c.** John Love **8 b.** Denny Hulme
9 c. Brabham-Repco **10 a.** First

QUIZ 13

Answers on page 60

1. **Which British driver dominated the 1969 season to claim his first World Championship title?**
   a. Vic Elford   *b.* Jackie Stewart   *c.* Jacky Oliver

2. **How many of the 11 races did he win?**
   a. 10   *b.* Eight   *c.* Six

3. **Who won the 1969 Constructors' Championship?**
   a. Tyrrell   *b.* Brabham   *c.* Matra

4. **Who finished runner-up in the 1969 World Drivers' Championship?**
   a. Jochen Rindt   *b.* Graham Hill   *c.* Jacky Ickx

5. **Which British driver, whose son is now a leading motorsport photographer, finished sixth at Silverstone in 1969 for McLaren?**
   a. Michael Tee   *b.* Tim Parnell   *c.* Vic Elford

6. **Which American star driver crashed his four-wheel-drive Lotus on the first lap of the 1969 German Grand Prix?**
   a. Pete Lovely   *b.* Mario Andretti   *c.* Michael Andretti

7. **Which blonde French 'bombshell' drove the four-wheel-drive Matra to sixth place in the 1969 Canadian Grand Prix?**
   a. Jean-Pierre Beltoise   *b.* Johnny Servoz-Gavin   c. Guy Ligier

8. **Who became the first Austrian driver ever to win a Grand Prix at Watkins Glen in 1969?**
   a. Gerhard Berger   *b.* Niki Lauda   *c.* Jochen Rindt

9. **Which courageous Englishman finished second in the race?**
   a. Derek Bell   *b.* Piers Courage   *c.* John Surtees

10. **Which famous British driver suffered a puncture, was flung from his car and broke both legs, near the end of the 1969 race at Watkins Glen?**
    a. John Surtees   *b.* Jackie Stewart   *c.* Graham Hill

Answers to page 58

1 *c.*Graham Hill **2** *b.*Richie Ginther **3** *a.*Honda **4** *b.*Mike Spence **5** *c.*Jack Brabham **6** *c.*Denny Hulme **7** *c.*The Bear **8** *.b.*Serenissima **9** *b.*Four **10** *b.*Mike Parkes

FACT FILE 1

British drivers dominated the record books in the sixties.

England and Scotland shared the decade's Championship honours with three Drivers' titles each.

Graham Hill won for England twice (in 1962 and 1968) and 'Big John' Surtees cheered the Ferrari faithful with his triumph in 1964.

Scotland produced two more maestros - Jim Clark and Jackie Stewart. Clark starred for Lotus in 1963 and 1965 and Stewart gave the tartan army further joy in 1969.

But the Southern hemisphere took up the Championship cudgels with a vengeance!

Jack Brabham became the first and, to date, the only man to win the World Drivers' Championship in a car bearing his own name in 1966. It was his third title in eight years.

His Kiwi team-mate, Denny Hulme, pipped him to the post in 1967, the first and to date, the only, New Zealander to claim the World Drivers' crown.

Tragically, the sixties claimed far too many drivers' lives.

The loss of Jim Clark in a Formula 2 race at Hockenheim on April 7th 1968 left an indelible mark on the sport.

Wolfgang von Trips died at Monza, on the threshold of World Championship glory.

Stirling Moss cheated death at Goodwood on Easter Monday in 1962. He would never drive in a Grand Prix again.

Spa claimed two young British lives, Chris Bristow and Alan Stacey, in 1960. Mike Spence died in practice for Indianapolis in 1968. Fire claimed two other popular drivers, Lorenzo Bandini at Monaco in 1967 and France's Jo Schlesser in France in 1968.

The terrible waste inspired Jackie Stewart to begin his life-long, much respected, crusade for greater safety in motor sport.

FACT FILE 2

Britain's Cliff Allison took a career best second place in the opening round of the Grand Prix season in 1960 for Ferrari in Argentina. He had a busy weekend. Before that, he had taken his Testa Rossa to a superb victory in the 'support' event, the 1000 Kilometres sports car race!

Sadly, his promising career was cut short when he suffered a badly broken arm in a practice crash before the next race at Monaco in which he was flung from his car

Stirling Moss recorded the first ever victory for Lotus in Monaco.

He drove a privately-entered Lotus 18 for Rob Walker, heir to the Johnny Walker whiskey empire, painted a deep navy blue!

Rain played havoc with the race and only four of the original 16 starters were running at the end.

Bruce McLaren finished second in his Cooper-Climax and, after his victory in Argentina, led the Drivers' title chase.

A 24-year-old Scot was given his first Formula One drive for the works Lotus team in the 1960 Dutch Grand Prix. His name was Jim Clark...

The 1960 Belgian Grand Prix at Spa was one of the most tragic in history.

Stirling Moss suffered serious injuries in a practice accident and Lotus privateer, Mike Taylor, was lucky to escape with his life when his car suffered steering failure.

But worse was to come during the race. Britain's Chris Bristow lost control of his Cooper and died instantly and Alan Stacey crashed to death in his works Lotus after being hit in the face by a bird.

Australia's Jack Brabham was in hot pursuit of a second World Drivers' title and took his third successive race win in the 1960 French Grand Prix at Reims. He was so quick that he brought his Cooper home in record time - under the stipulated two hours!

FACT FILE 3

Stirling Moss, still recovering from his Spa injuries, dropped the flag at the start of the 1960 British Grand Prix at Silverstone.

Graham Hill, Tony Brooks and Henry Taylor all stalled their engines!

Hill stormed from 21st to first but spun out of the race six laps from the end.

Stirling Moss, ever the epitome of the Bulldog spirit, did his utmost in the 1960 Portuguese Grand Prix. An escape road excursion saw him stall his Lotus five laps from home, he push-started the car, downhill, against race traffic, finished fifth, but was disqualified for driving in the wrong direction!

British teams boycotted the 1960 Italian Grand Prix at Monza. Lotus, Cooper and BRM all said that they would not compete on the circuit if the notorious banking, which they thought too dangerous, was used.

Ferrari took a carefully orchestrated one-two-three win.

And Phil Hill became the first American driver ever to win a World Championship race.

Cooper won the Constructor's title for a second successive year in 1960 but the Italians were out for revenge in 1961...

Innes Ireland broke a leg in practice for the opening round of the year in Monaco - and Stirling Moss took the side panels out of his dark blue Lotus -to keep cool in the Mediterranean heat. It worked! He won, heading home all three works Ferraris.

But the Italians gained revenge in the next round in Holland. Wolfgang von Trips headed home his Ferrari team-mate Phil Hill. And all of the 15 starters finished.

And the Prancing Horse was to hammer home its advantage three weeks later in Spa, filling the first four places. This time it was Phil Hill's turn to finish ahead of von Trips.

FACT FILE 4

A 22-year-old Italian, making his Championship debut, hit the headlines in the 1961 French Grand Prix at Reims. Giancarlo Baghetti took his ageing Ferrari to victory over the Porsche of the experienced Dan Gurney by just one tenth of a second.

Baghetti crashed in his next Grand Prix, at Aintree, in torrential rain. The Ferrari works cars of von Trips, Phil Hill and Richie Ginther took the podium placings.

Stirling Moss won the last Grand Prix victory of his career at the Nurburgring in 1961.

Taffy von Trips finished second for Ferrari and seemed to be en route for the Drivers' title.

Tragically, it was not to be. The charasmatic German took pole position at Monza. On the second lap of the race, he clipped Clark's Lotus. The car hurtled into the crowd, killing 14 spectators. von Trips was flung from the car and died instantly.

America's Phil Hill won the race and became the first US World Champion.

Ferrari won the World Constructors' title for the first time in history in 1961.

The feisty Scot, Innes Ireland, won the final round of the year in the USA. It was to prove his one and only World Championship win but the first of many for the works Lotus team.

The 1962 season started on a sad note for British motor sport. Stirling Moss was severely injured in a crash at Goodwood which would terminate his Grand Prix career.

But Jim Clark and Graham Hill took up the torch for Lotus and BRM and thrilled the crowds all over the world with their duels.

And Jim Clark became the first driver to race lying down in the pace-setting Lotus 25!

FACT FILE 5

Graham Hill took his first Grand Prix win at Zandvoort in 1962.

It was the first of four victories in the season which would see Hill take the Drivers' crown and his team, BRM, the Constructors' title for the first, and only, time in history.

Jim Clark won his very first Grand Prix for Team Lotus at Spa in 1962.

But his Yorkshire team-mate, Trevor Taylor, was lucky to escape unscathed when a telegraph pole smashed across the nose of his car after a collision with the Ferrari of Belgium's Willy Mairesse.

A young Mexican brought his Ferrari home in fourth place at Spa. Ricardo Rodriguez was just 19 years old. Sadly, he would lose his life in practice for his home, non-Championship, Grand Prix, later in the season.

Dan Gurney took Porsche's first Grand Prix win at Rouen in 1962.

The lanky American described his experience as 'like a giraffe sitting on a plate!'

Jim Clark won the 1962 British Grand Prix at Aintree - from start to finish. It was to become a familiar sight for motor sport fans!

Landslides, caused by torrential rain, delayed the start of the 1962 German Grand Prix at the Nurburgring.

Front-row man, Jim Clark, forgot to switch on his fuel pump at the start and lost 13 seconds - now what was that problem you had in Japan Herr Schumacher..???

South Africa hosted its first ever World Championship race at the season's end in 1962.

Jim Clark had to win for Lotus to prevent Graham Hill taking the title for BRM. A tiny loose bolt prevented the Scot from achieving his aim. And Hill became the first Englishman to win the World Championship in a British car.

An unsung South African, Tony Maggs, brought his Cooper home in third place at East London to finish in seventh place overall in the Drivers' Championship, ahead of Ginther and Brabham.

FACT FILE 6

British drivers won each and every one of the 10 rounds of the 1963 World Championship.

Jim Clark won seven of them for Lotus!

Only six of the 20 starters finished the 1963 Spa race. Need we say, it was wet!

Jim Clark lapped the entire field for victory.

And he won from start to finish in the next race at Reims.

In second place was that South African, Tony Maggs, who finished ahead of Graham Hill's BRM. He had incurred a one-minute penalty for being push-started on the grid!

Graham Hill's BRM ran out of petrol on the final lap of the 1963 British Grand Prix at Silverstone and freewheeled over the line into third place. It was a British one-two-three: Clark; Surtees: Hill. What would the fans make of that result today?

John Surtees took his first Grand Prix victory for Ferrari at the Nurburgring in 1963.

Drivers petitioned against the dangers of the Monza banking. The race was run on the original road circuit. Jim Clark won, clinched his first World Drivers' title and the first Constructors' Championship for Lotus.

Jim Clark started last, due to engine failure, in the 1963 US Grand Prix. One lap in arrears, he finished third overall. What a Champion!

Mexico City hosted a Grand Prix for the first time in 1963.

Jim Clark pipped Fangio's record in the final round of 1963 in East London, South Africa.

He claimed seven wins in one season. Jimmy was only 27.

FACT FILE 7

1964 was a classic Championship year.

John Surtees won the Drivers' title by just one point from Graham Hill and Ferrari finished three points ahead of BRM to take the Constructors' crown.

Surtees thrilled the Italians with his win on their home 'turf' at Monza.

Five different drivers shared the ten victory garlands during the season - three British, one American and one Italian.

And 1964 marked the arrival in Grand Prix racing of the 'Ditton Road Flyers'. The happy trio of Britain's Mike Hailwood, New Zealand's Chris Amon and America's Peter Revson shared a flat in Surrey and an unconventional year under the despairing eye of team boss Tim Parnell!

Results were modest. Hailwood finished sixth in Monaco and Amon fifth in Holland - but the parties were legendary!

Britain's Peter Arundell joined Clark in the Lotus Team in 1964 and seemed set for future stardom, finishing third at Monaco and Spa. His career was blighted by a terrible accident mid-season in a Formula 2 race at Spa, when the likeable man from Ilford suffered major injuries when he was flung from his car.

America's Dan Gurney gave Brabham its first Grand Prix victory in France.

Brands Hatch hosted the British Grand Prix for the first time in 1964.

And Jim Clark notched up his third successive win in Britain's premier motor sport event.

The clumsy Honda made its debut at the 1964 Grand Prix at the Nurburgring in the hands of America's Ronnie Bucknum.

Sadly, the 'Ring claimed yet another victim. Holland's Count Carel Godin de Beaufort succumbed to his injuries after crashing his private Porsche in practice.

FACT FILE 8

Austria hosted a full round of the World Championship in 1964. And the fans thrilled to the skills of their home driver, Jochen Rindt, who had powered his private Brabham up to third place in his first Grand Prix before the steering broke.

The airfield circuit at Zeltweg was primitive, to say the least. Austria would have to wait another six years before it held another Grand Prix on a proper circuit!

The first round of 1965 took place in South Africa on January 1st. And Hogmanay was celebrated in style, with a crushing victory for Clark and a Grand Prix debut for one John Young Stewart.

And excited official waved the chequered flag a lap too soon! Happily, Clark ignored it.

Stewart finished sixth for BRM.

Clark went on to dominate the 1965 season for Lotus, with six wins - he was World Champion by August 1st - and he took time out to become the first British driver to win the Indianapolis 500 too!

Stewart went on to win his first Grand Prix in only his eighth outing - at Monza.

He finished his first Formula One season third overall in the drivers' title chase.

And America's Richie Ginther had his finest hour in the final round of the year in Mexico.

He led the race from start to finish and scored his first and only Grand Prix win.

It was the first ever victory for a Honda-powered car - a portent of even greater triumphs to come in the eighties and nineties.

FACT FILE 9

Fifteen cars started the 1966 Belgian Grand Prix at Spa. But, thanks to torrential rain, only seven finished the first lap!

Jackie Stewart had an horrendous accident , ending up in a ditch, trapped in his petrol-soaked BRM. Fortunately, Graham Hill and Bob Bondurant were able to free him before the car caught fire.

This accident inspired Stewart to become the passionate, tireless, campaigner for greater motor sport safety for which he is now revered.

Jim Clark failed to start the 1965 French Grand Prix after being hit in the eye by a bird in practice.

Jack Brabham became the first man ever to win a Grand Prix in a car bearing his own name.

By the end of the year, he would become the first and, to date the only, man to win the World Drivers' title in car bearing his own name!

Tired of media jibes about his age, the 40-year-old Australian turned up on the grid for the 1966 Dutch Grand Prix, sporting a false beard and limping on a walking stick. He promptly went out and won his third successive race of the year!

Ludovico Scarfiotti won at Monza in front of the Ferrari faithful. His was the first victory for an Italian driver at the famous home of Italian motor racing since Ascari in 1952.

John Surtees, who had left Ferrari in a huff earlier in the season, threw a wobbly when he collided with Peter Arundell early in the 1966 US Grand Prix. He stomped off down to the Lotus pit to register his discontent, whilst his Cooper was checked out. He was the fastest man on the circuit on his return to race - but his tantrum had been costly. He finished third.

However, he won the final race of the year in Mexico.

FACT FILE 10

Lotus started the 1967 season with the Dream Team for British fans.

Graham Hill left BRM to join Jim Clark to campaign Colin Chapman's revolutionary Ford-Cosworth - powered Lotus 49s.

Hangovers were put on hold for the first round of the year in South Africa, on the new, twisty circuit of Kyalami, on the outskirts of Johannesburg.

But many doubted their eyes when Pedro Rodriguez scored his first ever World Championship win for Cooper ahead of all the big names in the sport.

New Zealand's Denny Hulme took his first Grand Prix win for Brabham in Monaco in 1967.

But, sadly, his triumph was marred by the terrible accident which claimed the life of Lorenzo Bandini, when his Ferrari crashed upside down in flames.

The 1967 Dutch Grand Prix marked the debut of what was to become one of the all-time great racing engines - the Ford-Cosworth, fitted as an integral part of the new Lotus 49.

The car, which had only turned a wheel two days earlier, wove its magic. Graham Hill qualified on pole and Jim Clark won the race, a first-time out triumph for the power unit which was to claim 155 Grands Prix wins.

Dan Gurney proudly took the honours for his Eagle-Weslake for the only time at Spa.

Jim Clark won his fifth British Grand Prix in six years in his Lotus-Ford. Little did anyone know that it would be his last Formula 1 win on home ground.

Former French Rugby international, Guy Ligier, scored the sole Championship point of his career, when he finished sixth in the 1967 race at the Nurburgring in a Brabaham.

FACT FILE 11

Canada hosted a Grand Prix for the first time in 1967 at the primitive Mosport Park Circuit outside Toronto.

Jack Brabham splashed to victory.

Jim Clark performed miracles at Monza, making up a whole lost lap on the high-speed circuit after a tyre change to take the lead. He ran out of fuel just half a lap from the flag and free-wheeled home in third.

Graham Hill and Jim Clark proved so dominant in their Lotus 49s at Watkins Glen that they tossed to decide who should win! Hill won the toss but mechanical problems saw Clark take the victory, even though his rear-wheel collapsed two laps from the end of the race. Chapman's boys still managed a one-two win

Big Bear, Denny Hulme, became the first, and to date the only, New Zealander to win the World Drivers' title.

The drivers headed south for some fun in the sun in the Tasman series in New Zealand and Australia to escape Europe's winter gloom. 1967 lived up to all expectations, with Jim Clark learning to drive a trotting sulky (the horse was called Royal Scot!) and to fly a light aircraft. Some highly dubious cricket matches also formed part of the curriculum...

Brewing heir Piers Courage joined in the revelry and established his credentials with some fine racing results, finally outdriving his illustrious opposition to win the last round of the series.

FACT FILE 12

April 7th, 1968 and May 1st, 1994 are two of the blackest dates in motor racing history.

Jim Clark was killed in a Formula Two race at Hockenheim in 1968 and, 26 years later, Ayrton Senna lost his life in the San Marino Grand Prix at Imola.

They were two of the greatest drivers Formula One has ever known.

Clark, headed home a Lotus one-two in the opening round of 1968 at Kyalami, and broke Fangio's total with 25 Championship wins. Then came Hockenheim.

Graham Hill gave Team Lotus one of its most emotional Grands Prix victories in history by winning the next round in the series, the Spanish Grand Prix at Jarama.

And he clinched his fourth Monaco win just two weeks later.

Bruce McLaren won the first Grand Prix for his McLaren in Spa.

And Jackie Stewart, wearing an arm brace, took a famous first for Matra at Zandvoort.

The 1968 season was to witness further tragedy in the French Grand Prix at Rouen. Jo Schlesser died when flames enveloped his overturned Porsche.

Huge wings had sprouted from the back of the Lotus and McLarens.

Jo Siffert became the first Swiss driver to win a Grand Prix at Brands Hatch in 1968.

Graham Hill's 100th Grand Prix, at Monza, ended just as his first. He lost a wheel.

However, with gritty determination, he claimed victory in the final race of the year in Mexico to take not only the Drivers' but also the Constructors' title for Team Lotus.

It was a brave, brave ending to a year which had begun so sadly.

FACT FILE 13

1969 was to prove a monopoly for Jackie Stewart and the Ford Cosworth engine.

The power unit was to win each and every round of the 11-race series, albeit in four different chassis.

The Scot was to win six Grands Prix and clinch his first World Drivers' Championship. And his legendary relationship with Ken Tyrrell was securely affirmed.

Jochen Rindt joined Hill in the Lotus works team but suffered a a nasty shock when the huge rear wing on his car buckled during the Spanish Grand Prix and the car overturned.

Chris Amon's Ferrari engine seized whilst he was streets ahead. Jackie Stewart inherited the win in his Matra-Ford but was so embarrassed that he gave the trophy away!

Wings were banned for the next round in Monaco. Graham Hill claimed his fifth win in the event and Piers Courage took an excellent best for Frank Williams in a Brabham-Ford.

Jackie Stewart was on a mission. Yet there were new men in his mirrors, with Belgium's Jacky Ickx triumphant in Germany and Canada for Brabham, Austria's Jochen Rindt, victorious in the USA and young British chargers in Jackie Oliver and Piers Courage coming up through the ranks.

The year belonged to Stewart and the gleaming blue Matra-Ford.

But there was yet another twist in the tail for British fans. Graham Hill broke both legs when he was flung from his Lotus near the end of the US Grand Prix. He had stopped seconds earlier to push his car back onto the circuit - and neglected to fasten his safety belts...

1960s

RESULTS

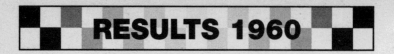

RESULTS 1960

1960 The names of Lotus and Stirling Moss were united in two famous victories in a year dominated by Brabham and Cooper once again. British teams boycotted Monza because the banking was perceived as too dangerous. There were ten rounds (including Indy). Points were awarded for the first *six* places: 8-6-4-3-2-1 for the first time. The point for fastest lap was dropped from the scoring system.

ROUND 1/ARGENTINE GRAND PRIX
BUENOS AIRES, 7 FEBRUARY

1. MCLAREN(NZ)	COOPER-CLIMAX	2HR 17MIN 49.5SEC
2. ALLISON (GB)	FERRARI	2HR 18MIN 16.8SEC
3. MOSS(GB)/TRINTIGNANT(FRA)	COOPER-CLIMAX	2HR 18MIN 26.4SEC
4. MENDITEGUY(ARG)	COOPER-MASERATI	2HR 18MIN 42.2SEC
5. VON TRIPS(GER)	FERRARI	79 LAPS
6. IRELAND(GB)	LOTUS-CLIMAX	79 LAPS

Race: 80 laps of 2.42mile/3.91km (194miles/313kms)
Fastest lap: Moss, 1min 38.9sec, 88.4mph/142.39kph
Pole position: Moss, 1min 36.9sec 22 starters, 14 classified finishers

ROUND 2/MONACO GRAND PRIX
MONTE CARLO, 29 MAY

1. MOSS (GB)	LOTUS-CLIMAX	2HR 53MIN 45.5SEC
2. MCLAREN(NZ)	COOPER-CLIMAX	2HR 54MIN 37.6SEC
3. P.HILL(USA)	FERRARI	2HR 54MIN 47.4SEC
4. BROOKS(GB)	COOPER-CLIMAX	99 LAPS
5. BONNIER(SWE)	BRM	83 LAPS
6. GINTHER(USA)	FERRARI	70 LAPS

Race: 100 laps of 1.95mile/3.15km (195miles/315kms)
Fastest lap: McLaren, 1min 36.2sec, 73.1mph/117.6kph
Pole position: Moss, 1min 36.3sec 16 starters, 9 classified finishers

ROUND 3/INDIANAPOLIS 500
INDIANAPOLIS, 30 MAY

1. J. RATHMANN(USA)	KEN-PAUL	3HR 36MIN 11.36SEC
2. WARD(USA)	LEADER CARD	
3. GOLDSMITH(USA)	DEMLER	
4. BRANSON(USA)	BOB ESTES	
5. THOMSON(USA)	ADAM QUARTER HORSE	
6. E.JOHNSON(USA)	JIM ROBBINS	

Race: 200 laps of 2.5mile/4.02km
Fastest lap: J.Rathmann, 1min 01.59sec, 146.13mph/235.17kph
Pole position: Sachs(USA), Dean Van Lines 33 starters, 17 classified finishers

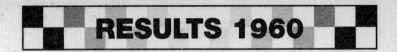
RESULTS 1960

ROUND 4/ DUTCH GRAND PRIX
ZANDVOORT, 6 JUNE

1. BRABHAM(AUS)	COOPER-CLIMAX	2HR 1MIN 47.2SEC
2. IRELAND (GB)	LOTUS-CLIMAX	2HR 2MIN 11.2SEC
3. G.HILL(GB)	BRM	2HR 2MIN 43.8SEC
4. MOSS (GB)	LOTUS-CLIMAX	2HR 2MIN 44.9SEC
5. VON TRIPS(GER)	FERRARI	74 LAPS
6. GINTHER(USA)	FERRARI	74 LAPS

Race: 75 laps of 2.6mile/4.19km (195miles/314kms)
Fastest lap: Moss,1min 33.8sec,99.9mph/160.9kph
Pole position: Moss,1min 33.2sec 17 starters, 8 classified finishers

ROUND 5/BELGIAN GRAND PRIX
SPA-FRANCORCHAMPS,19 JUNE

1. BRABHAM(AUS)	COOPER-CLIMAX	2HR 21MIN 37.3SEC
2. MCLAREN(NZ)	COOPER-CLIMAX	2HR 22MIN 40.6SEC
3. GENDEBIEN(BEL)	COOPER-CLIMAX	35 LAPS
4. P.HILL(USA)	FERRARI	35 LAPS
5. CLARK (GB)	LOTUS-CLIMAX	34 LAPS
6. BIANCHI(BEL)	COOPER-CLIMAX	28 LAPS

Race: 36 laps of 8.76mile/14.1km (315miles/508kms)
Fastest lap: Brabham/P.Hill/Ireland,3min51.9sec,136.0mph/217.96kph
Pole position: Brabham, 3min 50.0sec 17 starters, 6 classified finishers.
*Britain's Chris Bristow and Alan Stacey were killed during the race.

ROUND 6/FRENCH GRAND PRIX
REIMS,3 JULY

1. BRABHAM(AUS)	COOPER-CLIMAX	1HR 57MIN 24.9SEC
2. GENDEBIEN(BEL)	COOPER-CLIMAX	1HR 58MIN 13.2SEC
3. MCLAREN(NZ)	COOPER-CLIMAX	1HR 58MIN 16.8SEC
4. H.TAYLOR(GB)	COOPER-CLIMAX	49 LAPS
5. CLARK(GB)	LOTUS-CLIMAX	49 LAPS
6. FLOCKHART(GB)	LOTUS-CLIMAX	49 LAPS

Race: 50 laps of 5.16mile/8.3km (258miles/415kms)
Fastest lap: Brabham, 2min 17.5sec, 135.0mph/217.3kph
Pole position: Brabham, 2min 16.8sec 20 starters, 12 classified finishers

ROUND 7/BRITISH GRAND PRIX
SILVERSTONE,16 JULY

1. BRABHAM(AUS)	COOPER-CLIMAX	2HR 4MIN 24.6SEC
2. SURTEES (GB)	LOTUS-CLIMAX	2HR 5MIN 14.2SEC
3. IRELAND (GB)	LOTUS-CLIMAX	2HR 5MIN 54.2SEC
4. MCLAREN(NZ)	COOPER-CLIMAX	76 LAPS
5. BROOKS (GB)	COOPER-CLIMAX	76 LAPS
6. VON TRIPS (GER)	FERRARI	75 LAPS

Race: 77 laps of 2.9mile/4.7km (225miles/362kms)
Fastest lap: G.Hill(GB),BRM, 1min 34.4sec,111.6mph/179.6kph
Pole position: Brabham, 1min 34.6sec 24 starters, 16 classified finishers

RESULTS 1960

ROUND 8/ PORTUGUESE GRAND PRIX

OPORTO, 14 AUGUST

1. BRABHAM(AUS)	COOPER-CLIMAX	2HR 19MIN 00.03SEC
2. MCLAREN (NZ)	COOPER-CLIMAX	2HR 19MIN 58.00SEC
3. CLARK (GB)	LOTUS-CLIMAX	2HR 20MIN 53.26SEC
4. VON TRIPS(GER)	FERRARI	2HR 20MIN 58.84SEC
5. BROOKS (GB)	COOPER-CLIMAX	49 LAPS
6. IRELAND (GB)	LOTUS-CLIMAX	48 LAPS

Race: 55 laps of 4.6mile/7.4km (253miles/407kms)
Fastest lap: Surtees(GB)Lotus-Climax,2min 27.53sec,112.3mph/180.7kph
Pole position: Surtees, 2min 25.56sec 15 starters, 7 classified finishers

ROUND 9/EUROPEAN GRAND PRIX

MONZA, 4 SEPTEMBER

1. P.HILL(USA)	FERRARI	2HR 21MIN 09.2SEC
2. GINTHER(USA)	FERRARI	2HR 23MIN 36.8SEC
3. MAIRESSE(BEL)	FERRARI	49 LAPS
4. CABIANCA (ITA)	COOPER-FERRARI	48 LAPS
5. VON TRIPS(GER)	FERRARI F2	48 LAPS
6. HERRMANN(GER)	PORSCHE F2	47 LAPS

Race: 50 laps of 6.2mile/10km (310miles/500kms)
Fastest lap: P.Hill, 2min 43.6sec, 136.7mph/220kph
Pole position: P.Hill, 2min 41.4sec 16 starters, 10 classified finishers

ROUND 10/US GRAND PRIX

RIVERSIDE, CALIFORNIA,20 NOVEMBER

1. MOSS(GB)	LOTUS-CLIMAX	2HR 52MIN 52.2SEC
2. IRELAND (GB)	LOTUS-CLIMAX	2HR 53MIN 30.0SEC
3. MCLAREN(NZ)	COOPER-CLIMAX	2HR 54MIN 12.0SEC
4. BRABHAM(AUS)	COOPER-CLIMAX	74 LAPS
5. BONNIER(SWE)	BRM	74 LAPS
6. P.HILL (USA)	COOPER-CLIMAX	74 LAPS

Race: 75 laps of 3.3mile/5.28km (245miles/396kms)
Fastest lap: Brabham, 1min 56.03sec, 101.3mph/163.1kph
Pole position: Moss, 1min 54min 04sec 23 starters, 16 classified finishers

---

DRIVERS' WORLD CHAMPIONSHIP 1960

1. BRABHAM	43 *points*	5. P.HILL 16 *points*
2. MCLAREN	34 *points*	6. GENDEBIEN 10 *points*
3. MOSS	19 *points*	6. VON TRIPS 10 *points*
4. IRELAND	18 *points*	

CONSTRUCTORS' WORLD CHAMPIONSHIP 1960

1. COOPER/CLIMAX	48 *points*	3. FERRARI 26 *points*
2. LOTUS-CLIMAX	34 *points*	4. BRM 8 *points*

RESULTS 1961

1961 Taffy von Trips lost his life in a tragic accident at Monza in which 14 spectators also died. Ferrari were *the* team to beat. Indianapolis was dropped from the rankings and the winner's points tally went up to nine. Points: 9-6-4-3-2-1 for first six places. There were eight Grands Prix. Best five placings of the eight rounds counted.

ROUND 1/MONACO GRAND PRIX
MONTE CARLO, 14 MAY

1. MOSS(GB)	LOTUS-CLIMAX	2HR 45MIN 50.1SEC
2. GINTHER(USA)	FERRARI	2HR 45MIN 53.7SEC
3. P.HILL(USA)	FERRARI	2HR 46MIN 31.4SEC
4. VON TRIPS (GER)	FERRARI	98 LAPS
5. GURNEY(USA)	PORSCHE	98 LAPS
6. MCLAREN(NZ)	COOPER-CLIMAX	95 LAPS

Race: 100 laps of 1.95mile/3.15km (195miles/315kms)
Fastest lap: Moss/Ginther, 1min 36.3sec, 73.0mph/117.5kph
Pole position: Moss, 1min 39.1sec 16 starters, 10 classified finishers

ROUND 2/DUTCH GRAND PRIX
ZANDVOORT, 22 MAY

1. VON TRIPS(GER)	FERRARI	2HR 01MIN 52.1SEC
2. P.HILL(USA)	FERRARI	2HR 01MIN 53.0SEC
3. CLARK(GB)	LOTUS-CLIMAX	2HR 02MIN 05.2SEC
4. MOSS (GB)	LOTUS-CLIMAX	2HR 02MIN 14.3SEC
5. GINTHER(USA)	FERRARI	2HR 02MIN 14.4SEC
6. BRABHAM (AUS)	COOPER-CLIMAX	2HR 03MIN 12.2SEC

Race: 75 laps of 2.6mile/4.19km (195miles/314kms)
Fastest lap: Clark, 1min 35.5sec, 98.2mph/158kph
Pole position: P.Hill, 1min 35.7sec 15 starters, 15 classified finishers

ROUND 3/BELGIAN GRAND PRIX
SPA-FRANCORCHAMPS, 18 JUNE

1. P.HILL(USA)	FERRARI	2HR 03MIN 03.8SEC
2. VON TRIPS (GER)	FERRARI	2HR 03MIN 04.5SEC
3. GINTHER(USA)	FERRARI	2HR 03MIN 23.3SEC
4. GENDEBIEN(BEL)	FERRARI	2HR 03MIN 49.4SEC
5. SURTEES(GB)	COOPER-CLIMAX	2HR 04MIN 30.6SEC
6. GURNEY (USA)	PORSCHE	2HR 04MIN 34.8SEC

Race: 30 laps of 8.76mile/14.1km (263miles/423kms)
Fastest lap: Ginther, 3min 59.8sec, 137.5mph/211.7kph
Pole position: P.Hill, 3min 59.3sec 21 starters, 13 classified finishers

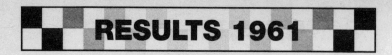

RESULTS 1961

ROUND 4/FRENCH GRAND PRIX

REIMS, 2 JULY

1. BAGHETTI(ITA)	FERRARI	2HR 14MIN 17.5SEC
2. GURNEY(USA)	PORSCHE	2HR 14MIN 17.6SEC
3. CLARK (GB)	LOTUS-CLIMAX	2HR 15MIN 18.6SEC
4. IRELAND(GB)	LOTUS-CLIMAX	2HR 15MIN 27.8SEC
5. MCLAREN(NZ)	COOPER-CLIMAX	2HR 15MIN 59.3SEC
6. G.HILL(GB)	BRM	2HR 15MIN 59.4SEC

Race: 52 laps of 5.16mile/8.3km (268miles/432kms)
Fastest lap: P.Hill, 2min 27.1sec, 126.25mph/203.18kph
Pole position: P.Hill, 2min 24.9sec 26 starters, 14 classified finishers

ROUND 5/BRITISH GRAND PRIX

AINTREE, 15 JULY

1. VON TRIPS(GER)	FERRARI	2HR 40MIN 53.6SEC
2. P.HILL(USA)	FERRARI	2HR 41MIN 39.6SEC
3. GINTHER(USA)	FERRARI	2HR 41MIN 40.4SEC
4. BRABHAM(AUS)	COOPER-CLIMAX	2HR 42MIN 02.2SEC
5. BONNIER(SWE)	PORSCHE	2HR 42MIN 09.8SEC
6. SALVADORI(GB)	COOPER-CLIMAX	2HR 42MIN 19.8SEC

Race: 75 laps of 3mile/4.83km (225 miles/362kms)
Fastest lap: Brooks(GB),BRM, 1min 57.8sec, 91.6mph/147.5kph
Pole position: P.Hill, 1min 58.8sec 30 starters, 17 classified finishers

ROUND 6/EUROPEAN GRAND PRIX

NURBURGRING, 6 AUGUST

1. MOSS(GB)	LOTUS-CLIMAX	2HR 18MIN 12.4SEC
2. VON TRIPS(GER)	FERRARI	2HR 18MIN 33.8SEC
3. P.HILL(USA)	FERRARI	2HR 18MIN 34.9SEC
4. CLARK(GB)	LOTUS-CLIMAX	2HR 19MIN 29.5SEC
5. SURTEES(GB)	COOPER-CLIMAX	2HR 20MIN 05.5SEC
6. MCLAREN (NZ)	COOPER-CLIMAX	2HR 20MIN 53.8SEC

Race: 15 laps of 14.17mile/22.81km (213miles/342kms)
Fastest lap: P.Hill, 8min 57.8sec, 94.9mph/152.7kph
Pole position: P. Hill, 8min 55.2sec 25 starters, 17 classified finishers

ROUND 7/ITALIAN GRAND PRIX

MONZA, 10 SEPTEMBER

1. P.HILL(USA)	FERRARI	2HR 3MIN 13.0SEC
2. GURNEY (USA)	PORSCHE	2HR 3MIN 44.2SEC
3. MCLAREN(NZ)	COOPER-CLIMAX	2HR 5MIN 41.4SEC
4. JACK LEWIS(GB)	COOPER-CLIMAX	2HR 5MIN 53.4SEC
5. BROOKS(GB)	BRM-CLIMAX	2HR 5MIN 53.5SEC
6. SALVADORI (GB)	COOPER-CLIMAX	42 LAPS

Race: 43 laps of 6.2mile/10km (267miles/430kms)
Fastest lap: Baghetti(ITA), Ferrari,2min 48.4sec,132.8mph/213.8kph
Pole position: von Trips,(GER), Ferrari, 2min 46.03sec 32 starters, 12 classified finishers
*von Trips killed during race, also 14 spectators.

RESULTS 1961/2

ROUND 8/US GRAND PRIX
WATKINS GLEN, 8 OCTOBER

1. IRELAND(GB)	LOTUS-CLIMAX	2HR 13MIN 45.8SEC
2. GURNEY (USA)	PORSCHE	2HR 13MIN 50.1SEC
3. BROOKS (GB)	BRM-CLIMAX	2HR 14MIN 34.8SEC
4. MCLAREN (NZ)	COOPER-CLIMAX	2HR 14MIN 43.8SEC
5. G. HILL (GB)	BRM-CLIMAX	99 LAPS
6. BONNIER(SWE)	PORSCHE	98 LAPS

Race: 100 laps of 2.3mile/3.7km (230miles/370kms)
Fastest lap: Brabham(AUS), Cooper-Climax, 1min 18.2sec,105.9mph/170kph
Pole position: Brabham(AUS), 1min 17.0sec 19 starters, 11 classified finishers

 DRIVERS' WORLD CHAMPIONSHIP 1961

1. P.HILL	34 *points*	3. MOSS	21 *points*
2. VON TRIPS	33 *points*	5. GINTHER	16 *points*
3. GURNEY	21 *points*	6. IRELAND	12 *points*

CONSTRUCTORS' WORLD CHAMPIONSHIP 1961

1. FERRARI	40 *points*	4. COOPER/CLIMAX	14 *points*
2. LOTUS-CLIMAX	32 *points*	5. BRM-CLIMAX	7 *points*
3. PORSCHE	22 *points*		

1962 The season started under a cloud for British fans. Stirling Moss suffered serious injuries in a crash at Goodwood on Easter Monday. He would never race in another Grand Prix. But two new British stars were waiting in the wings - Graham Hill and Jim Clark. There were nine rounds. South Africa hosted a Championship race for the first time. Points: 9-6-4-3-2-1 for first six places. Best five scores from nine.

ROUND 1/EUROPEAN GRAND PRIX
ZANDVOORT, 20 MAY

1. G. HILL(GB)	BRM	2HR 11MIN 02.1SEC
2. T. TAYLOR(GB)	LOTUS-CLIMAX	2HR 11MIN 29.3SEC
3. P. HILL (USA)	FERRARI	2HR 12MIN 23.2SEC
4. BAGHETTI(ITA)	FERRARI	79 LAPS
5. MAGGS(SA)	COOPER-CLIMAX	78 LAPS
6. DE BEAUFORT(HOL)	PORSCHE	76 LAPS

Race: 80 laps of 2.6-mile/4.19km (208miles/335kms)
Fastest lap: McLaren(NZ), Cooper-Climax, 1min34sec, 99.36mph/159.9kph
Pole position: Surtees(GB), Lola Climax, 1min 32.5sec 20 starters, 9 classified finishers

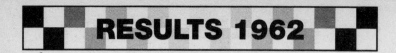

RESULTS 1962

ROUND 2/MONACO GRAND PRIX
MONTE CARLO, 3 JUNE

1. MCLAREN(NZ)	COOPER-CLIMAX	2HR 46MIN 29.7SEC
2. P.HILL(USA)	FERRARI	2HR 46MIN 31.0SEC
3. BANDINI(ITA)	FERRARI	2HR 47MIN 53.8SEC
4. SURTEES(GB)	LOLA-CLIMAX	99 LAPS
5. BONNIER(SWE)	PORSCHE	93 LAPS
6. G. HILL(GB)	BRM	92 LAPS

Race: 100 laps of 1.95mile/3.15km (195miles/315kms)
Fastest lap: Clark(GB),Lotus-Climax, 1min 35.5sec,73.7mph/118.5kph
Pole position: Clark, 1min 35.4sec 16 starters, 9 classified finishers

ROUND 3/BELGIAN GRAND PRIX
SPA-FRANCORCHAMPS, 17 JUNE

1. CLARK(GB)	LOTUS-CLIMAX	2HR 7MIN 32.5SEC
2. G.HILL(GB)	BRM	2HR 8MIN 16.4SEC
3. P.HILL(USA)	FERRARI	2HR 9MIN 38.8SEC
4. R. RODRIGUEZ(MEX)	FERRARI	2HR 9MIN 38.9SEC
5. SURTEES(GB)	LOLA-CLIMAX	31 LAPS
6. BRABHAM(AUS)	LOTUS-CLIMAX	30 LAPS

Race: 32 laps of 8.76mile/14.1km (280miles/451kms)
Fastest lap: Clark, 3min 55.6sec, 133.9mph/215.5kph
Pole position: G.Hill 3min 57.0sec 19 starters, 11 classified finishers

ROUND 4/FRENCH GRAND PRIX
ROUEN-LES-ESSARTS, 8 JULY

1. GURNEY (USA)	PORSCHE	2HR 7MIN 35.5SEC
2. MAGGS (SA)	COOPER-CLIMAX	53 LAPS
3. GINTHER (USA)	BRM	52 LAPS
4. MCLAREN(NZ)	COOPER-CLIMAX	51 LAPS
5. SURTEES(GB)	LOLA-CLIMAX	51 LAPS
6. DE BEAUFORT(HOL)	PORSCHE	51 LAPS

Race: 54 laps of 4.07mile/6.54km (220miles/353kms)
Fastest lap: G.Hill(GB), BRM,2min 16.9sec, 106.9mph/172.03kph
Pole position: Clark(GB), Lotus-Climax, 2min 14.8sec 17 starters, 10 classified finishers

ROUND 5, BRITISH GRAND PRIX
AINTREE, 21 JULY

1. CLARK(GB)	LOTUS-CLIMAX	2HR 26MIN 20.8SEC
2. SURTEES(GB)	LOLA-CLIMAX	2HR 27MIN 10.0SEC
3. MCLAREN(NZ)	COOPER-CLIMAX	2HR 28MIN 05.6SEC
4. G.HILL(GB)	BRM	2HR 28MIN 17.6SEC
5. BRABHAM(AUS)	LOTUS-CLIMAX	74 LAPS
6. MAGGS (SA)	COOPER-CLIMAX	74 LAPS

Race: 75 laps of 3mile/4.83km (225miles/ 362kms)
Fastest lap: Clark, 1min 55sec, 93.9mph/151.1kph
Pole position: Clark, 1min 53.6sec 21 starters, 16 classified finishers

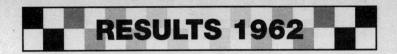
RESULTS 1962

ROUND 6/GERMAN GRAND PRIX
NURBURGRING, 5 AUGUST

1. G. HILL(GB)	BRM	2HR 38MIN 45.3SEC
2. SURTEES(GB)	LOLA-CLIMAX	2HR 38MIN 47.8SEC
3. GURNEY(USA)	PORSCHE	2HR 38MIN 49.7SEC
4. CLARK(GB)	LOTUS-CLIMAX	2HR 39MIN 27.4SEC
5. MCLAREN(NZ)	COOPER-CLIMAX	2HR 40MIN 04.9SEC
6. R. RODRIGUEZ(MEX)	FERRARI	2HR 40MIN 09.1SEC

Race: 15 laps of 14.17mile/22.81km (213 miles/342kms)
Fastest lap: G. Hill, 10min 12.2sec, 83.3mph/134.1kph
Pole position: Gurney, 8min 47.2sec 26 starters, 17 classified finishers

ROUND 7/ITALIAN GRAND PRIX
MONZA, 16 SEPTEMBER

1. G. HILL(GB)	BRM	2HR 29MIN 08.4SEC
2. GINTHER(USA)	BRM	2HR 29MIN 38.2SEC
3. MCLAREN(NZ)	COOPER-CLIMAX	2HR 30MIN 06.2SEC
4. MAIRESSE(BEL)	FERRARI	2HR 30MIN 06.6SEC
5. BAGHETTI(ITA)	FERRARI	2HR 30MIN 39.7SEC
6. BONNIER(SWE)	PORSCHE	85 LAPS

Race: 86 laps of 3.57mile/5.75km (307miles/495kms)
Fastest lap: G. Hill, 1min 42.3sec, 125.7mph/202.3kph
Pole position: Clark(GB), Lotus-Climax, 1min 40.35sec 21 starters, 12 classified finishers

ROUND 8/US GRAND PRIX
WATKINS GLEN,7 OCTOBER

1. CLARK(GB)	LOTUS-CLIMAX	2HR 7MIN 13.0SEC
2. G.HILL(GB)	BRM	2HR 7MIN 22.2SEC
3. MCLAREN(NZ)	COOPER-CLIMAX	99 LAPS
4. BRABHAM(AUS)	BRABHAM-CLIMAX	99 LAPS
5. GURNEY(USA)	PORSCHE	99 LAPS
6. GREGORY(USA)	LOTUS-BRM	99 LAPS

Race: 100 laps of 2.3mile/3.7km (230miles/370kms)
Fastest lap: Clark, 1min 15sec, 110.4mph/177.67kph
Pole position: Clark, 1min 15.8sec 18 starters, 13 classified finishers

ROUND 8/SOUTH AFRICAN GRAND PRIX
EAST LONDON, 29 DECEMBER

1. G. HILL(GB)	BRM	2HR 8MIN 03.3SEC
2. MCLAREN(NZ)	COOPER-CLIMAX	2HR 8MIN 53.1SEC
3. MAGGS(SA)	COOPER-CLIMAX	2HR 8MIN 53.6SEC
4. BRABHAM(AUS)	BRABHAM-CLIMAX	2HR 8MIN 57.1SEC
5. IRELAND(GB)	LOTUS-CLIMAX	81 LAPS
6. LEDERIE (SA)	LOTUS-CLIMAX	78 LAPS

Race: 82 laps of 2.43mile/3.9km (200miles/320kms)
Fastest lap: Clark(GB), Lotus-Climax, 1min 31sec,96.3mph/155kph
Pole position: Clark, 1min 29.3sec 17 starters, 11 classified finishers

RESULTS 1962/3

DRIVERS' WORLD CHAMPIONSHIP 1962

1. G. HILL	42 points	4.	SURTEES	19 points
2. CLARK	30 points	5.	GURNEY	15 points
3. MCLAREN	27 points	6.	P. HILL	14 points

CONSTRUCTORS' WORLD CHAMPIONSHIP 1962

1. BRM-CLIMAX	42 points	4.	LOLA/CLIMAX	19 points
2. LOTUS-CLIMAX	36 points	5.	PORSCHE	18 points
3. COOPER/CLIMAX	29 points	5.	FERRARI	18 points

1963 Jim Clark and Lotus monopolised the season with seven outright victories. Mexico hosted a Grand Prix for the first time. There were ten rounds, best six scores counted. Points: 9-6-4-3-2-1 for first six places.

ROUND 1/EUROPEAN GRAND PRIX
MONTE CARLO, 26 MAY

1. G. HILL(GB)	BRM	2HR 41MIN 49.7SEC
2. GINTHER(USA)	BRM	2HR 41MIN 54.3SEC
3. MCLAREN(NZ)	COOPER-CLIMAX	2HR 42MIN 02.5SEC
4. SURTEES(GB)	FERRARI	2HR 42MIN 03.8SEC
5. MAGGS(SA)	COOPER-CLIMAX	98 LAPS
6. T.TAYLOR(GB)	LOTUS-CLIMAX	98 LAPS

Race: 100 laps of 1.95mile/3.15km (195miles/315kms)
Fastest lap: Surtees, 1min 34.5sec, 74.4mph/119.8kph
Pole position: Clark(GB), Lotus-Climax, 1min 34.3sec 15 starters, 9 classified finishers

ROUND2/BELGIAN GRAND PRIX
SPA-FRANCORCHAMPS, 9 JUNE

1. CLARK(GB)	LOTUS-CLIMAX	2HR 27MIN 47.6SEC
2. MCLAREN(NZ)	COOPER-CLIMAX	2HR 32MIN 41.6SEC
3. GURNEY(USA)	BRABHAM-CLIMAX	31 LAPS
4. GINTHER(USA)	BRM	31 LAPS
5. BONNIER(SWE)	COOPER-CLIMAX	30 LAPS
6. DE BEAUFORT(HOL)	PORSCHE	30 LAPS

Race: 32 laps of 8.76mile/14.1km (280miles/451kms)
Fastest lap: Clark,3min 58.1sec, 132.5mph/213.2kph
Pole position: G. Hill(GB), BRM, 3min 54.1sec 20 starters, 6 classified finishers

ROUND 3/DUTCH GRAND PRIX
ZANDVOORT, 23 JUNE

1. CLARK(GB)	LOTUS-CLIMAX	2HR 8MIN 13.07SEC
2. GURNEY(USA)	BRABHAM-CLIMAX	79 LAPS
3. SURTEES(GB)	FERRARI	79 LAPS
4. IRELAND(GB)	BRP-BRM	79 LAPS
5. GINTHER(USA)	BRM	79 LAPS
6. SCARFIOTTI(ITA)	FERRARI	78 LAPS

Race: 80 laps of 2.6mile/4.19km (280miles/35kms)
Fastest lap: Clark 1min 33.7sec, 100.1mph/161.1kph
Pole position: Clark, 1min 31.6sec 19 starters, 11 classified finishers

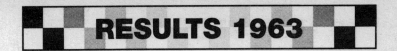

RESULTS 1963

ROUND 4/FRENCH GRAND PRIX

REIMS, 30 JUNE

1. CLARK(GB)	LOTUS-CLIMAX	2HR 10MIN 54.3SEC
2. MAGGS(SA)	COOPER-CLIMAX	2HR 11MIN 59.2SEC
3. G. HILL(GB)	BRM	2HR 13MIN 08.2SEC
4. BRABHAM(AUS)	BRABHAM-CLIMAX	2HR 13MIN 09.5SEC
5. GURNEY(USA)	BRABHAM-CLIMAX	2HR 13MIN 27.7SEC
6. SIFFERT(SWISS)	LOTUS-BRM	52 LAPS

Race: 53 laps of 5.16mile/8.3km (273miles/440kms)
Fastest lap: Clark, 2min 21.6sec, 131.1mph/211kph
Pole position: Clark, 2min 20.2sec 19 starters, 12 classified finishers

ROUND 5/BRITISH GRAND PRIX

SILVERSTONE, 20 JULY

1. CLARK(GB)	LOTUS-CLIMAX	2HR 14MIN 09.6SEC
2. SURTEES(GB)	FERRARI	2HR 14MIN 35.4SEC
3. G. HILL(GB)	BRM	2HR 14MIN 47.2SEC
4. GINTHER(USA)	BRM	81 LAPS
5. BANDINI(ITA)	BRM	81 LAPS
6. HALL(USA)	LOTUS-BRM	80 LAPS

Race: 82 laps of 2.9mile/4.7km (240 miles/385kms)
Fastest lap: Surtees, 1min 36sec, 109.7mph/176kph
Pole position: Clark, 1min 34.4sec 23 starters, 13 classified finishers

ROUND 6/GERMAN GRAND PRIX

NURBURGRING,4 AUGUST

1. SURTEES(GB)	FERRARI	2HR 13MIN 06.8SEC
2. CLARK (GB)	LOTUS-CLIMAX	2HR 14MIN 24.3SEC
3. GINTHER(USA)	BRM	2HR 15MIN 51.7SEC
4. MITTER(GER)	PORSCHE	2HR 21MIN 18.3SEC
5. HALL(USA)	LOTUS-BRM	14 LAPS
6. BONNIER(SWE)	COOPER-CLIMAX	14 LAPS

Race: 15 laps of 14.17mile/22.81km (213miles/342kms)
Fastest lap: Surtees, 8m8in 47sec, 96.8mph/155.8kph
Pole position: Clark, 8min 45.8sec 22 starters,10 classified finishers

ROUND 7/ITALIAN GRAND PRIX

MONZA, 8 SEPTEMBER

1. CLARK(GB)	LOTUS-CLIMAX	2HR 24MIN 19.6SEC
2. GINTHER(USA)	BRM	2HR 25MIN 54.6SEC
3. MCLAREN(NZ)	COOPER-CLIMAX	85 LAPS
4. IRELAND(GB)	BRP-BRM	84 LAPS
5. BRABHAM(AUS)	BRABHAM-CLIMAX	84 LAPS
6. MAGGS(SA)	COOPER-CLIMAX	84 LAPS

Race: 86 laps of 3.57mile/5.75km (307 miles/ 494.5kms)
Fastest lap: Clark, 1min 38.9sec, 130.0mph/209kph
Pole position: Surtees(GB), Ferrari, 1min 37.3sec 20 starters, 16 classified finishers

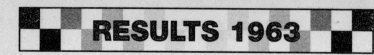

RESULTS 1963

ROUND 8/US GRAND PRIX

WATKINS GLEN, 6 OCTOBER

1. G. HILL(GB)	BRM	2HR 19MIN 22.1SEC
2. GINTHER(USA)	BRM	2HR 19MIN 56.4SEC
3. CLARK(GB)	LOTUS-CLIMAX	109 LAPS
4. BRABHAM(AUS)	BRABHAM-CLIMAX	108 LAPS
5. BANDINI(ITA)	FERRARI	106 LAPS
6. DE BEAUFORT(HOL)	PORSCHE	99 LAPS

Race: 110 laps of 2.3mile/3.7km (253miles/407kms)
Fastest lap: Clark, 1min 14.5sec, 111.1mph/178.9kph
Pole position: G. Hill, 1min 13.4sec 21 starters, 11 classified finishers

ROUND 9/MEXICAN GRAND PRIX

MEXICO CITY, 27 OCTOBER

1. CLARK(GB)	LOTUS-CLIMAX	2HR 09MIN 52.1SEC
2. BRABHAM(AUS)	BRABHAM-CLIMAX	2HR 11MIN 33.2SEC
3. GINTHER(USA)	BRM	2HR 11MIN 46.8SEC
4. G. HILL(GB)	BRM	64 LAPS
5. BONNIER(SWE)	COOPER-CLIMAX	62 LAPS
6. GURNEY(USA)	BRABHAM-CLIMAX	62 LAPS

Race: 65 laps of 3.1mile/5km (203 miles/325kms)
Fastest lap: Clark, 1min 58.1sec, 94.7mph/152.4kph
Pole position: Clark, 1min 58.8sec 21 starters, 11 classified finishers

ROUND 10/SOUTH AFRICAN GRAND PRIX

EAST LONDON, 28 DECEMBER

1. CLARK(GB)	LOTUS-CLIMAX	2HR 10MIN 36.9SEC
2. GURNEY(USA)	BRABHAM-CLIMAX	2HR 11MIN 43.7SEC
3. G.HILL(GB)	BRM	84 LAPS
4. MCLAREN(NZ)	COOPER-CLIMAX	84 LAPS
5. BANDINI(ITA)	FERRARI	84 LAPS
6. BONNIER(SWE)	COOPER-CLIMAX	83 LAPS

Race: 85 laps of 2.44mile/3.92km (207 miles/333kms)
Fastest lap: Gurney, 1min 29.1sec, 98.4mph/158.3kph
Pole position: Clark, 1min 28.9sec 20 starters, 13 classified finishers

DRIVERS' WORLD CHAMPIONSHIP 1963

1. CLARK	54 points	4. SURTEES	22 points
2. G. HILL	29 points	5. GURNEY	19 points
2. GINTHER	29 points	6. MCLAREN	17 points

CONSTRUCTORS' WORLD CHAMPIONSHIP 1963

1. LOTUS-CLIMAX	54 points	4. FERRARI	26 points
2. BRM-CLIMAX	36 points	5. COOPER-CLIMAX	25 points
3. BRABHAM-CLIMAX	28 points	6. BRP-BRM	6 points

RESULTS 1964

1964 Three British drivers fought out the Championship (makes you think!). And the series went right down to the wire in Mexico. Austria hosted its first round, in place of South Africa, at the primitive former military airfield at Zeltweg, and Brands Hatch staged the British Grand Prix for the first time. The Japanese influence arrived in Formula One, in low-key fashion, at the Nurburgring. There were ten rounds to the Championship. Points: 9-6-4-3-2-1 for first six places. Best six results from ten.

ROUND 1/MONACO GRAND PRIX
MONTE CARLO, 10 MAY

1. G. HILL(GB)	BRM	2HR 41MIN 19.5SEC
2. GINTHER(USA)	BRM	99 LAPS
3. ARUNDELL(GB)	LOTUS-CLIMAX	97 LAPS
4. CLARK(GB)	LOTUS-CLIMAX	96 LAPS
5. BONNIER(SWE)	COOPER-CLIMAX	96 LAPS
6. HAILWOOD(GB)	LOTUS-BRM	96 LAPS

Race: 100 laps of 1.95mile/3.15km (195miles/315kms)
Fastest lap: G. Hill, 1min 33.9sec, 74.9mph/120.5kph
Pole position: Clark, 1min 34.0sec 16 starters, 10 classified finishers

ROUND 2/DUTCH GRAND PRIX
ZANDVOORT, 24 MAY

1. CLARK(GB)	LOTUS-CLIMAX	2HR 7MIN 35.4SEC
2. SURTEES(GB)	FERRARI	2HR 8MIN 29.0SEC
3. ARUNDELL(GB)	LOTUS-CLIMAX	79 LAPS
4. G. HILL(GB)	BRM	79 LAPS
5. AMON (NZ)	LOTUS-BRM	79 LAPS
6. ANDERSON(GB)	BRABHAM-CLIMAX	78 LAPS

Race: 80 laps of 2.6mile/4.19km (208 miles/ 335kms)
Fastest lap: Clark, 1min 32.8sec, 101.0mph/162kph
Pole position: Gurney(USA), Brabham-Climax, 1min 31.2sec 17 starters, 13 classified finishers

ROUND 3/BELGIAN GRAND PRIX
SPA-FRANCORCHAMPS, 14 JUNE

1. CLARK(GB)	LOTUS-CLIMAX	2HR 6MIN 40.5SEC
2. MCLAREN (NZ)	COOPER-CLIMAX	2HR 6MIN 43.9SEC
3. BRABHAM(AUS)	BRABHAM-CLIMAX	2HR 7MIN 28.6SEC
4. GINTHER(USA)	BRM	2HR 8MIN 39.1SEC
5. G.HILL(GB)	BRM	31 LAPS
6. GURNEY(USA)	BRABHAM-CLIMAX	31 LAPS

Race: 32 laps of 8.76mile/14.1km (280 miles/451kms)
Fastest lap: Gurney, 3min 49.2sec, 137.6mph/221.5kph
Pole position: Gurney, 3min 50.9sec 18 starters, 10 classified finishers

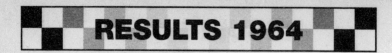

RESULTS 1964

ROUND 4/FRENCH GRAND PRIX
ROUEN-LES-ESSARTS, 28 JUNE

1. GURNEY(USA)	BRABHAM-CLIMAX	2HR 7MIN 49.1SEC
2. G. HILL(GB)	BRM	2HR 8MIN 13.2SEC
3. BRABHAM(AUS)	BRABHAM-CLIMAX	2HR 8MIN 14.0SEC
4. ARUNDELL(GB)	LOTUS-CLIMAX	2HR 8MIN 59.7SEC
5. GINTHER(USA)	BRM	2HR 10MIN 01.2SEC
6. MCLAREN(NZ)	COOPER-CLIMAX	56 LAPS

Race: 57 laps of 4.06mile/6.54km (231miles/373kms)
Fastest lap: Brabham, 2min 11.4sec, 111.37mph/179.23kph
Pole position: Clark(GB), Lotus-Climax, 2min 09.6sec 17 starters, 12 classified finishers

ROUND 5/BRITISH GRAND PRIX
BRANDS HATCH, 11 JULY

1.CLARK(GB)	LOTUS-CLIMAX	2HR 15MIN 07.0SEC
2.G. HILL(GB)	BRM	2HR 15MIN 09.8SEC
3.SURTEES(GB)	FERRARI	2HR 16MIN 27.6SEC
4.BRABHAM(AUS)	BRABHAM-CLIMAX	79 LAPS
5.BANDINI(ITA)	FERRARI	78 LAPS
6.P.HILL(USA)	COOPER-CLIMAX	78 LAPS

Race: 80 laps of 2.65mile/4.27km (212 miles/342kms)
Fastest lap: Clark, 1min 38.8sec, 96.5mph/155.4kph
Pole position: Clark, 1min 38.1sec 23 starters, 14 classified finishers

ROUND 6/GERMAN GRAND PRIX
NURBURGRING, 2 AUGUST

1. SURTEES(GB)	FERRARI	2HR 12MIN 04.8SEC
2. G.HILL(GB)	BRM	2HR 13MIN 20.4SEC
3. BANDINI(ITA)	FERRARI	2HR 16MIN 56.6SEC
4. SIFFERT(SWISS)	BRABHAM-BRM	2HR 17MIN 27.9SEC
5. TRINTIGNANT(FRA)	BRM	14 LAPS
6. MAGGS(SA)	BRM	14 LAPS

Race: 15 laps of 14.17mile/22.81km (213miles/342kms)
Fastest lap: Surtees, 8min 39sec, 98.3mph/158.2kph
*Privateer de Beaufort was fatally injured during practice

ROUND 7/AUSTRIAN GRAND PRIX
ZELTWEG, 23 AUGUST

1. BANDINI(ITA)	FERRARI	2HR 6MIN 18.23SEC
2. GINTHER(USA)	BRM	2HR 6MIN 24.41SEC
3. ANDERSON(GB)	BRABHAM-CLIMAX	102 LAPS
4. MAGGS(SA)	BRM	102 LAPS
5. IRELAND(GB)	BRP-BRM	102 LAPS
6; BONNIER(SWE)	BRABHAM-CLIMAX	101 LAPS

Race: 105 laps of 1.99mile/3.2km (209miles/ 336kms)
Fastest lap: Gurney (USA), Brabham-Climax,1min 10.56sec, 101.5mph/163kph
Pole position: G. Hill(GB), BRM, 1min 09,8sec 20 starters, 9 classified finishers

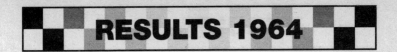

RESULTS 1964

ROUND 8/ITALIAN GRAND PRIX

MONZA, 6 SEPTEMBER

1. SURTEES(GB)	FERRARI	2HR 10MIN 51.8SEC
2. MCLAREN(NZ)	COOPER-CLIMAX	2HR 11MIN 57.8SEC
3. BANDINI(ITA)	FERRARI	77 LAPS
4. GINTHER(USA)	BRM	77 LAPS
5. IRELAND(GB)	BRP-BRM	77 LAPS
6. SPENCE(GB)	LOTUS-CLIMAX	77 LAPS

Race: 78 laps of 3.57mile/5.75km (278miles/448.5kms)
Fastest lap: Surtees, 1min 38.8sec, 130.1mph/209kph
Pole position: Surtees, 1min 37.04sec 20 starters,14 classified finishers

ROUND 9/US GRAND PRIX

WATKINS GLEN, 4 OCTOBER

1. G. HILL(GB)	BRM	2HR 16MIN 38.0SEC
2. SURTEES(GB)	FERRARI	2HR 17MIN 08.5SEC
3. SIFFERT(SWISS)	BRABHAM-BRM	109 LAPS
4. GINTHER(USA)	BRM	107 LAPS
5. HANGSEN(USA)	LOTUS-CLIMAX	107 LAPS
6. T. TAYLOR(GB)	BRP-BRM	106 LAPS

Race: 110 laps of 2.3mile/3.7km (253miles/407kms)
Fastest lap: Clark(GB), Lotus-Climax, 1min 13.2sec, 113.1mph/183kph
Pole position: Clark, 1min 12.6sec 19 starters, 8 classified finishers

ROUND 10/MEXICAN GRAND PRIX

MEXICO CITY, 25 OCTOBER

1. GURNEY(USA)	BRABHAM-CLIMAX	2HR 09MIN 50.32SEC
2. SURTEES(GB)	FERRARI	2HR 10MIN 59.26SEC
3. BANDINI(ITA)	FERRARI	2HR 10MIN 59.95SEC
4. SPENCE (GB)	LOTUS-CLIMAX	2HR 11MIN 12.18SEC
5. CLARK(GB)	LOTUS-CLIMAX	64 LAPS
6. P.RODRIGUEZ(MEX)	FERRARI	64 LAPS

Race: 65 laps of 3.1mile/5km (203miles/325kms)
Fastest lap: Clark, 1min 58.37sec, 95.6mph/152kph
Pole position: Clark, 1min 57.24sec 19 starters, 14 classified finishers

DRIVERS' WORLD CHAMPIONSHIP 1964

1. SURTEES	40 *points*	4. BANDINI	23 *points*
2. G.HILL	39 *points*	4. GINTHER	23 *points*
3. CLARK	32 *points*	6. GURNEY	19 *points*

CONSTRUCTORS' WORLD CHAMPIONSHIP 1963

1. FERRARI	45 *points*	4. BRABHAM-CLIMAX	30 *points*
2. BRM	42 *points*	5. COOPER-CLIMAX	16 *points*
3. LOTUS-CLIMAX	37 *points*	6. BRABHAM-BRM	7 *points*

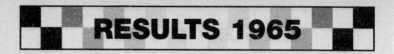

RESULTS 1965

1965 Jim Clark took his second world title with six wins in a row (he did miss out on Monaco because he was busy becoming the first Brit ever to triumph at Indianapolis!). One John Young Stewart made his Championship debut -and how! To say British drivers dominated the year was an understatement... The season kick-started in South Africa, Austria was dropped from the calendar. There were 10 rounds, best six scores counted. Points: 9-6-4-3-2-1 for first six places.

ROUND 1/SOUTH AFRICAN GRAND PRIX
EAST LONDON,1 JANUARY

1. CLARK(GB)	LOTUS-CLIMAX	2HR 6MIN 46.0SEC
2. SURTEES(GB)	FERRARI	2HR 7MIN 15.0SEC
3. G. HILL(GB)	BRM	2HR 7MIN 17.8SEC
4. SPENCE(GB)	LOTUS-CLIMAX	2HR 7MIN 40.4SEC
5. MCLAREN(NZ)	COOPER-CLIMAX	84 LAPS
6. STEWART (GB)	BRM	83 LAPS

Race: 85 laps of 2.44mile/3.92km (207miles/333kms)
Fastest lap: Clark, 1min 27.6sec, 100.1mph/161.09kph
Pole position: Clark, 1min 27min 2.0sec 20 starters, 15 classified finishers

ROUND 2/MONACO GRAND PRIX
MONTE CARLO, 30 MAY

1. G. HILL(GB)	BRM	2HR 37MIN 39.6SEC
2. BANDINI(ITA)	FERRARI	2HR 38MIN 43.6SEC
3. STEWART(GB)	BRM	2HR 39MIN 21.5SEC
4. SURTEES(GB)	FERRARI	99 LAPS
5. MCLAREN(NZ)	COOPER-CLIMAX	98 LAPS
6. SIFFERT(SWISS)	BRABHAM-BRM	98 LAPS

Race: 100 laps of 1.95mile/3.15km (195miles/315kms)
Fastest lap: G. Hill, 1min 31.7sec, 76.8mph/123.5kph
Pole position: G. Hill, 1min 31.07sec 16 starters, 10 classified finishers

ROUND 3/BELGIAN GRAND PRIX PRIX
SPA-FRANCORCHAMPS, 13 JUNE

1. CLARK(GB)	LOTUS-CLIMAX	2HR 23MIN 34.8SEC
2. STEWART(GB)	BRM	2HR 24MIN 19.6SEC
3. MCLAREN(NZ)	COOPER-CLIMAX	31 LAPS
4. BRABHAM(AUS)	BRABHAM-CLIMAX	31 LAPS
5. G. HILL(GB)	BRM	31 LAPS
6. GINTHER(USA)	HONDA	31 LAPS

Race: 32 laps of 8.76mile/14.1km circuit-280 miles/451kms)
Fastest lap: Clark, 4min 12.9sec, 124.7mph/200kph
Pole position: G. Hill, 3min 45.4sec 19 finishers, 14 classified finishers

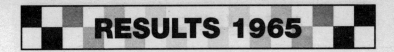
RESULTS 1965

ROUND 4/FRENCH GRAND PRIX
CLERMONT FERRAND, 27 JUNE

1.CLARK(GB)	LOTUS-CLIMAX	2HR 14MIN 38.4SEC
2.STEWART(GB)	BRM	2HR 15MIN 04.7SEC
3.SURTEES(GB)	FERRARI	2HR 17MIN 11.9SEC
4.HULME(NZ)	BRABHAM-CLIMAX	2HR 17MIN 31.5SEC
5.G. HILL(GB)	BRM	39 LAPS
6.SIFFERT (SWISS)	BRABHAM-BRM	39 LAPS

Race: *40 laps of 5mile/8km (200 miles/320kms)*
Fastest lap: *Clark, 3min 18.09sec, 90.6mph/145.8kph*
Pole position: *Clark, 2min 18.3sec 17 starters, 9 classified finishers*

ROUND 5/BRITISH GRAND PRIX
SILVERSTONE, 10 JULY

1. CLARK(GB)	LOTUS-CLIMAX	2HR 5MIN 25.4SEC
2. G. HILL(GB)	BRM	2HR 5MIN 28.6SEC
3. SURTEES(GB)	FERRARI	2HR 5MIN 53.0SEC
4. SPENCE(GB)	LOTUS-CLIMAX	2HR 6MIN 05.0SEC
5. STEWART(GB)	BRM	2HR 6MIN 40.0SEC
6. GURNEY(USA)	BRABHAM-CLIMAX	79 LAPS

Race: *80 laps of 2.9mile/4.71km (232miles/377kms)*
Fastest lap: *G. Hill, 1min 32.2sec, 114.3mph/184kph*
Pole position: *Clark, 1min 30.8sec 20 starters, 14 classified finishers*

ROUND 6/DUTCH GRAND PRIX
ZANDVOORT, 18 JULY

1. CLARK (GB)	LOTUS-CLIMAX	2HR 3MIN 59.1SEC
2. STEWART(GB)	BRM	2HR 4MIN 07.1SEC
3. GURNEY(USA)	BRABHAM-CLIMAX	2HR 4MIN 12.1SEC
4. G. HILL(GB)	BRM	2HR 4MIN 44.2SEC
5. HULME(NZ)	BRABHAM-CLIMAX	79 LAPS
6. GINTHER(USA)	HONDA	79 LAPS

Race: *80 laps of 2.6mile/4.19km (208miles/335kms)*
Fastest lap: *Clark, 1min 30.6sec, 103.5mph/166.6kph*
Pole position: *G. Hill, 1min 30.7sec 17 starters, 13 classified finishers*

ROUND 7/GERMAN GRAND PRIX
NURBURGRING, 1 AUGUST

1. CLARK(GB)	LOTUS-CLIMAX	2HR 07MIN 52.4SEC
2. G.HILL(GB)	BRM	2HR 08MIN 08.3SEC
3. GURNEY(USA)	BRABHAM-CLIMAX	2HR 08MIN 13.8SEC
4. RINDT(AUT)	COOPER-CLIMAX	2HR 11MIN 22.0SEC
5. BRABHAM(AUS)	BRABHAM-CLIMAX	2HR 12MIN 33.6SEC
6. BANDINI(ITA)	FERRARI	2HR 13MIN 01.0SEC

Race: *15 laps of 14.17mile/22.81km (213miles/342kms)*
Fastest lap: *Clark, 8min 24.01sec, 101.2mph/162.9kph*
Pole position: *Clark, 8min 22.7sec 19 starters, 8 classified finishers*

RESULTS 1965

ROUND 8/ITALIAN GRAND PRIX
MONZA, 12 SEPTEMBER

1. STEWART(GB)	BRM	2HR 4MIN 52.8SEC
2. G.HILL(GB)	BRM	2HR 4MIN 56.1SEC
3. GURNEY(USA)	BRABHAM-CLIMAX	2HR 5MIN 09.3SEC
4. BANDINI(ITA)	FERRARI	2HR 6MIN 08.7SEC
5. MCLAREN(NZ)	COOPER-CLIMAX	75 LAPS
6. ATTWOOD(GB)	LOTUS-BRM	75 LAPS

Race: 76 laps of 3.57mile/5.75km (271 miles/437kms)
Fastest lap: Clark, 1min 36.4sec,133.4mph/214.7kph
Pole position: Clark, 1min 35.09sec 23 starters, 14 classified finishers

ROUND 9/US GRAND PRIX
WATKINS GLEN, 3 OCTOBER

1. G. HILL(GB)	BRM	2HR 20MIN 36.1SEC
2. GURNEY(USA)	BRABHAM-CLIMAX	2HR 20MIN 48.6SEC
3. BRABHAM(AUS)	BRABHAM-CLIMAX	2HR 21MIN 33.6SEC
4. BANDINI(ITA)	FERRARI	109 LAPS
5. P. RODRIGUEZ(MEX)	FERRARI	109 LAPS
6. RINDT(AUT)	COOPER-CLIMAX	108 LAPS

Race: 110 laps of 2.3mile/3.7km (253miles/407kms)
Fastest lap: G. Hill, 1min 11.09sec, 115.1mph/185.33kph
Pole position: G.Hill, 1min 11.25sec 18 starters, 13 classified finishers

ROUND 10/MEXICAN GRAND PRIX
MEXICO CITY, 24 OCTOBER

1. GINTHER(USA)	HONDA	2HR 08MIN 32.10SEC
2. GURNEY(USA)	BRABHAM-CLIMAX	2HR 08MIN 34.99SEC
3. SPENCE(GB)	LOTUS-CLIMAX	2HR 09MIN 32.25SEC
4. SIFFERT(SWISS)	BRABHAM-BRM	2HR 10MIN 26.52SEC
5. BUCKNUM(USA)	HONDA	64 LAPS
6. ATTWOOD(GB)	LOTUS-BRM	64 LAPS

Race: 65 laps of 3.1mile/5km (203miles/ 325kms)
Fastest lap: Gurney, 1min 55.84sec, 96.6mph/155.4kph
Pole position: Clark(GB), Lotus-Climax, 1min 56.17sec 18 starters, 11 class. finishers

---

 DRIVERS' WORLD CHAMPIONSHIP 1965

1. CLARK	54 *points*	4. GURNEY	25 *points*
2. G.HILL	40 *points*	5. SURTEES	17 *points*
3. STEWART	33 *points*	6. BANDINI	13 *points*

CONSTRUCTORS' WORLD CHAMPIONSHIP 1965

1. LOTUS-CLIMAX	54 *points*	4. FERRARI	26 *points*
2. BRM	45 *points*	5. COOPER-CLIMAX	14 *points*
3. BRABHAM-CLIMAX	27 *points*	6. HONDA	11 *points*

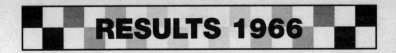

RESULTS 1966

1966 Jack Brabham, at 40 years of age, took his third title in a car of his own manufacture, powered by an Aussie company, Repco.
Bruce McLaren and Dan Gurney went into the construction business for themselves. South Africa was dropped from the calendar. There were nine rounds, best five scores counted. Points: 9-6-4-3-2-1 for first six places.

ROUND 6/MONACO GRAND PRIX
MONTE CARLO, 22 MAY

1. STEWART(GB)	BRM	2HR 33MIN 10.5SEC
2. BANDINI(ITA)	FERRARI	2HR 33MIN 50.7SEC
3. G.HILL(GB)	BRM	99 LAPS
4. BONDURANT(USA)	BRM	95 LAPS
5. GINTHER(USA)	COOPER-MASERATI	80 LAPS*
6. LIGIER(FRA)	COOPER-MASERATI	75 LAPS*

Race: 100 laps of 1.95mile/3.15km (195miles/315kms)
Fastest lap: Bandini, 1min 29.8sec, 78.3mph/126kph
Pole position: Clark(GB), Lotus-Climax, 1min 29.9sec 16 starters, 4 classified finishers
* Neither Ginther nor Ligier were classified finishers

ROUND 2/BELGIAN GRAND PRIX
SPA-FRANCORCHAMPS, 12 JUNE

1. SURTEES(GB)	FERRARI	2HR 9MIN 11.3SEC
2. RINDT(AUT)	COOPER-MASERATI	2HR 9MIN 53.4SEC
3. BANDINI(ITA)	FERRARI	27 LAPS
4. BRABHAM(AUS)	BRABHAM-REPCO	26 LAPS
5. GINTHER(USA)	COOPER-MASERATI	25 LAPS
6. LIGIER(FRA)	COOPER-MASERATI	24 LAPS*

Race: 28 laps of 8.76mile/14.1km (245miles/395kms)
Fastest lap: Surtees, 4min 18.7sec, 121.9mph/196.2kph
Pole position: Surtees, 3min 38.0sec 15 starters, 5 classified finishers
*Ligier was non-classified finisher

ROUND 3/FRENCH GRAND PRIX
REIMS, 3 JULY

1. BRABHAM(AUS)	BRABHAM-REPCO	1HR 48MIN 31.3SEC
2. PARKES(GB)	FERRARI	1HR 48MIN 40.8SEC
3. HULME(NZ)	BRABHAM-REPCO	46 LAPS
4. RINDT(AUT)	COOPER-MASERATI	46 LAPS
5. GURNEY(USA)	EAGLE-CLIMAX	45 LAPS
6. J. TAYLOR(GB)	BRABHAM-BRM	45 LAPS

Race: 48 laps of 5.16mile/8.3km (247 miles/398 kms)
Fastest lap: Bandini, 2min 11.3sec,141.4mph/227.6kph
Pole position: Bandini, 2min 07.8sec 17 starters, 8 classified finishers

RESULTS 1966

ROUND 4/BRITISH GRAND PRIX

BRANDS HATCH, 16 JULY

1. BRABHAM(AUS)	BRABHAM-REPCO	2HR 13MIN 13.4SEC
2. HULME(NZ)	BRABHAM-REPCO	2HR 13MIN 23.0SEC
3. G. HILL(GB)	BRM	79 LAPS
4. CLARK(GB)	LOTUS-CLIMAX	79 LAPS
5. RINDT(AUT)	COOPER-MASERATI	79 LAPS
6. MCLAREN(NZ)	MCLAREN-SERENISSIMA	78 LAPS

Race: 80 laps of 2.65mile/4.27km (212 miles/342kms)
Fastest lap: Brabham,1min 37sec,98.3mph/158kph
Pole position: Brabham,1min 34.5sec 20 starters, 11 classified finishers

ROUND 5/DUTCH GRAND PRIX

ZANDVOORT, 24 JULY

1. BRABHAM(AUS)	BRABHAM-REPCO	2HR 20MIN 32.5SEC
2. G. HILL(GB)	BRM	89 LAPS
3. CLARK(GB)	LOTUS-CLIMAX	88 LAPS
4. STEWART(GB)	BRM	88 LAPS
5. SPENCE(GB)	LOTUS-BRM	87 LAPS
6. BANDINI(ITA)	FERRARI	87 LAPS

Race: 90 laps of 2.6 mile/4.19km (234 miles/377kms)
Fastest lap: Hulme(NZ), Brabham-Repco, 1min 30.6sec, 103.5mph/167kph
Pole position: Brabham, 1min 28.1sec 17 starters, 9 classified finishers

ROUND 6/GERMAN GRAND PRIX

NURBURGRING, 7 AUGUST

1. BRABHAM(AUS)	BRABHAM-REPCO	2HR 27MIN 03.0SEC
2. SURTEES(GB)	COOPER-MASERATI	2HR 27MIN 47.4SEC
3. RINDT(AUT)	COOPER-MASERATI	2HR 29MIN 35.6SEC
4. G.HILL(GB)	BRM	2HR 33MIN 44.4SEC
5. STEWART(GB)	BRM	2HR 35MIN 31.9SEC
6. BANDINI(ITA)	FERRARI	2HR 37MIN 59.4SEC

Race: 15 laps of 14.17mile/22.81km (213 miles/342kms)
Fastest lap: Surtees, 8min 49.0sec, 96.4mph/155kph
Pole position: Clark(GB), Lotus-Climax, 8min, 16.5sec 27 starters, 12 class. finishers
Britain's John Taylor died of burns after an accident.

ROUND 7/ITALIAN GRAND PRIX

MONZA, 4 SEPTEMBER

1.SCARFIOTTI(ITA)	FERRARI	1HR 47MIN 14.8SEC
2.PARKES(GB)	FERRARI	1HR 47MIN 20.6SEC
3.HULME(NZ)	BRABHAM-REPCO	1HR 47MIN 20.9SEC
4.RINDT(AUT)	COOPER-MASERATI	67 LAPS
5.SPENCE(GB)	LOTUS-BRM	67 LAPS
6.ANDERSON(GB)	BRABHAM-CLIMAX	66 LAPS

Race: 68 laps of 3.57 mile/5.75km (243 miles/391kms)
Fastest lap: Scarfiotti,1min 32.4sec, 139.2mph/224.03kph
Pole position: Parkes, 1min 31.3sec 20 starters, 9 classified finishers

RESULTS 1966/7

ROUND 8/US GRAND PRIX
WATKINS GLEN, 2 OCTOBER

1. CLARK(GB)	LOTUS-BRM	2HR 09MIN 40.1SEC
2. RINDT(AUT)	COOPER-MASERATI	2HR 11MIN 26.9SEC
3. SURTEES(GB)	COOPER-MASERATI	107 LAPS
4. SIFFERT (SWISS)	COOPER-MASERATI	105 LAPS
5. MCLAREN(NZ)	MCLAREN-FORD	105 LAPS
6. ARUNDELL(GB)	LOTUS-CLIMAX	101 LAPS

Race: 108 laps of 2.3mile/3.7km (248miles/400 kms)
Fastest lap: Surtees, 1min 9.67sec, 118.8mph/191kph
Pole position: Brabham(AUS), Brabham-Climax, 1min 08.42sec 19 starters, 6 classified finishers

ROUND 9/MEXICAN GRAND PRIX
MEXICO CITY, 23 OCTOBER

1. SURTEES(GB)	COOPER-MASERATI	2HR 6MIN 35.34SEC
2. BRABHAM(AUS)	BRABHAM-REPCO	2HR 6MIN 43.22SEC
3. HULME(NZ)	BRABHAM-REPCO	64 LAPS
4. GINTHER(USA)	HONDA	64 LAPS
5. GURNEY(USA)	EAGLE-WESLAKE	64 LAPS
6. BONNIER(SWE)	COOPER-MASERATI	63 LAPS

Race: 65 laps of 3.1mile/5km (203miles/325kms)
Fastest lap: Ginther, 1min 53.75sec, 98.3mph/158.2kph
Pole position: Surtees, 1min 53.18sec 18 starters, 8 classified finishers

---

DRIVERS' WORLD CHAMPIONSHIP 1966

1. BRABHAM	42 *points*	4. HULME	18 *points*
2. SURTEES	28 *points*	5. G.HILL	17 *points*
3. RINDT	22 *points*	6. CLARK	16 *points*

CONSTRUCTORS' WORLD CHAMPIONSHIP 1966

1. BRABHAM-REPCO	42 *points*	4. BRM	22 points
2. FERRARI	31 *points*	5. LOTUS-BRM	13 points
3. COOPER-MASERATI	30 *points*	6. LOTUS-CLIMAX	8 points

1967 Graham Hill joined Jim Clark in the Lotus 'Dream Team'. The Ford-Cosworth engine made its triumphant entry. Antipodean team-mates, Brabham and Hulme tussled for the title. Italy's Lorenzo Bandini tragically lost his life in a fiery accident at Monaco. Canada hosted a Grand Prix for the first time. South Africa kicked off the season with new Kyalami circuit outside Johannesburg. There were 11 rounds. The season was divided into two halves. Best five out of first six scores. Best four out of second five scores. Points: 9-6-4-3-2-1.

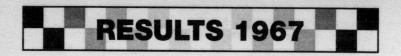

RESULTS 1967

ROUND 1/SOUTH AFRICAN GRAND PRIX

KYALAMI, 2 JANUARY

1. P. RODRIGUEZ(MEX)	COOPER-MASERATI	2HR 5MIN 45.9SEC
2. LOVE (RHO)	COOPER-CLIMAX	2HR 6MIN 12.3SEC
3. SURTEES(GB)	HONDA	79 LAPS
4. HULME(NZ)	BRABHAM-REPCO	78 LAPS
5. ANDERSON(GB)	BRABHAM-CLIMAX	78 LAPS
6. BRABHAM(AUS)	BRABHAM-REPCO	76 LAPS

Race: 80 laps of 2.55mile/4.09km (204miles/327kms)
Fastest lap: Hulme, 1min 29.9sec, 101.8mph/163.9kph
Pole position: Brabham, 1min 28.3sec 18 starters, 6 classified finishers

ROUND 2/MONACO GRAND PRIX

MONTE CARLO, 7 MAY

1. HULME(NZ)	BRABHAM-REPCO	2HR 34MIN 34.3SEC
2. G. HILL(GB)	LOTUS-BRM	99 LAPS
3. AMON (NZ)	FERRARI	98 LAPS
4. MCLAREN(NZ)	MCLAREN-BRM	97 LAPS
5. P. RODRIGUEZ(MEX)	COOPER-MASERATI	96 LAPS
6. SPENCE(GB)	BRM	96 LAPS

Race: 100 laps of 1.95 mile/3.15km (195 miles/315 kms)
Fastest lap: Clark(GB), Lotus-Climax, 1min 29.5sec,78.6mph/126.5kph
Pole position: Brabham(AUS),Brabham-Repco, 1min 27.6sec 16 starters, 6 class. finishers

ROUND 3/DUTCH GRAND PRIX

ZANDVOORT, 4 JUNE

1. CLARK (GB)	LOTUS-FORD	2HR 14MIN 45.1SEC
2. BRABHAM(AUS)	BRABHAM-REPCO	2HR 15MIN 08.7SEC
3. HULME (NZ)	BRABHAM-REPCO	2HR 15MIN 10.8SEC
4. AMON (NZ)	FERRARI	2HR 15MIN 12.4SEC
5. PARKES(GB)	FERRARI	89 LAPS
6. SCARFIOTTI (ITA)	FERRARI	89 LAPS

Race: 90 laps of 2.6 mile/4.19 km (234 miles/377 kms)
*Fastest lap:*Clark, 1min 28.08sec, 106.5mph/171.4 kph
Pole position: G. Hill(GB), Lotus-Ford, 1min 24.6sec 17 starters, 10 classified finishers

ROUND 4/BELGIAN GRAND PRIX

SPA-FRANCORCHAMPS, 18 JUNE

1. GURNEY (USA)	EAGLE-WESLAKE	1HR 40MIN 49.4SEC
2. STEWART(GB)	BRM	1HR 41MIN 52.4SEC
3. AMON (NZ)	FERRARI	1HR 42MIN 29.4SEC
4. RINDT (AUT)	COOPER-MASERATI	1HR 43MIN 03.3SEC
5. SPENCE (GB)	BRM	27 LAPS
6. CLARK (GB)	LOTUS-FORD	27 LAPS

Race: 28 laps of 8.76 mile/14.1 km (245 miles/395 kms)
Fastest lap: Gurney, 3min 31.9sec, 148.8mph/239.5kph
Pole position: Clark, 3min 28.1sec 18 starters, 10 classified finishers

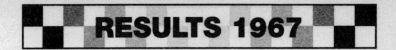

RESULTS 1967

ROUND 5/FRENCH GRAND PRIX
LE MANS, BUGATTI CIRCUIT, 2 JULY

1. BRABHAM(AUS)	BRABHAM-REPCO	2HR 13MIN 21.3SEC
2. HULME(NZ)	BRABHAM-REPCO	2HR 14MIN 10.8SEC
3. STEWART(GB)	BRM	79 LAPS
4. SIFFERT (SWISS)	COOPER-MASERATI	77 LAPS
5. IRWIN (GB)	BRM	76 LAPS
6. P .RODRIGUEZ(MEX)	COOPER-MASERATI	76 LAPS

Race: 80 laps of 2.74 mile/4.4km (220 miles/ 352kms)
Fastest lap: G. Hill(GB),Lotus-Ford, 1min 36.7sec, 102.3mph/164.6kph
Pole position: G. Hill, 1min 36.2 sec 15 starters, 7 classified finishers

ROUND 6/BRITISH GRAND PRIX
SILVERSTONE, 15 JULY

1. CLARK(GB)	LOTUS-FORD	1HR .59MIN 25.6SEC
2. HULME(NZ)	BRABHAM-REPCO	1HR 59MIN 38.4SEC
3. AMON(NZ)	FERRARI	1HR 59MIN 42.2SEC
4. BRABHAM(AUS)	BRABHAM-REPCO	1HR 59MIN 47.4SEC
5. P .RODRIGUEZ(MEX)	COOPER-MASERATI	79 LAPS
6. SURTEES(GB)	HONDA	78 LAPS

Race: 80 laps of 2.9 mile/4.71 km (234 miles/ 377 kms)
Fastest lap: Hulme, 1min 27.0sec, 121.1mph/194.9kph
Pole position: Clark, 1min 25.3sec 20 starters, 10 classified finishers

ROUND 7/GERMAN GRAND PRIX
NURBURGRING, 6 AUGUST

1. HULME(NZ)	BRABHAM-REPCO	2HR 05MIN 55.7SEC
2. BRABHAM(AUS)	BRABHAM-REPCO	2HR 06MIN 34.2SEC
3. AMON (NZ)	FERRARI	2HR 06MIN 34.7SEC
4. SURTEES(GB)	HONDA	2HR 08MIN 21.4SEC
5. BONNIER(SWE)	COOPER-MASERATI	2HR 14MIN 37.8SEC
6. LIGIER (FRA)	BRABHAM-REPCO	14 LAPS

Race: 15 laps of 14.19mile/22.84km (213 miles/343 kms)
Fastest lap: Gurney(USA), Eagle-Weslake, 8min 15.1sec, 103.1mph/166kph
Pole position: Clark(GB), Lotus-Ford,8min 04.1sec 25 starters, 11 classified finishers

ROUND 8/CANADIAN GRAND PRIX
MOSPORT PARK, TORONTO, 27 AUGUST

1.BRABHAM(AUS)	BRABHAM-REPCO	2HR 40MIN 40.0SEC
2.HULME(NZ)	BRABHAM-REPCO	2HR 41MIN 41.9SEC
3.GURNEY(USA)	EAGLE-WESLAKE	89 LAPS
4.G. HILL(GB)	LOTUS-FORD	88 LAPS
5.SPENCE(GB)	BRM	87 LAPS
6.AMON(NZ)	FERRARI	87 LAPS

Race: 90 laps of 2.46mile/3.96km (221 miles/356 kms)
*Fastest lap:*Clark(GB), Lotus-Ford, 1min 23.1sec, 106.5mph/171.5kph
Pole position: Clark, 1min 22.4sec 18 starters, 11 classified finishers

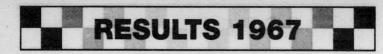

RESULTS 1967

ROUND 9/ITALIAN GRAND PRIX
MONZA, 10 SEPTEMBER

1. SURTEES(GB)	HONDA	1HR 43MIN 45.0SEC
2. BRABHAM(AUS)	BRABHAM-REPCO	1HR 43MIN 45.2SEC
3. CLARK(GB)	LOTUS-FORD	1HR 44MIN 08.1SEC
4. RINDT(AUT)	COOPER-MASERATI	1HR 44MIN 41.6SEC
5. SPENCE(GB)	BRM	67 LAPS
6. ICKX(BEL)	COOPER-MASERATI	66 LAPS

Race: 68 laps of 3.57mile/5.75km (243 miles/391 kms)
Fastest lap: Clark, 1min 28.5sec, 145.3mph/233.9kph
Pole position: Clark, 1min 28.5sec 18 starters, 7 classified finishers

ROUND 10/US GRAND PRIX
WATKINS GLEN, 1 OCTOBER

1. CLARK(GB)	LOTUS-FORD	2HR 3MIN 13.2SEC
2. G.HILL(GB)	LOTUS-FORD	2HR 3MIN 19.5SEC
3. HULME(NZ)	BRABHAM-REPCO	107 LAPS
4. SIFFERT(SWISS)	COOPER-MASERATI	106 LAPS
5. BRABHAM(AUS)	BRABHAM-REPCO	104 LAPS
6. BONNIER(SWE)	COOPER-MASERATI	101 LAPS

Race: 108 laps of 2.3mile/3.7km (248 miles-400 km)
Fastest lap: G. Hill, 1min 06sec, 125.4mph/201.9kph
Pole position: G.Hill, 1min 05.48sec 18 starters, 7 classified finishers

ROUND 11/MEXICAN GRAND PRIX
MEXICO CITY, 22 OCTOBER

1.CLARK(GB)	LOTUS-FORD	1HR 59MIN 28.70SEC
2.BRABHAM(AUS)	BRABHAM-REPCO	2HR 00MIN 54.06SEC
3.HULME(NZ)	BRABHAM-REPCO	64 LAPS
4.SURTEES(GB)	HONDA	64 LAPS
5.SPENCE(GB)	BRM	63 LAPS
6.P.RODRIGUEZ(MEX)	COOPER-MASERATI	63 LAPS

Race: 65 laps of 3.1 mile/5km (203 miles/325kms)
Fastest lap: Clark:1min 48.13sec, 103.4mph/166.4kph
Pole position: Clark: 1min 47.56sec 18 starters, 13 classified finishers

 DRIVERS' WORLD CHAMPIONSHIP 1967

1.	HULME	51 *points*	4. SURTEES	20 *points*
2.	BRABHAM	46 *points*	6. G.HILL	15 *points*
3.	CLARK	41 *points*	6. P.RODRIGUEZ	15 *points*
4.	AMON	20 *points*		

CONSTRUCTORS' WORLD CHAMPIONSHIP 1967

1. BRABHAM-REPCO	63 *points*	4. FERRARI	20 *points*
2. LOTUS-FORD	44 *points*	4. HONDA	20 *points*
3. COOPER-MASERATI	28 *points*	6. BRM	17 *points*

RESULTS 1968

1968 April 7 was a sad day for Britain's motor sport fans. Jim Clark lost his life at Hockenheim in a Formula 2 race. But the devastated Lotus team fought back to take both titles, thanks to Clark's life-long friend, Graham Hill. Britain's Mike Spence died in an accident at Indianapolis. World Champion Hulme joined his fellow Kiwi at McLaren and Bruce McLaren became the second man in history to win a race in a car bearing his own name. Jackie Stewart teamed up with Ken Tyrrell, in what would prove to be an historic partnership. Young Jacky Ickx gained the title of rain-master with Ferrari and became the first Belgian to win a Grand Prix, and Switzerland's Jo Siffert gave Rob Walker his first triumph since Moss in 1961. Spain hosted a Grand Prix for the first time since 1954, at the spartan Jarama track outside Madrid. There were 12 rounds. The season was divided into two; best five results from first six, best five results from second six. Points: 9-6-4-3-2-1 for first six places.

ROUND 1/SOUTH AFRICAN GRAND PRIX
KYALAMI, 1 JANUARY

1. CLARK(GB)	LOTUS-FORD	1HR 53MIN 56.6SEC
2. G. HILL(GB)	LOTUS-FORD	1HR 54MIN 21.9SEC
3. RINDT(AUT)	BRABHAM-REPCO	1HR 54MIN 27.0SEC
4. AMON(NZ)	FERRARI	78 LAPS
5. HULME(NZ)	MCLAREN-BRM	78 LAPS
6. BELTOISE(FRA)	MATRA-FORD	77 LAPS

Race: 80 laps of 2.55mile/4.1km (204miles/328 kms)
Fastest lap: Clark, 1min 23.7sec, 109.6mph/176.5kph
Pole position: Clark,1min 21.6sec 23 starters, 9 classified finishers

ROUND/2 SPANISH GRAND PRIX
JARAMA, MADRID, 12 MAY

1. G.HILL(GB)	LOTUS-FORD	2HR 15MIN 20.1SEC
2. HULME(NZ)	MCLAREN-FORD	2HR 15MIN 36.0SEC
3. REDMAN(GB)	COOPER-BRM	89 LAPS
4. SCARFIOTTI(ITA)	COOPER-BRM	89 LAPS
5. BELTOISE(FRA)	MATRA-FORD	81 LAPS

Race: 90 laps of 2.12mile/3.4km (191miles/306kms)
Fastest lap: Beltoise, 1min 28.3sec,86.2mph/138.8kph
Pole position: Amon(NZ), Ferrari, 1min 27.9sec 13 starters, 5 classified finishers

ROUND 3/MONACO GRAND PRIX
MONTE CARLO, 26 MAY

1. G. HILL(GB)	LOTUS-FORD	2HR 0MIN 32.3SEC
2. ATTWOOD(GB)	BRM	2HR 0MIN 34.5SEC
3. BIANCHI(BEL)	COOPER-BRM	76 LAPS
4. SCARFIOTTI(ITA)	COOPER-BRM	76 LAPS
5. HULME(NZ)	MCLAREN-FORD	73 LAPS

Race: 80 laps of 1.95mile/3.15km (156miles/252kms)
Fastest lap: Attwood, 1min 28.1sec, 79.8mph/128.5kph
Pole position: G. Hill, 1min 28.2sec 16 starters, 5 classified finishers

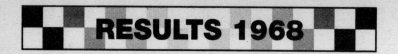

RESULTS 1968

ROUND 4/BELGIAN GRAND PRIX

SPA-FRANCORCHAMPS, 9 JUNE

1. MCLAREN(NZ)	MCLAREN-FORD	1HR 40MIN 02.1SEC
2. P. RODRIGUEZ(MEX)	BRM	1HR 40MIN 14.2SEC
3. ICKX(BEL)	FERRARI	1HR 40MIN 41.7SEC
4. STEWART(GB)	MATRA-FORD	27 LAPS
5. OLIVER(GB)	LOTUS-FORD	26 LAPS
6. BIANCHI(BEL)	COOPER-BRM	26 LAPS

Race: 28 laps of 8.76mile/14.1km (245 miles/395kms)
Fastest lap: Surtees(GB), Honda, 3min 30.5sec, 149.8mph/241.1kph
Pole position: Amon(NZ), Ferrari, 3min 28.6sec 18 starters, 8 classified finishers

ROUND 5/DUTCH GRAND PRIX

ZANDVOORT, 23 JUNE

1. STEWART(GB)	MATRA-FORD	2HR 46MIN 11.26SEC
2. BELTOISE(FRA)	MATRA-V12	2HR 47MIN 45.19SEC
3. P. RODRIGUEZ(MEX)	BRM	89 LAPS
4. ICKX(BEL)	FERRARI	88 LAPS
5. MOSER(SWISS)	BRABHAM-REPCO	87 LAPS
6. AMON(NZ)	FERRARI	85 LAPS

Race: 90 laps of 2.6mile/4.19km (234miles/377kms)
Fastest lap: Beltoise, 1min 45.91sec, 88.6mph/142.5kph
Pole position: Amon, 1min 23.54sec 19 starters, 9 classified finishers

ROUND 6/FRENCH GRAND PRIX

ROUEN-LES-ESSARTS, 7 JULY

1. ICKX(BEL)	FERRARI	2HR 25MIN 40.9SEC
2. SURTEES(GB)	HONDA	2HR 27MIN 39.5SEC
3. STEWART(GB)	MATRA-FORD	59 LAPS
4. ELFORD(GB)	COOPER-BRM	58 LAPS
5. HULME(NZ)	MCLAREN-FORD	58 LAPS
6. COURAGE(GB)	BRM	57 LAPS

Race: 60 laps of 4.06mile/6.54km (243 miles/392kms)
Fastest lap: P.Rodriguez(MEX), BRM, 2min 11.5sec, 111.2mph/179.1kph
Pole position: Rindt(AUT), Brabham-Repco, 1min 56.1sec 17 starters, 11 class. finishers

ROUND 7/BRITISH GRAND PRIX

BRANDS HATCH, 20 JULY

1. SIFFERT(SWISS)	LOTUS-FORD	2HR 1MIN 20.3SEC
2. AMON (NZ)	FERRARI	2HR 1MIN 24.7SEC
3. ICKX(BEL)	FERRARI	79 LAPS
4. HULME(NZ)	MCLAREN-FORD	79 LAPS
5. SURTEES(GB)	HONDA	78 LAPS
6. STEWART(GB)	MATRA-FORD	77 LAPS

Race: 80 laps of 2.65mile/4.27km (212 miles/342 kms)
Fastest lap: Siffert, 1min 29.7sec, 106.3mph/171.2kph
Pole position: G. Hill(GB), Lotus-Ford, 1min 28.9sec 20 starters, 8 classified finishers

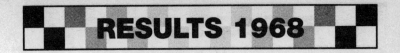

RESULTS 1968

ROUND 8/GERMAN GRAND PRIX

NURBURGRING, 4 AUGUST

1. STEWART(GB)	MATRA-FORD	2HR 19MIN 03.2SEC
2. G. HILL(GB)	LOTUS-FORD	2HR 23MIN 06.4SEC
3. RINDT(AUT)	BRABHAM-REPCO	2HR 23MIN 12.6SEC
4. ICKX(BEL)	FERRARI	2HR 24MIN 58.4SEC
5. BRABHAM(AUS)	BRABHAM-REPCO	2HR 25MIN 24.3SEC
6. P. RODRIGUEZ(MEX)	BRM	2HR 25MIN 28.2SEC

Race: 14 laps of 14.19mile/2.84km (199miles/320kms)
Fastest lap: Stewart 9min 36sec, 88.6mph/142.7kph
Pole position: Ickx, 9min 04sec 20 starters,14 classified finishers

ROUND 9/ITALIAN GRAND PRIX

MONZA, 8 SEPTEMBER

1. HULME(NZ)	MCLAREN-FORD	1HR 40MIN 14.8SEC
2. SERVOZ-GAVIN(FRA)	MATRA-FORD	1HR 41MIN 43.2SEC
3. ICKX(BEL)	FERRARI	1HR 41MIN 43.4SEC
4. COURAGE(GB)	BRM	67 LAPS
5. BELTOISE(FRA)	MATRA-V12	66 LAPS
6. BONNIER(SWE)	MCLAREN-BRM	64 LAPS

Race: 68 laps of 3.57mile/5.75km (243 miles/391kms)
Fastest lap: Oliver(GB), Lotus-Ford,1min 26.5sec,148.7mph/239.3kph
Pole position: Surtees(GB), Honda,1min 26.07sec 20 starters, 6 classified finishers

ROUND10/CANADIAN GRAND PRIX

MONT TREMBLANT-ST JOVITE,QUEBEC, 22 SEPTEMBER

1. HULME(NZ)	MCLAREN-FORD	2HR 27MIN 11.2SEC
2. MCLAREN(NZ)	MCLAREN-FORD	89 LAPS
3. P. RODRIGUEZ(MEX)	BRM	88 LAPS
4. G.HILL(GB)	LOTUS-FORD	86 LAPS
5. ELFORD(GB)	COOPER-BRM	86 LAPS
6. STEWART(GB)	MATRA-FORD	83 LAPS

Race: 90 laps of 2.65mile/4.26km (238 miles/383 kms)
Fastest lap: Siffert(SWISS), Lotus-Ford,1min 35.1sec, 100.3mph/161.4kph
*Pole position:*Rindt(AUT), Brabham-Repco, 1min 33.8sec 20 starters, 6 classified finishers

ROUND 11/US GRAND PRIX

WATKINS GLEN, 6 OCTOBER

1. STEWART(GB)	MATRA-FORD	1HR 59MIN 20.29SEC
2. G.HILL(GB)	LOTUS-FORD	1HR 59MIN 44.97SEC
3. SURTEES(GB)	HONDA	107 LAPS
4. GURNEY(USA)	MCLAREN-FORD	107 LAPS
5. SIFFERT(SWISS)	LOTUS-FORD	105 LAPS
6. MCLAREN(NZ)	MCLAREN-FORD	103 LAPS

Race: 108 laps of 2.3mile/3.7km (248 miles/400 kms)
Fastest lap: Stewart, 1min 5.22sec, 126.9mph/205kph
Pole position: Mario Andretti, Lotus-Ford, 1min 04.20sec 19 starters,6 classified finishers

RESULTS 1968/9

ROUND 12/MEXICAN GRAND PRIX
MEXICO CITY, 3 NOVEMBER

1. G.HILL(GB)	LOTUS-FORD	1HR 56MIN 43.95SEC
2. MCLAREN(NZ)	MCLAREN-FORD	1HR 58MIN 03.27SEC
3. OLIVER(GB)	LOTUS-FORD	1HR 58MIN 24.06SEC
4. P. RODRIGUEZ(MEX)	BRM	1HR 58MIN 25.04SEC
5. BONNIER(SWE)	HONDA	64 LAPS
6. SIFFERT(SWISS)	LOTUS-FORD	64 LAPS

Race: 65 laps of 3.1mile/5km (203 miles/325kms)
Fastest lap: Siffert, 1min 44.23sec, 107.3mph/172.7kph
Pole position: Siffert, 1min 45.22sec 21 starters, 10 classified finishers

DRIVERS' WORLD CHAMPIONSHIP 1968

1.	G.HILL	48 points	4.	ICKX	27 points
2.	STEWART	36 points	5.	MCLAREN	22 points
3.	HULME	33 points	6.	P.RODRIGUEZ	12 points

CONSTRUCTORS' WORLD CHAMPIONSHIP 1968

1.	LOTUS-FORD	62 points	5.	BRM	28 points
2.	MCLAREN-FORD	49 points	6.	COOPER-BRM	14 points
3.	MATRA-FORD	45 points	6.	HONDA	14 points
4.	FERRARI	45 points			

1969 Jackie Stewart dominated the season to take the first of his three World Championship titles. The Ford-Cosworth powered each and every car to win the 11 rounds. Jochen Rindt signed for Lotus alongside Graham Hill. The Lotus team arrived in Spain with the most ridiculous rear wings anyone had ever seen - and they broke! Hill broke both legs in an end of season accident at Watkins Glen. Ickx rejoined the Brabham team. Britain's Frank Williams appeared on the entry list for the first time as entrant for Piers Courage's Brabham Cooper. Eagle and Porsche withdrew from Grand Prix racing. The season was divided into two halves once more. Best five scores from first six races and best four scores from last five races. Points: 9-6-4-3-2-1 for first six races.

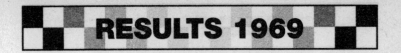

RESULTS 1969

ROUND 1/SOUTH AFRICAN GRAND PRIX

KYALAMI,JOHANNESBURG,1 MARCH

1. STEWART(GB)	MATRA-FORD	1HR 50MIN 39.1SEC
2. G.HILL(GB)	LOTUS-FORD	1HR 50MIN 57.9SEC
3. HULME(NZ)	MCLAREN-FORD	1HR 51MIN 10.9SEC
4. SIFFERT(SWISS)	LOTUS-FORD	1HR 51MIN 28.3SEC
5. MCLAREN(NZ)	MCLAREN-FORD	79 LAPS
6. BELTOISE(FRA)	MATRA-FORD	78 LAPS

Race: 80 laps of 2.55mile/4.1km (204 miles/328 kms)
Fastest lap: Stewart, 1min 21.6sec,112.5mph/181.05kph
Pole position: Brabham(AUS), Brabham-Ford, 1min 20.0sec 18 starters, 8 class. finishers

ROUND 2/SPANISH GRAND PRIX

MONTJUICH PARK,BARCELONA, 4 MAY

1. STEWART(GB)	MATRA-FORD	2HR 16MIN 53.0SEC
2. MCLAREN(NZ)	MCLAREN-FORD	88 LAPS
3. BELTOISE(FRA)	MATRA-FORD	87 LAPS
4. HULME(NZ)	MCLAREN-FORD	87 LAPS
5. SURTEES(GB)	BRM	84 LAPS
6. ICKX(BEL)	BRABHAM-FORD	83 LAPS

Race: 90 laps of 2.36mile/3.79km
Fastest lap: Rindt(AUT), Lotus-Ford,1min 28.3sec,96.0mph/154.5kph
Pole position: Rindt, 1min 25.7sec 14 starters, 6 classified finishers

ROUND 3/MONACO GRAND PRIX

MONTE CARLO, 18 MAY

1. G.HILL(GB)	LOTUS-FORD	1HR 56MIN 59.4SEC
2. COURAGE(GB)	BRABHAM-FORD	1HR 57MIN 16.7SEC
3. SIFFERT(SWISS)	LOTUS-FORD	1HR 57MIN 34.0SEC
4. ATTWOOD(GB)	LOTUS-FORD	1HR 57MIN 52.3SEC
5. MCLAREN(NZ)	MCLAREN-FORD	79 LAPS
6. HULME(NZ)	MCLAREN-FORD	78 LAPS

Race: 80 laps of 1.95 mile/3.15km (156 miles/252 kms)
Fastest lap: Stewart(GB), Matra-Ford,1min 25.1sec,82.6mph/133.0kph
Pole position: Stewart, Matra-Ford, 1min 24.6sec 16 starters, 7 classified finishers

ROUND 4/DUTCH GRAND PRIX

ZANDVOORT, 21 JUNE

1. STEWART(GB)	MATRA-FORD	2HR 6MIN 42.08SEC
2. SIFFERT(SWISS)	LOTUS-FORD	2HR 7MIN 06.06SEC
3. AMON(NZ)	FERRARI	2HR 7MIN 12.59SEC
4. HULME(NZ)	MCLAREN-FORD	2HR 7MIN 19.24SEC
5. ICKX(BEL)	BRABHAM-FORD	2HR 7MIN 19.75SEC
6. BRABHAM(AUS)	BRABHAM-FORD	2HR 7MIN 52.89SEC

Race: 90 laps of 2.6mile/4.19km (234 miles/377 kms)
Fastest lap: Stewart, 1min 22.94sec, 113.0mph/182kph
Pole position: Rindt(AUT), Lotus-Ford, 1min 20.85sec 15 starters, 10 class. finishers

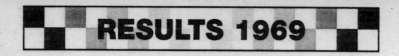

RESULTS 1969

ROUND 5/ FRENCH GRAND PRIX
CLERMONT-FERRAND,6 JULY

1. STEWART(GB)	MATRA-FORD	1HR 56 MIN 47.4SEC
2. BELTOISE(FRA)	MATRA-FORD	1HR 57MIN 44.5SEC
3. ICKX(BEL)	BRABHAM-FORD	1HR 57MIN 44.7SEC
4. MCLAREN(NZ)	MCLAREN-FORD	37 LAPS
5. ELFORD(GB)	MCLAREN-FORD	37 LAPS
6. G. HILL(GB)	LOTUS-FORD	37 LAPS

Race: 38 laps of 5-mile/8km (190 miles/ 304kms)
Fastest lap: Stewart, 3min 2.7sec, 98.6mph/158.7kph
Pole position: Stewart, 3min 00.6sec 13 starters, 10 classified finishers

ROUND 6/BRITISH GRAND PRIX
SILVERSTONE, 19 JULY

1. STEWART(GB)	MATRA-FORD	1HR 55MIN 55.6SEC
2. ICKX(BEL)	BRABHAM-FORD	83 LAPS
3. MCLAREN(NZ)	MCLAREN-FORD	83 LAPS
4. RINDT(AUT)	LOTUS-FORD	83 LAPS
5. COURAGE(GB)	BRABHAM-FORD	83 LAPS
6. ELFORD(GB)	MCLAREN-FORD	82 LAPS

Race: 84 laps of 2.9mile/4.71km (246 miles/350kms)
Fastest lap: Stewart, 1min 21.3sec, 129.6mph/208.6kph
Pole position: Rindt, 1min 20.8sec 17 starters, 10 classified finishers

ROUND 7/GERMAN GRAND PRIX
NURBURGRING, 3 AUGUST

1. ICKX(BEL)	BRABHAM-FORD	1HR 49MIN 55.4SEC
2. STEWART(GB)	MATRA-FORD	1HR 50MIN 53.1SEC
3. MCLAREN(NZ)	MCLAREN-FORD	1HR 53MIN 17.0SEC
4. G. HILL(GB)	LOTUS-FORD	1HR 53MIN 54.2SEC
5. SIFFERT(SWISS)	LOTUS-FORD	12 LAPS
6. BELTOISE(FRA)	MATRA-FORD	12 LAPS

Race: 14 laps of 14.19mile/22.8km (199 miles/319kms)
Fastest lap: Ickx,7min 43.8sec, 110.1mph/177.2kph
Pole position: Ickx, 7min 42.1sec 13 starters, 6 classified finishers

ROUND 8/ITALIAN GRAND PRIX
MONZA, 7 SEPTEMBER

1. STEWART(GB)	MATRA-FORD	1HR 39MIN 11.26SEC
2. RINDT(AUT)	LOTUS-FORD	1HR 39MIN 11.34SEC
3. BELTOISE(FRA)	MATRA-FORD	1HR 39MIN 11.43SEC
4. MCLAREN(NZ)	MCLAREN-FORD	1HR 39MIN 11.45SEC
5. COURAGE(GB)	BRABHAM-FORD	1HR 39MIN 44.70SEC
6. P. RODRIGUEZ(MEX)	FERRARI	66 LAPS

Race: 68 laps of 3.57mile/5.75km (243 miles/391kms)
Fastest lap: Beltoise, 1min 25.2sec, 150.9mph/242.9kph
Pole position: Rindt, 1min 25.48sec 15 starters, 10 classified finishers

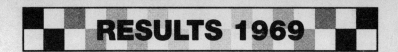

RESULTS 1969

ROUND 9/CANADIAN GRAND PRIX
MOSPORT, TORONTO, 20 SEPTEMBER

1. ICKX(BEL)	BRABHAM-FORD	1HR 59MIN 29.7SEC
2. BRABHAM(AUS)	BRABHAM-FORD	2HR 00MIN 11.9SEC
3. RINDT(AUT)	LOTUS-FORD	2HR 00MIN 17.7SEC
4. BELTOISE(FRA)	MATRA-FORD	89 LAPS
5. MCLAREN(NZ)	MCLAREN-FORD	87 LAPS
6. SERVOZ-GAVIN(FRA)	MATRA-FORD	84 LAPS

Race: 90 laps of 2.46 mile/3.96 km (221miles/356 kph)
Fastest lap: Ickx/Brabham, 1min 18.1sec, 114.7mph/184.7kph
Pole position: Ickx, 1min 17.4sec 20 starters, 7 classified finishers

ROUND 10/US GRAND PRIX
WATKINS GLEN, 5 OCTOBER

1. RINDT(AUT)	LOTUS-FORD	1HR 57MIN 56.84SEC
2. COURAGE(GB)	BRABHAM-FORD	1HR 58MIN 43.83SEC
3. SURTEES(GB)	BRM	106 LAPS
4. BRABHAM(AUS)	BRABHAM-FORD	106 LAPS
5. P .RODRIGUEZ(MEX)	FERRARI	101 LAPS
6. MOSER(SWISS)	BRAHAM-FORD	98 LAPS

Race: 108 laps of 2.3mile/3.7km (248 miles/400kms)
Fastest lap: Rindt, 1min 4.34sec,128.6mph/207kph
Pole position: Rindt, 1min 03.62sec 17 starters, 7 classified finishers

ROUND 11/MEXICAN GRAND PRIX
MEXICO CITY, 19 OCTOBER

1. HULME(NZ)	MCLAREN-FORD	1HR 54MIN 08.80SEC
2. ICKX(BEL)	BRABHAM-FORD	1HR 54MIN 11.36SEC
3. BRABHAM(AUS)	BRABHAM-FORD	1HR 54MIN 47.28SEC
4. STEWART(GB)	MATRA-FORD	1HR 54MIN 55.84SEC
5. BELTOISE(FRA)	MATRA-FORD	1HR 55MIN 47.32SEC
6. OLIVER(GB)	BRM	63 LAPS

Race: 65 laps of 3.1 mile/5 km (203 miles/325 kms)
Fastest lap: Ickx,1min 43.05sec,108.5mph/146.7kph
Pole position: Brabham, 1min 42.90sec 16 starters, 11 classified finishers

DRIVERS' WORLD CHAMPIONSHIP 1969

1. STEWART	63 *points*	4. RINDT	22 *points*
2. ICKX	37 *points*	5. BELTOISE	21 *points*
3. MCLAREN	26 *points*	6. HULME	20 *points*

CONSTRUCTORS' WORLD CHAMPIONSHIP 1969

1. MATRA-FORD	66 *points*	4. MCLAREN-FORD	38 *points*
2. BRABHAM-FORD	49 *points*	5. BRM	7 *points*
3. LOTUS-FORD	47 *points*	5. FERRARI	7 *points*

1970s

QUIZ & FACT

QUIZ 1

Answers on page 112

1 **Who won the opening round of the 1970 World Championship?**
   a. Jackie Stewart   *b.* Graham Hill   *c.* Jack Brabham

2 **Where was the race held?**
   a. South Africa   *b.* Argentina   *c.* Monaco

3 **Which new British team made its debut at the start of the season, with five cars on the grid?**
   a. Tyrrell   *b.* March   *c.* Lotus

4 **Which British driver had to be lifted into his privately-entered Lotus before the race?**
   a. Piers Courage   *b.* John Surtees   *c.* Graham Hill

5 **Where did he finish in the race?**
   a. Did not finish   *b.* Sixth   *c.* Fourth

6 **Which French driver joined the Tyrrell team at the start of 1970?**
   a. Jean-Pierre Beltoise   *b.* Francois Cevert   *c.* Johnny Servoz-Gavin

7 **Which French driver replaced him at Tyrrell when he retired from the sport after failing to qualify for the 1970 Monaco Grand Prix?**
   a. Jean-Pierre Beltoise   *b.* Francois Cevert
   c. Johnny Servoz-Gavin

8 **Which Belgian driver returned to drive for Ferrari in 1970 after a season with Brabham.**
   a. Jacky Ickx   *b.* Thierry Boutsen   *c.* Olivier Gendebien

9 **Which perfume company sponsored the BRM team in 1970?**
   a. Chanel   *b.* Yardley   *c.* Givenchy

10 **Which cigarette livery did the works Lotus cars carry in 1970?**
   a. Marlboro   *b.* John Player Special   *c.* Gold Leaf

Answers to page 112
1 *c.*Mont Tremblant 2 *a.*Tyrrell-Ford 3 *b.*Surtees-Ford 4 *b.*23 5 *a.*Lotus-Ford
6 *b.*U.S. Grand Prix 7 *c.*Pedro Rodriguez 8 *b.*Jochen Rindt 9 *c.*Dunlop
10 *b.*Denny Hulme.

QUIZ 2

Answers on page 113

1 **Who scored the fledgling March concern's first victory in the second race of the season in Spain?**
   a. Johnny Servoz-Gavin   *b.* Chris Amon   *c.* Jackie Stewart

2 **Which American driver finished third in a works March in Spain and scored his first World Championship points?**
   a. Mario Andretti   *b.* Dan Gurney   *c.* George Eaton

3 **Which revolutionary car made its debut in the 1970 Spanish Grand Prix?**
   a. Lotus 72   *b.* Tyrrell-Ford   *c.* Surtees-Ford

4 **Who won the 1970 Monaco Grand Prix?**
   a. Graham Hill   *b.* Jackie Stewart   *c.* Jochen Rindt

5 **Who was killed testing a sports car at Goodwood five days before the 1970 Belgian Grand Prix?**
   a. Piers Courage   *b.* Bruce McLaren   *c.* Jochen Rindt

6 **Which Swiss driver finished fourth in his Formula One debut in the 1970 Dutch Grand Prix?**
   a. Silvio Moser   *b.* Clay Regazzoni   *c.* Reine Wisell

7 **Which car was he driving?**
   a. Ferrari   *b.* Matra-Simca   *c.* de Tomaso

8 **Which future World Champion made his Formula One debut in the 1970 British Grand Prix?**
   a. Wilson Fittipaldi   *b.* Emerson Fittipaldi   *c.* Ronnie Peterson

9 **Which Swiss driver replaced the late Piers Courage in the de Tomaso for the 1970 German Grand Prix?**
   a. Silvio Moser   *b.* Clay Regazzoni   *c.* Jo Siffert

10 **Which high-speed circuit in a fabulous mountain setting was used for the first time for a Grand Prix in 1970?**
   a. Clermont-Ferrand   *b.* Osterreichring   *c.* Hockenheim

---

Answers to page 113
1 *b.* Mario Andretti 2 *c.* Ferrari 3 *b.* Brabham 4 *b.* Tim Schenken 5 *b.* Six
6 *b.* Seven 7 *c.* Two 8 *b.* Ronnie Peterson 9 *a.* None 10 *c.* March-Ford

---

QUIZ 3

Answers on page 110

1 **On which circuit did the 1970 Canadian Grand Prix take place?**
   a. Montreal   *b.* Mosport   *c.* Mont Tremblant

2 **Which new car made its debut in Canada in 1970?**
   a. Tyrrell-Ford   *b.* Surtees-Ford   *c.* Williams-Ford

3 **And which new car made its first appearance in the 1970 British Grand Prix?**
   a. Tyrrell-Ford   *b.* Surtees-Ford   *c.* Williams-Ford

4 **How old was Emerson Fittipaldi when he won his first Grand Prix in 1970?**
   a. 21   *b.* 23   *c.* 25

5 **Which car was he driving?**
   a. Lotus-Ford   *b.* Ferrari   *c.* Tyrrell-Ford

6 **At which race?**
   a. Italian Grand Prix   *b.* U.S. Grand Prix   *c.* Mexican Grand Prix

7 **Who finished sixth in Mexico on a circuit named after his brother?**
   a. Pedro Diniz   *b.* Pedro Lamy   *c.* Pedro Rodriguez

8 **Who became the sport's only posthumous World Champion to date at the end of 1970?**
   a. Bruce McLaren   *b.* Jochen Rindt   *c.* Piers Courage

9 **Which tyre company withdrew from Formula One at the end of 1970?**
   a. Firestone   *b.* Goodyear   *c.* Dunlop

10 **Which gritty New Zealand driver suffered bad burns to his hands and feet in a practice crash at Indianapolis in 1970?**
   a. Howden Ganley   *b.* Denny Hulme   *c.* Chris Amon

Answers to page 110
1 *c.* Jack Brabham **2** *a.* South Africa **3** *b.* March **4** *c.* Graham Hill **5** *b.* Sixth
6 *c.* Johnny Servoz-Gavin **7** *b.* Francois Cevert **8** *a.* Jacky Ickx **9** *b.* Yardley
10 *c.* Gold Leaf

QUIZ 4

Answers on page 111

1 **Which American driver won the opening round of the 1971 World Championship in South Africa?**
   a. Dan Gurney   *b.* Mario Andretti   *c.* Mark Donohue

2 **Which car was he driving?**
   a. Lotus-Ford   *b.* Tyrrell-Ford   *c.* Ferrari

3 **Which team did Graham Hill join for the 1971 season?**
   a. Tyrrell   *b.* Brabham   *c.* BRM

4 **Who was his Antipodean team-mate?**
   a. Chris Amon   *b.* Tim Schenken   *c.* Howden Ganley

5 **How many pole positions did Jackie Stewart claim in the 1971 season?**
   a. None   *b.* Six   *c.* Ten

6 **How many races did the Tyrrell team win in 1971?**
   a. Six   *b.* Seven   *c.* Eight

7 **How many races did the BRM team win in 1971?**
   a. None   *b.* One   *c.* Two

8 **Who finished runner-up in the 1971 World Drivers' Championship?**
   a. Jacky Ickx   *b.* Ronnie Peterson   *c.* Emerson Fittipaldi

9 **How many races did he win in 1971?**
   a. None   *b.* One   *c.* Two

10 **Which car was he driving?**
   a. Lotus-Ford   *b.* Surtees-Ford   *c.* March-Ford

Answers to page 111
1 *c.*Jackie Stewart **2** *a.*Mario Andretti **3** *a.*Lotus **7** 2 **4** *c.*Jochen Rindt **5** *b.*Bruce McLaren **6** *b.*Clay Regazzoni **7** *a.*Ferrari **8** *b.*Emerson Fittipaldi **9** *c.*Jo Siffert **10** *b.*Osterreichring

QUIZ 5

Answers on page 116

1 **Which future World Champion failed to qualify for the 1971 Monaco Grand Prix?**
   a. Emerson Fittipaldi *b. Niki Lauda* *c. Mario Andretti*

2 **Where did Jackie Stewart score his first victory in a Tyrrell in 1971?**
   a. Monaco *b. Mexico* *c. Montjuich Park,Barcelona*

3 **In the 1971 season, which top team failed to win a race for the first time since 1960?**
   a. McLaren-Ford *b. Brabham-Ford* *c. Lotus-Ford*

4 **Which driver was forced to miss the 1971 Dutch Grand Prix due to injuries suffered in a nasty road accident?**
   a. Jacky Ickx *b. Clay Regazzoni* *c. Emerson Fittipaldi*

5 **On which circuit near Marseilles was the 1971 French Grand Prix held?**
   a. Rouen *b. Clermont Ferrand* *c. Paul Ricard*

6 **What is the name of the circuit's long, high-speed straight?**
   a. Mistral *b. Minstrel* *c. Millionaire*

7 **Which Swiss driver led the 1971 Austrian Grand Prix from start-to-finish?**
   a. Clay Regazzoni *b. Jo Siffert* *c. Silvio Moser*

8 **Which car was he driving?**
   a. Ferrari *b. Matra-Simca* *c. BRM*

9 **Which British driver took his one and only career Grand Prix victory in the 1971 Italian Grand Prix?**
   a. Mike Hailwood *b. Jackie Oliver* *c. Peter Gethin*

10 **What was the final gap between the first four cars in the race?**
   a. One thousandth of a second *b. one tenth of a second*
   c. one second

Answers to page 116
1 *c.*Marlboro 2 *b.*Black and Gold 3 *c.*Emerson Fittipaldi 4 *b.*Denny Hulme 5 *b.*
One 6 *c.*Yardley 7 *c.*Peter Revson 8 *c.*Bernie Ecclestone 9 *a.*Carlos Reutemann
10 *c.*Graham Hill

QUIZ 6

Answers on page 117

1 **Which French driver claimed the one and only victory of his career in the 1971 U.S. Grand Prix?**
   a. Jean-Pierre Beltoise *b. Francois Cevert* *c. Jean Alesi*

2 **What was the 'staggering'(in those days...)first prize money?**
   a. 5000 dollars *b. 50,000 dollars* *c. 500,000 dollars*

3 **Which American driver drove a third works Tyrrell in the 1971 U.S. Grand Prix?**
   a. Mario Andretti *b. Peter Revson* *c. Mark Donohue*

4 **And which American driver finished third for McLaren in the 1971 Canadian Grand Prix?**
   a. Mario Andretti *b. Peter Revson* *c. Mark Donohue*

5 **Which two young Austrians made their Formula One debuts in their home Grand Prix in 1971?**
   a. Helmut Marko *b. Gerhard Berger* *c. Niki Lauda*

6 **Whom did Niki Lauda persuade to finance him during the 1971 season?**
   a. A cigarette company *b. His grand-parents* *c. A bank*

7 **At which race did Jackie Stewart clinch the 1971 World Championship?**
   a. Italian Grand Prix *b. Canadian Grand Prix*
   c. Austrian Grand Prix

8 **He did not finish the race. Why?**
   a. Ran out of fuel *b. Broke down* *c. Lost a wheel*

9 **Which American driver drove a BRM in the 1971 U.S. Grand Prix?**
   a. John Cannon *b. Skip Barber* *c. Sam Posey*

10 **Which Antipodean BRM driver finished fourth in the race?**
   a. Jo Siffert *b. Howden Ganley* *c. Peter Gethin*

Answers to page 117

1 *b.*Denny Hulme **2** *b.*Wilson Fittipaldi **3** *b.*Jean-Pierre Beltoise **4** *a.*BRM **5** *c.*He had an ulcer **6** *a.*Patrick Depailler **7** *b.*He broke his wrist playing football **8** *a.*Helmut Marko **9** *a.*Arturo Merzario **10** *c.*Emerson Fittipaldi

---

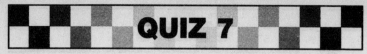

QUIZ 7

Answers on page

1 **Which international sponsor backed the BRM team in 1972?**
   a. Brooke Bond   *b.* Yardley   *c.* Marlboro

2 **And which colours did the Lotus team carry in 1972?**
   a. Red and white   *b.* Black and Gold   *c.* British Racing Green

3 **Who won the 1972 World Drivers' Championship?**
   a. Jackie Stewart   *b.* Denny Hulme   *c.* Emerson Fittipaldi

4 **Who finished third?**
   a. Jackie Stewart   *b.* Denny Hulme   *c.* Emerson Fittipaldi

5 **How many races did Ferrari win in 1972?**
   a. None   *b.* One   *c.* Three

6 **Who sponsored the McLaren team in 1972?**
   a. Typhoo   *b.* Marlboro   *c.* Yardley

7 **Which handsome American joined Hulme in the McLaren line-up for 1972?**
   a. Skip Barber   *b.* Mario Andretti   *c.* Peter Revson

8 **Which pint-sized entrepreneur took over the Brabham team in 1971?**
   a. Max Mosley   *b.* Robin Herd   *c.* Bernie Ecclestone

9 **Which dashing South American took pole postion in his very first race for Brabham?**
   a. Carlos Reutemann   *b.* Carlos Pace   *c.* Wilson Fittipaldi

10 **Who was his veteran team-mate for the season?**
   a. John Surtees   *b.* Denny Hulme   *c.* Graham Hill

Answers to page 114
1 *a.*Mario Andretti **2** *c.*Montjuich Park, Barcelona **3** *c.*Lotus-Ford **4** *c.*Emerson Fittipaldi **5** *c.*Paul Ricard **6** *a.*Mistral **7** *b.*Jo Siffert **8** *c.*BRM **9** *c.*Peter Gethin **10** *b.*One tenth of a second.

QUIZ 8

Answers on page 115

1 **Who won the 1972 South African Grand Prix for McLaren?**
   a. Jody Scheckter   b. Denny Hulme   c. Peter Revson

2 **Who finished seventh in the first World Championship Grand Prix ever contested between two brothers in Spain in 1972?**
   a. Emerson Fittipaldi   b. Wilson Fittipaldi   c. Christian Fittipaldi

3 **Who, in 1972 became the first French driver to win at Monaco since 1958?**
   a. Francois Cevert   b. Jean-Pierre Beltoise   c. Henri Pescarolo

4 **Which car was he driving?**
   a. BRM   b. Tyrrell-Ford   c. Matra-Simca

5 **Why did Jackie Stewart not take part in the 1972 Belgian Grand Prix?**
   a. He had flu   b. He was suspended   c. He had an ulcer

6 **Which French driver had his first Grand Prix outing in a third Tyrrell in his home Grand Prix in 1972?**
   a. Patrick Depailler   b. Andrea de Adamich   c. Francois Migault

7 **Why was Clay Regazzoni unable to participate in the 1972 French Grand Prix.**
   a. He had an ulcer   b. He had broken his wrist playing football
   c. He had broken his ankle in a charity karting match.

8 **Which young driver's career was ended when a stone pierced his visor during the 1972 French Grand Prix?**
   a. Helmut Marko   b. Tim Schenken   c. Nanni Galli

9 **Which diminutive Italian driver finished sixth in the 1972 British Grand Prix for Ferrari?**
   a. Arturo Merzario   b. Andrea de Adamich   c. Nanni Galli

10 **Whose car burst into flames during the 1972 German Grand Prix?**
   a. Jackie Stewart   b. Clay Regazzoni   c. Emerson Fittipaldi

---

Answers to page 115
1 *b.*Francois Cevert 2 *b.*50,000 dollars 3 *b.*Peter Revson 4 *c.*Mark Donohue
5 *a/c.*Helmut Marko/Niki Lauda 6 *c.*A Bank 7 *c.*Austrian Grand Prix 8 *c.*Lost a
wheel 9 *a.*John Cannon 10 *b.*Howden Ganley.

QUIZ 9

Answers on page 120

1 **What was the nickname of the McLaren M19A?**
   a. The Monster   *b.* The Coke Bottle   *c.* The Gin Palace

2 **What was the nickname of the Brabham BT34?**
   a. The Crab   *b.* The Lobster Claw   *c.* Bernie's Baby

3 **Which team did Britain's former two-wheel star, Mike Hailwood head in 1972?**
   a. Tyrrell   *b.* Surtees   *c.* Williams

4 **Who were the team's title sponsors?**
   a. Yardley   *b.* Tetleys   *c.* Brooke Bond -Oxo

5 **Which drinks company sponsored the new Tecno team in 1972?**
   a. Cinzano   *b.* Martini   *c.* Pernod

6 **On which circuit did the 1972 and 1974 Belgian Grands Prix take place?**
   a. Spa-Francorchamps   *b.* Zolder   *c.* Nivelles.

7 **Which driver won both races?**
   a. Jackie Stewart   *b.* Emerson Fittipaldi   *c.* Jacky Ickx

8 **Which British driver finished fifth in the 1972 German Grand Prix?**
   a. Jackie Stewart   *b.* Brian Redman   *c.* Derek Bell

9 **How old was Emerson Fittipaldi when he took his first world title in 1972?**
   a .22   *b.* 25   *c.* 26

10 **How many races did he win during the 1972 season?**
   a. Five   *b.* Six   *c.* Eight

Answers to page 120
1 *b.*Lord Hesketh   2 *a.*Le Patron   3 *b.*A teddy bear   4 *c.* The Fittipaldis, Emerson and Wilson   5 *c.* Clay Regazzoni   6 *a.*Ronnie Peterson   7 *b.*Denny Hulme   8 *a.*Clay Regazzoni   9 *c.* Mike Hailwood   10 *a.*George Medal

QUIZ 10

Answers on page 121

1 **Which driver joined Fittipaldi at Lotus at the start of the 1973 season?**
   a. Andretti   *b. Peterson*   *c. Wisell*

2 **Who designed the new McLaren M23 with the deformable structure for 1972?**
   a. Harvey Postlethwaite   *b. Gordon Coppuck*   *c. Tony Southgate*

3 **Which privateer team rocked the Establishment with their arrival in 1973?**
   a. Embassy-Shadow   *b. Ceramica Pagnossin*   *c. Hesketh Racing*

4 **Who was their chief designer?**
   a. Tony Southgate;   *b. Harvey Postlethwaite;*   *c. Gordon Murray*

5 **Which American driver headed the new Shadow team line-up?**
   a. Mario Andretti   *b. Peter Revson*   *c. George Follmer*

6 **Which future World Champion joined the BRM line-up for the season?**
   a. Mario Andretti   *b. Niki Lauda*   *c. Clay Regazzoni*

7 **And which former World Champion headed the Embassy-Shadow team?**
   a. Phil Hill   *b. Graham Hill*   *c. Jack Brabham*

8 **Which former Ferrari driver moved to BRM for 1973?**
   a. Jacky Ickx   *b. Arturo Merzario*   *c. Clay Regazzoni*

9 **Who took pole position in the first race of the year in Argentina?**
   a. Carlos Reutemann   *b. Jackie Stewart*   *c. Clay Regazzoni*

10 **Which South American driver joined Britain's Mike Hailwood at Surtees for the 1973 season?**
   a. Wilson Fittipaldi   *b. Carlos Pace*   *c. Luis Bueno*

Answers to page 121

1 *c.* Emerson Fittipaldi **2** *b.* Zolder **3** *c.* Track surface broke up **4** *b.* Monaco
5 *c.* March-Ford **6** *a.* 39 **7** *a.* Jody Scheckter **8** *c.* Peter Revson **9** *b.* David Purley
10 *b.* Tom Wheatcroft

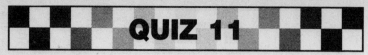

QUIZ 11

Answers on page 118

1 **Which English Lord sponsored the Hesketh Racing Team?**
   a. Lord March *b.* Lord Hesketh *c.* Lord Lichfield

2 **What was his nickname?**
   a. Le Patron *b.* Le Sponsor *c.* Le Professor

3 **What was the Hesketh team mascot?**
   a. A coronet *b.* A teddy bear *c.* A champagne bottle

4 **Which brothers finished first and sixth in the 1973 Argentine Grand Prix?**
   a. The Scheckters *b.* The Brambillas *c.* The Fittipaldis

5 **Which mustachioed hero took pole position for the race?**
   a. Graham Hill *b.* Henri Pescarolo *c.* Clay Regazzoni

6 **And who claimed the very first pole position of his career in Brazil?**
   a. Ronnie Peterson *b.* Francois Cevert *c.* Carlos Pace

7 **And who claimed his only pole position in a long and distinguished career in the 1973 South African Grand Prix?**
   a. Jean-Pierre Beltoise *b.* Denny Hulme *c.* Chris Amon

8 **Who was trapped in his blazing car during the race?**
   a. Clay Regazzoni *b.* Jackie Stewart *c.* Niki Lauda

9 **Which brave British driver helped pull him from the wreckage?**
   a. Guy Edwards *b.* Graham Hill *c.* Mike Hailwood

10 **How was his gallantry rewarded?**
   a. George Medal *b.* MBE *c.* KBE

Answers to page 118
1 *b.*The Coke Bottle **2** *b.*The Lobster Claw **3** *b.*Surtees **4** *c.*Brooke-Bond Oxo
5 *b.*Martini **6** *c.*Nivelles **7** *b.*Emerson Fittipaldi **8** *b.*Brian Redman **9** *b.*25
10 *a.*Five.

QUIZ 12

Answers on page 119

1 **Who was 'kidnapped' by the Brazilian navy after his victory in the Spanish Grand Prix?**
   a. Jackie Stewart   *b.* Carlos Pace   *c.* Emerson Fittipaldi

2 **Where was the 1973 Belgian Grand Prix held?**
   a. Spa-Francorchamps   *b.* Zolder   *c.* Nivelles

3 **Why was it nearly cancelled?**
   a. Drivers' strike   *b.* Torrential rain   *c.* Track surface broke up

4 **At which 1973 race did James Hunt make his Grand Prix debut?**
   a. British Grand Prix   *b.* Monaco Grand Prix   *c.* U.S.Grand Prix

5 **Which car was he driving?**
   a. Lotus-Ford   *b.* Hesketh-Ford   *c.* March-Ford

6 **How many Grand Prix did Ronnie Peterson contest before winning his first Grand Prix?**
   a. 39   *b.* 29   *c.* 49

7 **Who sparked off the massive accident at the end of the first lap of the 1973 British Grand Prix?**
   a. Jody Scheckter   *b.* James Hunt   *c.* John Watson

8 **Who won the restarted race?**
   a. Jackie Stewart   *b.* Emerson Fittipaldi   *c.* Peter Revson

9 **Who was awarded the George Medal for his heroic attempts to save Roger Williamson from his burning car during the 1973 Dutch Grand Prix?**
   a. Mike Hailwood   *b.* David Purley   *c.* Guy Edwards

10 **Who is the bluff Leicestershire businessman who had guided Williamson's career?**
   a. Tom Walkinshaw   *b.* Tom Wheatcroft   *c.* Tom Watson

Answers to page 119
1 *b.*Ronnie Peterson **2** *b.*Gordon Coppuck **3** *c.*Hesketh Racing **4** *b.*Harvey Postlethwaite **5** *c.*George Follmer **6** *b.*Niki Lauda **7** *b.*Graham Hill **8** *c.*Clay Regazzoni **9** *c.*Clay Regazzoni **10** *b.*Carlos Pace

QUIZ 13

Answers on page 124

1 **Which 1973 Grand Prix saw the introduction of the safety car for the first time in Formula One?**
a. German   b. Italian   c. Canadian

2 **Who collided with Francois Cevert in the 1973 Canadian Grand Prix?**
a. Jackie Stewart   b. Jody Scheckter   c. Arturo Merzario

3 **Who was tragically killed during practice for the 1973 U.S. Grand Prix?**
a. Francois Cevert   b. Peter Revson   c. Ronnie Peterson

4 **Where did James Hunt finish in the race?**
a. First   b. Second   c. Fourth

5 **Which former World Champion retired from Formula One at the end of 1973?**
a. Jack Brabham   b. Jacky Ickx   c. Jackie Stewart

6 **How many times did Jackie Stewart win the World Championship?**
a. Two   b. Three   c. Four

7 **For which team did Jody Scheckter drive in 1974?**
a. Ferrari   b. Tyrrell   c. McLaren

8 **Where did he finish in the Drivers' Championship?**
a. Third   b. Fifth   c. Sixth

9 **Which Welsh driver collided with James Hunt in two consecutive races in 1974?**
a. Jonathan Williams   b. Tom Pryce   c. John Watson

10 **Who carried the coveted 'number one' on his car in the absence of the 1973 World Champion?**
a. Emerson Fittipaldi   b. Jody Scheckter   c. Ronnie Peterson

---

Answers to page 124
1 *a.*James Hunt 2 *b.*John Watson 3 *c.*Did not finish 4 *c.*Mario Andretti
5 *b.*Fourth 6 *c.*Brazilian 7 *b.*Emerson Fittipaldi 8 *b.*McLaren-Ford 9 *c.*Denny Hulme 10 *b.*112

QUIZ 14

Answers on page 125

1 Who ran out of fuel half a lap before the end of the 1974 Argentine Grand Prix whilst leading much to the dismay of the crowd?
   a. Emerson Fittipaldi   *b.* Carlos Reutemann   *c.* Clay Regazzoni

2 Who won the race, the last victory in his long Grand Prix career?
   a. Graham Hill   *b.* Denny Hulme   *c.* Jean-Pierre Beltoise

3 Who was taken to hospital suffering from heat exhaustion at the end of the 1974 Brazilian Grand Prix?
   a. Emerson Fittipaldi   *b.* James Hunt   *c.* Ronnie Peterson

4 Which future World Champion claimed the first pole position of his career in the 1974 South African Grand Prix?
   a. Niki Lauda   *b.* Jody Scheckter   *c.* James Hunt

5 What relation is Ian Scheckter to Jody Schecter?
   a. Brother   *b.* Brother-in-law   *c.* Son

6 What nationality is Tom Belso who made his Grand Prix debut in the 1974 South African Grand Prix?
   a. Finnish   *b.* Danish   *c.* Swedish

7 Where did future World Champion, Niki Lauda, score his first Grand Prix victory?
   a. Monaco 1974   *b.* Nurburgring 1974   *c.* Jarama 1974

8 And where did future World Champion, Jody Scheckter, score his first Grand Prix victory in 1974?
   a. Sweden   *b.* Great Britain   *c.* USA.

9 Where was Niki Lauda's Ferrari when the flag fell at the end of the 1974 British Grand Prix?
   a. In the catch fencing   *b.* Out of fuel on the circuit
   c. Stuck at the exit to the pit lane.

10 Which New Zealand driver suffered severe foot and ankle injuries in a practice accident at the Nurburgring in 1974?
   a. Denny Hulme   *b.* Larry Perkins   *c.* Howden Ganley

Answers to page 125
1 *c.*Niki Lauda **2** *b.*Lotus **3** *c.*Jean-Pierre Jarier **4** *a.*Shadow **5** *c.*Broke down on warm-up lap **6** *b.*Carlos Pace **7** *c.*Jochen Mass **8** *b.*German **9** *c.*Five **10.** *b.*Spun off

---

QUIZ 15

Answers on page 122

1 **Which British driver finished third in the 1974 Austrian Grand Prix?**
   a. James Hunt.   *b. John Watson*   *c. David Hobbs*

2 **And which British driver finished fourth in the same race?**
   a. James Hunt   *b. John Watson*   *c. David Hobbs*

3 **Where did the two Ferraris finish in the 1974 Italian Grand Prix?**
   a. First and second   *b. Second and third*   *c. Did not finish*

4 **Who debuted the new Vel's Parnelli Jones car in the 1974 Canadian Grand Prix?**
   a. Mark Donohue   *b. Al Unser*   *c. Mario Andretti*

5 **Where did he qualify for the 1974 US Grand Prix?**
   a. On pole   *b. Fourth*   *c. Did not qualify*

6 **Carlos Pace finished second to his team-mate, Reutemann in the US Grand Prix. What was Pace's nationality?**
   a. Argentinian   *b. Spanish*   *c. Brazilian*

7 **Who finished fourth to clinch the 1974 World Drivers' Championship?**
   a. Niki Lauda   *b. Emerson Fittipaldi*   *c. Clay Regazzoni*

8 **What car was he driving?**
   a. Lotus-Ford   *b. McLaren-Ford*   *c. Ferrari*

9 **Which former World Champion hung up his Formula One helmet at the end of the 1974 season?**
   a. Graham Hill   *b. Chris Amon*   *c. Denny Hulme*

10 **How many Grands Prix did he contest in his Formula One career?**
   a. 99   *b. 112*   *c. 150*

Answers to page 122
1 *c.*Canadian 2 *b.*Jody Scheckter 3 *a.*Francois Cevert 4 *b.*Second 5 *c.*Jackie Stewart 6 *b.*Three 7 b Tyrrell 8 *a.*Third 9 *b.*Tom Pryce 10 *c.*Ronnie Peterson

---

QUIZ 16

Answers on page 123

1 **Who won the 1975 World Drivers' Championship?**
a. James Hunt *b. Emerson Fittipaldi* *c. Niki Lauda*

2 **Which top team failed to win a Grand Prix for the first time during a season since 1960?**
a. Brabham *b. Lotus* *c. Surtees*

3 **Who qualified on pole for both the 1975 Argentine and Brazilian Grands Prix?**
a. Emerson Fittipaldi *b. Carlos Reutemann* *c. Jean-Pierre Jarier*

4 **With which car?**
a. Shadow *b. McLaren* *c. Brabham*

5 **Where did he finish in Argentina?**
a. Did not finish *b. Fourth* *c. Broke down on warm-up lap*

6 **Which Brazilian driver won the 1975 Brazilian Grand Prix?**
a. Emerson Fittipaldi *b. Carlos Pace* *c. Wilson Fittipaldi*

7 **Who joined the McLaren team alongside Fittipaldi for 1975?**
a. James Hunt *b. Patrick Tambay* *c. Jochen Mass*

8 **What was his nationality?**
a. Austrian *b. German* *c. Swiss*

9 **How many South African drivers took part in the 1975 South African Grand Prix?**
a. Three *b. Four* *c. Five*

10 **Jody Scheckter won the race in front of his home fans but where did big brother Ian finish?**
a. Sixth *b. Spun off* *c. Ran out of fuel*

Answers to page 123
1 *b.*Carlos Reutemann **2** *b.*Denny Hulme **3** *c.*Ronnie Peterson **4** *a.*Niki Lauda **5** *a.*and *b.*(The two brothers married two sisters!. **6** *b.*Danish **7** *c.*Jarama (Spain) **8** *a.*Sweden **9** *c.*Stuck at the exit to the pit lane (unable to get through the milling hordes of people who were obstructing it!). **10** *c.*Howden Ganley

QUIZ 17

Answers on page 128

1 **Whose car vaulted the barrier in the 1975 Spanish Grand Prix, killing five spectators?**
   a. Merzario   *b.* Stommelen   *c.* Brambilla

2 **For which team was he driving?**
   a. Hill-Ford   *b.* Williams-Ford   *c.* March-Ford

3 **Who won the race, his only Grand Prix victory in 105 races?**
   a. Jean-Pierre Jarier   *b.* Jochen Mass   *c.* Chris Amon

4 **Who finished sixth?**
   a. Tony Brise   *b.* Lella Lombardi   *c.* Emerson Fittipaldi

5 **Which team-mates collided at the first corner of the race?**
   a. Scheckter and Depailler(Tyrrell)   *b.* Hunt and Jones(Hesketh)
   c. Lauda and Regazzoni(Ferrari)

6 **Which British driver was Graham Hill's protege in 1975?**
   a. Jim Crawford   *b.* Bob Evans   *c.* Tony Brise

7 **Where did he finish in the 1975 Swedish Grand Prix?**
   a. Did not finish   *b.* Fifth   *c.* Sixth

8 **At which sea-side circuit did James Hunt give the Hesketh team its one and only Grand Prix victory?**
   a. Paul Ricard   *b.* Brands Hatch   *c.* Zandvoort

9 **Whom did he beat into second place?**
   a. Emerson Fittipaldi   *b.* Niki Lauda   *c.* Mario Andretti

10 **Where was Emerson Fittipaldi when he won the 1975 British Grand Prix?**
   a. In the lead   *b.* In the armco   *c.* In the pits

Answers to page 128
1 *c.*James Hunt 2 *b.*Ferrari 3 *c.*McLaren 4 *c.*Mario Andretti 5 *b.*March
6 *c.*Gunnar Nilsson 7 *c.*Long Beach 8 *a.*Two(the Scheckter brothers! 9 *b.*Sixth
10 *b.*Copersucar

QUIZ 18

Answers on page 129

1 **Which great British driver announced that he was hanging up his helmet at the 1975 British Grand Prix?**
a. John Surtees b. Graham Hill c. Brian Henton

2 **How many Grands Prix had he contested in his career?**
a. 175 b. 176 c. 177

3 **Which driver gave the Williams-Ford team its best result to date at the Nurburgring in 1974?**
a. Tom Belso b. Ian Scheckter c. Jacques Laffite

4 **Which Italian driver took the only Grand Prix victory of his career in the rain interrupted 1975 Austrian Grand Prix?**
a. Vittorio Brambilla b. Tino Brambilla c. Arturo Merzario

5 **What colour was the car that he was driving?**
a. Red b. Blue c. Orange

6 **Which Vietnam 'veteran' made his Grand Prix debut in the 1975 Austrian Grand Prix in a Hesketh?**
a. Brett Lunger b. Jo Vanlanthen c. Harald Ertl

7 **Ferrari clinched the Drivers' and Constructors' Championship double at the 1975 Italian Grand Prix. When was the last time they had achieved the double?**
a. 1963 b. 1964 c. 1970

8 **Who was the previous Ferrari World Drivers' Champion?**
a. Jacky Ickx b. Lorenzo Bandini c. John Surtees

9 **Which former World Champion was killed in a light aircraft crash in November 1975?**
a. Denny Hulme b. Jack Brabham c. Graham Hill

10 **Which former World Champion shocked the Formula One world by announcing that he was to run his own Grand Prix team at the end of the year?**
a. Jackie Stewart b. Emerson Fittipaldi c. Phil Hill

Answers to page 129
1 *a.*Car adjudged to be millimetres too wide 2 *b.*Tyrrell six-wheeler 3 *c.*Sweden
4 *c.*James Hunt 5 *c.*Alan Jones 6 *b.*Alfa Romeo 7 *c.*Arturo Merzario 8 *b.*John Watson 9 *c.*Shave off his beard 10 *b.*James Hunt

---

QUIZ 19

Answers on page 126

1 **Who won the 1976 World Drivers' Championship?**
   a. Niki Lauda   *b.* Jody Scheckter   *c.* James Hunt

2 **Who won the 1976 World Constructors' Championship?**
   a. McLaren   *b.* Ferrari   *c.* Tyrrell

3 **For which team did James Hunt drive in 1976?**
   a. Hesketh   *b.* Tyrrell   *c.* McLaren

4 **Which American driver joined Lotus for the 1976 season?**
   a. Johnny Rutherford   *b.* A.J Foyt   *c.* Mario Andretti

5 **Upset by the situation, which team did Ronnie Peterson leave Lotus for early in the season?**
   a. Tyrrell   *b.* March   *c.* Williams

6 **Who replaced him at Lotus?**
   a. Jim Crawford   *b.* Brian Henton   *c.* Gunnar Nilsson

7 **Which plush American seaside resort hosted its first round of the World Championship in 1976?**
   a. Miami Beach   *b.* Venus Beach   *c.* Long Beach

8 **How many South African drivers contested the 1975 South African Grand Prix?**
   a. Two   *b.* Three   *c.* Five

9 **Where did Emerson Fittipaldi finish in the 1976 US Grand Prix West?**
   a. Second   *b.* Sixth   *c.* Did not finish

10 **Which car was he driving?**
   a. McLaren   *b.* Copersucar   *c.* Lotus

Answers to page 126
1 *b.*Rolf Stommelen   2 *a.*Hill-Ford   3 *b.*Jochen Mass   4 *b.*Lella Lombardi
5 *c.*Lauda and Regazzoni (Ferrari)   6 *c.*Tony Brise   7 *c.*Sixth   8 *c.*Zandvoort
9 *b.*Niki Lauda   10 *c.*In the pit

QUIZ 20

Answers on page 127

1 **James Hunt won the 1976 Spanish Grand Prix but was initially disqualified. Why?**
   a. Overtaking under a yellow flag   *b. Fuel irregularities*
   c. Car adjudged to be millimetres too wide

2 **Which revolutionary car made its first Grand Prix appearance at the 1976 Spanish Grand Prix?**
   a. Brabham fan car   *b. Tyrrell six-wheeler*   *c. March six-wheeler*

3 **In which race did the Tyrrell six-wheeler gain its first victory in 1976?**
   a. Monaco   *b. Belgium*   *c. Sweden*

4 **Who won the 1976 British Grand Prix after a restart but was later disqualified?**
   a. Niki Lauda   *b. Jody Scheckter*   *c. James Hunt*

5 **Which future World Champion finished fifth in the race for Surtees?**
   a. John Watson   *b. Carlos Reutemann*   *c. Alan Jones*

6 **Which engine manufacturer returned to the sport after an absence of 25 years in 1976?**
   a. Maserati   *b. Alfa Romeo*   *c. Mercedes*

7 **Which brave little Italian driver plunged into the flames to undo Niki Lauda's seat belts after his horrific crash at the Nurburgring in 1976?**
   a. Vittorio Brambilla   *b. Alessandro Pessenti-Rossi*
   c. Arturo Merzario.

8 **Who won the Penske team's only Grand Prix victory at the Osterreichring in 1976?**
   a. Mario Andretti   *b. John Watson*   *c. Brett Lunger*

9 **What did he have to do after a bet with team boss, Roger Penske?**
   a. Drink the bar dry   *b. Kiss the boss's feet*   *c. Shave off his beard*

10 **Who won the Dutch Grand Prix for a second successive year in 1976?**
   a. Clay Regazzoni   *b. James Hunt*   *c. Jody Scheckter*

Answers to page 127

1 *b.*Graham Hill **2** *b.*176 **3** *c.*Jacques Laffite **4** *a.*Vittorio Brambilla **5** *c.*Orange
6 *a.*Brett Lunger **7** *b.*1964 **8** *c.*John Surtees **9** *c.*Graham Hill **10** *b.*Emerson Fittipaldi

---

QUIZ 21

Answers on page 132

1 **Which manufacturer returned to Grand Prix racing in 1977 after an absence of 70 years?**
   a. Maserati   *b.* Vanwall   *c.* Renault

2 **Which highly talented Brazilian lost his life in a light aircraft crash early in the 1977 season?**
   a. Carlos Pace   *b.* Ingo Hoffman   *c.* Alex Ribiero

3 **Who replaced Chris Amon in the Ensign Team at the start of the 1977 season?**
   a. Alan Jones   *b.* Clay Regazzoni   *c.* Jody Scheckter

4 **How many Grands Prix did the Kiwi, Chris Amon, contest during his career?**
   a. 90   *b.* 96   *c.* 106

5 **Who joined the Ferrari team full-time for 1977?**
   a. Jody Scheckter   *b.* Gilles Villeneuve   *c.* Carlo Reutemann

6 **Which British team bid the sport adieu in 1977?**
   a. Hesketh   *b.* BRM   *c.* Lotus

7 **Which South African driver signed to drive for March for the 1977 season?**
   a. Ian Scheckter   *b.* Dave Charlton   *c.* Eddie Keizan

8 **At which circuit did the talented Tom Pryce lose his life in 1977?**
   a. Long Beach   *b.* Hockenheim   *c.* Kyalami

9 **Who won the first race of the year in his first drive for his new team?**
   a. Emerson Fittipaldi   *b.* Jody Scheckter   *c.* Ronnie Peterson

10 **Which team?**
   a. Wolf-Ford   *b.* Fittipaldi-Ford   *c.* Tyrrell-Ford

Answers to page 132
1 *b.* One **2** *c.* Niki Lauda **3** *b.* British Grand Prix **4** *c.* Jean-Pierre Jabouille **5** *c.* Six
6 *b.* Four **7** *c.* Alan Jones **8** *c.* Shadow-Ford **9** *c.* Only victory in team's history
10 *b.* Osterreichring

QUIZ 22

Answers on page 133

1 **How many Grands Prix did Jody Scheckter win in 1977?**
   a. none *b. one* *c. three*

2 **Who was the Swedish driver who won the 1977 Belgian Grand Prix, the only victory of his all-too brief career?**
   a. Torsten Palm *b. Gunnar Nilsson* *c. Ronnie Peterson*

3 **Who drove the third works McLaren in the 1977 British Grand Prix?**
   a. Keke Rosberg *b. Patrick Tambay* *c. Gilles Villeneuve*

4 **Which British driver won the race?**
   a. James Hunt *b. John Watson* *c. Rupert Keegan*

5 **How many British drivers took part in the 1977 British Grand Prix?**
   a. Three *b. Four* *c. Five*

6 **Who crashed his LEC in practice for the race and sustained multiple leg injuries which ended his Grand Prix career?**
   a. Mike Hailwood *b. Jacques Laffite* *c. David Purley*

7 **Who designed the Wolf WR1 for the 1977 season?**
   a. Patrick Head *b. Harvey Postlethwaite* *c. John Barnard*

8 **Who realised a childhood dream when he won the 1977 Italian Grand Prix?**
   a. Bruno Giacomelli *b. Vittorio Brambilla* *c. Mario Andretti*

9 **Which car was he driving?**
   a. Lotus-Ford *b. Parnelli-Ford* *c. Penske-Ford*

10 **How many World Championship rounds were there on the 1977 Grand Prix calendar?**
   a. 15 *b. 16* *c. 17*

Answers to page 133
1 *b.*Niki Lauda 2 *b.*Brabham 3 *c.*Lotus 4 *b.*Lotus 5 *c.*Monza 6 *a.*Riccardo Patrese 7 *c.*Lotus-Ford 8 *b.*Brabham-Alfa 9 *c.*Niki Lauda 10 *c.*Threw too much dirt onto the track

---

QUIZ 23

Answers on page 130

1 **How many races did Carlos Reutemann win for Ferrari in 1977?**
   a. None *b.* one *c.* Four

2 **Who won the 1977 World Championship?**
   a. Mario Andretti *b.* Jody Scheckter *c.* Niki Lauda

3 **In which race did the Renault Turbo car make its debut?**
   a 1977 French Grand Prix *b.* 1977 British Grand Prix
   c. 1977 Monaco Grand Prix

4 **Who drove it?**
   a. Jean-Pierre Jarier *b.* Jean-Pierre Beltoise
   c. Jean-Pierre Jabouille

5 **How many years did Clay Regazzoni drive for the Ferrari team?**
   a. Four *b.* Five *c.* Six

6 **How many years did Niki Lauda drive for the Ferrari team?**
   a. Three *b.* Four *c.* Five

7 **Who became the first Australian since Jack Brabham to win a Grand Prix in 1977?**
   a. Larry Perkins *b.* Brian McGuire *c.* Alan Jones

8 **In which car?**
   a. Surtees-Ford *b.* Williams-Ford *c.* Shadow-Ford

9 **What was significant about the victory?**
   a. He led from start-to-finish *b.* There were only three finishers
   c. It was the only victory in the team's history.

10 **Where was it held?**
   a. Nurburgring *b.* Osterreichring *c.* Hockenheim

Answers to page 130
1 *c.* Renault 2 *a.* Carlos Pace 3 *b.* Clay Regazzoni 4 *b.* 96 5 *c.* Carlos Reutemann
6 *b.* BRM 7 *a.* Ian Scheckter 8 *c.* Kyalami 9 *b.* Jody Scheckter 10 *a.* Wolf-Ford

---

QUIZ 24

Answers on page 131

1 **Who refused to drive in the 1977 Canadian Grand Prix?**
   a. Carlos Reutemann   *b.* Niki Lauda   *c.* Ronnie Peterson

2 **Which team did he join for 1978?**
   a. Tyrrell   *b.* Brabham   *c.* Williams

3 **Who won the 1978 Constructors' Championship?**
   a. Ferrari   *b.* McLaren   *c.* Lotus

4 **Which team did Ronnie Peterson drive for in 1978?**
   a. Tyrrell   *b.* Lotus   *c.* March

5 **On which circuit was he involved in the tragic accident which claimed his life?**
   a. Nurburgring   *b.* Osterreichring   *c.* Monza

6 **Which driver was unfairly blamed for the accident and banned by his peers from competing in the U.S. Grand Prix?**
   a. Riccardo Patrese   *b.* Vittorio Brambilla   *c.* Arturo Merzario

7 **Which team was the first to run a car with sliding 'Skirts'?**
   a. Wolf-Ford   *b.* Tyrrell-Ford   *c.* Lotus-Ford

8 **Which team ran the controversial 'Fan' car in the 1978 Swedish Grand Prix?**
   a. Lotus-Ford   *b.* Brabham-Alfa   *c.* Renault

9 **Who drove it?**
   a. Mario Andretti   *b.* Jean-Pierre Jabouille   *c.* Niki Lauda

10 **Why was it later banned from competition?**
   a. Too expensive   *b.* Too noisy
   c. Threw too much dirt onto the track

Answers to page 131

1 *c.*Three   2 *b.*Gunnar Nilsson   3 *a.*Gilles Villeneuve   4 *a.*James Hunt   5 *a.*Three
6 *c.*David Purley   7 *b.*Harvey Postlethwaite   8 *c.*Mario Andretti   9 *a.*Lotus-Ford
10 *c.*17

QUIZ 25

Answers on page 136

1 **Which team did Alan Jones join for 1978?**
   a. Ferrari *b.* Arrows-Ford *c.* Williams-Ford

2 **Who was the team's chief designer?**
   a. John Barnard *b.* Harvey Postlethwaite *c.* Patrick Head

3 **Which French driver joined the Tyrrell team for 1978?**
   a. Jean-Pierre Jarier *b.* Didier Pironi *c.* Jacques Laffite

4 **In which race did James Hunt score his last Grand Prix victory?**
   a. Japan 1977 *b.* Brazil 1978 *c.* Japan 1978

5 **Which future World Champion made his debut in the 1978 South African Grand Prix?**
   a. Ayrton Senna *b.* Keke Rosberg *c.* Nelson Piquet

6 **Which car did he drive?**
   a. Williams-Ford *b.* Hesketh-Ford *c.* Theodore-Ford

7 **Which future multi-World Champion made his Formula One debut in an Ensign-Ford in the 1978 German Grand Prix?**
   a. Keke Rosberg *b.* Alain Prost *c.* Nelson Piquet

8 **Which team decided to call it a day after the 1978 South African Grand Prix?**
   a. Surtees-Ford *b.* Hesketh-Ford *c.* Shadow-Ford

9 **And which team left the scene at the end of the 1978 season?**
   a. Surtees-Ford *b.* Hesketh-Ford *c.* Tyrrell-Ford

10 **Who made his Formula One debut in a Shadow at the 1978 Argentine Grand Prix?**
   a. Keke Rosberg *b.* Elio de Angelis *c.* Nelson Piquet

Answers to page 138
1 *a.*Jody Scheckter 2 *c.*Niki Lauda 3 *b.*He had lost interest 4 *b.*Ricardo Zunino
5 *c.*Argentinian 6 *c.*Wolf 7 *c.*Five 8 *b.*Dijon-Prenois 9 *a.*Jean-Pierre Jabouille
10 *a.*One

QUIZ 26

Answers on page 137

1 **Who won the 1978 World Drivers' title?**
   a. Mario Andretti   *b. Niki Lauda*   *c. Jody Scheckter*

2 **Who won the 1978 Monaco Grand Prix?**
   a. Ronnie Peterson   *b. Patrick Depailler*   *c. Jody Scheckter*

3 **Who won his very first Grand Prix on 'home' territory in 1978?**
   a. Gilles Villeneuve   *b. Rolf Stommelen*   *c. Rene Arnoux*

4 **Where?**
   a. France   *b. Germany*   *c. Canada*

5 **Rene Arnoux made his Grand Prix debut in 1978For which team?**
   a. Renault   *b. Martini*   *c. Surtees*

6 **For which team did Jochen Mass drive in 1978?**
   a. ATS-Ford   *b. McLaren-Ford*   *c. Arrows-Ford*

7 **Mario Andretti was first across the finish-line in the 1978 Italian Grand Prix but was classified sixth. Why?**
   a. Ran out of fuel   *b. Spun backwards over the line*
   c. Penalised one minute for jump start

8 **Who was credited with the victory?**
   a. Gilles Villeneuve   *b. Carlos Reutemann*   *c. Niki Lauda*

9 **Who was credited with second place?**
   a. John Watson   *b. James Hunt*   *c. Clay Regazzoni*

10 **How many major teams took part in the 1978 World Championship?**
   a. 12   *b. 15*   *c. 17*

Answers to page 137

1 *c.*Four 2 *a.*Patrick Depailler 3 *c.*James Hunt 4 *c.*92 5 *b.* 7 , 6 *a.*Gilles
Villeneuve 7 *a.*Jody Scheckter 8 *c.*Alan Jones 9 *a.*Williams-Ford 10 *b.*Clay
Regazzoni

QUIZ 27

Answers on page 138

1 **Which former World Champion received a knighthood in 1979?**
   a. Jackie Stewart *b. John Surtees* *c. Jack Brabham*

2 **Which French driver won the opening round of the season in Argentina?**
   a. Jean-Pierre Jabouille *b. Jacques Laffite* *c. Patrick Depailler*

3 **And which French driver won the second round, in Brazil?**
   a. Jean-Pierre Jabouille *b. Jacques Laffite* *c. Patrick Depailler*

4 **At which race did Renault claim the first ever pole position for a turbo-charged Formula 1 car in 1979?**
   a. French Grand Prix *b. Monaco Grand Prix*
   c. South African Grand Prix

5 **Which French driver joined the Renault team line-up for 1979?**
   a. Patrick Tambay *b. Jacques Laffite* *c. Rene Arnoux*

6 **How many French drivers scored Championship points in 1979?**
   a. Four *b. Six* *c. Seven*

7 **Which South American driver joined Lotus in 1979?**
   a. Nelson Piquet *b. Emerson Fittipaldi* *c. Carlos Reutemann*

8 **And which team did South Africa's Jody Scheckter join?**
   a. McLaren *b. Williams* *c. Ferrari*

9 **How many points did the Copersucar team score in 1979?**
   a. None *b. one* *c. Three*

10 **Who was the title sponsor of the Lotus team in 1979?**
   a. John Player Special *b. Essex* *c. Martini*

Answers to page 134
1 *c.*Williams-Ford 2 *c.*Patrick Head 3 *b.*Didier Pironi 4 *a.*Japan 1977 5 *b.*Keke
Rosberg 6 *c.*Theodore-Ford 7 *c.*Nelson Piquet 8 *b.*Hesketh 9 *a.*Surtees
10 *b.*Elio de Angelis.

QUIZ 28

Answers on page 135

1 **How many of the 1978 top six in the Constructors' Championship failed to win a race in 1979?**
   a. Two   b. Three   c. Four

2 **Who badly injured his legs in a hang-gliding accident, mid season?**
   a. Patrick Depailler   b. Didier Pironi   c. Jacques Laffite

3 **Who quit racing in Formula One after the 1979 Monaco Grand Prix?**
   a. Niki Lauda   b. Mario Andretti   c. James Hunt

4 **How many Grands Prix had he contested?**
   a. 72   b. 82   c. 92

5 **In how many years?**
   a. Six   b. Seven   c. Eight

6 **Who won the 1979 South African Grand Prix?**
   a. Gilles Villeneuve   b. Jody Scheckter   c. Carlos Reutemann

7 **Who took his second Monaco win (on 'home' territory) in 1979?**
   a. Jody Scheckter   b. Gilles Villeneuve   c. Patrick Depailler

8 **Who took pole position for the 1979 British Grand Prix?**
   a. Jody Scheckter   b. Rene Arnoux   c. Alan Jones

9 **In which car?**
   a. Williams-Ford   b. Renault   c. Ferrari

10 **Who won the race?**
   a. Jean-Pierre Jabouille   b. Clay Regazzoni   c. John Watson

VROOM VROOM!

Answers to page 135

1 *a.*Mario Andretti 2 *b.*Patrick Depailler 3 *a.*Gilles Villeneuve 4 *c.*Canada
5 *b.*Martini 6 *a.*ATS-Ford 7 *c.*Penalised one minute for jump start 8 *c.*Niki Lauda
9 *a.*John Watson 10 *b.*15

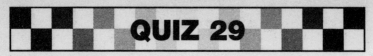

QUIZ 29

Answers on page 134

1 **Who won the 1979 World Drivers' title?**
   a. Jody Scheckter   b. Niki Lauda   c. Alan Jones

2 **Who 'retired' from Formula One during practice for the 1979 Canadian Grand Prix?**
   a. James Hunt   b. Emerson Fittipaldi   c. Niki Lauda

3 **What was the reason he gave for his retirement?**
   a. It was too dangerous   b. He had lost interest
   c. He was not being paid enough.

4 **Who replaced him in the team?**
   a. Bruno Giacomelli   b. Ricardo Zunino   c. Keke Rosberg

5 **What was his nationality?**
   a. Italian   b. Colombian   c. Argentinian

6 **Which team folded at the end of the 1979 season?**
   a. ATS   b. Theodore   c. Wolf

7 **How many Grands Prix did the Williams team win in 1979?**
   a. One   b. Three   c. Five

8 **At which circuit in France did the Formula One Renault Turbo car win for the first time?**
   a. Le Castellet   b. Dijon-Prenois   c. Clermont-Ferrand

9 **Who drove it?**
   a. Jean-Pierre Jabouille   b. Rene Arnoux   c. Jacques Laffite

10 **How many races did Renault win in the 1979 season?**
   a. One   b Two   c. Three

Answers to page 136
1 *c.*Brabham **2** *b.*Jacques Laffite **3** *b.*Jacques Laffite **4** *c.* South Africa **5** *c.*Rene Arnoux **6** *b.*Six **7** *c.*Carlos Reutemann **8** *c.*Ferrari **9** *b.*One **10** *c.*Martini

---

FACT FILE 1

The first year of the new decade was full of triumph and tragedy.

The sport mourned its first and to-date its only posthumous World Drivers' Champion.

Jochen Rindt enjoyed an uneasy alliance with Colin Chapman at Lotus.

"A monkey could have won in your car," he was reported to have told his team-boss, after he offered congratulations on Rindt's fine win in the German Grand Prix at Hockenheim.

Rindt had defied his Championship rival, Belgium's Jacky Ickx in the Ferrari, in a breathtaking battle by just 0.7seconds.

Ickx had made a brave recovery from burns received in a crash with Jacky Oliver's BRM earlier in the year.

Rindt had won in Monaco, Holland, France and Britain to give him his Championship advantage.

His race in Monaco is the subject of legend.

Just one and a half seconds behind Brabham at the start of the last lap, he pressurised the former World Champion into overbraking at the final corner. Brabham hit the straw bales. Rindt took the victory laurels.

But Rindt was deeply distressed by the death of both his great friend Bruce McLaren in a testing accident at Goodwood and that of his brother-in-law, Piers Courage in an horrendous, fiery crash in the Dutch Grand Prix.

Jochen Rindt was born for speed.

Over 100,000 fans drove through the Styrian mountains to cheer him on at his home Grand Prix at the new Osterreichring circuit.

Despite setting pole, Jochen retired with engine failure.

Then came Monza.

Something broke on the Lotus at the entry to the Parabolica during practice and he slammed into the guard rail at high speed.

FACT FILE 2

A new young team joined the fray at the beginning of 1970.

MARCH Engineering, piloted by four young men whose initials formed the name. Max Moseley (son of Sir Oswald,former leader of the British Fascist movement); former Formula Two drivers, Alan Rees and Graham Coaker and ex-McLaren designer, Robin Herd.

There were no less than five March cars on the grid in the opening round of the season.

Jackie Stewart finished third in South Africa in one for the Tyrrell team.

But the 'old man', Jack Brabham took the victory laurels, at the age of 44.

He would retire at the end of the season after contesting 126 Grands Prix. He had won three World Drivers' Championships.

And a total of 14 Grands Prix.'Not a lot' - Fangio won 24, and Five titles...Life could only get harder for everyone in Formula One.

South Africa at the start of the season was a heaven-sent venue. away from the European winter. But for one man more than most.

Graham Hill, 'recuperating' from two broken legs in the 1969 U.S. Grand Prix persuaded privateer Rob Walker to let him 'practise' in the Lotus.

He practised - the whole race - and finished sixth.

Hill had to be lifted in and out of the car...

FACT FILE 3

After 20 consecutive victories the Ford Cosworth engine was to be beaten in Belgium.

French play-boy Johnny Servoz-Gavin failed to qualify for Monaco and quit the sport.

Francois Cevert, brother-in-law of Jean-Pierre Beltoise, moved into the Tyrrell team alongside Stewart in what would prove to be a superb pairing.

Pedro Rodriguez took the second Grand Prix win of his career for BRM in Belgium.

It was BRM's first victory in four years.

Italy's Ignazio Giunti finished fourth on his Formula One debut for Ferrari. The talented Roman would lose his life in a sports car accident in 1971 in Buenos Aires.

Sadly, Pedro Rodriguez was also destined to lose his life later in 1971 in a sports car race at the Norisring in Germany .

Dan Gurney and Peter Gethin drove the McLarens at the 1970 Dutch Grand Prix in place of the team's lost leader, Bruce McLaren, who had been killed whilst testing a sports car at Goodwood and Denny Hulme, who had sustained severe burns to his hands and feet whilst practising for the Indy 500.

Piers Courage died in the race when his de Tomaso overturned and caught fire.

FACT FILE 4

The Derek Gardner-designed Tyrrell made its first appearance in the 1970 Canadian Grand Prix.

Jackie Stewart claimed pole position.

But Ickx and Regazzoni were to finish one and two for Ferrari.

John Surtees notched up the first points for *his* new team with a fourth-place finish in Canada.

Britain's Derek Bell captured the only point of his Grand Prix experiments in the USA. He finished sixth for Surtees at Watkins Glen.

Sweden's newcomer, Reine Wisell, finished third in his very first Grand Prix in the US behind winner and team-leader, Fittipaldi.

The final round of the year was held in Mexico. At the circuit named after the younger of the Rodriguez brothers, Ricardo, who lost his life in qualifying for the non-Championship Mexican Grand Prix in 1962. He was 20 years old.

The crowd of over 200,00 were totally out of control.

They were having picnics *in front* of the guard rails.

Some even ran across the circuit during the race.

Jackie Stewart retired from the race after hitting a dog which ran across the track.

Ickx and Regazzoni finished first and second for Ferrari and the team finished just four points short of Lotus in the Constructors' battle.

FACT FILE 5

Jack Brabham was hoping to add a fourth Drivers' title to his tally in 1970. But his expectations were blighted in the British Grand Prix at Brands Hatch.

He ran out of fuel with two corners to go.

Jochen Rindt couldn't believe his eyes as he passed the stationary Brabham and took the victory flag.

The scrutineers initially disqualified Rindt's Lotus, claiming that the wing was too high. Four hours later they reinstated him as winner.

There was an emotional return to Hockenheim, the circuit which had claimed the life of Jim Clark in 1978, for the German Grand Prix.

Emerson Fittipaldi finished fourth in only his second Grand Prix but Clay Regazzoni finished fourth in his very first Grand Prix at Zandvoort.

John Surtees driving the car bearing his own name just lost third place in Germany when the engine let go four laps from the end of the race.

The Tyrrell team appeared with a car bearing the name of the boss in Canada. It took pole position. Jackie Stewart flew into a commanding lead but a stub-axle broke on the bumpy circuit.

Jacky Ickx won the race for Ferrari and was challenging for the late Rindt's crown.

Stewart took pole in the USA but Emerson Fittipaldi scored a notable first win at the age of 23.

It was only the Brazilian's fourth Grand Prix. Again that other 'new boy' Clay Regazzoni had also won a round in his first season, at Monza. It was only his fifth Grand Prix.

Only seven drivers to date have won a Grand Prix in their first season.

Five went on to become World Champions.

The amazing Jacques Villeneuve won an amazing record four rounds in his first season in 1996 - although, of course, he did not win the title until the following year.

FACT FILE 6

The Ferrari one-two in Mexico at the end of 1970 had left the pundits forecasting a Ferrari whitewash in 1971.

How wrong they would prove to be!

Jackie Stewart in Ken Tyrrell's own car won six Grands Prix, notched up six pole positions, and amassed 62 points in the Drivers' Championship.

Stewart had been approached by Ferrari during the closed season but opted to stay with Tyrrell - a wise move!

Tyrrell ran away with the Constructors' crown, scoring more than twice as many points as their nearest rival, BRM, to give the Ford Cosworth its fourth successive title.

And Francois Cevert picked up his first and, sadly, his only Grand Prix victory in the USA.

It was a good race to win. The prize money was 50,000 dollars.

A vast amount back in the 'seventies - albeit chicken-feed by today's standards!

The Tyrrell 'twins' finished in first and second places in France and Germany.

Ferrari had an 'all star line-up' of three drivers.

America's Mario Andretti joined Ickx and Regazzoni in the scarlet cars.

And the team were ecstatic when their 'new boy' won the opening round of the year in South Africa, smashing the lap record in the process.

His victory came at the expense of Denny Hulme. The Kiwi had a two second lead with just four laps to go, when a bolt fell out of his suspension.

He limped home, a frustrated sixth.

FACT FILE 7

Ferrari arrived at the second round in Spain brimful of confidence.

Clay Regazzoni had also scored a runaway win in the 'Race of Champions' at Brands Hatch.

In the early 'seventies, the Grand Prix calendar was embellished by a number of Non-Championship Formula One races, which gave a number of young hopefuls the chance to pit their skills against the big boys.

British fans were treated to three opportunities to see their heroes on home soil - sadly, something which is out of the question on today's crowded calendar.

The V12 brigade dominated practice, with Ickx and Regazzoni lined up alongside the Matra Simca of Kiwi Chris Amon.

Yes, these were the days when you did see *three* cars on the front row of the grid!

But it was to be Tyrrell's day, with Stewart registering a famous first victory for the little Surrey-based team, and bringing that famous toothy grin to 'Uncle Ken's face'. It was a smile which would become very familiar indeed in the future...

But there would be little to smile about in the Ferrari camp during the rest of the season.

There would be just one more victory. Ickx ('the Rain Master') needed all his wet weather skills to win the Dutch Grand Prix on a sodden track at Zandvoort.

The Prancing Horse would only finish fourth in the Championship and another 14 rounds would elapse before Ickx would take the chequered flag again.

Rain decimated practice for the 1971 Monaco Grand Prix.

Mario Andretti didn't even qualify his Ferrari for the race!

Sweden's Ronnie Peterson hounded Stewart round the streets of the Principality, the young March driver on a charge which swept him through the pack to second place. Stewart led from start to finish.

The March had been developed by Frank Costin (the 'COS' of Cosworth) who had worked with Vanwall in the 1950s.

Denny Hulme finished fourth in the McLaren M19A. The car was nicknamed 'The Coke Bottle' by the press because of the huge bulges on either side of the cockpit which housed the fuel tanks.

The new Brabham BT34 was nicknamed the 'Lobster Claw' because of its distinctive nose.

But, despite the addition of Graham Hill to its driving force, the team struggled for points.

The former double World Champion only finished in the points once all season - fifth in Austria.

Emerson Fittipaldi and his wife were involved in a nasty road accident in France on their way to their home in Switzerland after the Monaco race.

Emerson(heavily bandaged) crashed his Lotus 72 heavily after just two laps of practice for the Dutch Grand Prix and was forced to sit out the race. He, obviously needed a little more time to convalesce.

And convalesce he did, returning to the fray two weeks later in France and finishing third after a very brave drive through the pain barrier in stifling heat.

The 1971 French Grand Prix was held at a new circuit, built high in the mountains above Marseilles at Le Castellet by multi-millionaire Paul Ricard.

The circuit boasted the most modern facilities in Europe and the longest straight, the Mistral (named after the infamous wind which rakes Provence). Sadly, today, it is sadly run-down and has not hosted a French Grand Prix since 1990.

FACT FILE 9

The 1971 British Grand Prix had an unlikely sponsor - Woolmark!

Switzerland's 'Seppi' Siffert won the Austrian Grand Prix, despite having to nurse a rear puncture.But Stewart won his second title, despite crashing unhurt at 100mph when his left rear wheel parted company with the car after a drive shaft broke.

Wife Helen greeted him,as he walked into the pits, with the news: "You are Champion. Ickx retired four laps ago!"

The 1971 Italian Grand Prix at Monza was a corker!

Mike Hailwood, who had held lap records at Monza in his bike racing day's("It's such an easy circuit to learn," he claimed, with typical candour!) joined the Surtees line-up.

At one point 'Mike the Bike' actually led the race, ahead of his old flat-mate Chris Amon.

There were no less than EIGHT different leaders on this high-speed, slipstreaming circuit. And you could have tossed a blanket over the first four as they howled over the line.

Poor Chris Amon's jinx had struck again. The likeable Kiwi had seemed en route for his first Grand Prix victory at last when, seven laps from the flag, he tore off one of his visor strips and the whole lot came away. He had to settle for sixth.

Britain's Peter Gethin won the race by one-hundreth of a second in his BRM from the March of 'Super Swede' Peterson. It was Gethin's only Grand Prix triumph of his career.

He would win one more Formula One race - the end of year non-Championship 'Victory Race' at Brands Hatch.

But there was no reason to smile on that occasion. His BRM team-mate, Jo Siffert perished in the flames when suspension failure sent him hurtling into a bank at the Kent circuit.

FACT FILE 10

The Lotus Team had not won a race in 1971. Who would predict that they would turn Formula One on its head in 1972?

Emerson Fittipaldi, at 25, became the youngest World Champion in the history of the sport (Michael Schumacher was 11 months older when he took his first title in 1994).

The beaming Brazilian won six Grands Prix to Jackie Stewart's four in the ageing Lotus 72 in his black-and-gold liveried car.

This was the year when sponsorship started to get serious. Marlboro backed no fewer than five drivers with BRM and Yardley switched their support to McLaren.

Hailwood and Amon welcomed the third member of the 'Ditton Road Flyers' back to full-time competition, as Revlon heir, Peter Revson crossed the 'Pond' to join the Yardley-McLaren team (and his former flat-mates, now rivals!)

One Bernard Ecclestone had taken over at Brabham and he had an exciting new driver on his books. The moody but magnificent Carlos Reutemann.

And it was the Argentinian, Reutemann, who shook the competition by taking pole position in his very first Grand Prix in front of his home crowd in the season-opener in Buenos Aires.

Just four drivers in the history of the sport have taken pole in their first Grand Prix. Guiseppe Farina for Alfa Romeo (well, it was the very first official Grand Prix at Silverstone in 1950!); Mario Andretti for Lotus in the USA in 1968; Reutemann for Brabham in Argentina and young Jacques Villeneuve for Williams in Australia in 1996.

Only Farina actually won the race (but the strength in depth was not exactly comparable)

And 'Happy Jacques' almost completed a dream debut, finally finishing second after leading for much of the race in Melbourne.

No such luck for Reutemann. A wrong tyre-choice stymmied 'Lole's' chances and he had to settle for seventh.

But up at the front, it was situation normal. Stewart won the race, set a new lap record and returned to the head of the Championship which he had headed since May 1971.

FACT FILE 11

Suddenly, it seemed that the South Americans were on the march again in Formula One.

Fittipaldi led Lotus; Reutemann was at Brabham and a young Brazilian, Carlo Pace joined the Frank Williams team.

But in South Africa, it was some of the 'old order' who hit the headlines. Denny Hulme won the race for McLaren; Peter Revson finished third in his sister car but his ex-flat-mate Hailwood was flying in the Surtees and was just about to overtake Stewart for the lead on Lap 29 when a rear suspension bolt sheared... He found little consolation in recording fastest lap!

Reutemann suffered a bad ankle injury in a Formula Two race at Thruxton. His seat at Brabham was taken by Wilson Fittipaldi.

Two brothers raced against each other for the first time in Formula One history in Spain in 1972 - Emerson and Wilson Fittipaldi.

But it was small brother Emerson who took the victory laurels for the second time in his career in Spain - big brother, Wilson, brought his Brabham home a creditable seventh.

The race itself at Monaco in 1972 was very, very wet this year.

Jean-Pierre Beltoise slithered to his one and only Grand Prix victory in the BRM.

His was the first victory by a French driver in the event since 1958!

And the last ever for the once great British team.

Jackie Stewart was forced to miss the 1972 Belgian Grand Prix because of an ulcer.

Clay Regazzoni missed the 1972 French Grand Prix because he had broken his wrist playing football! (Are you reading this Herr Schumacher???)

But the promising young Austrian, Helmut Marko, lost the sight of one eye and his racing career when a small stone pierced his visor in France.

FACT FILE 12

Emerson Fittipaldi won the 1972 British Grand Prix - then had a front puncture on the slowing down lap!

The Brazilian's car caught fire during the next race in Germany but he escaped unscathed.

Jackie Stewart was seething at the end of the race. The obdurate Clay Regazzoni and he had touched wheels. Stewart ended up in the armco barrier, the Swiss went on to take second place behind his Ferrari team-leader, Ickx.

The Lotus team's transporter crashed on its way to Monza. Fittipaldi's car had to be rebuilt on the grid ten minutes before the start because of a fuel leak (shades of Australia 1999...)

Jackie Stewart's clutch failed on the grid!

An exuberant Mike Hailwood took the best result of his four-wheel career, finishing second behind the newly crowned Champion, Fittipaldi.

This was the first time that the title would go to Latin America since 1957 (when one J-M Fangio took the honours).

Peter Revson took the only pole position of his career for McLaren in Canada - but John Young Stewart beat him to the line.Reutemann ran out of fuel on the last lap and Denny Hulme took third place.

McLaren had surrendered their Can-Am supremacy for the first time in years earlier in the season, so second and third was some recompense.

A burly, curly-haired South African made his Grand Prix debut in the 1971 U.S. Grand Prix. He was just 22. He qualified his McLaren on the third row of the grid and finished ninth.

How could anyone predict what lay in store for young Jody Scheckter?

FACT FILE 13

The 1973 season was dogged by triumph and tragedy again.

Jackie Stewart took his third World Championship. But his team-mate and great friend, Francois Cevert, died in a practice accident in the last race of the year in America.

Young British hopeful, Roger Williamson, died in an horrendous accident during the Dutch Grand Prix. David Purley desperately tried to pull him from his flaming car, to no avail. Williamson's sponsor, friend and mentor, Tom Wheatcroft was devastated.

Purley was awarded the George Medal for his efforts, as was another brave man, Mike Hailwood, who managed to extricate Clay Regazzoni from his burning Ferrari in South Africa.

The season did have its lighter moments...

The Hesketh team, complete with champagne and caviar and a Rolls Royce, arrived to inject a welcome sense of fun (and some serious racing).

And Hailwood, ever the joker, took to practising with a detective novel tucked inside his overalls, to wile away the time when his unreliable Surtees broke down during practice.

At the 1973 Austrian Grand Prix, marshalls found him sunbathing on the nose of his beached car at the back of the circuit, reading his book. And, later that evening, he confounded some local fans by happily signing their programme - underneath a photograph of Chris Amon!

Clay Regazzoni had left Ferrari to join BRM - and many wondered why?

But Ronnie Peterson had moved over to join Fittipaldi at Lotus, and *nobody* wondered why.

'Regga' would only score two points in the whole season. But he did raise hopes in the BRM camp when he grabbed pole position in Argentina.

But it was business as usual. Fittipaldi,Emerson,won the race for Lotus and big brother Wilson finished sixth for Brabham.

Ronnie Peterson took his first ever pole in Brazil but had to give best to the local hero. Emerson led the first Grand Prix to be held in his home country from start to finish and the samba parties in Sao Paulo lasted for a week!

The all-black 'masked crusader' of the American Shadow team joined the circus in South Africa and George Follmer took sixth place.

But the 'Big Bear' Denny Hulme amazed himself and the pundits by taking pole position for the very first and ONLY time in his long career in the new McLaren M23.

And local boy,Scheckter, 'Baby Bear', was on the front row too. To the fans delight, he led the race, after Regazzoni's accident, but exited with a blown engine.

Stewart won but Revson gave notice of McLaren's intent, with a fine second place.

The Spanish Grand Prix in Barcelona was a fun place to be in 1973!

The Brazilian navy just 'happened' to have an aircraft carrier in port during the race, and the stands rocked happily to the beat of the samba drums as their national hero Fittipaldi roared to victory. The ever-smiling Brazilian was later hijacked to the wardroom of the ship - much to the consternation of his team PRO!

Double World Champion, Graham Hill, arrived with his own Embassy-Shadow car, which he qualified an inauspicious last on the grid.

FACT FILE 15

Political correctness decreed that the 1973 Belgian Grand Prix should be held in Flemish territory rather than French. And what a shambles it proved to be.

The track at the arcane Zolder circuit was resurfaced far too late and broke up during first practice. JCBs were spotted at dawn!

The drivers were undecided as to whether the race should go ahead.

It did. Eight of them flew off the crumbling surface. Stewart and Cevert finished first and second.

A young Austrian, Niki Lauda, finished fifth for BRM.

Another young man, named Hunt,Master James, made his Grand Prix debut in Monaco in 1973.

The team, Hesketh, had all the trappings, large yacht, Silver Shadow, beautiful women, buckets of champagne. And a real live English Lord in charge...could they be serious?

They were. And they proceeded to rock the establishment later in the year with James finishing a brilliant third in Holland and a stunning second behind Peterson in the final round of the year in the USA.

Jackie Stewart won the Monaco Grand Prix for the third time in 1973, and then collided with second-place man, Fittipaldi, in the tunnel as he started to take his driving gloves off!

Sweden's Ronnie Peterson set pole position in his home country's first ever Grand Prix in 1973. But he was denied victory by the wily Denny Hulme. Denny Bear rocketed past with just four of the 199 miles to go.

FACT FILE 16

The 1973 French Grand Prix marked the beginning of a nightmare season for South Africa's young Jody Scheckter.

He collided with the reigning World Champion, Fittipaldi, and took him out of the race.

Ronnie Peterson, in the second black-and-gold Lotus won his first Grand Prix at his 40th attempt. And James Hunt claimed the first points for Hesketh by finishing sixth.

But for Jody, worse, much worse was yet to come!

Trying his utmost in the British Grand Prix, he lost control of his McLaren in the middle of the pack at the end of the first lap at Woodcote Corner. In those days, Woodcote was mega fast - no chicane!

The resulting accident was probably one of the biggest ever witnessed in Formula One (saving the 1998 Belgian Grand Prix debacle).

Amazingly, only poor Andrea de Adamich was injured. He suffered a broken ankle.

But the car carnage was mind-boggling. Nine cars were eliminated, including the entire Surtees team of three.

Jody ran and hid in the McLaren motor-home for the rest of the afternoon.

But he emerged, sheepishly, for the celebration barbecue later, when Peter Revson took the chequered flag for the McLaren team, after scoring his first Grand Prix victory.

Denny Hulme finished third, after scrapping with two young lions, Hunt and Peterson, to the flag!

Emerson Fittipaldi crashed in practice for Holland and suffered two badly swollen ankles; Niki Lauda broke a bone in his hand in Germany.

For the first and only time in his career, Emerson would finish behind his big brother, Wilson, in a Grand Prix, in Germany.

Stewart and Cevert were the class act, finishing first and second for the third time in the year.

Stewart clinched his third Drivers' title with a fourth-place finish in Monza - and legged it down the pit lane as the 'tifosi'tried to 'congratulate' him.

An 'Indy-style' pace car was introduced to Formula One in Canada - and it caused mayhem.

Patrick Depailler had injured himself in a motorcycle accident, so his place in a third Tyrrell was taken by the hard-working Chris Amon.

Canada was wet - very wet - and the positioning of the pace Car (after one Scheckter J. had collided with Francois Cevert, ouch!) was questionable to say the least.

Instead of the leading Fittipaldi, it took up station in front of the Iso-Ford of Kiwi Howden Ganley. "I figured that I had at least better drive like a race leader," commented the laconic Kiwi later.

Revson, using his Indy car experience, had pitted and, we think, made up a lap. Fittipaldi took the flag but Revvie was awarded the victory in what must rate as the most confused Grand Prix of all time.

The season ended on an all-time low.

Cevert's death in practice saw the Tyrrell team withdraw from the race at Watkins Glen. Jackie Stewart's celebratory 100th Grand Prix was aborted.

The triple World Champion announced his retirement one week later.

FACT FILE 18

1974 was a real year of change.

Stewart's retirement and Cevert's death meant a new line-up at Tyrrell.

Surprisingly, Uncle Ken chose two young chargers, the much maligned Jody Scheckter and Frenchman, Patrick Depailler, in deference to his Elf sponsors. They would not let him down.

Big news was the major sponsorship move of Marlboro from BRM to McLaren.

And they boasted a line-up of two World Champions. Emerson Fittipaldi and Denny Hulme.

Ronnie Peterson was running the coveted number one on his car, in deference to the Lotus' team success in 1973 and was joined by Ferrari refugee Jacky Ickx.

Niki Lauda joined Ferrari, and 'El Bandito' Clay Regazzoni, returned to the 'Prancing Horse' fold.

Hesketh Racing proudly fronted up with their own car for James Hunt, designed by 'The Doc', Harvey Postlethwaite.

And 'Revvie' (Peter Revson) left his Yardley McLaren seat clear for his mate Mike Hailwood, whilst he moved to the American Shadow team.

The handsome American had claimed the headlines when he became engaged to 'Miss World' Marjie Wallace.

But all would turn to terrible sadness, when he was killed in testing at Kyalami in March.

Denny Bear won the final Grand Prix of his career in Argentina, when super star Reutemann ran out of fuel with five laps to go.

Argentine President Peron, comforted the Brabham-driver and wife Mimicha at the end of the race. The fans were distraught.

FACT FILE 19

The 1974 Brazilian Grand Prix started an hour late. The over-zealous home fans, thrilled by the news of Emerson's pole position had strewn broken glass all over the track after their all-night party revellry.

Pouring rain stopped the race early but the debilitating heat had taken its toll on poor Ronnie Peterson, who finished sixth but was then rushed to hospital suffering from dehydration and heat stroke.

Ian Scheckter, brother and brother-in-law to Jody! - jumped into a Lotus for the South African Grand Prix.

Reutemann won the race for Brabham, but he had a nasty déjà vu moment: "As I came round the last corner, the man put out the flag. Then he put it away again. I thought 'oh, no, it's going to be another Argentina. But he stuck it out again and I had won. I could hardly believe it !"

Spain witnessed a Ferrari one-two, after a race of rain-plagued pit stops (maybe this is where Bernie got his ideas..) and young Niki Lauda gained the first of his 25 Grand Prix victories.

Jody Scheckter also scored his first Formula One points, finishing fifth.

The 1974 Belgian Grand Prix turned into something of a dog's breakfast with timing errors. A flying Mike Hailwood ran out of fuel. And Emerson Fittipaldi, fending of an on-form Lauda, had to duck a balance weight from a back marker which nearly smashed his visor.

Emerson won by less than half a second "I did it for the photographers," he grinned. Young Scheckter finished third.

Ronnie Peterson won in Monaco for Lotus. And 'Safety Car' driver, Vic Elford (father of Martin, whose Pix you now see in 'Autosport') spun on oil and *almost* halted the race.

Jody Scheckter headed home a Tyrrell one-two in Sweden. It was his first win at his 13th attempt.

But 'Uncle Ken' had won in Sweden himself, way back in 1955 in a Cooper-Norton!

FACT FILE 20

Everyone thought that Ferrari had overcome the Ford supremacy at last. But there were plenty of shocks in store.

Peterson drove a blinder in France to take first place; and young Mr Scheckter won the British Grand Prix.

Niki Lauda was left fuming in the pits, as an autocratic official wielding a red flag refused his exit - and hordes of stumbling'extras' blocked his route.

He would later be awarded two points for fifth place.

Carlos Reutemann just knew he would win from start to finish in Austria. What a shame that the magnificent driver's self-belief didn't last longer.

Monza proved to be Ferrari's nightmare. The scarlet chargers both retired with engine failure much to team manager Luca Montezemolo's chagrin (yes, he was around then too!!)

Peterson beat Fittipaldi by less than a second.

But it was to be the Brazilian's year.

He won in Canada, finished fourth in the USA and took his second World Championship in three years.

Sadly, Austria's young Helmuth Koinigg died in the US race.

Jody Scheckter finished third in the Drivers' Chamionship - and who would have predicted that after his 1973 disasters?

Denny Hulme hung up his Grand Prix helmet at the end of the year and retired to his beloved home-country, New Zealand, secure in the knowledge that he had helped make his compatriot, Bruce McLaren's dream come true.

McLaren won both the Drivers' and the Constructors' titles in 1974.

FACT FILE 21

1975 was Niki Lauda's first Championship year. He won five races but had to give best to a flying Hunt in Holland.

'Master James' won a nail-biting battle with 'The Rat' in the rain to give the Hesketh team its one and only victory in Formula One. It was truly a sight to savour (and my nails still bear the scars!).

'Jumper' Jarier had set pole position in both Argentina and Brazil for Shadow but the car let him down in both races.

His transmission broke on the warm-up lap in Buenos Aires, so he did not even make the start!

Carlos Pace became an overnight national hero when he won in Brazil for Brabham.

And Jody Scheckter had his home fans celebrating into the night when he won in Kyalami for Tyrrell (big brother Ian was not too impressed, he spun out of the race.)

The Spanish Grand Prix was a total shambles.

Arrogance and ignorance saw the sport's governing body fail to acknowledge the desperately poor safety features of the Barcelona track.

And the Press didn't help either with their petulant pontificating.

Dawn saw the Tyrrell mechanics hammering bolts into the weathered armco barriers on race day

Tragically, five people would die during the race, when Rolf Stommelen's Hill-Ford vaulted the barriers when its rear wing failed.

Jochen Mass was given the victory and Lella Lombardi became the first (and to date the only)woman to score World Championship points.

The race was stopped after 29 laps, so half points were awarded.

Reigning World Champion,Emerson Fittipaldi, withdrew at the end of the first lap in protest at the appalling lack of safety conditions, with the full support of his team and sponsors.

Ferrari team-mates Niki Lauda and Clay Regazzoni managed to collide with each other at the first corner ...

FACT FILE 22

Murray may have called Melbourne 1999 Fred Karno's circus. But the 1975 British Grand Prix at Silverstone was spectacularly silly.

Fittipaldi won the race - sitting in the pits - know the feeling Michael?!

The world and its wife skated off the track as a mega hail storm struck at the back of the circuit. Fortunately, no-one was injured.

Graham Hill announced his retirement after 176 Grands Prix to concentrate on running his own team, with protege Tony Brise in the hot seat and Embassy backing.

The rains came again in Austria.

The 'Monza Gorilla', Vittorio Brambilla, won the shortened race in his orange Beta Tools sponsored March. And managed to derange the front end in his exuberance on the slowing down lap!

But the sport was shocked to learn that the gentle American, Mark Donohue, had succumbed to injuries received in a practice crash on the Styrian mountain circuit.

The year had yet more tragic news to offer.

Graham Hill, piloting his own plane, crashed in thick fog not far from home, after returning from a test session in the south of France. All on board perished, including young Tony Brise.

And Emerson Fittipaldi rocked the motor sport world by announcing that he was to quit McLaren to link up with big brother Wilson for 1976 at Copersucar

Hesketh were running short of funds, so Hunt joined McLaren for 1976. And' Master James' overcame a tortured year to take the World Drivers' title in the rain-lashed Japanese Grand Prix.

Mario Andretti joined Lotus and Ronnie Peterson left in a huff to rejoin his mates at March.

Another young Swede replaced him at Lotus. Gunnar Nilsson had talent in abundance and Ken Tyrrell had him down as a future World Champion. Sadly, it was not to be.

Jody Scheckter took the revolutionary six-wheel Tyrrell to victory in Sweden.

The 1976 British Grand Prix at Brands Hatch was yet another debacle. Hunt 'won' the race after a restart but was disqualified by the Stewards for irregulaities after the race.

Niki Lauda's horrific crash at the Nurburgring needs no embellishment. But one little Italian driver did not seek the headlines which he deserves. Arturo Merzario was the one man who *knew* how to release the Ferrari seat belts. He did.

Northern Ireland's John Watson took his first Grand Prix victory for Penske at the Osterreichring and had to shave off his beard after a bet with team-boss,Roger Penske.

Lauda returned to Formula One at Monza and finished an incredibly brave fourth.

Hunt won in Canada and the USA.

Japan saw the Austrian lose his Drivers' title but Ferrari kept the Constructors' Crown.

James Hunt finished third and won the Drivers' Championship by just one point.

FACT FILE 24

Renault returned to the Grand Prix scene in 1977.

Formula One would follow the turbo route - for a while.

Chris Amon, one of the sport's stalwarts, retired with eyesight problems back to New Zealand (and some fun times with Denny Hulme and Mike Hailwood)

Chris had contested 96 Grands Prix , had five pole positions to his credit, finished second three times but, inexplicably, had never taken that coveted chequered flag.

Tragedy dogged the sport once more.

The Brazilian, Carlos Pace was killed in a light aircraft crash in his home country at the start of the year.

And young Welshman Tom Pryce was the victim of an awful accident in South Africa when a young fire marshall ran across the track in front of him, trying to reach Pryce's Shadow team-mate, Renzo Zorzi. Two young men lost their lives.

South Africa marked the swan song for the once mighty BRM team. Australia's Larry Perkins qualified the sole entry but could only finish 15th.

The Scheckter brothers enjoyed mixed fortunes in 1977. Jody signed for Wolf and won, first time out, in Argentina. Ian signed for March and only managed one finish all season, 11th in Spain. His signature was not required on any Formula One contracts at the end of the year.

Jody went on to win three races during the year, thanks to the inventive mind of former Hesketh designer, Harvey Postlethwaite, and finished runner-up in the Championship behind the resurgent Niki Lauda in his Ferrari.

A wiry little French-Canadian had thrashed one James Hunt in a Formula Atlantic race at Trois Riviéres in 1976. James had told the McLaren management to sign him up. They did. And Gilles Villeneuve made his Formula One debut at Silverstone in 1977 - at the wheel of a McLaren.

Team-boss, Teddy Mayer, wasn't impressed by his 11th place finish but Ferrari spotted the spark. Gilles would become one of Enzo Ferrari's favourites. His guts and skill endearing him to the 'Old Man'. But first he had to endure a horrible accident in Japan in 1977 when his car ran into Ronnie Peterson's Tyrrell, somersaulted into the crowd and killed two spectators. Gilles was uninjured. He would drive for Ferrari for all of his life.

Mario Andretti won four races for Lotus in 1977. But it was his victory at Monza which really kindled his childhood dream. The son of an Italian immigrant to the USA, he had never forgotten his roots - and where his love of motorsport was born.

His team-mate, Sweden's Gunnar Nilsson, won the 1977 Belgian Grand Prix, to help Lotus finish second overall in the Constructors' Championship. Little did anyone know that Gunnar had a cancer which would take his life in 1978. But not before the brave young Swede had established his Gunnar Nilsson Cancer Treatment Campaign. He persuaded his fellow countryman Bjorn Borg to take part in a fund-raising tennis match with the likes of James Hunt, Emerson Fittipaldi and Jody Scheckter in his memory.

James Hunt won the 1977 British Grand Prix but poor David Purley, crashed his LEC in practice and sustained dreadful multiple injuries. Typically, the man returned to racing in 1979 in the Aurora series. He then took up aerobatics in a Pitts Special but crashed into the sea in 1985.

1977 was Ferrari's year. But the combination of Lauda and Reutemann did not make for happy families. The acerbic Austrian and the sensitive South American never hit it off. Niki won three races; Carlos won one. Niki won the Drivers' title; Ferrari won the Constructors' title. But, after four years with the Prancing Horse, Lauda announced his intentions of leaving for Brabham at the end of the season. The split was acrimonious. Niki did not drive in the last two rounds of the year.

FACT FILE 26

No Australian had won a Grand Prix since Jack Brabham in South Africa in 1970. Alan Jones set the record straight by taking his first ever victory at the Osterreichring. It would be the one and only triumph in the Shadow team's history. Mr Jones was on his way to Williams for 1978.

His seat at Shadow would be taken by former Ferrari star Clay Regazzoni, who had a torrid time at Ensign in 1977.

Ronnie Peterson struggled with the six-wheeler at Tyrrell and, thankfully, returned to Lotus for 1978, albeit as number two to Andretti.

Colin Chapman's design team had come up with 'the car' in the Lotus 79, complete with sliding skirts -the epitome of the ground effect era.

Ronnie picked up wins in South Africa and Austria, whilst Mario happily headed for the Championship.

Then came Monza.

Drivers at the back of the grid were still rolling as the start lights came on. There was a multiple pile-up.

Ronnie's Lotus caught fire and James Hunt and others helped pull him out. Both legs were badly broken.

Vittorio Brambilla was hit by a flying wheel, suffering severe concussion which would effectively end his racing career.

Italian rookie, Riccardo Patrese, was blamed for causing the accident in his Arrows by his peers. An unfair accusation in an era which demanded an immediate review of starting procedures.

But it would be too late. Ronnie Peterson developed a serious embollism overnight and died the following morning.

Mario Andretti won the World title for Lotus but no-on in the sport was in party mood.

FACT FILE 27

Gordon Murray designed the Brabham' fan' car for 1978 to combat the ground effect of skirts.

It was quick. Lauda won in Sweden. But rivals protested that the turbulence of the 'fan' threw surface dirt into the radiators of following cars and it was banned from competition.

Alan Jones won the Can-Am title in 1978 but also put in some rugged performances in the Patrick Head-designed Williams, finishing an excellent second at Watkins Glen.

Little did he know but there were a couple of future World Champions in the offing in 1978.

Finland's Keke Rosberg stunned everybody by winning the non-Championship 'Race of Champions' at Silverstone in pouring rain for the fledgling Theodore Team.

Keke's 1978 Grand Prix year was not exactly memorable- but he left no-one in any doubt as to his potential. So laid back 'he should be horizontal', the mustachioed Finn struggled with a series of uncompetitive cars.

A young Formula 3 star from Brazil was also intent on making his mark on the sport. He ended the year on Bernie Ecclestone's shopping list at Brabham. Nelson Piquet has always seemed to be in the right place at the right time.

Winner of the 1977 Monaco Formula 3 race, showcase for young hopefuls, Didier Pironi had a 1978 contract with Tyrrell and scored points in five races.

Whilst arch-rival, fellow-Frenchman, Rene Arnoux had a frustrating season. He finished off driving for the Surtees Team but Big John would be forced to pull out at the end of the year due to lack of sponsorship. Arnoux would head for greater things at Renault in 1979.

The Hesketh team too had faded from the scene. After Eddie Cheever's sad showing in South Africa, Alexander Hesketh headed back to the House of Lords to back Mrs Thatcher...

FACT FILE 28

Mario Andretti and Gilles Villeneuve finished first and second in the restarted Italian Grand Prix in 1978 but both were penalised one minute for jumping the start.

Gilles made up for his disappointment by winning his 'home' round in Montreal.

The 1979 season saw Renault's hopes come true.

Jean-Pierre Jabouille won the first victory for a turbo-charged car - in France!

And Ligier's hopes were raised when Jacques Laffite won both opening races, in Argentina and Brazil.

The French, with their superb sponsored backing for 'Junior' drivers were beginning to reap the rewards.

The South Americans were struggling.

Emerson Fittipaldi could only salvage one point at Copersucar.

Carlos Reutemann moved to the Martini-sponsored Lotus team but had an uninspired year for him.

Nelson Piquet won the non-Championship Race of Champions at Brands Hatch but fourth-place in Holland was his best Grand Prix result.

However, when Niki Lauda walked away from the Brabham team in Montreal, Nelson found himself team leader. He would respond accordingly.

James Hunt, too, walked away from the sport in 1979. He had joined up with his old chum Harvey Postlethwaite at Wolf at the start of the year but became increasingly disillusioned as the season progressed.

Monaco 1979 would prove to be his last outing.

FACT FILE 29

Whilst the 'Old Guard' were on their way out, the new boys were on a charge.

Gilles Villeneuve won three races, the little French-Canadian happily trawling the European circuits with his family in his camper van.

But it was his 'new' team leader, Jody Scheckter who would win the World Championship for Ferrari (a feat which has yet to be repeated after 20 years).

South African, Jody was 29 and had come a long way since that unforgettable Woodcote incident...

And he won on his new 'home turf' - in Monaco - much to the delight of the Italian fans who had streamed across the border.

Meanwhile, over at Wolf, young Mr Rosberg, who had taken over from Mr Hunt, failed to score a point.

A disillusioned Walter Wolf pulled the plug on the team at the end of the season

Clay Regazzoni scored what would, sadly, prove to be the last win of his Grand Prix career but a very proud first for Williams in the 1979 British Grand Prix.

And Alan Jones promptly underlined the team's potential by winning *four* more races at the end of the year.

Patrick Depailler gave Ligier their third win of the season in Spain and then suffered badly broken legs in a hang-gliding accident!

1970s

RESULTS

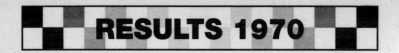

RESULTS 1970

1970 The 21st birthday of the World Championship was a sad year.
New Zealand's Bruce McLaren was killed testing his Can-Am car at
Goodwood. Britain's genial Piers Courage died in a fiery accident during
the Dutch Grand Prix. And Austria's Jochen Rindt became the sport's first
and, to date, only posthumous World Drivers' Champion when a high
speed accident claimed his life at Monza in practice for the Italian Grand
Prix. But, as always in motor sport, there were new names in the wings.
A smiling Brazilian named Fittipaldi; a tall blonde Swede called Peterson;
a roguish italian-speaking Swiss driver, Clay Regazzoni; a dashing
Frenchman, Francois Cevert; and American extrovert, Mario Andretti. All
would soon appear in the record books. Two new Constructors joined the
fray: March (under one,Max Mosley) and Tyrrell (brainchild of 'Uncle Ken').
The series returned to Austria, to the glorious Osterreichring in Styria.
Hockenheim hosted the German Grand Prix for the first time. There were
13 rounds. Best five results from first seven races. Best five results from
second six. Points: 9-6-4-3-2-1.

ROUND 1/SOUTH AFRICAN GRAND PRIX
KYALAMI, 7 MARCH

1. BRABHAM(AUS)	BRABHAM-FORD	1HR 49MIN 34.6SEC
2. HULME(NZ)	MCLAREN-FORD	1HR 49MIN 42.7SEC
3. STEWART(GB)	MARCH-FORD	1HR 49MIN 51.7SEC
4. BELTOISE(FRA)	MATRA-SIMCA	1HR 50MIN 47.7SEC
5. MILES(GB)	LOTUS-FORD	79 LAPS
6. G. HILL(GB)	LOTUS-FORD	79 LAPS

Race: 80 laps of 2.55mile/4.1km (204miles/328kms)
Fastest lap: Surtees(GB), McLaren-Ford/Brabham, 1min 20.8sec, 113.6mph/182.8kph
Pole position: Stewart, 1min 19.3sec 23 starters, 13 classified finishers

ROUND 2/SPANISH GRAND PRIX
JARAMA,MADRID,19 APRIL

1. STEWART(GB)	MARCH-FORD	2HR 10MIN 58.2SEC
2. MCLAREN(NZ)	MCLAREN-FORD	89 LAPS
3. ANDRETTI(USA)	MARCH-FORD	89 LAPS
4. G. HILL(GB)	LOTUS-FORD	89 LAPS
5. SERVOZ-GAVIN(FRA)	MARCH-FORD	88 LAPS

Race: 90 laps of 2.11mile/3.4km (190miles/306kms)
Fastest lap: Brabham(AUS), Brabham-Ford, 1min 24.3sec,90.3mph/145.3kph
Pole position: Brabham, 1min 23.9sec 16 starters, 5 classified finishers

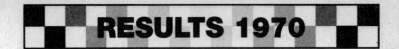

RESULTS 1970

ROUND 3/MONACO GRAND PRIX
MONTE CARLO, 10 MAY

1.RINDT(AUT)	LOTUS-FORD	1HR 54MIN 36.6SEC
2.BRABHAM(AUS)	BRABHAM-FORD	1HR 54MIN 59.7SEC
3.PESCAROLO(FRA)	MATRA-SIMCA	1HR 55MIN 28.0SEC
4.HULME(NZ)	MCLAREN-FORD	1HR 56MIN 04.9SEC
5.G.HILL(GB)	LOTUS-FORD	79 LAPS
6.P. RODRIGUEZ(MEX)	BRM	78 LAPS

Race: 80 laps of 1.95mile/3.15km (156miles/252kms)
Fastest lap: Rindt(last lap!), 1min 23.2sec,84.6mph/136.1kph
*Pole position:*Stewart(GB), March-Ford,1min 24.0sec 16 starters, 8 classified finishers

ROUND 4/BELGIAN GRAND PRIX
SPA-FRANCORCHAMPS, 7 JUNE

1. P. RODRIGUEZ(MEX)	BRM	1HR 38MIN 09.9SEC
2. AMON(NZ)	MARCH-FORD	1HR 38MIN 11.0SEC
3. BELTOISE(FRA)	MATRA-SIMCA	1HR 39MIN 53.6SEC
4. GIUNTI(ITA)	FERRARI	1HR 40MIN 48.4SEC
5. STOMMELEN(GER)	BRABHAM-FORD	1HR 41MIN 41.7SEC
6. PESCAROLO(FRA)	MATRA-SIMCA	27 LAPS

Race: 28 laps of 8.76mile/14.1km (245miles/395kms)
Fastest lap: Amon,3min 27min 27.4sec,152.1mph/244.7kph
Pole position: Stewart(GB), March-Ford,3min 28.0sec 17 starters, 8 classified finishers

ROUND 5/DUTCH GRAND PRIX
ZANDVOORT, 21 JUNE

1. RINDT(AUT)	LOTUS-FORD	1HR 50MIN 43.41SEC
2. STEWART(GB)	MARCH-FORD	1HR 51MIN 13.41SEC
3. ICKX(BEL)	FERRARI	79 LAPS
4. REGAZZONI(ITA)	FERRARI	79 LAPS
5. BELTOISE(FRA)	MATRA-SIMCA	79 LAPS
6. SURTEES(GB)	MCLAREN-FORD	79 LAPS

Race: 80 laps of 2.6mile/4.19km (208 miles/335kms)
Fastest lap: Ickx, 1min 19.23sec, 118.3mph/190.5kph
Pole position: Rindt,1min 18.30sec 20 starters, 11 classified finishers

ROUND 6/FRENCH GRAND PRIX
CLERMONT-FERRAND, 5 JULY

1. RINDT(AUT)	LOTUS-FORD	1HR 55MIN 57.00SEC
2. AMON(NZ)	MARCH-FORD	1HR 56MIN 04.61SEC
3. BRABHAM(AUS)	BRABHAM-FORD	1HR 56MIN 41.83SEC
4. HULME(NZ)	MCLAREN-FORD	1HR 56MIN 42.66SEC
5. PESCAROLO(FRA)	MATRA-SIMCA	1HR 57MIN 16.42SEC
6. GURNEY(USA)	MCLAREN-FORD	1HR 57MIN 16.65SEC

Race: 38 laps of 5.0mile/8.05km (190 miles/306 kms)
Fastest lap: Brabham, 3min 0.75sec, 99.7mph/160.4kph
Pole position: Ickx(BEL), Ferrari, 2min 58.22sec 20 starters, 15 classified finishers

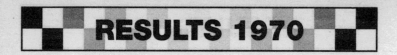

RESULTS 1970

ROUND 7/ BRITISH GRAND PRIX
BRANDS HATCH, 18 JULY

1. RINDT(AUT)	LOTUS-FORD	1HR 57MIN 02.0SEC
2. BRABHAM(AUS)	BRABHAM-FORD	1HR 57MIN 34.9SEC
3. HULME(NZ)	MCLAREN-FORD	1HR 57MIN 56.4SEC
4. REGAZZONI(SWISS)	FERRARI	1HR 57MIN 56.8SEC
5. AMON(NZ)	MARCH-FORD	79 LAPS
6. G. HILL(GB)	LOTUS-FORD	79 LAPS

Race: 80 laps of 2.65 mile/4.27km (212 miles/342 kms)
Fastest lap: Brabham,1min 25.9sec, 111.0mph/178.7kph
Pole position: Rindt, 1min 24.8sec 22 starters, 10 classified finishers

ROUND 8/GERMAN GRAND PRIX
HOCKENHEIM, 2 AUGUST

1. RINDT(AUT)	LOTUS-FORD	1HR 42MIN 00.3SEC
2. ICKX(BEL)	FERRARI	1HR 42MIN 01.0SEC
3. HULME(NZ)	MCLAREN-FORD	1HR 43MIN 22.1SEC
4. FITTIPALDI(BRA)	LOTUS-FORD	1HR 43MIN 55.4SEC
5. STOMMELEN(GER)	BRABHAM-FORD	49 LAPS
6. PESCAROLO(FRA)	MATRA-SIMCA	49 LAPS

Race: 50 laps of 4.22mile/6.79km (211 miles/339.5kms)
Fastest lap: Ickx, 2min 0.5sec, 126.0mph/202.8kph
Pole position: Ickx, 1min 59.5sec 21 starters, 9 classified finishers

ROUND 9/AUSTRIAN GRAND PRIX
OSTERREICHRING, 16 AUGUST

1. ICKX(BEL)	FERRARI	1HR 42MIN 17.32SEC
2. REGAZZONI(SWISS)	FERRARI	1HR 42MIN 17.93SEC
3. STOMMELEN(GER)	BRABHAM-FORD	1HR 43MIN 45.20SEC
4. P. RODRIGUEZ(MEX)	BRM	59 LAPS
5. OLIVER(GB)	BRM	59 LAPS
6. BELTOISE(FRA)	MATRA-SIMCA	59 LAPS

Race: 60 laps of 3.67mile/5.91km (220 miles/355kms)
Fastest lap: Ickx/Regazzoni, 1min 40.4sec, 131.7mph/211.9kph
Pole position: Rindt(AUT), Lotus-Ford, 1min 39.2sec 24 starters, 15 classified finishers

ROUND 10/ITALIAN GRAND PRIX
MONZA, 6 SEPTEMBER

1. REGAZZONI(SWISS)	FERRARI	1HR 39MIN 06.88SEC
2. STEWART(GB)	MARCH-FORD	1HR 39MIN 12.61SEC
3. BELTOISE(FRA)	MATRA-SIMCA	1HR 39MIN 12.68SEC
4. HULME(NZ)	MCLAREN-FORD	1HR 39MIN 13.03SEC
5. STOMMELEN(GER)	BRABHAM-FORD	1HR 39MIN 13.29SEC
6. CEVERT(FRA)	MARCH-FORD	1HR 40MIN 10.34SEC

Race: 68 laps of 3.57mile/5.75km (243 miles/391kms)
Fastest lap: Regazzoni, 1min 25.2sec, 150.9mph/242.9kph
Pole position: Ickx(BEL), Ferrari, 1min 24.14sec 20 starters, 9 classified finishers
*Team Lotus did not start the race after the death of Jochen Rindt in practice.

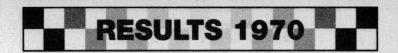

RESULTS 1970

ROUND 11/CANADIAN GRAND PRIX
MONT TREMBLANT-ST JOVITE, QUEBEC, 20 SEPTEMBER

1. ICKX(BEL)	FERRARI	2HR 21MIN 18.4SEC
2. REGAZZONI(SWISS)	FERRARI	2HR 21MIN 33.2SEC
3. AMON(NZ)	MARCH-FORD	2HR 22MIN 16.3SEC
4. P. RODRIGUEZ(MEX)	BRM	89 LAPS
5. SURTEES(GB)	SURTEES-FORD	89 LAPS
6. GETHIN(GB)	MCLAREN-FORD	88 LAPS

Race: 90 laps of 2.65mile/4.27km (238miles/384kms)
Fastest lap: Regazzoni, 1min 32.2sec, 103.4mph/166.5kph
Pole position: Stewart(GB), Tyrrell-Ford, 1min 31.5sec 20 starters,10 classified finishers

ROUND12/US GRAND PRIX
WATKINS GLEN, 4 OCTOBER

1. E.FITTIPALDI(BRA)	LOTUS-FORD	1HR 57MIN 32.79SEC
2. P. RODRIGUEZ(MEX)	BRM	1HR 58MIN 09.18SEC
3. WISELL(SWE)	LOTUS-FORD	1HR 58MIN 17.96SEC
4. ICKX(BEL)	FERRARI	107 LAPS
5. AMON(NZ)	MARCH-FORD	107 LAPS
6. D. BELL(GB)	SURTEES-FORD	107 LAPS

Race: 108 laps of 2.3mile/3.7km (248 miles/400 kms)
Fastest lap: Ickx,1min 2.74sec, 131.9mph/213kph
Pole position: Ickx, 1min 03.07sec 24 starters, 14 classified finishers

ROUND 13/MEXICAN GRAND PRIX
RICARDO RODRIGUEZ CIRCUIT, MEXICO CITY, 25 OCTOBER

1. ICKX(BEL)	FERRARI	1HR 53MIN 28.36SEC
2. REGAZZONI(SWISS)	FERRARI	1HR 54MIN 13.82SEC
3. HULME(NZ)	MCLAREN-FORD	1HR 54MIN 14.33SEC
4. AMON(NZ)	MARCH-FORD	1HR 54MIN 15.41SEC
5. BELTOISE(FRA)	MATRA-SIMCA	1HR 54MIN 18.47SEC
6. P. RODRIGUEZ(MEX)	BRM	1HR 54MIN 53.12SEC

Race: 65 laps of 3.1mile/5km (203miles/ 325kms)
Fastest lap: Ickx, 1min 43.11sec, 108.45ph/175kph
Pole position: Regazzoni, 1min 41.86sec 18 starters, 9 classified finishers

DRIVERS' WORLD CHAMPIONSHIP 1970

1.	RINDT	45 *points*	4.	HULME	27 *points*
2.	ICKX	40 *points*	5.	BRABHAM	25 *points*
3.	REGAZZONI	33 *points*	5.	STEWART	25 *points*

CONSTRUCTORS' WORLD CHAMPIONSHIP 1970

1.	LOTUS-FORD	59 *points*	4.	MCLAREN-FORD	35 *points*
2.	FERRARI	52 *points*	5.	BRM	23 *points*
3.	MARCH-FORD	48 *points*	5.	MATRA	23 *points*
4.	BRABHAM-FORD	35 *points*			

RESULTS 1971

1971 Andretti's victory in the opening round for Ferrari left few hints that the Tyrrell team would dominate the season. Stewart claimed his second Championship with six wins and helped Ken's fledgling operation to a handsome Constructors' triumph together with team-mate, Cevert, who claimed the only victory of what was to prove a tragically all-too brief career in the USA. Sweden's Ronnie Peterson emerged as a leading contender, despite not winning a race. Reigning World Champions, Lotus,failed to score a victory for the first time since 1960. Two more brave drivers lost their lives: Mexico's Pedro Rodriguez in a sports car race at the Norisring in Germany and Switzerland's Jo Siffert in a non-Championship Formula One race at Brands Hatch. There were 11 rounds. Best five results from first six places. Best four from second five. Points: 9-6-4-3-2-1.

ROUND 1/SOUTH AFRICAN GRAND PRIX
KYALAMI, 6 MARCH

1. ANDRETTI(USA)	FERRARI	1HR 47MIN 35.5SEC
2. STEWART(GB)	TYRRELL-FORD	1HR 47MIN 56.4SEC
3. REGAZZONI(SWISS)	FERRARI	1HR 48MIN 06.9SEC
4. WISELL(SWE)	LOTUS-FORD	1HR 48MIN 44.9SEC
5. AMON(NZ)	MATRA-SIMCA	78 LAPS
6. HULME(NZ)	MCLAREN-FORD	78 LAPS

Race: 79 laps of 2.55mile/4.1km (201miles/324kms)
Fastest lap: Andretti, 1min 20.3sec, 114.3mph/184kph
*Pole position:*Stewart,1min 17.8sec 25 starters, 13 classified finishers

ROUND 2/SPANISH GRAND PRIX
MONTJUICH PARK, BARCELONA, 18 MAY

1. STEWART(GB)	TYRRELL-FORD	1HR 49MIN 03.4SEC
2. ICKX(BEL)	FERRARI	1HR 49MIN 06.8SEC
3. AMON(NZ)	MATRA-SIMCA	1HR 50MIN 01.5SEC
4. P.RODRIGUEZ(MEX)	BRM	1HR 50MIN 21.3SEC
5. HULME(NZ)	MCLAREN-FORD	1HR 50MIN 30.4SEC
6. BELTOISE(FRA)	MATRA-SIMCA	74 LAPS

Race: 75 laps of 2.36mile/3.79km (177 miles/284kms)
Fastest lap: Ickx, 1min 25.1sec, 99.6mph/160.4kph
Pole position: Ickx, 1min 25.9sec 22 starters, 11 classified finishers

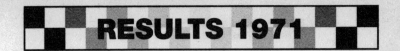

RESULTS 1971

ROUND 3/MONACO GRAND PRIX
MONTE CARLO, 23 MAY

1. STEWART(GB)	TYRRELL-FORD	1HR 52MIN 21.3SEC
2. PETERSON(SWE)	MARCH-FORD	1HR 52MIN 46.9SEC
3. ICKX(BEL)	FERRARI	1HR 53MIN 14.6SEC
4. HULME(NZ)	MCLAREN-FORD	1HR 53MIN 28.0SEC
5. E. FITTIPALDI(BRA)	LOTUS-FORD	79 LAPS
6. STOMMELEN(GER)	SURTEES-FORD	79 LAPS

Race: 80 laps of 1.95 mile/3.15 km (156 miles/252 kms)
Fastest lap: Stewart, 1min 22.2sec,85.6mph/137.7kph
Pole position: Stewart, 1min 23.2sec 18 starters,10 classified finishers

ROUND 4/DUTCH GRAND PRIX
ZANDVOORT, 20 JUNE

1. ICKX(BEL)	FERRARI	1HR 56MIN 20.09SEC
2. P. RODRIGUEZ(MEX)	BRM	1HR 56MIN 28.08SEC
3. REGAZZONI(SWISS)	FERRARI	69 LAPS
4. PETERSON(SWE)	MARCH-FORD	68 LAPS
5. SURTEES(GB)	SURTEES-FORD	68 LAPS
6. SIFFERT(SWISS)	BRM	68 LAPS

Race: 70 laps of 2.6mile/4.19km (182 miles/293kms)
Fastest lap: Ickx, 1min 34.95sec, 98.8mph/159kph
Pole position: Ickx, 1min 17.42sec 24 starters,12 classified finishers

ROUND 5/FRENCH GRAND PRIX
PAUL RICARD CIRCUIT, 4 JULY

1. STEWART(GB)	TYRRELL-FORD	1HR 46MIN 41.68SEC
2. CEVERT(FRA)	TYRRELL-FORD	1HR 47MIN 09.80SEC
3. E.FITTIPALDI(BRA)	LOTUS-FORD	1HR 47MIN 15.75SEC
4. SIFFERT(SWISS)	BRM	1HR 47MIN 18.85SEC
5. AMON(NZ)	MATRA-SIMCA	1HR 47MIN 22.76SEC
6. WISELL(SWE)	LOTUS-FORD	1HR 47MIN 57.66SEC

Race: 55 laps of 3.6 mile/5.8 km (198 miles/319 kms)
Fastest lap: Stewart, 1min 54.09sec, 113.9mph/183.3kph
Pole position: Stewart,1min 54.09sec 23 starters, 13 classified finishers

ROUND 6/BRITISH GRAND PRIX
SILVERSTONE, 17 JULY

1. STEWART(GB)	TYRRELL-FORD	1HR 31MIN 31.5SEC
2. PETERSON(SWE)	MARCH-FORD	1HR 32MIN 07.6SEC
3. E. FITTIPALDI(BRA)	LOTUS-FORD	1HR 32MIN 22.0SEC
4. PESCAROLO(FRA)	MARCH-FORD	67 LAPS
5. STOMMELEN(GER)	SURTEES-FORD	67 LAPS
6. SURTEES(GB)	SURTEES-FORD	67 LAPS

Race: 68 laps of 2.9mile/4.71km (199 miles/320 kms)
Fastest lap: Stewart, 1min 19.9sec, 131.9mph/212.4kph
Pole position: Regazzoni(SWISS), Ferrari, 1min 18.01sec 24 starters, 12 class. finishers

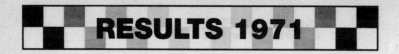

RESULTS 1971

ROUND 7/GERMAN GRAND PRIX
NURBURGING, 1 AUGUST

1. STEWART(GB)	TYRRELL-FORD	1HR 29MIN 15.7SEC
2. CEVERT(FRA)	TYRRELL-FORD	1HR 29MIN 45.8SEC
3. REGAZZONI(SWISS)	FERRARI	1HR 29MIN 52,8SEC
4. ANDRETTI(USA)	FERRARI	1HR 31MIN 20.7SEC
5. PETERSON(SWE)	MARCH-FORD	1HR 31MIN 44.8SEC
6. SCHENKEN(AUS)	BRABHAM-FORD	1HR 32MIN 14.3SEC

Race: 12 laps of 14.19 mile/22.84 km (170 miles/274 kms)
Fastest lap: Cevert, 7min 20.1sec, 116.1mph/186.8kph
Pole position: Stewart, 7min 19.0sec 22 starters, 12 classified finishers

ROUND 8/AUSTRIAN GRAND PRIX
OSTERREICHRING, 15 AUGUST

1. SIFFERT(SWISS)	BRM	1HR 30MIN 23.91SEC
2. E. FITTIPALDI(BRA)	LOTUS-FORD	1HR 30MIN 28.03SEC
3. SHENKEN(AUS)	BRABHAM-FORD	1HR 30MIN 43.68SEC
4. WISELL(SWE)	LOTUS-FORD	1HR 30MIN 55.78SEC
5. G. HILL(GB)	BRABHAM-FORD	1HR 31MIN 12.34SEC
6. PESCAROLO(FRA)	MARCH-FORD	1HR 31MIN 48.42SEC

Race: 54 laps of 3.67mile/5.91km (198 miles/319.2kms)
Fastest lap: Siffert, 1min 38.47sec, 134.28mph/216.1kph
Pole position: Siffert, 1min 37.44sec 21 starters, 12 classified finishers

ROUND 9/ITALIAN GRAND PRIX
MONZA, 5 SEPTEMBER

1. GETHIN(GB)	BRM	1HR 18MIN 12.60SEC
2. PETERSON(SWE)	MARCH-FORD	1HR 18MIN 12.61SEC
3. CEVERT(FRA)	TYRRELL-FORD	1HR 18MIN 12.69SEC
4. HAILWOOD(GB)	SURTEES-FORD	1HR 18MIN 13.21SEC
5. GANLEY(NZ)	BRM	1HR 18MIN 13.21SEC
6. AMON(NZ)	MATRA-SIMCA	1HR 18MIN 44.96SEC

Race: 55 laps of 3.57mile/5.75km (196miles/316kms)
Fastest lap: Pescarolo(FRA), March-Ford, 1min 23.8sec/153.49mph/247.02kph
Pole position: Amon, 1min 22.40sec 23 starters, 10 classified finishers

ROUND 10/CANADIAN GRAND PRIX
MOSPORT, TORONTO, 19 SEPTEMBER

1. STEWART(GB)	TYRRELL-FORD	1HR 55MIN 12.9SEC
2. PETERSON(SWE)	MARCH-FORD	1HR 55MIN 51.2SEC
3. DONOHUE(CAN)	MCLAREN-FORD	1HR 56MIN 48.7SEC
4. HULME(NZ)	MCLAREN-FORD	63 LAPS
5. WISELL(SWE)	LOTUS-FORD	63 LAPS
6. CEVERT(FRA)	TYRRELL-FORD	62 LAPS

Race: *64 laps of 2.46mile/3.96km (157 miles/253.4kms)
Fastest lap: Hulme, 1min 43.5sec, 85.5mph/137.4kph
Pole position: Stewart, 1min 15.3sec 24 starters, 16 classified finishers
*race foreshortened because of heavy rain and failing light

RESULTS 1971/2

ROUND 11/US GRAND PRIX
WATKINS GLEN, 3 OCTOBER

1. CEVERT(FRA)	TYRRELL-FORD	1HR 43MIN 51.99SEC
2. SIFFERT(SWISS)	BRM	1HR 44MIN 32.05SEC
3. PETERSON(SWE)	MARCH-FORD	1HR 44MIN 36.06SEC
4. GANLEY(NZ)	BRM	1HR 44MIN 48.74SEC
5. STEWART(GB)	TYRRELL-FORD	1HR 44MIN 51.99SEC
6. REGAZZONI(SWISS)	FERRARI	1HR 45MIN 08.42SEC

Race: 59 laps of 3.38mile/5.44km (199 miles/320.4kms)
Fastest lap: Ickx(BEL), Ferrari, 1min 43.47mph/117.5mph/189.1kph
Pole position: Stewart, 1min 42.64sec 29 starters, 17 classified finishers

DRIVERS' WORLD CHAMPIONSHIP 1971

1.	STEWART	62 points	4. ICKX	19 points
2.	PETERSON	33 points	4. SIFFERT	19 points
3.	CEVERT	26 points	6. E. FITTIPALDI	16 points

CONSTRUCTORS' WORLD CHAMPIONSHIP 1971

1. TYRRELL-FORD	73 points	3. FERRARI	33 points
2. BRM	36 points	5. LOTUS-FORD	21 points
3. MARCH-FORD	33 points	6. MCLAREN-FORD	10 points

1972 Lotus bounced back into the limelight, thanks to five wins by their Brazilian star, Emerson Fittipaldi. He became the youngest World Champion in history at the age of 25. Jean-Pierre Beltoise gained his only Grand Prix victory in the rain at Monaco. It would prove to be the last ever win for BRM. Bernie Ecclestone took over the reins at Brabham and signed up the dashing Argentinian, Carlos Reutemann to drive alongside Graham Hill. The Argentine Grand Prix returned to the calendar for the first time since 1960. There were 12 rounds, best five out of six results in both halves of the season to score. Points: 9-6-4-3-2-1 for first six places.

ROUND 1/ARGENTINE GRAND PRIX
BUENOS AIRES,23 JANUARY

1. STEWART(GB)	TYRRELL-FORD	1HR 57MIN 58.82SEC
2. HULME(NZ)	MCLAREN-FORD	1HR 58MIN 24.78SEC
3. ICKX(BEL)	FERRARI	1HR 58MIN 58.21SEC
4. REGAZZONI(SWISS)	FERRARI	1HR 59MIN 05.54SEC
5. SCHENKEN(AUS)	SURTEES-FORD	1HR 59MIN 07.93SEC
6. PETERSON(SWE)	MARCH-FORD	94 LAPS

Race: 95 laps of 2.08mile/3.35km circuit -198miles/318kms)
Fastest lap: Stewart,1min 13.66sec, 101.59mph/163.5kph
Pole position: Reutemann(ARG), Brabham-Ford, 1min 12.46sec 21 starters,11 class. finishers

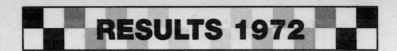

RESULTS 1972

ROUND 2/SOUTH AFRICAN GRAND PRIX
KYALAMI, 4 MARCH

1. HULME(NZ)	MCLAREN-FORD	1HR 45MIN 49.1SEC
2. E. FITTIPALDI(BRA)	LOTUS-FORD	1HR 46MIN 03.2SEC
3. REVSON(USA)	MCLAREN-FORD	1HR 46MIN 14.9SEC
4. ANDRETTI(USA)	FERRARI	1HR 46MIN 27.6SEC
5. PETERSON(SWE)	MARCH-FORD	1HR 46MIN 38.1SEC
6. G. HILL(GB)	BRABHAM-FORD	78 LAPS

Race: 79 laps of 2.55mile/4.1km (201.45miles/324kms)
Fastest lap: Hailwood(GB), Surtees-Ford, 1min 18.9sec,116.35mph/187.25kph
Pole position: Stewart(GB), Tyrrell-Ford, 1min 17.0sec 26 starters, 17 classified finishers

ROUND 3/SPANISH GRAND PRIX
JARAMA, MADRID, 1 MAY

1. E. FITTIPALDI(BRA)	LOTUS-FORD	2HR 3MIN 41.23SEC
2. ICKX(BEL)	FERRARI	2HR 4MIN 00.15SEC
3. REGAZZONI(SWISS)	FERRARI	89 LAPS
4. DE ADAMICH(ITA)	SURTEES-FORD	89 LAPS
5. REVSON(USA)	MCLAREN-FORD	89 LAPS
6. PACE(BRA)	MARCH-FORD	89 LAPS

Race: 90 laps of 2.12mile/3.4km (189miles/306kms)
Fastest lap: Ickx, 1min 21.01sec, 94.00mph/151.3kph
Pole position: Ickx, 1min 18.43sec 25 starters, 11 classified finishers

ROUND 4/MONACO GRAND PRIX
MONTE CARLO, 14 MAY

1. BELTOISE(FRA)	BRM	2HR 26MIN 54.7SEC
2. ICKX(BEL)	FERRARI	2HR 27MIN 32.9SEC
3. E.FITTIPALDI(BRA)	LOTUS-FORD	79 LAPS
4. STEWART(GB)	TYRRELL-FORD	78 LAPS
5. REDMAN(GB)	MCLAREN-FORD	77 LAPS
6. AMON(NZ)	MATRA-SIMCA	77 LAPS

Race: 80 laps of 1.95mile/3.15km (156 miles/ 252kms)
Fastest lap: Beltoise, 1min 40.0sec, 70.35mph/113.21kph
Pole position: E.Fittipaldi, 1min 21.4sec 26 starters,17 classified finishers

ROUND 5/BELGIAN GRAND PRIX
NIVELLES, BRUSSELS, 4 JUNE

1. E. FITTIPALDI(BRA)	LOTUS-FORD	1HR 44MIN 06.7SEC
2. CEVERT(FRA)	TYRRELL-FORD	1HR 44MIN 33.3SEC
3. HULME(NZ)	MCLAREN-FORD	1HR 45MIN 04.8SEC
4. HAILWOOD(GB)	SURTEES-FORD	1HR 45MIN 18.7SEC
5. PACE(BRA)	MARCH-FORD	84 LAPS
6. AMON(NZ)	MATRA-SIMCA	84 LAPS

Race: 85 laps of 2.32mile/3.72km (196.69miles/316.54kms)
Fastest lap: Amon, 1min 12.12sec, 115.38mph/185.68kph
Pole position: E.Fittipaldi, 1min 11.43sec 25 starters, 14 classified finishers

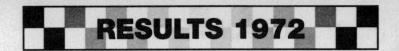

RESULTS 1972

ROUND 6/FRENCH GRAND PRIX

CLERMONT-FERRAND, 2 JULY

1. STEWART(GB)	TYRRELL-FORD	1HR 52MIN 21.5SEC
2. E. FITTIPALDI(BRA)	LOTUS-FORD	1HR 52MIN 49.2SEC
3. AMON(NZ)	MATRA-SIMCA	1HR 52MIN 53.4SEC
4. CEVERT(FRA)	TYRRELL-FORD	1HR 53MIN 10.8SEC
5. PETERSON(SWE)	MARCH-FORD	1HR 53MIN 18.3SEC
6. HAILWOOD(GB)	SURTEES-FORD	1HR 53MIN 57.6SEC

Race: 38 laps of 5.01mile/8.06km (190.19 miles/306.09kms)
Fastest lap: Amon, 2min 53.9sec, 103.61mph/166.75kph
Pole position: Amon, 2min 53.4sec 24 starters, 20 classified finishers

ROUND 7/BRITISH GRAND PRIX

BRANDS HATCH, 15 JULY

1.E. FITTIPALDI(BRA)	LOTUS-FORD	1HR 47MIN 50.2SEC
2.STEWART(GB)	TYRRELL-FORD	1HR 47MIN 54.3SEC
3.REVSON(USA)	MCLAREN-FORD	1HR 49MIN 02.7SEC
4.AMON(NZ)	MATRA-SIMCA	75 LAPS
5.HULME(NZ)	MCLAREN-FORD	75 LAPS
6.MERZARIO(ITA)	FERRARI	75 LAPS

Race: 76 laps of 2.65 mile/4.27km (201.4miles/324.14kms)
Fastest lap: Stewart, 1min 24.0sec, 113.57mph/182.78kph
Pole position: Ickx(BEL), Ferrari, 1min 22.2sec 26 starters, 13 classified finishers

ROUND 8/GERMAN GRAND PRIX

NURBURGRING, 30 JULY

1. ICKX(BEL)	FERRARI	1HR 42MIN 12.3SEC
2. REGAZZONI(SWISS)	FERRARI	1HR 43MIN 00.6SEC
3. PETERSON(SWE)	MARCH-FORD	1HR 43MIN 19.0SEC
4. GANLEY(NZ)	BRM	1HR 44MIN 32.5SEC
5. REDMAN(GB)	MCLAREN-FORD	1HR 44MIN 48.0SEC
6. G. HILL(GB)	BRABHAM-FORD	1HR 45MIN 11.9SEC

Race: 14 laps of 14.9mile/22.84km (198.66miles/319.69kms)
Fastest lap: Ickx, 7min 13.6sec,117.81mph/189.95kph
Pole position: Ickx, 7min 07.0sec 27 starters, 15 classified finishers

ROUND 9/AUSTRIAN GRAND PRIX

OSTERREICHRING, 13 AUGUST

1. E. FITTIPALDI(BRA)	LOTUS-FORD	1HR 29MIN 16.7SEC
2. HULME(NZ)	MCLAREN-FORD	1HR 29MIN 17.8SEC
3. REVSON(USA)	MCLAREN-FORD	1HR 29MIN 53.2SEC
4. HAILWOOD(GB)	SURTEES-FORD	1HR 30MIN 01.4SEC
5. AMON(NZ)	MATRA-SIMCA	1HR 30MIN 02.3SEC
6. GANLEY(NZ)	BRM	1HR 30MIN 17.8SEC

Race: 54 laps of 3.67mile/5.91km (198.18miles/319kms)
Fastest lap: Hulme, 1min 38.32sec, 134.48mph/216.43kph
Pole position: E. Fittipaldi (BRA), Lotus-Ford, 1min 35.97sec 25 starters, 14 class. finishers

RESULTS 1972

ROUND 10/ITALIAN GRAND PRIX
MONZA, 10 SEPTEMBER

1. E.FITTIPALDI(BRA)	LOTUS-FORD	1HR 29MIN 58.4SEC
2. HAILWOOD(GB)	SURTEES-FORD	1HR 30MIN 12.9SEC
3. HULME(NZ)	MCLAREN-FORD	1HR 30MIN 12.9SEC
4. REVSON(USA)	MCLAREN-FORD	1HR 30MIN 34.1SEC
5. G. HILL(GB)	BRABHAM-FORD	1HR 31MIN 04.0SEC
6. GETHIN(GB)	BRM	1HR 31MIN 20.3SEC

Race: 55 laps of 3.59mile/5.78km (197.45miles/318kms)
Fastest lap: Ickx(BEL), Ferrari, 1min 36.3sec, 134.14mph/215.89kph
Pole position: Ickx, 1min 35.65sec 25 starters, 13 classified finishers

ROUND 11/CANADIAN GRAND PRIX
MOSPORT PARK, ONTARIO, 24 SEPTEMBER

1. STEWART(GB)	TYRRELL-FORD	1HR 43MIN 16.9SEC
2. REVSON(USA)	MCLAREN-FORD	1HR 44MIN 05.1SEC
3. HULME(NZ)	MCLAREN-FORD	1HR 44MIN 11.5SEC
4. REUTEMANN(ARG)	BRABHAM-FORD	1HR 44MIN 17.6SEC
5. REGAZZONI(SWISS)	FERRARI	1HR 44MIN 23.9SEC
6. AMON(NZ)	MATRA-SIMCA	79 LAPS

Race: 80 laps of 2.46mile/3.96km (196.8miles/316.8kms)
Fastest lap: Stewart, 1min 15.7sec, 116.9mph/188.2kph
Pole position: Revson, 1min 13.6sec 24 starters, 13 classified finishers

ROUND 12/US GRAND PRIX
WATKINS GLEN, 8 OCTOBER

1.STEWART(GB)	TYRRELL-FORD	1HR 41MIN 43.35SEC
2.CEVERT(FRA)	TYRRELL-FORD	1HR 42MIN 22.78SEC
3.HULME(NZ)	MCLAREN-FORD	1HR 42MIN 28.08SEC
4.PETERSON(SWE)	MARCH-FORD	1HR 43MIN 07.87SEC
5.ICKX(BEL)	FERRARI	1HR 43MIN 08.47SEC
6.ANDRETTI(USA)	FERRARI	58 LAPS

Race: 59 laps of 3.38mile/5.44km (199.4miles/320.96kms)
Fastest lap: Stewart, 1min 41.64sec, 119.61mph/192.5kph
*Pole position:*Stewart, 1min 40.48sec 31 starters, 18 classified finishers

---

DRIVERS' WORLD CHAMPIONSHIP 1972

1. E. FITTIPALDI	61 points	5.	REVSON	23 points
2. STEWART	45 points	6.	CEVERT	15 points
3. HULME	39 points	6.	REGAZZONI	15 points
4. ICKX	27 points			

CONSTRUCTORS' WORLD CHAMPIONSHIP 1972

1. LOTUS-FORD	61 points	4.	FERRARI	33 points
2. TYRRELL-FORD	51 points	5.	SURTEES-FORD	33 points
3. MCLAREN-FORD	47 points	6.	MARCH-FORD	15 points

RESULTS 1973

1973 Jackie Stewart's fouth place at Monza clinched his third World Championship in five years. But triumph turned to tragedy at the final round of the series at Watkins Glen. Francois Cevert was killed in an horrific practice accident. The Tyrrell team withdrew from the race and, seven days later, Stewart announced his retirement from the sport. It was the end of an era. And Britain's young hopeful Roger Williamson lost his life during the season when his car caught fire during the Dutch Grand Prix. On a happier note, the year marked the arrival of the extrovert (some thought outrageous) Hesketh team - and one James Hunt - to the Championship chase. A young South African, Jody Scheckter, left an indelible mark on the Championship at Silverstone! There were 15 rounds. Brazil went wild as they hosted a round of the series for the first time - and their 1972 Champion did them proud. Emerson Fittipaldi led the race from start to finish. Sweden, too,was on the calendar for the first time but Scandinavia's favourite son, Ronnie Peterson, couldn't quite emulate his team-mate's 'home win'. He finished second! Best seven results from first eight races. Best six results from second seven. Points: 9-6-4-3-2-1 for first six places.

ROUND 1/ARGENTINE GRAND PRIX
BUENOS AIRES,28 JANUARY

1. E. FITTIPALDI(BRA)	LOTUS-FORD	1HR 56MIN 18.22SEC
2. CEVERT(FRA)	TYRRELL-FORD	1HR 56MIN 22.91SEC
3. STEWART(GB)	TYRRELL-FORD	1HR 56MIN 51.41SEC
4. ICKX(BEL)	FERRARI	1HR 57MIN 00.79SEC
5. HULME(NZ)	MCLAREN-FORD	95 LAPS
6. W. FITTIPALDI(BRA)	BRABHAM-FORD	95 LAPS

Race: 96 laps of 2.078mile/3.35km (199.56miles/322kms)
Fastest lap: E.Fittipaldi, 1min 11.22sec, 105.08mph/169.11kph
Pole position: Regazzoni (SWISS), BRM,1min 10.54sec 19 starters, 10 classified finishers

ROUND 2/BRAZILIAN GRAND PRIX
INTERLAGOS,SAO PAULO,11 FEBRUARY

1.E. FITTIPALDI(BRA)	LOTUS-FORD	1HR 43MIN 55.6SEC
2.STEWART(GB)	TYRRELL-FORD	1HR 44MIN 09.1SEC
3.HULME(NZ)	MCLAREN-FORD	1HR 45MIN 42.0SEC
4.MERZARIO(ITA)	FERRARI	39 LAPS
5.ICKX(BEL)	FERRARI	39 LAPS
6.REGAZZONI(SWISS)	BRM	39 LAPS

Race: 40 laps of 4.95mile/7.96km (197.84miles/318.4kms)
Fastest lap: E.Fittipaldi/Hulme 2min 35.0sec,114.88mph/184.88kph
Pole position: Peterson(SWE), Lotus-Ford,2min 30.5sec 20 starters,12 classified finishers

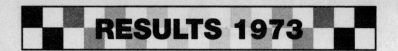

RESULTS 1973

ROUND 3/SOUTH AFRICAN GRAND PRIX
KYALAMI, 3 MARCH

1. STEWART(GB)	TYRRELL-FORD	1HR 43MIN 11.07SEC
2. REVSON(USA)	MCLAREN-FORD	1HR 43MIN 35.62SEC
3. E. FITTIPALDI(BRA)	LOTUS-FORD	78 LAPS
4. MERZARIO(ITA)	FERRARI	78 LAPS
5. HULME(NZ)	MCLAREN-FORD	77 LAPS
6. FOLLMER	SHADOW-FORD	

Race: 79 laps of 2.55mile/4.1km (201.45miles/324kms)
Fastest lap: E. Fittipaldi, 1min 17.10sec, 119.07mph/191.6kph
Pole position: Hulme, 1min 16.28sec 25 starters, 11 classified finishers

ROUND 4/SPANISH GRAND PRIX
MONTJUICH,BARCELONA, 29 APRIL

1.E. FITTIPALDI(BRA)	LOTUS-FORD	1HR 48MIN 18.7SEC
2.CEVERT(FRA)	TYRRELL-FORD	1HR 49MIN 01.4SEC
3.FOLLMER(USA)	SHADOW-FORD	1HR 49MIN 31.8SEC
4.REVSON(USA)	MCLAREN-FORD	74 LAPS
5.BELTOISE(BEL)	BRM	74 LAPS
6.HULME(NZ)	MCLAREN-FORD	74 LAPS

Race: 75 laps of 2.36mile/3.79km (177 miles/284.25kms)
Fastest lap: Peterson(SWE), Lotus-Ford,1min 23.8sec, 101.9mph/162.8kph
Pole position: Peterson, 1min 21.8sec 22 starters, 12 classified finishers

ROUND 5/BELGIAN GRAND PRIX
ZOLDER, 20 MAY

1.STEWART(GB)	TYRRELL-FORD	1HR 42MIN 13.43SEC
2.CEVERT(FRA)	TYRRELL-FORD	1HR 42MIN 45.27SEC
3.E. FITTIPALDI(BRA)	LOTUS-FORD	1HR 44MIN 16.22SEC
4.DE ADAMICH(ITA)	BRABHAM-FORD	69 LAPS
5.LAUDA(AUT)	BRM	69 LAPS
6.AMON(NZ)	TECNO	67 LAPS

Race: 70 laps of 2.62mile/4.22km (183.6miles/295.5kms)
Fastest lap: Cevert, 1min 25.42sec,110.51mph/177.85kph
Pole position: Peterson, Lotus-Ford,1min 22.46sec 23 starters, 11 classified finishers

ROUND 6/MONACO GRAND PRIX
MONTE CARLO, 3 JUNE

1. STEWART(GB)	TYRRELL-FORD	1HR 57MIN 44.3SEC
2. E. FITTIPALDI(BRA)	LOTUS-FORD	1HR 57MIN 45.6SEC
3. PETERSON(SWE)	LOTUS-FORD	77 LAPS
4. CEVERT(FRA)	TYRRELL-FORD	77 LAPS
5. REVSON(USA)	MCLAREN-FORD	76 LAPS
6. HULME(NZ)	MCLAREN-FORD	76 LAPS

Race: 78 laps of 2.04mile/3.28km (158.89miles/255.68kms)
Fastest lap: E. Fittipaldi, 1min 28.1sec, 83.23mph/133.95kph
Pole positition: Stewart, 1min 27.5sec 25 starters,11 classified finishers

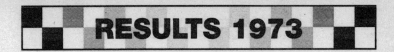
RESULTS 1973

ROUND 7/SWEDISH GRAND PRIX
ANDERSTORP, 17 JUNE

1. HULME(NZ)	MCLAREN-FORD	1HR 56MIN 46.1SEC
2. PETERSON(SWE)	LOTUS-FORD	1HR 56MIN 50.1SEC
3. CEVERT(FRA)	TYRRELL-FORD	1HR 57MIN 00.7SEC
4. REUTEMANN(ARG)	BRABHAM-FORD	1HR 57MIN 04.1SEC
5. STEWART(GB)	TYRRELL-FORD	1HR 57MIN 12.1SEC
6. ICKX(BEL)	FERRARI	79 LAPS

Race: 80 laps of 2.5mile/4.02km (200 miles/322kms)
Fastest lap: Hulme, 1min 26.15sec, 104.6mph/168.3kmh
Pole position: Peterson, 1min 23.81sec 20 starters, 14 classified finishers

ROUND 8/FRENCH GRAND PRIX
PAUL RICARD, 1 JULY

1. PETERSON(SWE)	LOTUS-FORD	1HR 41MIN 36.52SEC
2. CEVERT(FRA)	TYRRELL-FORD	1HR 42MIN 17.44SEC
3. REUTEMANN(ARG)	BRABHAM-FORD	1HR 42MIN 23.00SEC
4. STEWART(GB)	TYRRELL-FORD	1HR 42MIN 23.40SEC
5. ICKX(BEL)	FERRARI	1HR 42MIN 25.42SEC
6. HUNT(GB)	MARCH-FORD	1HR 42MIN 59.06SEC

Race: 54 laps of 3.61mile/5.81km (195miles/314kms)
Fastest lap: Hulme(NZ), McLaren-Ford,1min 50.99sec,117.5mph/189.1kph
Pole position: Stewart, 1min 48.37sec 25 starters, 16 classified finishers

ROUND 9/BRITISH GRAND PRIX
SILVERSTONE, 14 JULY

1. REVSON(USA)	MCLAREN-FORD	1HR 29MIN 18.5SEC
2. PETERSON(SWE)	LOTUS-FORD	1HR 29MIN 21.3SEC
3. HULME(NZ)	MCLAREN-FORD	1HR 29MIN 21.5SEC
4. HUNT(GB)	MARCH-FORD	1HR 29MIN 21.9SEC
5. CEVERT(FRA)	TYRRELL-FORD	1HR 29MIN 55.1SEC
6. REUTEMANN(ARG)	BRABHAM-FORD	1HR 30MIN 03.2SEC

Race: 67* laps of 2.93mile/4.71km (196miles/316kms)
Fastest lap: Hunt,1min 18.6sec, 134.06sec/215.75kph
Pole position: Peterson,1min 16.3sec 28 starters, 13 classified finishers
*Major incident at end of first lap. Race re-started

ROUND 10/DUTCH GRAND PRIX
ZANDVOORT, 29 JULY

1. STEWART(GB)	TYRRELL-FORD	1HR 39MIN 12.5SEC
2. CEVERT(FRA)	TYRRELL-FORD	1HR 39MIN 28.3SEC
3. HUNT(GB)	MARCH-FORD	1HR 40MIN 15.5SEC
4. REVSON(USA)	MCLAREN-FORD	1HR 40MIN 21.6SEC
5. BELTOISE(FRA)	BRM	1HR 40MIN 25.8SEC
6. VAN LENNEP(HOL)	WILLIAMS-FORD	70 LAPS

Race: 72 laps of 2.63mile/4.23km (189miles/305kms)
Fastest lap: Peterson(SWE), Lotus-Ford, 1min 20.31sec, 117.71mph/189.44kph.
Pole position: Peterson, 1min 19.47sec 23 starters, 11 classified finishers

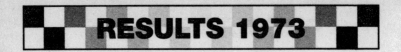

RESULTS 1973

ROUND 12/AUSTRIAN GRAND PRIX
OSTERREICHRING, 19 AUGUST

1. PETERSON(SWE)	LOTUS-FORD	1HR 28MIN 48.07SEC
2. STEWART(GB)	TYRRELL-FORD	1HR 28MIN 57.79SEC
3. PACE(BRA)	SURTEES-FORD	1HR 29MIN 35.42SEC
4. REUTEMANN(ARG)	BRABHAM-FORD	1HR 29MIN 36.69SEC
5. BELTOISE(FRA)	BRM	1HR 30MIN 10.38SEC
6. REGAZZONI(SWISS)	BRM	1HR 30MIN 21.01SEC

Race: 54 laps of 3.67mile/5.91km (198.3miles/319kms)
Fastest lap: Pace, 1min 37.29sec, 135.9mph/218.7kph
Pole position: E.Fittipaldi(BRA), Lotus-Ford,1min 34.98sec 23 starters, 10 class. finishers

ROUND 13/ITALIAN GRAND PRIX
MONZA, 9 SEPTEMBER

1. PETERSON(SWE)	LOTUS-FORD	1HR 29MIN 17.0SEC
2. E. FITTIPALDI(BRA)	LOTUS-FORD	1HR 29MIN 17.8SEC
3. REVSON(USA)	MCLAREN-FORD	1HR 29MIN 45.8SEC
4. STEWART(GB)	TYRRELL-FORD	1HR 29MIN 50.2SEC
5. CEVERT(FRA)	TYRRELL-FORD	1HR 30MIN 03.2SEC
6. REUTEMANN(ARG)	BRABHAM-FORD	1HR 30MIN 16.8SEC

Race: 55 laps of 3.59mile/5.78km (197miles/318kms)
Fastest lap: Stewart, 1min 35.3sec, 135.55mph/218.15kph
Pole position: Peterson, 1min 34.8sec 24 starters, 15 classified finishers

ROUND 14/CANADIAN GRAND PRIX
MOSPORT PARK,ONTARIO, 23 SEPTEMBER

1. REVSON(USA)	MCLAREN-FORD	1HR 59MIN 04.1SEC
2. E. FITTIPALDI(BRA)	LOTUS-FORD	1HR 59MIN 36.8SEC
3. OLIVER(GB)	SHADOW-FORD	1HR 59MIN 38.6SEC
4. BELTOISE(FRA)	BRM	1HR 59MIN 40.6SEC
5. STEWART(GB)	TYRRELL-FORD	79 LAPS
6. GANLEY(NZ)	ISO-FORD	79 LAPS

Race: 80 laps of 2.46mile/3.96km (196.7miles/317kms)
Fastest lap: E.Fittipaldi, 1min 15.5sec, 117.26mph/188.71kph
Pole position: Peterson(SWE), Lotus-Ford, 1min 13.7sec 26 starters,18 class. finishers.

ROUND 15/US GRAND PRIX
WATKINS GLEN, 7 OCTOBER

1. PETERSON(SWE)	LOTUS-FORD	1HR 41MIN 15.8SEC
2. HUNT(GB)	MARCH-FORD	1HR 41MIN 16.5SEC
3. REUTEMANN(ARG)	BRABHAM-FORD	1HR 41MIN 38.7SEC
4. HULME(NZ)	MCLAREN-FORD	1HR 42MIN 06.0SEC
5. REVSON(USA)	MCLAREN-FORD	1HR 42MIN 36.2SEC
6. E. FITTIPALDI(BRA)	LOTUS-FORD	1HR 43MIN 03.7SEC

Race: 59 laps of 3.38mile/5.44km (199miles/321kms)
Fastest lap: Hunt, 1min 41.65sec,119.6mph/192.47kph
Pole position: Peterson,1min 39.66sec 25 starters, 16 classified finishers

RESULTS 1973/4

DRIVERS' WORLD CHAMPIONSHIP 1973

1.	STEWART	71 points	4.	CEVERT	47 points
2.	E.FITTIPALDI	55 points	5.	REVSON	38 points
3.	PETERSON	52 points	6.	HULME	26 points

CONSTRUCTORS' WORLD CHAMPIONSHIP 1973

1.	LOTUS-FORD	92 points	5.	MARCH-FORD	14 points
2.	TYRRELL-FORD	82 points	6.	BRM	12 points
3.	MCLAREN-FORD	58 points	6.	FERRARI	12 points
4.	BRABHAM-FORD	22 points			

1974 It was all systems change for the season. But Emerson Fittipaldi joined McLaren and won his second world title. Ken Tyrrell had employed South-African whizz-kid Jody Scheckter and France's new hope, Patrick Depailler. After Stewart's retirement, Sweden's Ronnie Peterson's Lotus carried the coveted Number 1. Peter Revson lost his life in testing his Shadow for the South African Grand Prix. It was a wicked waste of a delightful, talented driver. And Austria's young hopeful, Helmuth Koinigg, died in the last race of the year at Watkins Glen.Veteran Graham Hill set up his own team of Lolas. And Hesketh Racing entered their own car, with startling effect.Penske and Parnelli-Jones, American teams, entered the arena, late in the season. Carlos Reutemann became the first Argentinian driver since Fangio to win a Grand Prix. There were 15 Grands Prix. Best seven out of first eight and best six out of seven second. Points: 9-6-4-3-2-1 for first six places.

ROUND 1/ARGENTINE GRAND PRIX

BUENOS AIRES,13 JANUARY

1. HULME(NZ)	MCLAREN-FORD	1HR 41MIN 02.02SEC
2. LAUDA(AUT)	FERRARI	1HR 41MIN 11.03SEC
3. REGAZZONI(ITA)	FERRARI	1HR 41MIN 22.04SEC
4. HAILWOOD(GB)	MCLAREN-FORD	1HR 41MIN 33.08SEC
5. BELTOISE(FRA)	BRM	1HR 41MIN 53.9SEC
6. DEPAILLER(FRA)	TYRRELL-FORD	1HR 42MIN 54.5SEC

Race: 53 laps 0f 3.71mile/5.97km (196.52miles/316.30kms)
Fastest lap: Regazzoni, 1min 52.01sec, 119.09mph/191.66kph
Pole position: Peterson, 1min 50.78sec 25 starters, 13 classified finishers

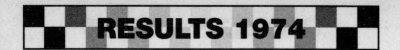

RESULTS 1974

ROUND 2/BRAZILIAN GRAND PRIX
INTERLAGOS,SAO PAULO, 27 JANUARY

1. E. FITTIPALDI(BRA)	MCLAREN-FORD	1HR 24MIN 37.1SEC
2. REGAZZONI(ITA)	FERRARI	1HR 24MIN 50.6SEC
3. ICKX(BEL)	LOTUS-FORD	31 LAPS
4. PACE(BRA)	SURTEES-FORD	31 LAPS
5. HAILWOOD(GB)	MCLAREN-FORD	31 LAPS
6. PETERSON(SWE)	LOTUS-FORD	31 LAPS

Race: 32 laps of 4.95mile/7.96km (158.27miles/254.72kms)
Fastest lap: Regazzoni, 2min 36.1sec,114.0mph/186.63kph
Pole position: E. Fittipaldi(BRA), 2min 32.97sec 25 starters, 17 classified finishers

ROUND 3/SOUTH AFRICAN GRAND PRIX
KYALAMI,30 MARCH

1. REUTEMANN(ARG)	BRABHAM-FORD	1HR 42MIN 40.96SEC
2. BELTOISE(FRA)	BRM	1HR 43MIN 14.09SEC
3. HAILWOOD(GB)	MCLAREN-FORD	1HR 43MIN 32.01SEC
4. DEPAILLER(FRA)	TYRRELL-FORD	1HR 43MIN 25.02SEC
5. STUCK(GER)	MARCH-FORD	1HR 43MIN 27.02SEC
6. MERZARIO(ITA)	WILLIAMS-FORD	1HR 43MIN 37.0SEC

Race: 78 laps of 2.55mile/4.1km (198.9miles/320.11kms)
Fastest lap: Reutemann, 1min 18.02 sec,117.46mph/189.03kph
Pole position: Lauda(AUT), Ferrari, 1min 16.58sec 27 starters, 19 classified finishers

ROUND 4/SPANISH GRAND PRIX
JARAMA,MADRID, 28 APRIL

1. LAUDA(AUT)	FERRARI	2HR 00MIN 29.6SEC
2. REGAZZONI(SWISS)	FERRARI	2HR 01MIN 05.2SEC
3. E. FITTIPALDI(BRA)	MCLAREN-FORD	83 LAPS
4. STUCK(GER)	MARCH-FORD	82 LAPS
5. J. SCHECKTER(SA)	TYRRELL-FORD	82 LAPS
6. HULME(NZ)	MCLAREN-FORD	82 LAPS

Race: 84 laps of 2.12mile/3.4km (178.08miles/285.6kms)
Fastest lap: Lauda, 1min 20.83sec, 94.21mph/151.62kph
Pole position: Lauda, 1min 18.44sec 25 starters, 14 classified finishers

ROUND 5/BELGIAN GRAND PRIX
NIVELLES, BRUSSELS, 12 MAY

1 E.FITTIPALDI(BRA)	MCLAREN-FORD	1HR 44MIN 20.6SEC
2. LAUDA(AUT)	FERRARI	1HR 44MIN 20.9SEC
3. J.SCHECKTER(SA)	TYRRELL-FORD	1HR 45MIN 06.2SEC
4. REGAZZONI(SWISS)	FERRARI	1HR 45MIN 12.6SEC
5. BELTOISE(FRA)	BRM	1HR 45MIN 28.6SEC
6. HULME(NZ)	MCLAREN-FORD	1HR 45MIN 31.1SEC

Race: 85 laps of 2.31mile/3.72km (196.35miles/316.2kms)
Fastest lap: Hulme, 1min 11.31sec, 116.82mph/188.00kph
Pole position: Regazzoni, 1min 09.82sec 31 starters, 18 classified finishers

RESULTS 1974

ROUND 6/MONACO GRAND PRIX
MONTE CARLO,26 MAY

1. PETERSON(SWE)	LOTUS-FORD	1HR 58MIN 03.7SEC
2. J. SCHECKTER(SA)	TYRRELL-FORD	1HR 58MIN 32.5SEC
3, JARIER(FRA)	SHADOW-FORD	1HR 58MIN 52.6SEC
4. REGAZZONI(SWISS)	FERRARI	1HR 59MIN 06.8SEC
5. E. FITTIPALDI(BRA)	MCLAREN-FORD	77 LAPS
6. WATSON(GB)	BRABHAM-FORD	77 LAPS

Race: 78 laps of 2.04mile/3.28km (159.12miles/255.84kms)
Fastest lap: Peterson, 1min 27.9sec, 83.42mph/134.25kph
Pole position: Lauda(AUT), Ferrari, 1min 26.3sec 25 starters, 9 classified finishers

ROUND 7/SWEDEN
ANDERSTORP, 9 JUNE

1. J. SCHECKTER(SA)	TYRRELL-FORD	1HR 58MIN 31.4SEC
2. DEPAILLER(FRA)	TYRRELL-FORD	1HR 58MIN 31.8SEC
3. HUNT(GB)	HESKETH-FORD	1HR 58MIN 34.7SEC
4. E. FITTIPALDI(BRA)	MCLAREN-FORD	1HR 59MIN 24.9SEC
5. JARIER(FRA)	SHADOW-FORD	1HR 59MIN 47.8SEC
6. G. HILL(GB)	LOLA-FORD	79 LAPS

Race: 80 laps of 2.5mile/4.02km (200miles/321.6kms)
Fastest lap: Depailler, 1min 27.26sec, 103.00mpn/165.76kph
Pole position: Depailler, 1min 24.76sec 25 starters, 11 classified finishers

ROUND 8/DUTCH GRAND PRIX
ZANDVOORT, 23 JUNE

1. LAUDA(AUT)	FERRARI	1HR 43MIN 00.4SEC
2. REGAZZONI(SWISS)	FERRARI	1HR 43MIN 08.6SEC
3. E. FITTIPALDI(BRA)	MCLAREN-FORD	1HR 43MIN 30.6SEC
4. HAILWOOD(GB)	MCLAREN-FORD	1HR 43MIN 31.6SEC
5. J. SCHECKTER(SA)	TYRRELL-FORD	1HR 43MIN 34.6SEC
6. DEPAILLER(FRA)	TYRRELL-FORD	1HR 43MIN 51.9SEC

Race: 75 laps of 2.63mile/4.23km (197.25miles/317.25kms)
Fastest lap: Peterson(SWE)Lotus-Ford, 1min 21.44sec, 116.08mph/186.9kph
Pole position: Lauda, 1min 18.31sec 25 starters/12 classified finishers

ROUND 9/FRENCH GRAND PRIX
DIJON-PRENOIS, 7 JULY

1. PETERSON(SWE)	LOTUS-FORD	1HR 21MIN 55.0SEC
2. LAUDA(AUT)	FERRARI	1HR 22MIN 15.4SEC
3. REGAZZONI(SWISS)	FERRARI	1HR 22MIN 22.9SEC
4. J. SCHECKTER(SA)	TYRRELL-FORD	1HR 22MIN 31.1SEC
5. ICKX(BEL)	LOTUS-FORD	1HR 22MIN 32.6SEC
6. HULME(NZ)	MCLAREN-FORD	1HR 22MIN 33.2SEC

Race: 80 laps of 2.04mile/3.29km (163.2miles/263.2kms)
Fastest lap: Scheckter, 1min 00.0sec, 122.62mph/197.34kph
Pole position: Lauda, 0min 58.79sec 22 starters, 16 classified finishers

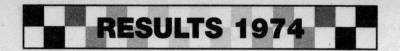

RESULTS 1974

ROUND 10/BRITISH GRAND PRIX
BRANDS HATCH, 20 JULY

1. J. SCHECKTER(SA)	TYRRELL-FORD	1HR 43MIN 02.2SEC
2. E. FITTIPALDI(BRA)	MCLAREN-FORD	1HR 43MIN 17.5SEC
3. ICKX(BEL)	LOTUS-FORD	1HR 44MIN 03.7SEC
4. REGAZZONI(SWISS)	FERRARI	1HR 44MIN 09.4SEC
5. LAUDA(AUT)	FERRARI	74 LAPS
6. REUTEMANN(ARG)	BRABHAM-FORD	74 LAPS

Race: 75 laps of 2.65mile-4.27km (198.75miles/320.25kms)
Fastest lap: Lauda, 1min 21.1sec, 117.63mph, 189.31kph
Pole position: Lauda, 1min 19.7sec 25 starters, 14 classified finishers

ROUND 11/GERMAN GRAND PRIX
NURBURGRING, 4 AUGUST

1. REGAZZONI(SWISS)	FERRARI	1HR 41MIN 35.0SEC
2. J. SCHECKTER(SA)	TYRRELL-FORD	1HR 42MIN 25.7SEC
3. REUTEMANN(ARG)	BRABHAM-FORD	1HR 42MIN 58.3SEC
4. PETERSON(SWE)	LOTUS-FORD	1HR 42MIN 59.2SEC
5. ICKX(BEL)	LOTUS-FORD	1HR 43MIN 00.0SEC
6. PRYCE(GB)	SHADOW-FORD	1HR 43MIN 53.1SEC

Race: 14 laps of 14.19mile/ 22.84km (198.66 miles/319.76kms)
Fastest lap: Scheckter, 7min 11.1sec,118.49mph/190.69kph
Pole position: Lauda(AUT),Ferrari, 7min 00.8sec 26 starters, 14 classified finishers

ROUND 12/AUSTRIAN GRAND PRIX
OSTERREICHRING, 18 AUGUST

1. REUTEMANN(ARG)	BRABHAM-FORD	1HR 28MIN 44.7SEC
2. HULME(NZ)	MCLAREN-FORD	1HR 29MIN 27.6SEC
3. HUNT(GB)	HESKETH-FORD	1HR 29MIN 46.3SEC
4. WATSON(GB)	BRABHAM-FORD	1HR 29MIN 54.1SEC
5. REGAZZONI(SWISS)	FERRARI	1HR 29MIN 57.8SEC
6 V. BRAMBILLA(ITA)	MARCH-FORD	1HR 29MIN 58.5SEC

Race: 54 laps of 3.67mile/5.91km (198.18miles/319.14kms)
Fastest lap: Regazzoni, 1min 37.22sec, 136.00mph/218.88kph
Pole position: Lauda(AUT),Ferrari,1min 35.4sec 25 starters, 10 classified finishers

ROUND 13 ITALIAN GRAND PRIX
MONZA, 8 SEPTEMBER

1. PETERSON(SWE)	LOTUS-FORD	1HR 22MIN 56.6SEC
2. E. FITTIPALDI(BRA)	MCLAREN-FORD	1HR 22MIN 57.4SEC
3. J. SCHECKTER(SA)	TYRRELL-FORD	1HR 23MIN 21.3SEC
4. MERZARIO(ITA)	WILLIAMS-FORD	1HR 24MIN 24.3SEC
5. PACE(BRA)	BRABHAM-FORD	51 LAPS
6. HULME(NZ)	MCLAREN-FORD	51 LAPS

Race: 52 laps of 3.59mile/5.78km (186.68miles/300.56kms)
Fastest lap: Pace, 1min 34.2sec,137.26mph/220.89kph
Pole position: Lauda(AUT), Ferrari, 1min 33.16sec 25 starters, 11 classified finishers

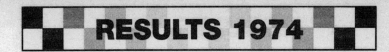

RESULTS 1974

ROUND 14/CANADIAN GRAND PRIX

MOSPORT PARK,ONTARIO, 22 SEPTEMBER

1. E. FITTIPALDI(BRA)	MCLAREN-FORD	1HR 40MIN 26.1SEC
2. REGAZZONI(SWISS)	FERRARI	1HR 40MIN 39.2SEC
3. PETERSON(SWE)	LOTUS-FORD	1HR 40MIN 40.6SEC
4. HUNT(GB)	HESKETH-FORD	1HR 40MIN 41.8SEC
5. DEPAILLER(FRA)	TYRRELL-FORD	1HR 41MIN 21.5SEC
6. HULME(NZ)	MCLAREN-FORD	79 LAPS

Race: 80 laps of 2.46mile/3.96km (196.64miles/316.48kms)
Fastest lap: Lauda(AUT), Ferrari, 1min 13.66sec, 120.18mph/193.41kph
Pole position: E.Fittipaldi, 1min 13.19sec 26 starters, 16 classified finishers

ROUND 15/US GRAND PRIX

WATKINS GLEN, 6 OCTOBER

1. REUTEMANN(ARG)	BRABHAM-FORD	1HR 40MIN 21.4SEC
2. PACE(BRA)	BRABHAM-FORD	1HR 40MIN 32.2SEC
3. HUNT(GB)	HESKETH-FORD	1HR 41MIN 31.8SEC
4. E. FITTIPALDI(BRA)	MCLAREN-FORD	1HR 41MIN 39.2SEC
5. WATSON(GB)	BRABHAM-FORD	1HR 41MIN 47.2SEC
6. DEPAILLER(FRA)	TYRRELL-FORD	1HR 41MIN 51.5SEC

Race: 59 laps of 3.38mile/5.44km (199.19miles/320.55kms)
Fastest lap: Pace, 1min 40.61sec,120.84mph/194.47kph
Pole position: Reutemann, 1min 38.97sec 27 starters,12 classified finishers*
*Helmuth Koinigg(AUT), Surtees, was killed during the race

DRIVERS' WORLD CHAMPIONSHIP 1974

1. E. FITTIPALDI 55 *points*	4. LAUDA 38 *points*
2. REGAZZONI 52 *points*	5. PETERSON 35 *points*
3. J.SCHECKTER 45 *points*	6. REUTEMANN 32 *points*

CONSTRUCTORS' WORLD CHAMPIONSHIP 1974

1. MCLAREN-FORD	73 *points*	4. LOTUS-FORD	42 *points*
2. FERRARI	65 *points*	5. BRABHAM-FORD	35 *points*
3. TYRRELL-FORD	52 *points*	6. HESKETH-FORD	15 *points*

1975 Tragedy struck the Grand Prix world both on and off the track. Former double World Champion Graham Hill, one of the most charismatic drivers to grace the sport, his young British protégé, Tony Brise, and four other members of the fledgling Hill team all perished in a light aircraft crash in November. Five spectators were killed when Rolf Stommelen's car flew into the crowd in Spain. One marshall was killed and another seriously injured when Mark Donohue's Penske somersaulted the barriers during practice for the Austrian Grand Prix. The likeable American succumbed to head injuries three days later. Niki Lauda won his first world title and Denny Hulme retired from Formula 1 at the end of the 1974 season. The Canadian Grand Prix was dropped from the calendar. There were 14 rounds, best six from seven races in each half of the season scored. Points: 9-6-4-3-2-1. Half points were awarded in Spain, when the race was stopped after Stommelen's accident and, in Austria when it was curtailed due to a violent rainstorm.

ROUND 1/ARGENTINE GRAND PRIX
BUENOS AIRES, 12 JANUARY

1.E. FITTIPALDI(BRA)	MCLAREN-FORD	1HR 39MIN 26.29SEC
2.HUNT(GB)	HESKETH-FORD	1HR 39MIN 32.20SEC
3.REUTEMANN(ARG)	BRABHAM-FORD	1HR 39MIN 43.35SEC
4.REGAZZONI(SWISS)	FERRARI	1HR 40MIN 02.08SEC
5.DEPAILLER(FRA)	TYRRELL-FORD	1HR 40MIN 20.54SEC
6.LAUDA(AUT)	FERRARI	1HR 40MIN 45.94SEC

Race: 53 laps of 3.71mile/5.97km (196.1miles/316.41kms)
Fastest lap: Hunt, 1min 50.91sec,120.37mph/193.72kph
Pole position: Jarier(FRA), Shadow-Ford, 1min 49.21sec* 21 starters, 14 classified finishers
*Jarier's transmission broke on the warm-up lap, so he was unable to take the start

ROUND 2/BRAZILIAN GRAND PRIX
INTERLAGOS, SAO PAULO, 26 JANUARY

1.PACE(BRA)	BRABHAM-FORD	1HR 44MIN 41.17SEC
2.E. FITTIPALDI(BRA)	MCLAREN-FORD	1HR 44MIN 46.96SEC
3.MASS(GER)	MCLAREN-FORD	1HR 45MIN 17.83SEC
4.REGAZZONI(SWISS)	FERRARI	1HR 45MIN 24.45SEC
5.LAUDA(AUT)	FERRARI	1HR 45MIN 43.05SEC
6.HUNT(GB)	HESKETH-FORD	1HR 45MIN 46.29SEC

Race: 40 laps of 4.95mile/7.96km (198 miles/318.4kms)
Fastest lap: Jarier(FRA), Shadow-Ford, 2min 34.16sec, 115.50mph/185.88kph
Pole position: Jarier, 2min 29.88sec 23 starters, 15 classified finishers

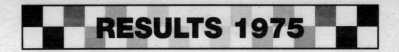
RESULTS 1975

ROUND 3/SOUTH AFRICAN GRAND PRIX
KYALAMI, 1 MARCH

1.J. SCHEKTER(SA)	TYRRELL-FORD	1HR 43MIN 16.90SEC
2.REUTEMANN(ARG)	BRABHAM-FORD	1HR 43MIN 20.64SEC
3.DEPAILLER(FRA)	TYRRELL-FORD	1HR 43MIN 33.82SEC
4.PACE(BRA)	BRABHAM-FORD	1HR 43MIN 34.21SEC
5.LAUDA(AUT)	FERRARI	1HR 43MIN 45.54SEC
6.MASS(GER)	MCLAREN-FORD	1HR 44MIN 20.24SEC

Race: 78 laps of 2.55/4.1km (198.9miles/320.11kms)
Fastest lap: Pace, 1min 17.20sec,118.92mph/191.38kph
Pole position: Pace, 1min 16.41sec 27 starters, 17 classified finishers

ROUND 4/SPANISH GRAND PRIX
MONTJUICH,BARCELONA, 27 APRIL

1. MASS(GER)	MCLAREN-FORD	29LAPS 42MIN 53.7SEC
2. ICKX(BEL)	LOTUS-FORD	29LAPS 42MIN 54.8SEC
3. REUTEMANN(ARG)	BRABHAM-FORD	28LAPS 42MIN 37.5SEC
4. JARIER(FRA)	SHADOW-FORD	28LAPS 43MIN 44.8SEC
5. BRAMBILLA(ITA)	MARCH-FORD	28LAPS
6. LELLA LOMBARDI(ITA)	MARCH-FORD	27LAPS

Race: *29 laps of 2.36mile/3.79km (68.44miles/109.91kms)
Fastest lap: Andretti(USA) Parnelli-Ford, 1min 25.1sec, 99.64mph/160.36kph
Pole position: Lauda(AUT), Ferrari, 1min 23.5sec 25 starters, 8 classified finishers
*Race halted due to serious accident

ROUND 5/MONACO GRAND PRIX
MONTE CARLO, 11 MAY

1.LAUDA(AUT)	FERRARI	2HR 1MIN 21.31SEC
2.E. FITTIPALDI(BRA)	MCLAREN-FORD	2HR 1MIN 24.09SEC
3.PACE(BRA	BRABHAM-FORD	2HR 1MIN 39.12SEC
4.PETERSON(SWE)	LOTUS-FORD	2HR 1MIN 59.76SEC
5.DEPAILLER(FRA)	TYRRELL-FORD	2HR 2MIN 02.17SEC
6.MASS(GER)	MCLAREN-FORD	2HR 2MIN 03.38SEC

Race: 75 laps of 2.04mile/3.28km (153 miles/246kms)
Fastest lap: Depailler, 1min 28.67sec, 82.7mph/113.1kph
Pole position: Lauda, 1min 26.4sec 18 starters, 9 classified finishers

ROUND 6/BELGIAN GRAND PRIX
ZOLDER, 25 MAY

1. LAUDA(AUT)	FERRARI	1HR 43MIN 53.98SEC
2. J. SCHECKTER(SA)	TYRRELL-FORD	1HR 44MIN 13.20SEC
3. REUTEMANN(ARG)	BRABHAM-FORD	1HR 44MIN 35.80SEC
4. DEPAILLER(FRA)	TYRRELL-FORD	1HR 44MIN 54.06SEC
5. REGAZZONI(SWISS)	FERRARI	1HR 44MIN 57.84SEC
6. PRYCE(GB)	SHADOW-FORD	1HR 45MIN 22.43SEC

Race: 70 laps of 2.65mile/4.26km (185.5miles/298.2kms)
Fastest lap: Regazzoni, 1min 26,76sec,109.88mph/176.85kph
Pole position: Lauda, 1min 25.43sec 24 starters, 12 classified finishers

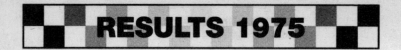

RESULTS 1975

ROUND 7/SWEDISH GRAND PRIX

ANDERSTORP, 8 JUNE

1. LAUDA(AUT)	FERRARI	1HR 59MIN 18.32SEC
2. REUTEMANN(ARG)	BRABHAM-FORD	1HR 59MIN 24.61SEC
3. REGAZZONI(SWISS)	FERRARI	1HR 59MIN 47.41SEC
4. ANDRETTI(USA)	PARNELLI-FORD	2HR 00MIN 02.69SEC
5. DONOHUE(USA)	PENSKE-FORD	2HR 00MIN 49.08SEC
6. BRISE(GB)	HILL-FORD	79 LAPS

Race: 80 laps of 2.5mile/4.02km (200miles/321.6kms)
Fastest lap: Lauda, 1min 28.27sec, 101.83mph/163.88kph
Pole position: Brambilla(ITA), March-Ford, 1min 24.63sec 26 starters, 17 class. finishers

ROUND 8/ DUTCH GRAND PRIX

ZANDVOORT, 22 JUNE

1. HUNT(GB)	HESKETH-FORD	1HR 46MIN 57.40SEC
2. LAUDA(AUT)	FERRARI	1HR 46MIN 58.46SEC
3. REGAZZONI(SWISS)	FERRARI	1HR 47MIN 52.46SEC
4. REUTEMANN(ARG)	BRABHAM-FORD	74 LAPS
5. PACE(BRA)	BRABHAM-FORD	74 LAPS
6. PRYCE(GB)	SHADOW-FORD	74 LAPS

Race: 75 laps of 2.63mile/4.23km (197.25miles/317.25kms)
Fastest lap: Lauda, 1min 21.54sec, 115.93mph/186.58kph
Pole position: Lauda, 1min 20.29sec 24 starters, 16 classified finishers

ROUND 9/FRENCH GRAND PRIX

PAUL RICARD, 6 JULY

1. LAUDA(AUT)	FERRARI	1HR 40MIN 18.84SEC
2. HUNT(GB)	HESKETH-FORD	1HR 40MIN 20.43SEC
3. MASS(GER)	MCLAREN-FORD	1HR 40MIN 21.15SEC
4. E. FITTIPALDI(BRA)	MCLAREN-FORD	1HR 40MIN 58.61SEC
5. ANDRETTI(USA)	PARNELLI-FORD	1HR 41MIN 20.92SEC
6. DEPAILLER(FRA)	TYRRELL-FORD	1HR 41MIN 26.24SEC

Race: 54 laps of 3.61mile/5.81km (194.94miles/313.74kms)
Fastest lap: Mass, 1min 50.6sec, 117.51mph/189.11kph
Pole position: Lauda, 1min 47.82sec 25 starters, 18 classified finishers

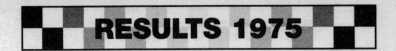

RESULTS 1975

ROUND 10/BRITISH GRAND PRIX

SILVERSTONE, 19 JULY

1. E. FITTIPALDI(BRA)	MCLAREN-FORD	1HR 22MIN 5.0SEC
2. PACE(BRA)	BRABHAM-FORD	55LAPS-ACCIDENT
3. J. SCHECKTER(SA)	TYRRELL-FORD	55LAPS-ACCIDENT
4. HUNT(GB)	HESKETH-FORD	55LAPS-ACCIDENT
5. DONOHUE(USA)	PENSKE-FORD	55LAPS-ACCIDENT
6. V. BRAMBILLA(ITA)	MARCH-FORD	55LAPS

Race: *56 laps of 2.93 mile/4.72km (164.08miles/264.32kms)*
Fastest lap: Regazzon(ITA), Ferrari, 1min 20.9sec,130.47mph/209.97kph
Pole position: Pryce(GB), Shadow-Ford, 1min 19.36sec 26 starters, 19 class. finishers*
12 of these crashed out but were classifed, including the 2nd, 3rd,4th and 5th place men
*Race halted after 56 of schedule 67 laps due to hail storm

ROUND 11/GERMAN GRAND PRIX

NURBURGRING, 3 AUGUST

1. REUTEMANN(ARG)	BRABHAM-FORD	1HR 41MIN 14.1SEC
2. LAFFITE(FRA)	WILLIAMS-FORD	1HR 42MIN 51.8SEC
3. LAUDA(AUT)	FERRARI	1HR 43MIN 37.4SEC
4. PRYCE(GB)	SHADOW-FORD	1HR 44MIN 45.5SEC
5. JONES(AUS)	HILL-FORD	1HR 45MIN 04.4SEC
6. VAN LENNEP(HOL)	ENSIGN-FORD	1HR 46MIN 19.6SEC

Race: 14 laps of 14.19mile/22.84km (198.66miles/319.76kms)
Fastest lap: Regazzoni(SWISS), Ferrari, 7min 6.4sec, 119.79mph/192.79kph
Pole position: Lauda, 6min 58.6sec 24 starters, 10 classified finshers

ROUND 12/AUSTRIAN GRAND PRIX

OSTERREICHRING, 17 AUGUST

1. V. BRAMBILLA(ITA)	MARCH-FORD	57MIN 56.69SEC
2. HUNT(GB)	HESKETH-FORD	58MIN 23.72SEC
3. PRYCE(GB)	SHADOW-FORD	58MIN 31.54SEC
4. MASS(GER)	MCLAREN-FORD	59MIN 09.35SEC
5. PETERSON(SWE)	LOTUS-FORD	59MIN 20.02SEC
6. LAUDA(AUT	FERRARI	59MIN 26.97SEC

Race: *29 laps of 3.67mile/5.91kms (106.43miles/171.39kms)*
Fastest lap: Brambilla, 1min 53.90sec, 116.10mph/186.63kph
Pole position: Lauda, 1min 34.85sec 26 starters, 17 classified finishers
*Race curtailed from 54 to 29 laps due to torrential rain

RESULTS 1975/6

ROUND 13/ITALIAN GRAND PRIX
MONZA, 7 SEPTEMBER

1. REGAZZONI(SWISS)	FERRARI	1HR 22MIN 42.6SEC
2. E. FITTIPALDI(BRA)	MCLAREN-FORD	1HR 22MIN 59.2SEC
3. LAUDA(AUT)	FERRARI	1HR 23MIN 05.8SEC
4. REUTEMANN(ARG)	BRABHAM-FORD	1HR 23MIN 37.7SEC
5. HUNT(GB)	HESKETH-FORD	1HR 23MIN 39.7SEC
6. PRYCE(GB)	SHADOW-FORD	1HR 23MIN 58.5SEC

Race: 52 laps of 3.59mile/5.78km (186.68miles/ 3.00.56kms)
Fastest lap: Regazzoni, 1min 33.1sec, 138.88mph/223.50kph
Pole position: Lauda, 1min 32.24sec 26 starters, 14 classified finishers

ROUND 14/US GRAND PRIX
WATKINS GLEN, 5 OCTOBER

1. LAUDA(AUT)	FERRARI	1HR 42MIN 58.18SEC
2. E. FITTIPALDI(BRA)	MCLAREN-FORD	1HR 43MIN 03.19SEC
3. MASS(GER)	MCLAREN-FORD	1HR 43MIN 45.81SEC
4. HUNT(GB)	HESKETH-FORD	1HR 43MIN 47.65SEC
5. PETERSON(SWE)	LOTUS-FORD	1HR 43MIN 48.16SEC
6. J. SCHECKTER(SA)	TYRRELL-FORD	1HR 43MIN 48.49SEC

Race: 59 laps of 3.38mile/5.44km (199.42miles/320.96kms)
Fastest lap: E. Fittipaldi, 1min 43.37sec, 117.60mph-189.27kph
Pole position: Lauda, 1min 42.00sec 22 starters, 11 classified finishers

DRIVERS' WORLD CHAMPIONSHIP 1975

1. LAUDA	64.5 points	4. HUNT	33 points
2. E.FITTIPALDI	45 points	5. REGAZZONI	25 points
3. REUTEMANN	37 points	6. PACE	24 points

CONSTRUCTORS' WORLD CHAMPIONSHIP 1975

1. FERRARI	72.5 points	4. HESKETH-FORD	33 points
2. BRABHAM-FORD	54 points	5. TYRRELL-FORD	25 points
3. MCLAREN-FORD	53 points	6. SHADOW-FORD	9.5 points

1976 The year will be engraved on the memories of motor sport fans throughout the world for many reasons. Niki Lauda cheated death after his horrendous Nurburing accident. James Hunt joined McLaren in the place of Emerson Fittipaldi who left to start his own team with brother Wilson. Hunt won the title by one point from Lauda. Mario Andretti joined Lotus and a disgruntled Peterson joined March. The year was fraught with controversy and argument both on and off the track, with protest and counter-protest making the headlines and detracting from some fine racing. The Japanese Grand Prix rounded off the calendar for the first time and an early-season race at picturesque Long Beach was introduced. There were 16 rounds. Best seven results from first eight, best seven from second eight. Points: 9-6-4-3-2-1.

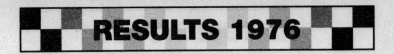

RESULTS 1976

ROUND 1/BRAZILIAN GRAND PRIX
INTERLAGOS/SAO PAULO, 25 JANUARY

1. LAUDA(AUT)	FERRARI	1HR 45MIN 16.78SEC
2. DEPAILLER(FRA)	TYRRELL-FORD	1HR 45MIN 38.25SEC
3. PRYCE(GB)	SHADOW-FORD	1HR 45MIN 40.62SEC
4. STUCK(GER	MARCH-FORD	1HR 46MIN 44.95SEC
5. J. SCHECKTER(SA)	TYRRELL-FORD	1HR 47MIN 13.24SEC
6. MASS(GER)	MCLAREN-FORD	1HR 47MIN 15.05SEC

Race: 40 laps of 4.95mile/7.96km (198miles/318.4kms)
Fastest lap: Jarier(FRA), Shadow-Ford, 2min 35.07sec, 114.83mph/184.80kph
Pole position: Hunt(GB), McLaren-Ford, 2min 32.5sec 22 starters, 13 class. finishers

ROUND 2/SOUTH AFRICAN GRAND PRIX
KYALAMI,6 MARCH

1. LAUDA(AUT)	FERRARI	1HR 42MIN 18.4SEC
2. HUNT(GB)	MCLAREN-FORD	1HR 42MIN 19.7SEC
3. MASS(GER)	MCLAREN-FORD	1HR 43MIN 04.3SEC
4. J. SCHECKTER	TYRRELL-FORD	1HR 43MIN 26.8SEC
5. WATSON(GB)	PENSKE-FORD	77 LAPS
6. ANDRETTI(USA)	PARNELLI-FORD	77 LAPS

Race: 78 laps of 2.22mile/4.1km (198.9miles/319.8kms)
Fastest lap: Lauda, 1min 17.97sec,117.4mph/189.5kph
Pole position: Hunt, 1min 16.10sec 25 starters, 17 classified finishers

ROUND 3/US GRAND PRIX(WEST)
LONG BEACH,CALIFORNIA, 28 MARCH

1. REGAZZONI(SWISS)	FERRARI	1HR 53MIN 18.5SEC
2. LAUDA(AUT)	FERRARI	1HR 54MIN 00.9SEC
3. DEPAILLER(FRA)	TYRRELL-FORD	1HR 54MIN 08.4SEC
4. LAFFITE(FRA)	LIGIER-MATRA	1HR 54MIN 32.3SEC
5. MASS(GER)	MCLAREN-FORD	1HR 54MIN 40.8SEC
6. E. FITTIPALDI(BRA)	COPERSUCAR-FORD	79LAPS

Race: 80 laps of 2.02mile/3.25km (161.6miles/260kms)
Fastest lap: Regazzoni, 1min 23.08sec,87.53mph/140.87kph
Pole position: Regazzoni, 1min 23.09sec 20 starters, 10 classified finishers

ROUND 4/SPANISH GRAND PRIX
JARAMA, 2MAY

1.*HUNT(GB)	MCLAREN-FORD	1HR 42MIN 20.43SEC
2. LAUDA(AUT	FERRARI	1HR 42MIN 51.40SEC
3 NILSSON(SWE)	LOTUS-FORD	1HR 43MIN 08.45SEC
4. REUTEMANN(ARG)	BRABHAM-ALFA	74 LAPS
5. AMON(NZ)	ENSIGN-FORD	74 LAPS
6. PACE(BRA)	BRABHAM-ALFA	74 LAPS

Race: 75 laps of 2.12mile/3.4km (159miles/255kms)
Fastest lap: Mass(GER), McLaren-Ford, 1min 29.93sec,94.1mph/151.43kph
Pole position: Hunt, 1min 18.52sec 24 starters, 13 classified finishers
Hunt was originally disqualified but reinstated after appeal.

RESULTS 1976

ROUND 5/BELGIAN GRAND PRIX

ZOLDER,16 MAY 1976

1. LAUDA(AUT)	FERRARI	1HR 42MIN 53.23SEC
2. REGAZZONI(SWISS)	FERRARI	1HR 42MIN 56.69SEC
3. LAFFITE(FRA)	LIGIER-MATRA	1HR 43MIN 28.61SEC
4. J. SCHECKTER(SA)	TYRRELL-FORD	1HR 44MIN 24.31SEC
5. JONES(AUS)	SURTEES-FORD	69 LAPS
6. MASS(GER)	SURTEES-FORD	69 LAPS

Race: 70 laps of 2.65mile/4.26km (185.5 miles/298.2kms)
Fastest lap: Lauda, 1min 25.98sec, 110.88mph/178.45kph
Pole position: Lauda, 1min 26.55sec 26 starters, 12 classified finishers

ROUND 6/MONACO GRAND PRIX

MONTE CARLO,30 MAY

1. LAUDA(AUT	FERRARI	1HR 59MIN 51.47SEC
2. J.SCHECKTER(SA)	TYRRELL-FORD	2HR 00MIN 02.60SEC
3. DEPAILLER(FRA)	TYRRELL-FORD	2HR 00MIN 56.31SEC
4. STUCK(GER)	MARCH-FORD	77 LAPS
5. MASS(GER)	MCLAREN-FORD	77 LAPS
6. E. FITTIPALDI	COPERSUCAR-FORD	77 LAPS

Race: 78 laps of 2.06mile/3.31km (160.68miles/258.18)
Fastest lap: Regazzoni(SWISS),Ferrari, 1min 30.28sec, 82.06mph/132.07kph
Pole position: Lauda, 1min 29.65sec 20 starters, 14 classified finishers

ROUND 7/SWEDISH GRAND PRIX

ANDERSTORP, 13 JUNE

1. J. SCHECKTER(SA)	TYRRELL-FORD	1HR 46MIN 53.73SEC
2. DEPAILLER(FRA)	TYRRELL-FORD	1HR 47MIN 13.5SEC
3. LAUDA(AUT)	FERRARI	1HR 47MIN 27.6SEC
4. LAFFITE(FRA)	LIGIER-MATRA	1HR 47MIN 49.55SEC
5. HUNT(GB)	MCLAREN-FORD	1HR 47MIN 53.21SEC
6. REGAZZONI(SWISS)	FERRARI	1HR 47MIN 54.01SEC

Race: 72 laps of 2.5mile/4.02km (180miles/ 289.44kms)
Fastest lap: Andretti(USA),Lotus-Ford, 1min 28s,102.14mph/164.37sec
Pole position: Scheckter 1min 25.66sec 26 starters, 15 classified finishers

RESULTS 1976

ROUND 8/FRENCH GRAND PRIX

PAUL RICAR, 4 JULY

1. HUNT(GB)	MCLAREN-FORD	1HR 40MIN 58.60SEC
2. DEPAILLER(FRA)	TYRRELL-FORD	1HR 41MIN 11.30SEC
3. *WATSON(GB)	PENSKE-FORD	1HR 41MIN 22.15SEC
4. PACE(BRA)	BRABHAM-ALFA	1HR 41MIN 23.42SEC
5. ANDRETTI(USA)	LOTUS-FORD	1HR 41MIN 42.52SEC
6. J. SCHECKTER(SA)	TYRRELL-FORD	1HR 41MIN 53.67SEC

Race: 54 laps of 3.61mile/5.81km (194.9miles/313,74kms)
Fastest lap: Lauda(AUT), Ferrari, 1min 51.0sec, 117.09mph/188.43kph
Pole position: Hunt, 1min 47.89sec 26 starters, 19 classified finishers
*Watson disqualified but reinstated after appeal

ROUND 9/BRITISH GRAND PRIX

BRANDS HATCH, 18 JULY

1* LAUDA(AUT)	FERRARI	1HR 44MIN 19.66SEC
2. J. SCHECKTER(SA)	TYRRELL-FORD	1HR 44MIN 35.84SEC
3. WATSON(GB)	PENSKE-FORD	75 LAPS
4. PRYCE (GB)	SHADOW-FORD	75 LAPS
5. JONES(AUS)	SURTEES-FORD	75 LAPS
6. E. FITTIPALDI(BRA)	COPERSUCAR-FORD	74 LAPS

Race: 76 laps of 2.61mile/4.21km (198.36miles/320kms)
Fastest lap: Lauda, 1min 19.91sec,117.74mph/189.49kph
Pole position: Lauda, 1min 19.35 sec 26 starters, 9 classified finishers
*The race was restarted after a major collision at the first corner. Hunt 'won' the second race but was disqualified by the Stewards for not completing the first lap of the original race.

ROUND 10/GERMAN GRAND PRIX

NURBURGRING, 1 AUGUST

1. HUNT(GB)	MCLAREN-FORD	1HR 41MIN 42.7SEC
2. J. SCHECKTER(SA)	TYRRELL-FORD	1HR 42MIN 10.4SEC
3. MASS(GER)	MCLAREN-FORD	1HR 42MIN 35.1SEC
4. PACE(BRA)	BRABHAM-ALFA	1HR 42MIN 36.9SEC
5. NILSSON(SWE)	LOTUS-FORD	1HR 43MIN 40.0SEC
6. STOMMELEN(GER)	BRABHAM-ALFA	1HR 44MIN 13.0SEC

Race: 14 laps of 14.9mile/22.84km (198.66miles/319.76kms)
Fastest lap: Scheckter,7min 10.8sec, 118.57mph/190.82kph
Pole position: Hunt, 7min 06.15sec *26 starters,15 classified finishers.
*The race was restarted after Lauda's crash on Lap 1.

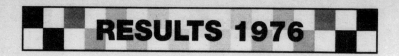

RESULTS 1976

ROUND 11/AUSTRIAN GRAND PRIX
OSTERREICHRING, 15 AUGUST

1. WATSON(GB)	PENSKE-FORD	1HR 30MIN 07.86SEC
2. LAFFITE(FRA)	LIGIER-MATRA	1HR 30MIN 18.65SEC
3. NILSSON(SWE)	LOTUS-FORD	1HR 30MIN 19.84SEC
4. HUNT(GB)	MCLAREN-FORD	1HR 30MIN 20.30SEC
5. ANDRETTI(USA)	LOTUS-FORD	1HR 30MIN 29.35SEC
6. PETERSON(SWE)	MARCH-FORD	1HR 30MIN 42.20SEC

Race: 54 laps of 3.67mile/5.91km (198.18miles/319.14kms)
Fastest lap: Hunt, 1min 35.91sec, 137.83mph/221.81kph
Pole position: Hunt, 1min 35.02sec 25 starters, 12 classified finishers

ROUND 12/DUTCH GRAND PRIX
ZANDVOORT, 29 AUGUST

1. HUNT(GB)	MCLAREN-FORD	1HR 44MIN 52.09SEC
2. REGAZZONI(SWISS)	FERRARI	1HR 44MIN 53.01SEC
3. ANDRETTI(USA)	LOTUS-FORD	1HR 44MIN 54.18SEC
4. PRYCE(GB)	SHADOW-FORD	1HR 44MIN 59.03SEC
5. J. SCHECKTER(SA)	TYRRELL-FORD	1HR 45MIN 14.55SEC
6. BRAMBILLA(ITA)	MARCH-FORD	1HR 45MIN 37.12SEC

Race: 75 laps of 2.62mile/4.23km (196.5miles/317.25kms)
Fastest lap: Regazzoni, 1min 22.59sec, 114.46mph/184.2kph
Pole position: Peterson(SWE), March-Ford, 1min 21.31sec 26 starters, 12 class. finishers

ROUND 13/ITALIAN GRAND PRIX
MONZA, 12 SEPTEMBER

1. PETERSON(SWE)	MARCH-FORD	1HR 30MIN 35.6SEC
2. REGAZZONI(SWISS)	FERRARI	1HR 30MIN 37.9SEC
3. LAFFITE(FRA)	LIGIER-MATRA	1HR 30MIN 38.6SEC
4. LAUDA(AUT	FERRARI	1HR 30MIN 55.0SEC
5. J. SCHECKTER(SA)	TYRRELL-FORD	1HR 30MIN 55.1SEC
6. DEPAILLER(FRA)	TYRRELL-FORD	1HR 31MIN 19.5SEC

Race: 52 laps of 3.6mile/5.8km (187.2miles/301.6kms)
Fastest lap: Peterson, 1min 41.3sec, 128.08mph/206.12kph
Pole position: Laffite, 1min 41.35sec 26 laps,19 classified finishers

ROUND 14/CANADIAN GRAND PRIX
MOSPORT, 3 OCTOBER

1. HUNT(GB)	MCLAREN-FORD	1HR 40MIN 09.63SEC
2. DEPAILLER(FRA)	TYRRELL-FORD	1HR 40MIN 15.96SEC
3. ANDRETTI(USA)	LOTUS-FORD	1HR 40MIN 19.99SEC
4. J. SCHECKTER(SA)	TYRRELL-FORD	1HR 40MIN 29.37SEC
5. MASS(GER)	MCLAREN-FORD	1HR 40MIN 51.44SEC
6. REGAZZONI(SWISS)	FERRARI	1HR 40MIN 55.88SEC

Race: 80 laps of 2.46mile/3.96km (196.8miles)
Fastest lap: Depailler, 1min 13.82sec, 119.92mph/192.99kph
Pole position: Hunt, 1min 12.39sec 24 starters, 20 classified finishers

RESULTS 1976/7

ROUND 15/US GRAND PRIX (EAST)
WATKINS GLEN, 10 OCTOBER

1. HUNT(GB)	MCLAREN-FORD	1HR 42MIN 40.74SEC
2. J. SCHECKTER(SA)	TYRRELL-FORD	1HR 42MIN 48.77SEC
3. LAUDA(AUT)	FERRARI	1HR 43MIN 43.07SEC
4. MASS(GER)	MCLAREN-FORD	1HR 43MIN 43.20SEC
5. STUCK(GER)	MARCH-FORD	1HR 43MIN 48.72SEC
6. WATSON(GB)	PENSKE-FORD	1HR 43MIN 48.93SEC

Race: 59 laps of 3.38mile/5.44km (199.42miles/320.96kms)
Fastest lap: Hunt, 1min 42.85sec, 118.20mph/190.23kph
Pole position: Hunt, 1min 12.39sec 24 starters, 20 classified finishers

ROUND 16/JAPANESE GRAND PRIX
FUJI, 24 OCTOBER

1. ANDRETTI(USA)	LOTUS-FORD	1HR 43MIN 58.86SEC
2. DEPAILLER(FRA)	TYRRELL-FORD	1HR 43MIN 59.14SEC
3. HUNT(GB)	MCLAREN-FORD	1HR 44MIN 00.06SEC
4. JONES(AUS)	SURTEES-FORD	1HR 44MIN 12.07SEC
5. REGAZZONI(SWISS)	FERRARI	1HR 44MIN 18.76SEC
6. NILSSON(SWE)	LOTUS-FORD	1HR 44MIN 18.92SEC

Race: 73 laps of 2.71mile/4.26km (197.83miles/318.28kms)
Fastest lap: Hasemi(JAP), Kojima-Ford,1min 18.23sec, 124.64mph/200.59kph
Pole position: Andretti, 1min 12.77sec 25 starters,11 classified finishers

DRIVERS' WORLD CHAMPIONSHIP 1976

1. HUNT	69 points	4. DEPAILLER	39 points
2. LAUDA	68 points	5. REGAZZONI	31 points
3. J.SCHECKTER	49 points	6. ANDRETTI	22 points

CONSTRUCTORS' WORLD CHAMPIONSHIP 1976

1. FERRARI	83 points	4. LOTUS-FORD	29 points
2. MCLAREN-FORD	74 points	5. LIGIER-MATRA	20 points
3. TYRRELL-FORD	71 points	5. PENSKE-FORD	20 points

1977 No fewer than eight drivers took the victory laurels. Lauda took his second title in a tight tussle with Andretti. Again, the sport lost two of its brightest stars. Carlos Pace was killed in a light-aircraft crash in Brazil and Tom Pryce was the victim of an horrendous accident in South Africa. Peterson joined Tyrrell, with their six-wheeler, and Jody Scheckter joined the new Wolf team, with startling effect. Reutemann had bolted to Ferrari at the end of 1976. Gunnar Nilsson took his one and only Grand Prix victory before cancer took its toll on this, genial, popular Swede at the age of 29 in 1978. The season extended to 17 races. Best eight out of nine in first half of season, best seven out of eight in second half. Points: 9-6-4-3-2-1.

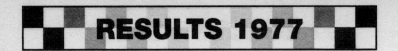

RESULTS 1977

ROUND 1/ARGENTINE GRAND PRIX
BUENOS AIRES,9 JANUARY

1. J. SCHECKTER(SA)	WOLF-FORD	1HR 40MIN 11.19SEC
2. PACE(BRA)	BRABHAM-ALFA	1HR 40MIN 54.43SEC
3. REUTEMANN(ARG)	FERRARI	1HR 40MIN 57.21SEC
4. E. FITTIPALDI(BRA)	COPERSUCAR-FORD	1HR 41MIN 06.67SEC
5. ANDRETTI(USA)	LOTUS-FORD	51 LAPS
6. REGAZZONI(SWISS)	ENSIGN-FORD	51 LAPS

Race: 53 laps of 71mile/5.97km (196.63miles/316.41kms)
Fastest lap: Hunt, 1min 51.06sec, 120.21mph/193.46kph
Pole position: Hunt, 1min 48.68sec 20 starters, 7 classified finishers

ROUND 2/BRAZILIAN GRAND PRIX
INTERLAGOS,SAO PAULO,23 JANUARY

1. REUTEMANN(ARG)	FERRARI	1HR 45MIN 07.72SEC
2. HUNT(GB)	MCLAREN-FORD	1HR 45MIN 18.43SEC
3. LAUDA(AUT)	FERRARI	1HR 46MIN 55.23SEC
4. E. FITTIPALDI(BRA)	COPERSUCAR-FORD	39 LAPS
5. NILSSON(SWE)	LOTUS-FORD	39 LAPS
6. ZORZI(ITA)	SHADOW-FORD	39 LAPS

Race: 40 laps of 4.95mile/7.96km (198miles/318.4kms)
Fastest lap: Hunt, 2min 34.55sec,115.22mph/185.443kph
Pole position: Hunt, 2min 30.11sec 22 starters, 7 classified finishers

ROUND 3/SOUTH AFRICAN GRAND PRIX
KYALAMI, 5 MARCH

1. LAUDA(AUT)	FERRARI	1HR 42MIN 21.6SEC
2. J. SCHECKTER(SA)	WOLF-FORD	1HR 42MIN 26.8SEC
3. DEPAILLER(FRA)	TYRRELL-FORD	1HR 42MIN 27.3SEC
4. HUNT(GB)	MCLAREN-FORD	1HR 42MIN 31.1SEC
5. MASS(GER)	MCLAREN-FORD	1HR 42MIN 41.5SEC
6. WATSON(GB)	BRABHAM-ALFA	1HR 42MIN 41.8SEC

Race: 75 laps of 2.55mile/4.1km (198.9miles/319.8km)
Fastest lap: Watson, 1min 17.63sec, 118.25mph/190.31kph
Pole position: Hunt, 1min 15.96sec 23 starters, 15 classified finishers

ROUND 4/US GRAND PRIX (WEST)
LONG BEACH, CALIFORNIA

1. ANDRETTI(USA)	LOTUS-FORD	1HR 51MIN 35.47SEC
2. LAUDA(AUT)	FERRARI	1HR 51MIN 36.24SEC
3. J. SCHECKTER(SA)	WOLF-FORD	1HR 51MIN 40.33SEC
4. DEPAILLER(FRA)	TYRRELL-FORD	1HR 52MIN 49.96SEC
5. E. FITTIPALDI(BRA)	COPERSUCAR-FORD	1HR 52MIN 56.38SEC
6. JARIER(FRA)	PENSKE-FORD	79 LAPS

Race: 80 laps of 2.02mile/3.25km (161.6miles/260kms)
Fastest lap: Lauda, 1min 22.75sec, 87.88mph/141.42kph
Pole position: Lauda, 1min 21.65sec 22 starters, 11 classified finishers

RESULTS 1977

ROUND 5/ SPANISH GRAND PRIX
JARAMA, 8 MAY

1. ANDRETTI(USA)	LOTUS-FORD	1HR 42MIN 52.22SEC
2. REUTEMANN(ARG)	FERRARI	1HR 43MIN 08.07SEC
3. J. SCHECKTER(SA)	WOLF-FORD	1HR 43MIN 16.73SEC
4. MASS(GER)	MCLAREN-FORD	1HR 43MIN 17.09SEC
5. NILSSON(SWE)	LOTUS-FORD	1HR 43MIN 58.05SEC
6. STUCK(GER)	BRABHAM-ALFA	74 LAPS

Race: 75 laps of 2.12mile/3.4km (159 miles/255kms)
Fastest lap: Laffite(FRA) Ligier-Matra, 1min 20.81sec, 94.24mph/151.66kph
Pole position: Andretti, 1min 18.7sec 24 starters, 14 classified finishers

ROUND 6/MONACO GRAND PRIX
MONTE CARLO, 22 MAY

1. J. SCHECKTER(SA)	WOLF-FORD	1HR 57MIN 52.77SEC
2. LAUDA(AUT)	FERRARI	1HR 57MIN 53.66SEC
3. REUTEMANN(ARG)	FERRARI	1HR 58MIN 25.57SEC
4. MASS(GER)	MCLAREN-FORD	1HR 58MIN 27.37SEC
5. ANDRETTI(USA)	LOTUS-FORD	1HR 58MIN 28.32SEC
6. JONES(AUS)	SHADOW-FORD	1HR 58MIN 29.38SEC

Race: 76 laps of 2.06mile/3.31km (156.56miles/251.56kms)
Fastest lap: Scheckter, 1min 31.07sec, 81.35mph/130.92kph
Pole position: Watson(GB), Brabham-Alfa, 1min 29.86sec 20 starters,12 class. finishers

ROUND 7/BELGIAN GRAND PRIX
ZOLDER,5 JUNE

1. NILSSON(SWE)	LOTUS-FORD	1HR 55MIN 05.71SEC
2. LAUDA (AUT)	FERRARI	1HR 55MIN 19.90SEC
3. PETERSON(SWE)	TYRRELL-FORD	1HR 55MIN 25.66SEC
4. BRAMBILLA(ITA)	SURTEES-FORD	1HR 55MIN 30.69SEC
5. JONES(AUS)	SHADOW-FORD	1HR 56MIN 21.18SEC
6. STUCK(GER)	BRABHAM-ALFA	69 LAPS

Race: 70 laps of 2.65mile/4.26km (185.5miles/298.2kms)
Fastest lap: Nilsson, 1min 27.36sec, 109.13mph/175.63kph
Pole position: Andretti(USA), Lotus-Ford,1min 24.64sec 26 starters, 14 class. finishers

ROUND 8/SWEDISH GRAND PRIX
ANDERSTORP, 19 JUNE

1. LAFFITE(FRA)	LIGIER-MATRA	1HR 46MIN 55.52SEC
2. MASS(GER)	MCLAREN-FORD	1HR 47MIN 03.97SEC
3. REUTEMANN(ARG)	FERRARI	1HR 47MIN 09.89SEC
4. DEPAILLER(FRA)	TYRRELL-FORD	1HR 47MIN 11.83SEC
5. WATSON(GB)	BRABHAM-ALFA	1HR 47MIN 14.26SEC
6. ANDRETTI(USA)	LOTUS-FORD	1HR 47MIN 20.80SEC

Race: 72 laps of 2.5mile/4.02km (180miles/289.44kms)
Fastest lap: Andretti, 1min 27.61sec, 102.59mph/165.11kph
Pole position: Andretti, 1min 25.40sec 24 starters, 18 classified finishers

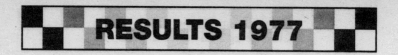

RESULTS 1977

ROUND 9/FRENCH GRAND PRIX
DIJON-PRENOIS, 3 JULY

1. ANDRETTI(USA)	LOTUS-FORD	1HR 39MIN 40.13SEC
2. WATSON(GB)	BRABHAM-ALFA	1HR 39MIN 41.68SEC
3. HUNT(GB)	MCLAREN-FORD	1HR 40MIN 14.00SEC
4. NILSSON(SWE)	LOTUS-FORD	1HR 40MIN 51.21SEC
5. LAUDA(AUT)	FERRARI	1HR 40MIN 54.58SEC
6. REUTEMANN(ARG)	FERRARI	79 LAPS

Race: 80 laps of 2.36mile/3.8km (188.8miles/304kms)
Fastest lap: Andretti, 1min 13.75sec, 115.26mph/185.49kph
Pole position: Andretti, 1min 12.21sec 22 starters, 13 classified finishers

ROUND 10/BRITISH GRAND PRIX
SILVERSTONE, 16 JULY

1. HUNT(GB)	MCLAREN-FORD	1HR 31MIN 46.06SEC
2. LAUDA (AUT)	FERRARI	1HR 32MIN 04.37SEC
3. NILSSON(SWE)	LOTUS-FORD	1HR 32MIN 05.63SEC
4. MASS(GER)	MCLAREN-FORD	1HR 32MIN 33.82SEC
5. STUCK(GER)	BRABHAM-ALFA	1HR 32MIN 57.79SEC
6. LAFFITE(FRA)	LIGIER-MATRA	67 LAPS

Race: 68 laps of 2.93mile/4.72km (199.24miles/320.96kms)
Fastest lap: Hunt, 1min 19.60sec, 132.60mph/213.40kph
Pole position: Hunt, 1min 18.49sec 26 starters, 15 classified finishers

ROUND 11/GERMAN GRAND PRIX
HOCKENHEIM, 31 JULY

1. LAUDA(AUT)	FERRARI	1HR 31MIN 48.62SEC
2. J.SCHECKTER(SA)	WOLF-FORD	1HR 32MIN 02.95SEC
3. STUCK(GER)	BRABHAM-ALFA	1HR 32MIN 09.52SEC
4. REUTEMANN(ARG)	FERRARI	1HR 32MIN 48.89SEC
5. BRAMBILLA(ITA)	SURTEES-FORD	1HR 33MIN 15.99SEC
6. TAMBAY(FRA)	ENSIGN-FORD	1HR 33MIN 18.43SEC

Race: 47 laps of 4.22mile/6.79km (198.34miles/319.13kms)
Fastest lap: Lauda, 1min 55.99sec, 130.93mph/210.71kph
Pole position: Scheckter, 1min 53.07sec 25 starters, 10 classified finishers

ROUND 12/AUSTRIAN GRAND PRIX
OSTERREICHRING, 14 AUGUST

1. JONES(AUS)	SHADOW-FORD	1HR 37MIN 16.49SEC
2. LAUDA (AUT)	FERRARI	1HR 37MIN 36.62SEC
3. STUCK(GER)	BRABHAM-ALFA	1HR 37MIN 50.99SEC
4. REUTEMANN(ARG)	FERRARI	1HR 37MIN 51.24SEC
5. PETERSON(SWE)	TYRRELL-FORD	1HR 38MIN 18.58SEC
6. MASS(GER)	MCLAREN-FORD	53 LAPS

Race: 54 laps of 3.69mile/5.94km (199.26 miles/320.76kms)
Fastest lap: Watson(GB), Brabham-Alfa, 1min 40.96sec,131.66mph/211.89kph
Pole position: Lauda, 1min 39.32sec 26 starters, 17 classified finishers

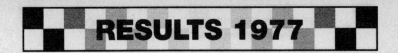

RESULTS 1977

ROUND 13/DUTCH GRAND PRIX
ZANDVOORT, 28 AUGUST

1. LAUDA(AUT)	FERRARI	1HR 41MIN 45.93SEC
2. LAFFITE(FRA)	LIGIER-MATRA	1HR 41MIN 47.82SEC
3. J. SCHECKTER(SA)	WOLF-FORD	74 LAPS
4. E. FITTIPALDI(BRA)	COPERSUCAR-FORD	74 LAPS
5. TAMBAY(FRA)	ENSIGN-FORD	73 LAPS
6. REUTEMANN(ARG)	FERRARI	73 LAPS

Race: 75 laps of 2.63mile/4.23km (196.5 miles/317.25kms)
Fastest lap: Lauda, 1min 19.99sec, 118.18mph/190.19kph
Pole position: Andretti(USA),Lotus-Ford,1min 18.65sec 26 starters, 11 class. finishers

ROUND 14/ITALIAN GRAND PRIX
MONZA, 11 SEPTEMBER

1. ANDRETTI(USA)	LOTUS-FORD	1HR 27MIN 50.30SEC
2. LAUDA(AUT)	FERRARI	1HR 28MIN 07.26SEC
3. JONES(AUS)	SHADOW-FORD	1HR 28MIN 13.93SEC
4. MASS(GER)	MCLAREN-FORD	1HR 28MIN 18.78SEC
5. REGAZZONI(SWISS)	ENSIGN-FORD	1HR 28MIN 21.41SEC
6. PETERSON(SWE)	TYRRELL-FORD	1HR 29MIN 09.42SEC

Race: 52 laps of 3.6mile/5.8km (187.21mile/301.6kms)
Fastest lap: Andretti, 1min 39.1sec, 130.92mph/210.7kph
Pole position: Hunt(GB),McLaren-Ford, 1min 38.08sec 24 starters, 9 class. finishers

ROUND 15/US GRAND PRIX (EAST)
WATKINS GLEN, 2 OCTOBER

1. HUNT(GB)	MCLAREN-FORD	1HR 58MIN 23.27SEC
2. ANDRETTI(USA)	LOTUS-FORD	1HR 58MIN 22.29SEC
3. J. SCHECKTER(SA)	WOLF-FORD	1HR 59MIN 42.15SEC
4. LAUDA(AUT)	FERRARI	2HR 00MIN 03.88SEC
5. REGAZZONI(SWISS)	ENSIGN-FORD	2HR 00MIN 11.40SEC
6. REUTEMANN(ARG)	FERRARI	58 LAPS

Race: 59 laps of 3.38mile/5.44km (199.42miles/320.96kms)
Fastest lap: Peterson(SWE), Tyrrell-Ford, 1min 51.85sec, 108.69mph/174.91kph
Pole position: Hunt, 1min 40.86sec 26 starters, 19 classified finishers

ROUND 16/CANADIAN GRAND PRIX
MOSPORT, ONTARIO, 9 OCTOBER

1. J. SCHECKTER(SA)	WOLF-FORD	1HR 40MIN 00.00SEC
2. DEPAILLER(FRA)	TYRRELL-FORD	1HR 40MIN 06.77SEC
3. MASS(GER)	MCLAREN-FORD	1HR 40MIN 15.76SEC
4. JONES(AUS)	SHADOW-FORD	1HR 40MIN 46.69SEC
5. TAMBAY(FRA)	ENSIGN-FORD	1HR 41MIN 03.26SEC
6. BRAMBILLA(ITA)	SURTEES-FORD	78LAPS

Race: 80 laps of 2.46mile/3.96km (196.8miles/316.8kms)
Fastest lap: Andretti(USA), 1min 13.3sec,130.77mph/194.36kph
Pole position: Andretti, 1min 11.38sec 25 starters, 12 classified finsihers

RESULTS 1977/8

ROUND 17/JAPANESE GRAND PRIX

FUJI, 23 OCTOBER

1. HUNT(GB)	MCLAREN-FORD	1HR 31MIN 51.68SEC
2. REUTEMANN(ARG)	FERRARI	1HR 32MIN 54.13SEC
3. DEPAILLER(FRA)	TYRRELL-FORD	1HR 32MIN 58.07SEC
4. JONES(AUS)	SHADOW-FORD	1HR 32MIN 58.29SEC
5. LAFFITE(FRA)	LIGIER-MATRA	72 LAPS
6. PATRESE(ITA)	SHADOW-FORD	72 LAPS

Race: 73 laps of 2.71mile/4.36km (197.83miles/318.28kms)
Fastest lap: J.Scheckter(SA), 1min 14.3sec,131.24mph/211.21kph
Pole position: Andretti(USA), Lotus-Ford,1min 12.23sec 23 starters,12 class. finishers

DRIVERS' WORLD CHAMPIONSHIP 1977

1.	LAUDA	72 points	4.	REUTEMANN	42 points
2.	J.SCHECKTER	55 points	5.	HUNT	40 points
3.	ANDRETTI	47 points	6.	MASS	25 points

CONSTRUCTORS' WORLD CHAMPIONSHIP 1977

1.	FERRARI	95 points	4.	WOLF-FORD	55 points
2.	LOTUS-FORD	62 points	5.	BRABHAM-ALFA	27 points
3.	MCLAREN-FORD	60 points	5.	TYRRELL-FORD	27 points

1978 Yet again the sport was to mourn one of its brightest stars.
Ronnie Peterson returned to Lotus as number two to Andretti and recovered all of his old sparkle. Andretti won the Championship but Peterson died after a catastrophic start-line shunt at Monza. Lauda left Ferrari for Brabham and Gilles Villeneuve took his place. Tambay joined Hunt at McLaren and Jones made what would later prove a highly significant career move to Williams. The Renault turbo continued to struggle to be competitive, even Jacky Oliver's new Arrows team proved more successful. Hesketh Racing made their final Grand Prix appearance in South Africa and 'Big John' Surtees pulled the plug at the end of the year after a dismal season. There were 16 rounds. Seven best results from first eight races, seven best from second eight. Points: 9-6-4-3-2-1.

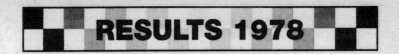

RESULTS 1978

ROUND 1/ARGENTINE GRAND PRIX
BUENOS AIRES, 15 JANUARY

1. ANDRETTI(USA)	LOTUS-FORD	1HR 37MIN 04.47SEC
2. LAUDA(AUT)	BRABHAM-ALFA	1HR 37MIN 17.68SEC
3. DEPAILLER(FRA)	TYRRELL-FORD	1HR 37MIN 18.11SEC
4. HUNT(GB)	MCLAREN-FORD	1HR 37MIN 20.52SEC
5. PETERSON(SWE)	LOTUS-FORD	1HR 38MIN 19.32SEC
6. TAMBAY(FRA)	MCLAREN-FORD	1HR 38MIN 24.37SEC

Race: 52 laps of 3.71mile/5.97km (196.63miles/316.41kms)
Fastest lap: Hunt, 1min 50.58sec, 120.73mph/194.3kph
Pole position: Andretti, 1min 47.75sec 24 starters, 18 classified

ROUND 2/BRAZILIAN GRAND PRIX
RIO DE JANEIRO, 29 JANUARY

1. REUTEMANN(ARG)	FERRARI	1HR 49MIN 59.86SEC
2. E. FITTIPALDI(BRA)	COPERSUCAR-FORD	1HR 50MIN 48.99SEC
3. LAUDA (AUT)	BRABHAM-ALFA	1HR 50MIN 56.88SEC
4. ANDRETTI(USA)	LOTUS-FORD	1HR 51MIN 32.98SEC
5. REGAZZONI(SWISS)	SHADOW-FORD	62 LAPS
6. PIRONI(FRA)	TYRRELL-FORD	62 LAPS

Race: 63 laps of 3.13mile/5.03km (197.19miles/316.89kms)
Fastest lap: Reutemann, 1min 43.07sec, 109.19mph/175.72kph
Pole position: Peterson(SWE), Lotus-Ford, 1min 40.45sec 22 starters, 11 class. finishers

ROUND 3/ SOUTH AFRICAN GRAND PRIX
KYALAMI, 4 MARCH

1. PETERSON(SWE)	LOTUS-FORD	1HR 42MIN 15.77SEC
2. DEPAILLER(FRA)	TYRRELL-FORD	1HR 42MIN 16.23SEC
3. WATSON(GB)	BRABHAM-ALFA	1HR 42MIN 20.21SEC
4. JONES(AUS)	WILLIAMS-FORD	1HR 42MIN 54.75SEC
5. LAFFITE(FRA)	LIGIER-MATRA	1HR 43MIN 24.99SEC
6. PIRONI(FRA)	TYRRELL-FORD	77 LAPS

Race: 78 laps of 2.55mile/4.1km (198.9miles/319.8kms)
Fastest lap: Andretti(USA), Lotus-Ford, 1min 17.09sec, 119.08mph/191.65kph
Pole position: Lauda(AUT), Brabham-Alfa, 1min 14.65sec 26 starters, 12 class. finishers

ROUND 4/US GRAND PRIX WEST
LONG BEACH, CALIFORNIA,2 APRIL

1. REUTEMANN(ARG)	FERRARI	1HR 52MIN 01.30SEC
2. ANDRETTI(USA)	LOTUS-FORD	1HR 52MIN 12.36SEC
3. DEPAILLER(FRA)	TYRRELL-FORD	1HR 52MIN 30.25SEC
4. PETERSON(SWE)	LOTUS-FORD	1HR 52MIN 46.90SEC
5. LAFFITE(FRA)	LIGIER-MATRA	1HR 53MIN 24.19SEC
6. PATRESE(ITA)	ARROWS-FORD	79 LAPS

Race: 80.5 laps of 2.02mile/3.25km (162.61miles/261.63kms)
Fastest lap: Jones(AUS), Williams-Ford,1min 22.22sec, 88.42mph/142.35kph
Pole position: Reutemann, 1min 20.64sec 22 starters, 12 classified finishers.

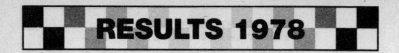

RESULTS 1978

ROUND 5/MONACO GRAND PRIX

MONTE CARLO, 7 MAY 1978

1. DEPAILLER(FRA)	TYRRELL-FORD	1HR 55MIN 14.66SEC
2. LAUDA(AUT)	BRABHAM-ALFA	1HR 55MIN 37.11SEC
3. J. SCHECKTER(SA)	WOLF-FORD	1HR 55MIN 46.95SEC
4. WATSON(GB)	BRABHAM-ALFA	1HR 55MIN 48.19SEC
5. PIRONI(FRA)	TYRRELL-FORD	1HR 56MIN 27.72SEC
6. PATRESE(ITA)	ARROWS-FORD	1HR 56MIN 23.42SEC

Race: 75 laps of 2.06mile/3.31km (156.56miles/251.56kms)
Fastest lap: Lauda, 1min 28.65sec,82.57mph/134.5kph
Pole position: Reutemann(ARG), Ferrari, 1min 34sec 20 starters, 11 classified finishers

ROUND 6/BELGIAN GRAND PRIX

ZOLDER, 21 MAY

1. ANDRETTI(USA)	LOTUS-FORD	1HR 39MIN 52.02SEC
2. PETERSON(SWE)	LOTUS-FORD	1HR 40MIN 01.92SEC
3. REUTEMANN(ARG)	FERRARI	1HR 40MIN 16.36SEC
4. G. VILLENEUVE(CAN)	FERRARI	1HR 40MIN 39.06SEC
5. LAFFITE(FRA)	LIGIER-MATRA	69 LAPS
6. PIRONI(FRA)	TYRRELL-FORD	69 LAPS

Race: 70 laps of 2.65mile/4.26km (185.5miles/298.2kms)
Fastest laps: Peterson, 1min 23.13sec, 144.69mph/184.57kph
Pole position: Andretti, 1min 20.9sec 24 starters, 13 classified finishers

ROUND 7/SPANISH GRAND PRIX

JARAMA, 4 JUNE

1. ANDRETTI(USA)	LOTUS-FORD	1HR 41MIN 47.06SEC
2. PETERSON(SWE)	LOTUS-FORD	1HR 42MIN 06.92SEC
3. LAFFITE(FRA)	LIGIER-MATRA	1HR 42MIN 24.30SEC
4. J. SCHECKTER(SA)	WOLF-FORD	1HR 42MIN 47.12SEC
5. WATSON(GB)	BRABHAM-ALFA	1HR 42MIN 52.98SEC
6. HUNT(GB)	MCLAREN-FORD	74 LAPS

Race: 75 laps of 2.12mile/3.4km (159miles/255kms)
Fastest lap: Andretti, 1min 20.06sec, 95.12mph/153.1kph
Pole position: Andretti, 1min 16.39sec 24 starters, 15 classified finishers

ROUND 8/SWEDISH GRAND PRIX

ANDERSTORP, 17 JUNE

1. LAUDA(AUT)	BRABHAM-ALFA	1HR 41MIN 00.61SEC
2. PATRESE(ITA)	ARROWS-FORD	1HR 41MIN 34.63SEC
3. PETERSON(SWE)	LOTUS-FORD	1HR 41MIN 34.71SEC
4. TAMBAY(FRA)	MCLAREN-FORD	69 LAPS
5. REGAZZONI(SWISS)	SHADOW-FORD	69 LAPS
6. E. FITTIPALDI(BRA)	COPERSUCAR-FORD	69 LAPS

Race: 70 laps of 2.51mile/4.03km (175.71miles/282.1kms)
Fastest lap: Lauda, 1min 24.84sec, 106.29mph/171.01kph
Pole position: Andretti(USA), Lotus-Ford, 1min 22.06sec 24 starters, 15 class. finshers

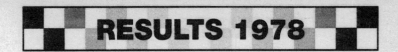

RESULTS 1978

ROUND 9/FRENCH GRAND PRIX
PAUL RICARD, 2 JULY

1. ANDRETTI(USA)	LOTUS-FORD	1HR 38MIN 51.92SEC
2. PETERSON(SWE)	LOTUS-FORD	1HR 38MIN 54.85SEC
3. HUNT(GB)	MCLAREN-FORD	1HR 39MIN 11.72SEC
4. WATSON(GB)	BRABHAM-ALFA	1HR 39MIN 28.80SEC
5. JONES(AUS)	WILLIAMS-FORD	1HR 39MIN 33.73SEC
6. J. SCHECKTER(SA)	WOLF-FORD	1HR 39MIN 46.45SEC

Race: 54 laps of 3.61mile/5.81km (194.94miles/313.74kms)
Fastest lap: Reutemann(ARG), Ferrari, 1min 48.56sec,119.72mph/192.67kph
Pole position: Watson, 1min 44.41sec 26 starters, 18 classified finishers

ROUND10/ BRITISH GRAND PRIX
BRANDS HATCH, 16 JULY

1. REUTEMANN(ARG)	FERRARI	1HR 42MIN 12.39SEC
2. LAUDA(AUT)	BRABHAM-ALFA	1HR 42MIN 13.62SEC
3. WATSON(GB)	BRABHAM-ALFA	1HR 42MIN 49.64SEC
4. DEPAILLER(FRA)	TYRRELL-FORD	1HR 43MIN 25.66SEC
5. STUCK(GER)	SHADOW-FORD	75 LAPS
6. TAMBAY(FRA)	MCLAREN-FORD	75 LAPS

Race: 76 laps of 2.61mile/4.21km (198.36miles/320kms)
Fastest lap: Lauda,1min 18.60sec, 119.8mph/192.65kph
Pole position: Peterson(SWE), Lotus-Ford,1min 16.8sec 26 starters, 10 class. finishers

ROUND 11/ GERMAN GRAND PRIX
HOCKENHEIM, 30 JULY

1. ANDRETTI(USA)	LOTUS-FORD	1HR 28MIN 00.90SEC
2. J. SCHECKTER(SA)	WOLF-FORD	1HR 28MIN 16.25SEC
3. LAFFITE(FRA)	LIGIER-MATRA	1HR 28MIN 28.91SEC
4. E.FITTIPALDI(BRA)	COPERSUCAR-FORD	1HR 28MIN 37.78SEC
5. PIRONI(FRA)	TYRRELL-FORD	1HR 28MIN 58.16SEC
6. REBAQUE(MEX)	LOTUS-FORD	1HR 29MIN 38.76SEC

Race: 45 laps of 4.22mile/6.79km (189.9miles/305.6kms)
Fastest lap: Peterson(SWE), Lotus-Ford,1min 55.62sec, 131.35mph/211.39kph
Pole position: Andretti, 1min 51.9sec 24 starters, 12 classified finishers

ROUND 12/AUSTRIAN GRAND PRIX
OSTERREICHRING, 13 AUGUST

1. PETERSON(SWE)	LOTUS-FORD	1HR 41MIN 21.57SEC
2. DEPAILLER(FRA)	TYRRELL-FORD	1HR 42MIN 09.01SEC
3. G. VILLENEUVE(CAN)	FERRARI	1HR 43MIN 01.33SEC
4. E. FITTIPALDI(BRA)	COPERSUCAR-FORD	53 LAPS
5. LAFFITE(FRA)	LIGIER-MATRA	53 LAPS
6. BRAMBILLA(ITA)	SURTEES-FORD	53 LAPS

Race: 54 laps of 3.69mile/5.94km (199.26miles/320.76kms)
Fastest lap: Peterson, 1min 43.12sec,128.91mph/207.45kph
Pole position: Peterson, 1min 37.71sec 26 starters, 9 classified finishers

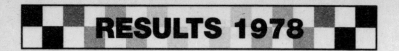
RESULTS 1978

ROUND 13/DUTCH GRAND PRIX
ZANDVOORT, 27 AUGUST

1. ANDRETTI(USA)	LOTUS-FORD	1HR 41MIN 04.23SEC
2. PETERSON(SWE)	LOTUS-FORD	1HR 41MIN 04.55SEC
3. LAUDA(AUT)	BRABHAM-ALFA	1HR 41MIN 16.44SEC
4. WATSON(GB)	BRABHAM-ALFA	1HR 41MIN 25.15SEC
5. E. FITTIPALDI(BRA)	COPERSUCAR-FORD	1HR 41MIN 25.73SEC
6. G. VILLENEUVE(CAN)	FERRARI	1HR 41MIN 50.18SEC

Race: 75 laps of 2.62mile/4.23km (196.5miles/317.25kms)
Fastest lap: Lauda,1min 19.57sec,118.81mph/191.20kph
Pole position: 26 starters, 12 classified finishers

ROUND 14/ITALIAN GRAND PRIX
MONZA, 10 SEPTEMBER

1. LAUDA(AUT)	BRABHAM-ALFA	1HR 07MIN 04.53SEC
2. WATSON(GB)	BRABHAM-ALFA	1HR 07MIN 06.02SEC
3. REUTEMANN(ARG)	FERRARI	1HR 07MIN 25.01SEC
4. LAFFITE(FRA)	LIGIER-MATRA	1HR 07MIN 42.07SEC
5. TAMBAY(FRA)	MCLAREN-FORD	1HR 07MIN 44.93SEC
6. ANDRETTI(USA)	LOTUS-FORD	1HR 07MIN 50.87SEC

Race: 40 laps of 3.6 mile/5.8km (144.1miles/232kms)
Fastest lap: Andretti, 1min 38.23sec,132.08mph/212.56kph
Pole position: Andretti, 1min 37.52sec 24 starters, 14 classified finishers*
*After the start incident which was to claim the life of Ronnie Peterson, the race was restarted. Andretti and G.Villeneuve finished first and second but were adjuged to have jumped the start light and were relegated to sixth and seventh place respectively.

ROUND 15/ US GRAND PRIX (EAST)
WATKINS GLEN, 1 OCTOBER

1. REUTEMANN(ARG)	FERRARI	1HR 40MIN 48.80SEC
2. JONES(AUS)	WILLIAMS-FORD	1HR 41MIN 08.54SEC
3 .J. SCHECKTER(SA)	WOLF-FORD	1HR 41MIN 34.50SEC
4. JABOUILLE(FRA)	RENAULT	1HR 42MIN 13.81SEC
5. E. FITTIPALDI(BRA)	COPERSUCAR-FORD	1HR 42MIN 16.89SEC
6. TAMBAY(FRA)	MCLAREN-FORD	1HR 42MIN 30.01SEC

Race: 59 laps of 3.38mile/5.44km (199.42miles/320.96kms)
Fastest lap: Jarier(FRA), Lotus-Ford, 1min 39.56sec, 122.11mph/196.52kph
Pole position: Andretti(USA), Lotus-Ford, 1min 38.11sec 26 starters, 16 class. finishers

RESULTS 1978/9

ROUND 16/CANADIAN GRAND PRIX
MONTREAL, 8 OCTOBER

1. G.VILLENEUVE(CAN)	FERRARI	1HR 57MIN 49.20SEC
2. J. SCHECKTER (SA)	WOLF-FORD	1HR 58MIN 02.57SEC
3. REUTEMANN(ARG)	FERRARI	1HR 58MIN 08.60SEC
4. PATRESE(ITA)	ARROWS-FORD	1HR 58MIN 13.86SEC
5. DEPAILLER(FRA)	TYRRELL-FORD	1HR 58MIN 17.75SEC
6. DALY(IRL)	ENSIGN-FORD	1HR 58MIN 43.67SEC

Race: 70 laps of 2.8mile/4.5km (196 miles/315kms)
Fastest lap: Jones(AUS), Williams-Ford,1min 38.07sec,102.64mph/165.17kph
Pole position: Jarier(FRA), Lotus-Ford,1min 38.2sec 22 starters, 12 classified finishers

DRIVERS' WORLD CHAMPIONSHIP 1978

1. ANDRETTI	64 *points*	4.	LAUDA	44 *points*
2. PETERSON	51 *points*	5.	DEPAILLER	34 *points*
3. REUTEMANN	48 *points*	6.	WATSON	25 *points*

CONSTRUCTORS' WORLD CHAMPIONSHIP 1978

1. LOTUS-FORD	86 *points*	4. TYRRELL-FORD	38 *points*
2. FERRARI	58 *points*	5. WOLF-FORD	24 *points*
3. BRABHAM-ALFA	53 *points*	6. LIGIER-MATRA	19 *points*

1979 This would prove to be a transitional year. Scheckter joined Ferrari and won the title for himself and the team, which is still waiting for a repeat 20 years on! Hunt and Lauda both quit the sport mid-season, one for good, the other to return to claim a third World title. A new order waited in the wings to take up the challenge: Gilles Villeneuve with Ferrari; Alan Jones at Williams; Finland's Keke Rosberg at Wolf; Italy's brilliant young Elio de Angelis at Shadow - and the Renault turbo car, claiming its first victory with Jabouille, with the energetic little man, Rene Arnoux about to take up the cudgels. The enegmatic Reutemann joined Andretti at Lotus, and a certain Brazilian, Nelson Piquet, joined Lauda at Brabham. The 'old-guard' triumphed - but no-one knew how much the sport would change in the '80s.
There were 15 rounds. Only the best four results from each half of the season counted. Points: 9-6-4-3-2-1. In the Constructors' Championship, all races counted and all cars finishing in the first six scored points.

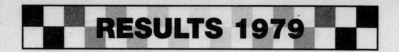

RESULTS 1979

ROUND 1/ARGENTINE GRAND PRIX
BUENOS AIRES, 21 JANUARY

1. LAFFITE(FRA)	LIGIER-FORD	1HR 36MIN 03.21SEC
2. REUTEMANN(ARG)	LOTUS-FORD	1HR 36MIN 18.15SEC
3. WATSON(GB)	MCLAREN-FORD	1HR 37MIN 32.02SEC
4. DEPAILLER(FRA)	LIGIER-FORD	1HR 37MIN 44.93SEC
5. ANDRETTI(USA)	LOTUS-FORD	52 LAPS
6. E. FITTIPALDI(BRA)	COPERSUCAR	52 LAPS

Race: 53 laps of 3.71mile/5.97km (196.63miles/316kms)
Fastest lap: Laffite, 1min 46.91sec,124.88mph/200.97kph
Pole position: Laffite, 1min 44.20sec 24 starters, 11 classified finishers

ROUND 2/BRAZILIAN GRAND PRIX
INTERLAGOS,SAO PAULO, 4 FEBRUARY

1. LAFFITE(FRA)	LIGIER-FORD	1HR 40MIN 09.64SEC
2. DEPAILLER(FRA)	LIGIER-FORD	1HR 40MIN 14.92SEC
3. REUTEMANN(ARG)	LOTUS-FORD	1HR 40MIN 53.78SEC
4. PIRONI(FRA)	TYRRELL-FORD	1HR 41MIN 35.52SEC
5. G.VILLENEUVE(CAN)	FERRARI	39 LAPS
6. J. SCHECKTER(SA)	FERRARI	39 LAPS

Race: 40 laps of 4.89mile/7.87km (195 miles/314.8kms)
Fastest lap: Laffite, 2min 28.76sec,118.4mph/190.55kph
Pole position: Laffite, 2min 23.07sec 24 starters, 15 classified finishers

ROUND 3/SOUTH AFRICAN GRAND PRIX
KYALAMI, 3 MARCH

1. G. VILLENEUVE(CAN)	FERRARI	1HR 41MIN 49.96SEC
2. J. SCHECKTER(SA)	FERRARI	1HR 41MIN 53.38SEC
3. JARIER(FRA)	TYRRELL-FORD	1HR 42MIN 12.07SEC
4. ANDRETTI(USA)	LOTUS-FORD	1HR 42MIN 17.84SEC
5. REUTEMANN(ARG)	LOTUS-FORD	1HR 42MIN 56.93SEC
6. LAUDA(AUT)	BRABHAM-ALFA	77 LAPS

Race: 78 laps of 2.55mile/4.1km (198.9miles/319.8kms)
Fastest lap: G.Villeneuve,1min 14.41sec, 123.37mph/198.54kph
Pole position: Jabouille(FRA), Renault Turbo, 1min 11.8sec 24 starters,13 class. finishers

ROUND 4/US GRAND PRIX (WEST)
LONG BEACH, CALIFORNIA, 8 APRIL

1. G.VILLENEUVE(CAN)	FERRARI	1HR 50MIN 24.40SEC
2. J. SCHECKTER(SA)	FERRARI	1HR 50MIN 54.78SEC
3. JONES(AUS)	WILLIAMS-FORD	1HR 51MIN 25.09SEC
4. ANDRETTI(USA)	LOTUS-FORD	1HR 51MIN 29.73SEC
5. DEPAILLER(FRA)	LIGIER-FORD	1HR 51MIN 48.92SEC
6. JARIER(FRA)	TYRRELL-FORD	79 LAPS

Race: 80.5 laps of 2.02mile/3.25km (162.61miles/261.63kms)
Fastest lap: Villeneuve, 1min 21min 21.2sec,89.56mph/144.28kph
Pole position: Villeneuve, 1min 18.83sec 24 starters, 10 classified finishers

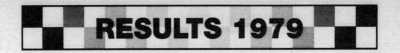

RESULTS 1979

ROUND 5/SPANISH GRAND PRIX

JARAMA, 29 APRIL, 29 APRIL

1. DEPAILLER(FRA)	LIGIER-FORD	1HR 39MIN 11.84SEC
2. REUTEMANN(ARG)	LOTUS-FORD	1HR 39MIN 32.78SEC
3. ANDRETTI(USA)	LOTUS-FORD	1HR 39MIN 39.15SEC
4. J. SCHECKTER(SA)	FERRARI	1HR 39MIN 40.52SEC
5. JARIER(FRA)	TYRRELL-FORD	1HR 39MIN 42.23SEC
6. PIRONI(FRA)	TYRRELL-FORD	1HR 40MIN 00.27SEC

Race: 75 laps of 2.12mile/3.4km (159miles/255kms)
Fastest lap: G.Villeneuve, (CAN),Ferrari, 1min 16.44sec,99.61mph/160.0kph
Pole position: Laffite (FRA), Ligier-Ford, 1min 14.50sec 24 starters, 14 classified finishers

ROUND 6/ BELGIAN GRAND PRIX

ZOLDER, 13 MAY

1. J. SCHECKTER(SA)	FERRARI	1HR 39MIN 59.53SEC
2. LAFFITE(FRA)	LIGIER-FORD	1HR 40MIN 14.89SEC
3. PIRONI(FRA)	TYRRELL-FORD	1HR 40MIN 34.70SEC
4. REUTEMANN(ARG)	LOTUS-FORD	1HR 40MIN 46.02SEC
5. PATRESE(ITA)	ARROWS-FORD	1HR 41MIN 03.84SEC
6. WATSON(GB)	MCLAREN-FORD	1HR 41MIN 05.38SEC

Race: 70 laps of 2.65mile/4.26km (185.5miles/298.2kms)
Fastest lap: G.Villeneuve(CAN), Ferrari,1min 23.09sec,114.74mph/184.66kph
Pole position: Laffite, 1min 1.13sec 24 starters, 11 classified finishers

ROUND 7/ MONACO GRAND PRIX

MONTE CARLO, 27 MAY

1.J. SCHECKTER(SA)	FERRARI	1HR 55MIN 22.48SEC
2.REGAZZONI (SWISS)	WILLIAMS-FORD	1HR 55MIN 22.92SEC
3.REUTEMANN(ARG)	LOTUS-FORD	1HR 55MIN 31.05SEC
4.WATSON(GB)	MCLAREN-FORD	1HR 56MIN 03.79SEC
5.DEPAILLER(FRA)	LIGIER-FORD	74 LAPS
6.MASS(GER)	ARROWS-FORD	69 LAPS

Race: 76 laps of 2.06mile/3.31km (156.56miles/251.56kms)
Fastest lap: Depailler, 1min 28.82sec,83.41mph/134.24kph
Pole position: Scheckter, 1min 26.45sec 20 starters, 8 classified finishers

ROUND 8/ FRENCH GRAND PRIX

DIJON-PRENOIS, 1 JULY

1. JABOUILLE(FRA)	RENAULT TURBO	1HR 35MIN 20.42SEC
2. G. VILLENEUVE(CAN)	FERRARI	1HR 35MIN 35.01SEC
3. ARNOUX(FRA)	RENAULT TURBO	1HR 35MIN 35.25SEC
4. JONES(AUS)	WILLIAMS-FORD	1HR 35MIN 57.03SEC
5. JARIER(FRA)	TYRRELL-FORD	1HR 36MIN 24.93SEC
6. REGAZZONI(SWISS)	WILLIAMS-FORD	1HR 36MIN 25.93SEC

Race: 80 laps of 2.36mile/3.8km (188.8miles/304kms)
Fastest lap: Arnoux, 1min 09.16sec, 122.9mph/197.8 kph
Pole position: Jabouille, 1min 07.19sec 24 starters, 18 classified finishers

RESULTS 1979

ROUND 9/BRITISH GRAND PRIX
SILVERSTONE, 14 JULY

1. REGAZZONI(SWISS)	WILLIAMS-FORD	1HR 26MIN 11.17SEC
2. ARNOUX (FRA)	RENAULT TURBO	1HR 26MIN 35.45SEC
3. JARIER(FRA)	TYRRELL-FORD	67 LAPS
4. WATSON(GB)	MCLAREN-FORD	67 LAPS
5. J. SCHECKTER(SA)	FERRARI	67 LAPS
6. ICKX(BEL)	LIGIER-FORD	67 LAPS

Race: 68 laps of 2.93mile/4.72km (199.24miles/320.96kms)
Fastest lap: Regazzoni, 1min 14.40sec, 141.87mph/228.32kph
Pole position: Jones(AUS), Williams-Ford, 1min 11.88sec 24 starters, 14 class. finishers

ROUND 10/GERMANY
HOCKENHEIM, 29 JULY

1. JONES(AUS)	WILLIAMS-FORD	1HR 24MIN 48.83SEC
2. REGAZZONI(SWISS)	WILLIAMS-FORD	1HR 24MIN 51.74SEC
3. LAFFITE(FRA)	LIGIER-FORD	1HR 25MIN 07.22SEC
4. J. SCHECKTER(SA)	FERRARI	1HR 25MIN 20.03SEC
5. WATSON(GB)	MCLAREN-FORD	1HR 26MIN 26.63SEC
6. MASS(GER)	ARROWS-FORD	44 LAPS

Race: 45 laps of 4.22mile/6.79km (189.9miles/305kms)
Fastest lap: G.Villeneuve(CAN), Ferrari,1min 51.89sec, 135.7mph/218.4kph
Pole position: Jabouille(FRA), Renault Turbo, 1min 48.48sec 24 starters, 12 class. finishers

ROUND 11 AUSTRIAN GRAND PRIX
OSTERREICHRING, 12 AUGUST

1. JONES(AUS)	WILLIAMS-FORD	1HR 27MIN 38.01SEC
2. G. VILLENEUVE(CAN)	FERRARI	1HR 28MIN 14.06SEC
3. LAFFITE(FRA)	LIGIER-FORD	1HR 28MIN 24.78SEC
4. J. SCHECKTER(SA)	FERRARI	1HR 28MIN 25.22SEC
5. REGAZZONI(SWISS)	WILLIAMS-FORD	1HR 28MIN 26.93SEC
6. ARNOUX(FRA)	RENAULT TURBO	53 LAPS

Race: 54 laps of 3.69mile/5.94kms (199.26miles/320.76kms)
Fastest lap: Arnoux, 1min 35.77sec, 138.8mph/223.38kph
Pole position: Arnoux, 1min 34.07sec 24 starters, 10 classified finishers

ROUND 12/DUTCH GRAND PRIX
ZANDVOORT, 26 AUGUST 1979

1. JONES(AUS)	WILLIAMS-FORD	1HR 41MIN 19.78SEC
2. J. SCHECKTER(SA)	FERRARI	1HR 41MIN 41.56SEC
3. LAFFITE(FRA)	LIGIER-FORD	1HR 42MIN 23.03SEC
4. PIQUET(BRA)	BRABHAM-ALFA	74 LAPS
5. ICKX(BEL)	LIGIER-FORD	74 LAPS
6. MASS(GER)	ARROWS-FORD	73 LAPS

Race: 75 laps of 2.63mile/4.23km (196.5miles/317.25kms)
Fastest lap: G. Villeneuve(CAN), Ferrari, 1min 19.44sec, 119.00mph/191.50kph
Pole position: Arnoux(FRA), Renault Turbo, 1min 15.46sec 24 starters, 7 class. finishers

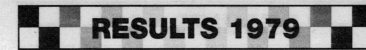

RESULTS 1979

ROUND 13/ITALIAN GRAND PRIX

MONZA, 9 SEPTEMBER

1. J.SCHECKTER(SA)	FERRARI	1HR 22MIN 00.22SEC
2. G. VILLENEUVE(CAN)	FERRARI	1HR 22MIN 00.68SEC
3. REGAZZONI(SWISS)	WILLIAMS-FORD	1HR 22MIN 05.00SEC
4. LAUDA(AUT)	BRABHAM-ALFA	1HR 22MIN 54.62SEC
5. ANDRETTI(USA)	LOTUS-FORD	1HR 22MIN 59.92SEC
6. JARIER(FRA)	TYRRELL-FORD	1HR 23MIN 01.77SEC

Race: 50 laps of 3.6mile/5.8km (180.0miles/290.0kms)
Fastest lap: Regazzoni, 1min 35.50sec, 135.71mph/218.4kph
Pole position: Jabouille (FRA) Renault Turbo, 1min 34.58sec 24 starters, 14 class. finishers

ROUND 14/CANADIAN GRAND PRIX

MONTREAL, 30 SEPTEMBER

1. JONES (AUS)	WILLIAMS-FORD	1HR 52MIN 06.89SEC
2. G. VILLENEUVE(CAN)	FERRARI	1HR 52MIN 07.97SEC
3. REGAZZONI(SWISS)	WILLIAMS-FORD	1HR 53MIN 20.55SEC
4. J. SCHECKTER(SA)	FERRARI	71 LAPS
5. PIRONI(FRA)	TYRRELL-FORD	71 LAPS
6. WATSON(GB)	MCLAREN-FORD	70 LAPS

Race: 72 laps of 2.74mile/4.41km (197.28miles/317.51kms)
Fastest lap: Jones, 1min 31.27sec, 108.08mph/173.92kph
Pole position: Jones, 1min 29.89sec 24 starters, 10 classified finishers

ROUND 15/US GRAND PRIX(EAST)

WATKINS GLEN, 7 OCTOBER

1. G. VILLENEUVE(CAN)	FERRARI	1HR 52MIN 17.73SEC
2. ARNOUX(FRA)	RENAULT TURBO	1HR 53MIN 06.52SEC
3. PIRONI(FRA)	TYRRELL-FORD	1HR 53MIN 10.93SEC
4. DE ANGELIS(ITA)	SHADOW-FORD	1HR 53MIN 48.25SEC
5. STUCK (GER)	ATS-FORD	1HR 53MIN 58.99SEC
6. WATSON(GB)	MCLAREN-FORD	58 LAPS

Race: 59 laps of 3.38mile/5.44km (199.42miles/320.96kms)
Fastest lap: Piquet(BRA),Brabham-Ford, 1min 40.05sec, 121.25mph/195.13kph
Pole position: Jones(AUS), Williams-Ford, 1min 35.61sec 24 starters, 7 class. finishers

---

DRIVERS' WORLD CHAMPIONSHIP 1979

1. J.SCHECKTER 51 *points*	4. J.LAFFITE 36 *points*
2. G.VILLENEUVE 47 *points*	5. C.REGAZZONI 34 *points*
3. A.JONES 40 *points*	6. C.REUTEMANN 25 *points*

RESULTS 1979

CONSTRUCTORS' WORLD CHAMPIONSHIP 1979

1. FERRARI	113 *points*	4. LOTUS	39 *points*
2. WILLIAMS	75 *points*	5. TYRELL	28 *points*
3. LIGIER	61 *points*	6. RENAULT	26 *points*

1980s

QUIZ & FACT

QUIZ 1

Answers on page 218

1 **Which South American driver joined Williams in 1980?**
   a. Emerson Fittipaldi   *b. Nelson Piquet*   *c. Carlos Reutemann*

2 **Which South American driver won three Grands Prix in 1980?**
   a. Emerson Fittipaldi   *b. Nelson Piquet*   *c. Carlos Reutemann*

3 **Which South American driver retired from Formula One at the end of the 1980 season?**
   a. Emerson Fittipaldi   *b. Nelson Piquet*   *c. Carlos Reutemann*

4 **Who won the 1980 World Drivers' Championship?**
   a. Jody Scheckter   *b. Alan Jones*   *c. Mario Andretti*

5 **Driving which car?**
   a. Williams-Ford   *b. Ferrari*   *c. Lotus-Ford*

6 **How many races did the Champion win in the 1980 season?**
   a. Five   *b. Six*   *c. Seven*

7 **Which French newcomer finished sixth in the opening round of the year in Argentina?**
   a. Rene Arnoux   *b. Didier Pironi*   *c. Alain Prost*

8 **Which French driver scored back-to-back victories in Brazil and South Africa in 1980?**
   a. Rene Arnoux   *b. Didier Pironi*   *c. Alain Prost*

9 **And which French driver claimed his maiden victory in the 1980 Belgian Grand Prix?**
   a. Rene Arnoux   *b. Didier Pironi*   *c. Alain Prost*

10 **In which car?**
   a. Renault   *b. Ligier*   *c. Alfa Romeo*

Answers to page 218
1 *b.*Rupert Keegan   **2** *b.*14   **3** *b.*144   **4** *c.*Silverstone   **5** *b.*1975   **6** *c.*Bruno Giacomelli   **7** *c.*Alfa Romeo   **8** *a.*Patrick Depailler   **9** *b.*Alfa Romeo   **10** *a.*Carlos Reutemann.

QUIZ 2

Answers on page 219

1 **Which 'wannabee' TV presenter drove an Ensign in the 1980 Belgian Grand Prix?**
   a. Martin Brundle   b. James Hunt   c. Tiff Needell

2 **Who finished third in a Fittipaldi-Ford in the 1980 Argentine Grand Prix?**
   a. Emerson Fittipaldi   b. Wilson Fittipaldi   c. Keke Rosberg

3 **Who finished second for Lotus in Brazil?**
   a. Emerson Fittipaldi   b. Elio de Angelis   c. Mario Andretti

4 **Which former World Champion scored only one point during the entire 1980 season?**
   a. Emerson Fittipaldi   b. Jody Scheckter   c. Mario Andretti

5 **And which former World Champion could only manage two points in the year?**
   a. Emerson Fittipaldi   b. Jody Scheckter   c. Mario Andretti

6 **Which team opted out of Formula One after the 1980 South African Grand Prix?**
   a. Fittipaldi   b. Ensign   c. Shadow

7 **Ricardo Zunino had replaced Niki Lauda at Brabham in 1979 Who, in turn, replaced him midway through 1980?**
   a. Bruno Giacomelli   b. John Watson   c. Hector Rebaque

8 **What was his nationality?**
   a. Spanish   b. Mexican   c. Italian

9 **Which former World Championship winning team driver failed to qualify in Monaco in 1980?**
   a. John Watson   b. Mario Andretti   c. Emerson Fittipaldi

10 **Which mustachioed front-runner crashed during the 1980 Long Beach Grand Prix and was paralysed from the waist down?**
   a. Keke Rosberg   b. Jan Lammers   c. Clay Regazzoni

Answers to page 219

1 *b.*He had a slow puncture 2 *a.*Alfred Neubauer 3 *a.*Raymond Mays 4 *a.*FISA did not acknowledge the race for 'political' reasons 5 *c.*Two 6 *c.*Jody Scheckter 7 *c.*Nelson Piquet 8 *a.*Internal motorsport politics 9 *a.*Nelson Piquet 10 *c.*Brabham

---

QUIZ 3

Answers on page 216

1 **Who drove a third Williams in the 1980 British Grand Prix?**
   a. Kevin Keegan **b.** *Rupert Keegan* **c.** *Tiff Needell*

2 **How many Grands Prix did Emerson Fittipaldi win in his career**
   a. 12 **b.** *14* **c.** *16*

3 **How many Grands Prix did he contest?**
   a. 140 **b.** *144* **c.** *150*

4 **Where was the smiling Brazilian's last Grand Prix victory?**
   a. Brands Hatch **b.** *Interlagos* **c.** *Silverstone*

5 **In which year?**
   a. 1974 **b.** *1975* **c.** *1976*

6 **Who qualified on pole for the 1980 U.S Grand Prix East?**
   a. Alan Jones **b.** *Mario Andretti* **c.** *Bruno Giacomelli*

7 **In which car?**
   a. Lotus-Ford **b.** *Williams-Ford* **c.** *Alfa Romeo*

8 **Which French driver lost his life in a testing accident at Hockenheim in 1980?**
   a. Patrick Depailler **b.** *Patrick Tambay* **c.** *Didier Pironi*

9 **In which car?**
   a. Tyrrell-Ford **b.** *Alfa Romeo* **c.** *McLaren-Ford*

10 **Which South American driver won the 1980 Monaco Grand Prix?**
   a. Carlos Reutemann **b.** *Nelson Piquet* **c.** *Ayrton Senna*

Answers to page 216
1 *c.* Carlos Reutemann 2 *b.* Nelson Piquet 3 *a.* Emerson Fittipaldi 4 *b.* Alan Jones
5 *a.* Williams 6 *a.* Five 7 *c.* Alain Prost 8 *a.* Rene Arnoux 9 *b.* Didier Pironi
10 *a.* Ligier.

QUIZ 4

Answers on page 217

1 **Why was Alan Jones lucky to win the 1980 German Grand Prix?**
   a. He was nearly out of fuel   b. He had a slow puncture
   c. He spun on the last lap.

2 **Which great German former team-manager died in 1980?**
   a. Alfred Neubauer   b. Hermann Lang   c. Hans Stuck Snr

3 **Which great British Team Manager died in his eighties in 1980?**
   a. Raymond Mays   b. Louis Stanley   c. Colin Chapman

4 **Why was the 1980 Spanish Grand Prix discounted from the World Championship?**
   a. FISA did not acknowledge it for political reasons
   b. Nobody wanted to race   c. Alan Jones won but was denied the honours because his mechanics won the pit-lane football match. (The answers are about as daft as the behaviour of the governing bodyduring the weekend.)

5 **How many Irish drivers competed in the 1980 World Championship?**
   a. None   b. One   c. Two

6 **Which reigning World Champion retired from Formula One at the end of 1980?**
   a. Gilles Villeneuve   b. Nigel Mansell   c. Jody Scheckter

7 **Who won the 1981 World Drivers' Championship?**
   a. Alan Jones   b. Carlos Reutemann   c. Nelson Piquet

8 **Why was the 1981 Argentine Grand Prix delayed until April?**
   a. Internal motorsport politics   b. The Falklands War   c. Fuel crisis

9 **Which South American driver won the race?**
   a. Nelson Piquet   b. Carlos Reutemann   c. Chico Serra

10 **Driving for which team?**
   a. Fittipaldi   b. Williams   c. Brabham

Answers to page 217

1 *c.* Tiff Needell   **2** *c.* Keke Rosberg   **3** *b.* Elio de Angelis   **4** *c.* Mario Andretti
5 *c.* Jody Scheckter   **6** *c.* Shadow   **7** *c.* Hector Rebaque   **8** *b.* Mexican   **9** *a.* John Watson   **10** *c.* Clay Regazzoni

---

219

QUIZ 5

Answers on page 222

1 **Which highly-popular former Formula One star and his little daughter died in a tragic road accident in 1981?**
   a. Mike Hailwood   *b.* Mike Hawthorn   *c.* Michele Alboreto

2 **The formerly lack-lustre McLaren team was re-vamped in 1981. Who was its leading light?**
   a. Bernie Ecclestone   *b.* Ron Dennis   *c.* Colin Chapman

3 **For whom was he chief mechanic in his 'former life'?**
   a. Bruce McLaren   *b.* Bernie Ecclestone   *c.* Jack Brabham

4 **Which driver won the 1981 Monaco Grand Prix?**
   a. Jody Scheckter   *b.* Alain Prost   *c.* Gilles Villeneuve.

5 **And which driver won the 1981 Spanish Grand Prix?**
   a. Jody Scheckter   *b.* Alain Prost   *c.* Gilles Villeneuve

6 **Which British driver finished third in Spain?**
   a. Tiff Needell   *b.* Nigel Mansell   *c.* John Watson

7 **Which British driver won the 1981 British Grand Prix at Silverstone?**
   a. Tiff Needell   *b.* Nigel Masell   *c.* John Watson

8 **How many races did Renault win in 1981?**
   a. None   *b.* Three   *c.* Four

9 **Which former Renault driver retired in the middle of the 1981 season?**
   a. Rene Arnoux   *b.* Jean-Pierre Jarier   *c.* Jean-Pierre Jabouille

10 **How many races did he win for the turbo warriors?**
   a. Two   *b.* Four   *c.* Five

Answers to page 222
1 *b.*16 **2** *b.*Seven **3** *c.*Niki Lauda **4** *c.*McLaren **5** *c.*Two **6** *a.*Alan Jones **7** *b.*They objected to the small print on their Superlicence forms **8** *c.*Elio de Angelis **9** *c.*Alain Prost **10** *c.*Renault.

QUIZ 6

Answers on page 223

1 **Which British hopeful made his Grand Prix debut in a Toleman in Las Vegas in 1981?**
   a. Derek Allsop *b. Derek Warwick* *c. David Warwick*

2 **Which former rock-star drove for ATS in 1981?**
   a. George Harrison *b. Slim Borgudd* *c. Nick Mason*

3 **Who was the title sponsor of the Lotus team in 1981?**
   a. John Player Special *b. Martini* *c. Essex*

4 **How many races did they win in the year?**
   a. None *b. One* *c. Two*

5 **Who was the Formula One team's leading driver?**
   a. Nigel Mansell *b. Mario Andretti* *c. Elio de Angelis*

6 **What was the name of the boss of the Lotus team's major sponsor in 1981?**
   a. David Essex *b. David Thieme* *c. Peter Dyke*

7 **Where did they hold their team launch?**
   a. Wembley *b. The Albert Hall* *c. Silverstone*

8 **Who finished second in the 1981 World Drivers' Championship by just one point?**
   a. Alan Jones *b. Gilles Villeneuve* *c. Carlos Reutemann*

9 **Which former rock star scored one point in the Drivers' Championship?**
   a. George Harrison *b. Slim Borgudd* *c. Nick Mason*

10 **Which band had he played for?**
   a. The Beatles *b. Pink Floyd* *c. Abba*

Answers to page 223

1 *c.*They were underweight 2 *b.*Alain Prost 3 *c.*Carlos Reutemann 4 *a.*Derek Daly
5 *a.*Niki Lauda 6 *c.*Didier Pironi 7 *a.*His team-mate did not respect team orders
8 *a.*Belgium 9 *b.*Riccardo Patrese 10 *c.*John Watson.

QUIZ 7

Answers on page 220

1 **How many Grand Prix races were there in 1982?**
   a. 12   b. 16   c. 17

2 **How many were won by turbo-charged cars?**
   a. None   b. Seven   c. Ten

3 **Which former World Champion returned to the scene in 1982?**
   a. Emerson Fittipaldi   b. Jody Scheckter   c. Niki Lauda

4 **With which team?**
   a. Ferrari   b. Lotus   c. McLaren

5 **How many races did he win during the season?**
   a. None   b. One   c. Two

6 **Which former World Champion announced his retirement from Formula One at the end of 1981?**
   a. Alan Jones   b. Nelson Piquet   c. John Watson

7 **Why did the drivers go one strike before the opening round of the 1982 season in South Africa?**
   a. The circuit was unsafe;   b. They objected to the small print on their Superlicence forms   c. The prize money was unacceptable

8 **Which driver entertained his chums by playing soothing Mozart on the piano, whilst they camped down in a hotel in downtown Jo'burg.**
   a. Nigel Mansell   b. Bruno Giacomelli   c. Elio de Angelis

9 **Who won the 1982 South African Grand Prix?**
   a. Keke Rosberg   b. Carlos Reutemann   c. Alain Prost

10 **In which car?**
   a. McLaren   b. Ferrari   c. Renault

Answers to page 220
1 *a.*Mike Hailwood 2 *b.*Ron Dennis 3 *c.*Jack Brabham 4 *c.*Gilles Villeneuve
5 *c.*Gilles Villeneuve 6 *c.*John Watson 7 *c.*John Watson 8 *b.*Three 9 *c.*Jean-
Pierre Jabouille 10 *a.*Two

QUIZ 8

Answers on page 221

1 **Why were Nelson Piquet's Brabham and Keke Rosberg's Williams disqualified from first and second place finishes in the 1982 Brazilian Grand Prix?**
   a. They were overweight.   *b.* They ignored black flags.
   c. They were underweight.

2 **Who 'won' the race?**
   a. Nigel Mansell   *b.* Alain Prost   *c.* Gilles Villeneuve

3 **Which South American driver walked out on Formula One after the Brazilian Grand Prix in 1982?**
   a. Emerson Fittipaldi   *b.* Nelson Piquet   *c.* Carlos Reutemann

4 **Who replaced him in the Williams Team?**
   a. Derek Daly   *b.* Andrea de Cesaris   *c.* Alan Jones

5 **Who won the 1982 U.S. Grand Prix at Long Beach?**
   a. Niki Lauda   *b.* Keke Rosberg   *c.* Gilles Villeneuve

6 **Which French driver won the San Marino Grand Prix in 1982?**
   a. Jean-Pierre Jarier   *b.* Patrick Tambay   *c.* Didier Pironi

7 **Why was Gilles Villeneuve furious about the result?**
   a. His team-mate did not respect team orders
   b. His car ran out of fuel   *c.* He was black-flagged

8 **Where was Gilles Villeneuve tragically killed in practice for a Grand Prix in 1982?**
   a. Belgium   *b.* Monaco   *c.* Detroit

9 **Which Italian driver won the first of his 256-race career in Monaco in 1982?**
   a. Andrea de Cesaris   *b.* Riccardo Patrese   *c.* Michele Alboreto

10 **And who made Ford's celebrations complete in 'Motown' in June?**
   a. Mario Andretti   *b.* Nigel Mansell   *c.* John Watson

Answers to page 221

1 *b.*Derek Warwick   **2** *b.*Slim Borgudd   **3** *c.*Essex   **4** *a.*None   **5** *c.*Elio de Angelis
6 *b.*David Thieme   **7** *b.*The Albert Hall   **8** *c.*Carlos Reutemann   **9** *b.*Slim Borgudd
10 *c.*Abba

223

QUIZ 9

Answers on page 226

1 **Which driver won the 1982 Grand Prix in France, totally against team orders?**
   a. Rene Arnoux   *b.* Patrick Tambay   *c.* Didier Pironi

2 **How many different drivers took the chequered flag in the 16-race season?**
   a. Six   *b.* Nine   *c.* Eleven

3 **Who won the 1982 World Drivers' title?**
   a. Niki Lauda   *b.* John Watson   *c.* Keke Rosberg

4 **How many races did he win in the year?**
   a. One   *b.* Three   *c.* Four

5 **Where?**
   a. France   *b.* Finland   *c.* Switzerland

6 **Which French driver finished joint runner-up in the Driver's title chase in 1982?**
   a. Alain Prost   *b.* Rene Arnoux   *c.* Didier Pironi

7 **Which team won the Constructors' title in 1982?**
   a. Williams   *b.* Ferrari   *c.* Lotus

8 **Whose Grand Prix career was terminated by a practice accident in the rain at Hockenheim in 1982?**
   a. Carlos Reutemann   *b.* Didier Pironi   *c.* Jaques Laffite

9 **Who won the 1982 German Grand Prix at Hockenheim?**
   a. Rene Arnoux   *b.* Keke Rosberg   *c.* Patrick Tambay

10 **In which car?**
   a. Williams   *b.* Ferrari   *c.* Renault

Answers to page 226
1 *c.*Nelson Piquet 2 *c.*Brabham-BMW 3 *b.*Johnny Cecotto 4 *a.*Venezuelan
5 *a.*Fittipaldi 6 *c.*Four 7 *b.*22nd 8 *a.*First 9 *b.*Received a push-start after a pit
stop 10 *a.*Failed to stop at weigh bridge.

QUIZ 10

Answers on page 227

1 Who was the first to congratulate the newly-crowned 1982 WorldChampion on the podium in Las Vegas 1982?
   a. The President of the USA   *b.* The President of the FIA
   c. Diana Ross

2 Which Italian driver won his first Grand Prix in Austria in 1982?
   a. Andrea de Cesaris   *b.* Mauro Baldi   *c.* Elio de Angelis

3 For which team?
   a. Ferrari   *b.* Lotus   *c.* Alfa Romeo

4 Who won the first Grand Prix of his career in Dijon in 1982?
   a. Nigel Mansell   *b.* Elio de Angelis   *c.* Keke Rosberg

5 And who won the first Grand Prix of his career in Las Vegas in 1982?
   a. Keke Rosberg   *b.* Eddie Cheever   *c.* Michele Alboreto

6 For which team?
   a. Ferrari   *b.* Tyrrell   *c.* Alfa Romeo

7 Which South American driver gave the Brabham BMW turbo its first win in Montreal in 1982?
   a. Nelson Piquet   *b.* Riccardo Patrese   *c.* Roberto Guerrero

8 Which Italian driver was tragically killed in a start-line accident in the same race?
   a. Riccardo Paletti   *b.* Bruno Giacomelli   *c.* Elio de Angelis

9 Which leading team manager died of a heart attack at the end of the 1982 season?
   a. Enzo Ferrari   *b.* Colin Chapman   *c.* Ted Toleman

10 How many Constructors' titles had his team won since 1958?
   a. .Five   *b.* Six   *c.* Seven

Answers to page 227
1 *b.*Johnny Cecotto **2** *c.*Venezuelan **3** *b.*Theodore-Ford **4** *c.*Eddie Cheever
5 *a.*Renault **6** *b.*McLaren **7** *c.*Niki Lauda **8** *b.*Keke Rosberg **9** *b.*Andrea de Cesaris **10** *c.*Three

---

QUIZ 11

Answers on page 224

1 **Who won the 1983 World Drivers' Championship?**
   a. Alain Prost   *b. Niki Lauda*   *c. Nelson Piquet*

2 **In which car?**
   a. Ferrari   *b. Brabham-Alfa*   *c. Brabham-BMW*

3 **Which former motor cycle World Champion made his Grand Prix debut in 1983 in Brazil?**
   a. Kenny Roberts   *b. Johnny Cecotto*   *c. Roberto Guerrero*

4 **What was his nationality?**
   a. Venezuelan   *b. Argentinian*   *c. Brazilian*

5 **Which famous name was missing from the scene in 1983?**
   a. Fittipaldi   *b. Tyrrell*   *c. Ligier*

6 **How many races did Alain Prost win in 1983?**
   a. None   *b. Three*   *c. Four*

7 **Where did Britain's John Watson qualify on the grid for the 1983 Long Beach Grand Prix?**
   a. Pole   *b. 22nd*   *c. 26th*

8 **Where did he finish?**
   a. First   *b. Last*   *c. Third*

9 **Why was Keke Rosberg disqualified from the 1983 Brazilian Grand Prix?**
   a. Ignored a black flag   *b. Received a push-start after a pit stop*
   c. Car underweight

10 **Why was Andrea de Cesaris not allowed to start in Brazil?**
   a. Failed to stop at weigh-bridge   *b. Failed to give urine sample*
   c. Failed to attend pre-race drivers' briefing

Answers to page 224
1 *a.*Rene Arnoux 2 *c.*Eleven 3 *c.*Keke Rosberg 4 *a.*One 5 *a.*France 6 *c.*Didier
Pironi 7 *b.*Ferrari 8 *b.*Didier Pironi 9 *c.*Patrick Tambay 10 *b.*Ferrari

---

QUIZ 12

Answers on page 225

1 **Which South American driver finished sixth at Long Beach in 1983?**
   a. Roberto Guerrero   *b. Johnny Cecotto*   *c. Raul Boesel*

2 **What was his nationality?**
   a. Brazilian   *b. Colombian*   *c. Venezuelan*

3 **Which car was he driving?**
   a. Toleman-Hart   *b. Theodore-Ford*   *c. Tyrrell-Ford*

4 **Which American driver finished third in the 1983 French Grand Prix?**
   a. Robert Guerrero   *b. Danny Sullivan*   *c. Eddie Cheever*

5 **In which car?**
   a. Renault   *b. Alfa Romeo*   *c. Theodore*

6 **Which former World Championship winning team was mortified when neither of its cars qualified for the 1983 Monaco Grand Prix?**
   a. Tyrrell   *b. McLaren*   *c. Ferrari*

7 **Which former double World Champion was at the helm of one of the offending cars?**
   a. Emerson Fittipaldi   *b. James Hunt*   *c. Niki Lauda*

8 **Who won in Monaco?**
   a. Alain Prost   *b. Keke Rosberg*   *c. Rene Arnoux*

9 **Which Italian driver surprised everyone by producing a stunning drive at Spa in 1983, setting fastest lap of the race before being forced to retire with engine failure ?**
   a. Elio de Angelis   *b. Andrea de Cesaris*   *c. Corrado Fabi*

10 **How many French drivers finished in the top three in the 1983 San Marino Grand Prix?**
   a. None   *b. Two*   *c. Three*

Answers to page 225
1 *c.*Diana Ross **2** *c.*Elio de Angelis **3** *b.*Lotus **4** *c.*Keke Rosberg **5** *c.*Michele Alboreto **6** *b.*Tyrrell **7** *a.*Nelson Piquet **8** *a.*Riccardo Paletti **9** *b.*Colin Chapman **10** *c.*Seven

---

QUIZ 13

Answers on page 230

1 **Which Italian driver won the 1983 US Grand Prix in Detroit?**
   a. Elio de Angelis   *b. Bruno Giacomelli*   *c. Michele Alboreto*

2 **In which car?**
   a. Ferrari   *b. Tyrrell*   *c. Alfa Romeo*

3 **Which engine powered the car?**
   a. Ford-Cosworth DFV   *b. Ford-Cosworth DFX*
   c. Ford-Cosworth DFY.

4 **How many Ford-powered cars finished in the top three in 'Motown'?**
   a. One   *b. Two*   *c. Three*

5 **How many turbo-powered cars finished in the top three in Montreal?**
   a. One   *b. Two*   *c. Three*

6 **Who took over from the late Colin Chapman at Lotus in 1983?**
   a. Gerard Ducarouge   *b. Patrick Head*   *c. Harvey Postlethwaite*

7 **Which engines did Lotus run in the second half of the 1983 season?**
   a. BMW   *b. Honda*   *c. Renault*

8 **Who scored one of the best results of his Formula One career, second in Hockenheim in 1983?**
   a. Andrea de Cesaris   *b. Derek Warwick*   *c. Stefan Johansson*

9 **Which German driver was disqualified from the 1983 Dutch Grand Prix for over-taking on the parade lap?**
   a. Michael Schumacher   *b. Manfred Winkelhock*
   c. Hans Stuck Jnr.

10 **Who collided with Nelson Piquet in the 1983 Dutch Grand Prix?**
   a. Alain Prost   *b. Andrea de Cesaris*   *c. Elio de Angelis.*

Answers to page 230
1 *b.*Martin Brundle **2** *c.*Tyrrell-Ford **3** *c.*Alain Prost **4** *a.*Niki Lauda **5** *a.*Half a point **6** *b.*Emerson Fittipaldi **7** *c.*Michele Alboreto **8** *a.*Johnny Cecotto **9** *a.*McLaren **10** *c.*Derek Warwick

---

QUIZ 14

Answers on page 231

1   **How many turbo cars finished in the top six at Monza in 1983?**
    a. Six   b. Five   c. One

2   **Who replaced Derek Daly at Williams in 1983?**
    a. Alan Jones   b. Jacques Laffite   c. Carlos Reutemann

3   **Who failed to qualify for both Monza and the European Grand Prix at Brands Hatch in 1983?**
    a. Alan Jones   b. Jacques Laffite   c. Carlos Reutemann

4   **Which gabby British driver made his Grand Prix debut for Williams at Brands Hatch in 1983?**
    a. Nigel Mansell   b. Martin Brundle   c. Jonathan Palmer

5   **What was his 'day job'?**
    a. Dentist   b. Doctor   c. Journalist

6   **Where did Nigel Mansell finish in the 1983 European Grand Prix at Brands Hatch?**
    a. First   b. Third   c. Sixth

7   **In which car?**
    a. Lotus   b. Williams   c. Ferrari

8   **Which British driver finished fourth in the final round of the season in South Africa?**
    a. Nigel Mansell   b. Derek Warwick c. John Watson

9   **Which French Canadian driver failed to qualify for the 1983 Canadian Grand Prix?**
    a. Jean-Pierre Villeneuve   b. Jacques Villeneuve
    c. Jean Villeneuve

10 **What relation was he to Gilles Villeneuve?**
    a. Brother   b. Son   c. Cousin

Answers to page 231
1 *a.*Ayrton Senna **2** *c.*Alfa Romeo **3** *a.*Alain Prost **4** *b.*Ayrton Senna **5** *b.*Torrential rain **6** *b.*Jacky Ickx **7** *a.*Tyrrell **8** *c.*Mike Thackwell **9** *b.*Dallas **10** *c.*Keke Rosberg

QUIZ 15

Answers on page 228

1 **Which driver finished fifth in his very first Grand Prix outing in 1984 in Brazil?**
   a. Ayrton Senna   b. Martin Brundle   c. Stefan Bellof

2 **In which car?**
   a. Toleman-Hart   b. Theodore-Ford   c. Tyrrell-Ford

3 **Who won seven Grands Prix in 1984 but just failed to win the Championship?**
   a. Niki Lauda   b. Nigel Mansell   c. Alain Prost

4 **Who did win the 1984 World Drivers' Championship?**
   a. Niki Lauda   b. Nigel Mansell   c. Alain Prost

5 **What was his victory margin?**
   a. Half a point   b. One point   c. Ten points

6 **Which former World Champion came out of retirement in 1984 to race at Indy?**
   a. James Hunt   b. Emerson Fittipaldi   c. Alan Jones

7 **Who joined Rene Arnoux at Ferrari for the 1984 season?**
   a. Patrick Tambay   b. Andrea de Cesaris   c. Michele Alboreto

8 **Who partnered Ayrton Senna at Toleman in the first half of the 1984 season?**
   a. Johnny Cecotto   b. Derek Warwick   c. Martin Brundle

9 **Which team finished first and second in the 1984 South African Grand Prix?**
   a. McLaren   b. Ferrari   c. Brabham

10 **Which driver finished third in the race - for Renault?**
   a. Rene Arnoux   b. Patrick Tambay   c. Derek Warwick

Answers to page 228
1 *c.* Michele Alboreto   **2** *b.* Tyrrell-Ford   **3** *c.* Ford-Cosworth DFY   **4** *c.* Three
5 *c.* Three   **6** *a.* Gerard Ducarouge   **7** *c.* Renault   **8** *a.* Andrea de Cesaris   **9** *b.* Manfred Winkelhock   **10** *a.* Alain Prost.

QUIZ 16

Answers on page 229

1 **Who scored his first World Championship points in South Africa in 1984?**
   a. Ayrton Senna   *b.* Stefan Johansson   *c.* Francois Hesnault

2 **Which team did Benetton sponsor in 1984?**
   a. Tyrrell   *b.* Toleman   *c.* Alfa Romeo

3 **Who won the 1984 Monaco Grand Prix?**
   a. Alain Prost   *b.* Ayrton Senna   *c.* Patrick Tambay

4 **Who finished second?**
   a. Alain Prost   *b.* Ayrton Senna   *c.* Patrick Tambay

5 **Why was the race foreshortened?**
   a. Accidents blocked the course   *b.* Torrential rain
   c. Fire in the pits

6 **Which former leading racing driver was Clerk of the Course in Monaco in 1984?**
   a. Jackie Stewart   *b.* Jacky Ickx   *c.* Jack Brabham

7 **Which team had all of its points annulled in 1984 by the FIA because of alleged irregularities in its fuel injection system?**
   a. Tyrrell   *b.* Ferrari   *c.* McLaren

8 **Which New Zealand driver qualified for the the 1984 Canadian Grand Prix in a RAM-Hart after four years' absence from Grand Prix racing?**
   a. Chris Amon   *b.* Denny Hulme   *c.* Mike Thackwell

9 **Which US City, notable for its soap opera popularity (and who really cares who shot JR?) hosted a round of the world series in 1984?**
   a. Denver   *b.* Dallas   *c.* San Diego

10 **Who bought himself a water-cooled skullcap to counteract the intense heat for the race?**
   a. Niki Lauda   *b.* Jonathan Palmer   *c.* Keke Rosberg

Answers to page 229
1 *a.*Six 2 *b.*Jacques Laffite 3 *b.*Jacques Laffite 4 *c.*Jonathan Palmer 5 *b.*Doctor
6 *b.*Third 7 *a.*Lotus 8 *b.*Derek Warwick 9 *b.*Jacques Villeneuve 10 *a.*Younger
brother

QUIZ 17

Answers on page 234

1   How many Grands Prix took place in the US in 1984?
    a. One   *b.* Two   *c.* Three

2   Which British driver suffered two broken ankles in a practice
    crash in Dallas?
    a. Derek Warwick   *b.* Nigel Mansell   *c.* Martin Brundle

3   Whose practice accident before the 1984 British Grand Prix at
    Brands Hatch left him with severe leg and ankle injuries which
    would terminate his Formula One career?
    a. Jacques Laffite   *b.* Johnny Cecotto   *c.* Jean-Pierre Jarier

4   Which British driver finished second in the 1984 British Grand
    Prix?
    a. Nigel Mansell   *b.* John Watson   *c.* Derek Warwick

5   How many normally-aspirated cars qualified for the 1984
    Austrian Grand Prix?
    a. None   *b.* One   *c.* Two

6   Who made his debut in Formula One in his home Grand Prix in
    Austria in 1984?
    a. Jochen Berger   *b.* Gerhard Berger   *c.* Jo Gartner

7   For which team?
    a. Arrows   *b.* Ferrari   *c.* ATS-BMW

8   Which brothers shared the Brabham-BMW drive in 1984?
    a. Emerson and Wilson Fittipaldi   *b.* Corrado and Teo Fabi
    c. Manfred and Jo Winkelhock

9   Who won the 1984 Constructors' title.?
    a. Ferrari   *b.* McLaren   *c.* Lotus

10 Who finished third in the 1984 Drivers' Championship?
    a. Ayrton Senna   *b.* Nelson Piquet   *c.* Elio de Angelis

---

Answers to page 234
1 *b.*Alain Prost **2** *b.*Elio de Angelis **3** *b.*Stefan Bellof **4***c.*Ayrton Senna **5** *c.* 65
6 *b.*He injured his wrist in a practice accident at the previous race in Spa **7**
*b.*Brands Hatch **8** *c.*Ayrton Senna **9** *b.*Nigel Mansell **10** *a.*Alain Prost

---

QUIZ 18

Answers on page 235

1 **Which tyre company pulled out of Formula One at the end of 1984?**
   a. Dunlop *b.* Pirelli *c.* Michelin

2 **Which British driver joined the Williams team for 1985,**
   a. Nigel Mansell *b.* Derek Warwick *c.* Martin Brundle

3 **Who joined Lotus in 1985?**
   a. Nigel Mansell *b.* Ayrton Senna *c.* Jonathan Palmer

4 **Which engine powered the Lotus team in 1985?**
   a. Ford *b.* Renault *c.* BMW

5 **Which tyres did the Brabham team choose to run in 1985?**
   a. Firestone *b.* Goodyear *c.* Pirelli

6 **Which driver won the 1985 World Drivers' title?**
   a. Niki Lauda *b.* Nigel Mansell *c.* Alain Prost

7 **How many races did he win in the 1985 season?**
   a. Five *b.* Six *c.* Seven

8 **Who claimed the first of his 41 Grands Prix victories in pouring rain in Estoril in 1985?**
   a. Ayrton Senna *b.* Michael Shumacher *c.* Nigel Mansell

9 **Which brilliant German driver finished sixth in the same Portuguese Grand Prix?**
   a. Manfred Winkelhock *b.* Stefan Bellof *c.* Jo Winkelhock

10 **Why was Alain Prost disqualifed from the 1985 San Marino Grand Prix after taking the chequered flag?**
   a. Ignored a black flag *b.* Push start in the pits
   c. Underweight at finish.

Answers to page 235

1 *c.*John Watson **2** *c.*Seventh **3** *a.*Stefan Bellof **4** *b.*Manfred Winkelhock **5** *b.*One
6 *b.*One **7** *b.*and *c.*Renault and Ligier **8** *b.*French government's protest against
apartheid **9** *c.*Australia **10** *b.*Philippe Streiff

QUIZ 19

Answers on page 232

1 **Who ran out of fuel on his victory lap in Monaco in 1985?**
   a. Ayrton Senna   *b.* Alain Prost   *c.* Andrea de Cesaris

2 **Which driver won the second Grand Prix victory of his career in the 1985 San Marino Grand Prix?**
   a. Eddie Cheever   *b.* Elio de Angelis   *c.* Mauro Baldi

3 **Who was suspended after a row with his team for the 1985 Brazilian Grand Prix?**
   a. Martin Brundle   *b.* Stefan Bellof   *c.* Jonathan Palmer

4 **Who recorded the first of what would be a record-breaking number of career pole positions in Portugal in 1985?**
   a. Nigel Mansell   *b.* Gerhard Berger   *c.* Ayrton Senna

5 **How many pole positions did he record?**
   a. 50   *b.* 60   *c.* 65

6 **Why did Niki Lauda miss the 1985 European Grand Prix?**
   a. He retired from Formula One (again!) in mid season
   b. He injured his wrist in a practice accident at the previous race in Spa   *c.* He had a previous commitment with his airline, Lauda Air.

7 **Where was the European Grand Prix held in 1985?**
   a. Zandvoort   *b.* Brands Hatch   *c.* Nurburgring

8 **Who qualified on pole?**
   a. Alain Prost   *b.* Nigel Mansell   *c.* Ayrton Senna

9 **Who won the race, the first of his Grand Prix career?**
   a. Alain Prost   *b.* Nigel Mansell   *c.* Ayrton Senna

10 **Who finished fourth to take his first ever World Drivers' title?**
   a. Alain Prost   *b.* Nigel Mansell   *c.* Ayrton Senna

Answers to page 232
1 *b.*Two 2 *c.*Martin Brundle 3 *b.*Johnny Cecotto 4 *c.*Derek Warwick 5 *a.*None
6 *b.*Gerhard Berger 7 *c.*ATS-BMW 8 *b.*Corrado and Teo Fabi 9 *b.*McLaren
10 *c.*Elio de Angelis.

QUIZ 20

Answers on page 233

1 **Which British driver took Niki Lauda's place in the 1985 European Grand Prix in what would prove to be his last Formula One race?**
   a. Martin Brundle *b.* Derek Warwick *c.* John Watson

2 **Where did he finish?**
   a. Second *b.* Sixth *c.* Seventh

3 **Which Formula One hopeful was killed in a Sports Car race at Spa in September 1985?**
   a. Stefan Bellof *b.* Manfred Winkelhock *c.* Jo Winkelhock

4 **Who had lost his life just a few weeks earlier in a Sports Car race in Mosport, Canada?**
   a. Stefan Bellof *b.* Manfred Winkelhock *c.* Jo Winkelhock

5 **How many French drivers won the World title between 1950 and 1985?**
   a. None *b.* One *c.* Two

6 **How many French teams won the Constructors' title between 1958 and 1985?**
   a. None *b.* One *c.* Two

7 **Which teams failed to take part in the 1985 South African Grand Prix?**
   a. Ferrari *b.* Renault *c.* Ligier

8 **Why?**
   a. In protest against the oil embargo *b.* In protest against apartheid *c.* The plane carrying the cars arrived too late for official practice

9 **Which country hosted a Grand Prix for the very first time at the end of the 1985 season?**
   a. China *b.* Malaysia *c.* Australia

10 **Which French driver finished third in the race?**
   a. Philippe Alliot *b.* Philippe Streiff *c.* Alain Prost

Answers to page 233
1 *c.*Michelin **2** *a.*Nigel Mansell **3** *b.*Ayrton Senna **4** *b.*Renault **5** *c.*Pirelli
6 *c.*Alain Prost **7** *a.*Five **8** *a.*Ayrton Senna **9** *b.*Stefan Bellof **10** *c.*Underweight at finish

---

QUIZ 21

Answers on page 238

1 **Which World Champion retired from Formula One at the end of the 1985 season?**
   a. Alain Prost   *b.* Nelson Piquet   *c.* Niki Lauda

2 **How many titles had he won in his career?**
   a. One   *b.* Three   *c.* Four

3 **Which high street name became a team owner in 1986?**
   a. Woolworth   *b.* Benetton   *c.* Marks and Spencer

4 **Who refused to accept one English driver as his team-mate for 1986?**
   a. Ayrton Senna   *b.* Alain Prost   *c.* Nigel Mansell

5 **Whom did he send on his way to the job centre?**
   a. Martin Brundle   *b.* Derek Warwick   *c.* Jonathan Palmer

6 **Which forceful former World Champion returned to Formula One for a full season in 1986 - but only managed to score four points?**
   a. James Hunt   *b.* Jackie Stewart   *c.* Alan Jones

7 **What was his nationality?**
   a. Irish   *b.* Australian   *c.* Scottish

8 **Which team did Nelson Piquet drive for in 1986?**
   a. Brabham   *b.* Lotus   *c.* Williams

9 **Who was paralysed in a road accident before the start of the 1986 season?**
   a. Frank Williams   *b.* Philippe Streiff   *c.* Clay Regazzoni

10 **What were banned for the 1986 season?**
   a. Turbo-charged engines   *b.* Normally aspirated engines
   c. Slick tyres

Answers to page 238
1 *b.*Five 2 *a.*Four 3 *c.*Nigel Mansell 4 *b.*There was a first lap accident
5 *b.*Jacques Laffite 6 *c.*Graham Hill 7 *a.*Nigel Mansell's 8 *c.*Keke Rosberg
9 *c.*Johnny Dumfries 10 *b.*Martin Brundle

QUIZ 22

Answers on page 239

1 Which 'Iron Curtain' country hosted a Grand Prix for the first time in 1986?
   a. Poland   *b.* Russia   *c.* Hungary

2 Elio de Angelis was tragically killed in a testing accident in 1986. At which circuit?
   a. Estoril   *b.* Paul Ricard   *c.* Imola

3 Who took his place in the Brabham team?
   a. Derek Warwick   *b.* John Watson   *c.* Nelson Piquet

4 Which leading designer left the McLaren team during the 1986 season?
   a. Gordon Murray   *b.* Patrick Head   *c.* John Barnard

5 Which top team did he join?
   a. Ferrari   *b.* Williams   *c.* Lotus

6 Whose Formula One career ended after he suffered serious injuries in a rallying accident in 1986 in which his co-driver was killed?
   a. Marc Surer   *b.* Patrick Tambay   *c.* Stefan Johansson

7 Who won the 1986 Constructors' Championship?
   a. Williams   *b.* McLaren   *c.* Lotus

8 For which 'trendy' team did Gerhard Berger claim a famous first win in 1986?
   a. Zakspeed   *b.* McLaren   *c.* Benetton

9 In which race?
   a. Mexico   *b.* Portugal   *c.* Spain

10 Who won the Monaco Grand Prix for the third year in a row in 1986?
   a. Ayrton Senna   *b.* Keke Rosberg   *c.* Alain Prost

Answers to page 239
1 *a.*Saturo Nakajima 2 *a.*Japanese 3 *b.*Renault 4 *b.*Honda 5 *c.*Two 6 *a.*Stefan Johansson 7 *a.*None 8 *a.*Riccardo Patrese 9 *a.*Goodyear 10 *c.*Ayrton Senna

---

QUIZ 23

Answers on page 236

1 **How many races did Nigel Mansell win in 1986?**
   a. Four   b. Five   c. Six

2 **How many races did Alain Prost win 1986?**
   a. Four   b. Five   c. Six

3 **Who won the 1986 British Grand Prix at Brands Hatch?**
   a. Ayrton Senna   b. Alain Prost   c. Nigel Mansell

4 **Why was the race re-started?**
   a. Someone stalled on the grid   b. There was a first lap accident
   c. The start lights failed

5 **Which popular French driver received severe leg injuries in an accident at the first corner of the race which would end his Formula One career?**
   a. Alain Prost   b. Jacques Laffite   c. Patrick Tambay

6 **Which former Champion's long standing record did he emulate by starting the race?**
   a. Juan-Manuel Fangio   b. Jackie Stewart   c. Graham Hill

7 **Whose rear tyre exploded with less than a quarter of the race to go in Adelaide in 1986?**
   a. Nigel Mansell's   b. Ayrton Senna's   c. Alain Prost's

8 **Who announced his decision to retire from Formula One at the Adelaide race?**
   a. John Watson   b. Nigel Mansell   c. Keke Rosberg

9 **Which British driver finished fifth in the 1986 Hungarian Grand Prix?**
   a. Derek Warwick   b. Martin Brundle   c. Johnny Dumfries

10 **Which British driver finished sixth in the 1986 Hungarian Grand Prix?**
   a. Derek Warwick   b. Martin Brundle   c. Johnny Dumfries

Answers to page 236

1 *c.*Niki Lauda 2 *b.*Three 3 *b.*Benetton 4 *a.*Ayrton Senna 5 *b.*Derek Warwick
6 *c.*Alan Jones 7 *b.*Australian 8 *c.*Williams 9 *a.*Frank Williams 10 *b.*Normally
aspirated engines

QUIZ 24

Answers on page 237

1 **Who was surprise fourth place finisher in the 1987 British Grand Prix at Silverstone?**
   a. Satoru Nakajima *b.* Christian Danner *c.* Adrian Campos

2 **What was his nationality?**
   a. Japanese *b.* Spanish *c.* German

3 **Which engine manufacturer withdrew from Formula One for 1987?**
   a. Ford *b.* Renault *c.* BMW

4 **Which engines did Lotus use in the 1987 season?**
   a. Ford *b.* Honda *c.* TAG Porsche

5 **How many races did Nigel Mansell miss in 1987?**
   a. None *b.* One *c.* Two

6 **Who finished sixth in the World Drivers' Championship?**
   a. Stefan Johansson *b.* Gerhard Berger *c.* Andrea de Cesaris

7 **How many races did he win during the season?**
   a. None *b.* One *c.*Two

8 **Who joined Nelson Piquet in the Williams team for the 1987 Australian Grand Prix?**
   a. Riccardo Patrese *b.* Ivan Capelli *c.* Teo Fabi

9 **Which tyre giant supplied all of the teams in the 1987 calendar?**
   a. Goodyear *b.* Michelin *c.* Dunlop

10 **Who collided with Nigel Mansell in the 1987 Belgian Grand Prix?**
   a. Alain Prost *b.* Gerhard Berger *c.* Ayrton Senna

Answers to page 237
1 *c.*Hungary **2** *b.*Paul Ricard **3** *a.*Derek Warwick **4** *c.*John Barnard **5** *a.*Ferrari
6 *a.*Surer **7** *a.*Williams **8** *c.*Benetton **9** *a.*Mexico **10** *c.*Alain Prost

QUIZ 25

Answers on page 242

1 **Which British driver drove for Zakspeed in 1987?**
   a. Jonathan Palmer   *b.* Derek Warwick   *c.* Martin Brundle

2 **How many starts were there in the 1987 Austrian Grand Prix?**
   a. One   *b.* Two   *c.* Three

3 **Which Williams driver was forced to miss out on the 1987 San Marino Grand Prix?**
   a. Nigel Mansell   *b.* Nelson Piquet   *c.* Riccardo Patrese

4 **How many races did Nigel Mansell win in 1987?**
   a. Five   *b.* Six   *c.* Seven

5 **How many drivers won Grands Prix in 1987?**
   a. Four   *b.* Five   *c.* Six

6 **Who won both the Japanese and Australian races back-to-back in 1987?**
   a. Gerhard Berger   *b.* Alain Prost   *c.* Michele Alboreto

7 **Driving for which team?**
   a. McLaren   *b.* Benetton   *c.* Ferrari

8 **Who won at Monaco for the first time in 1987?**
   a. Nelson Piquet   *b.* Nigel Mansell   *c.* Ayrton Senna

9 **How many times in his career did he win the Monaco Grand Prix?**
   a. Three   *b.* Four   *c.* Six

10 **At which race did the famous Lotus team score the last of its 79 victories in 1987?**
   a. Detroit Grand Prix   *b.* Mexican Grand Prix
   c. British Grand Prix

Answers to page 244
1 *b.*Alessandro Nannini 2 *a.*Reversing in the pit lane 3 *b.*Gerhard Berger 4 *c.*He received a one-race ban 5 *b.*Stefan Johansson 6 *b.*Onyx 7 *b.*Seven 8 *a.*Paul Ricard 9 *a.*Four 10 *c.*Thierry Boutsen

---

QUIZ 26

Answers on page 243

1. **Which of the sport's leading icons died in 1988?**
   a. Juan-Manuel Fangio b. Enzo Ferrari c. Colin Chapman

2. **How old was he?**
   a. 50 b. 80 c. 90

3. **For which team did Ayrton Senna drive in 1988?**
   a. Lotus b. McLaren c. Williams

4. **Who won the 1988 Constructors' Championship.**
   a. Lotus b. McLaren c. Williams

5. **How many races did the McLaren team win in the 1988 season?**
   a. 15 b. 16 c. 17

6. **Which team did Nelson Piquet join for the 1988 season?**
   a. Lotus b. Ferrari c. Arrows

7. **Which team saw both its cars disqualified from the 1988 Belgian Grand Prix?**
   a. McLaren b. Williams c. Benetton

8. **Why?**
   a. Overtaking each other on the parade lap
   b. Overtaking each other under yellow flags c. Illegal fuel

9. **Which British driver stood in for Nigel Mansell in the 1988 Belgian Grand Prix?**
   a. Johathan Palmer b. Julian Bailey c. Martin Brundle

10. **Which driver tripped over a back-marker whilst leading the 1988 Italian Grand Prix?**
    a. Ayrton Senna b. Alain Prost c. Andrea de Cesaris

Answers to page 243

1 *c.*Nigel Mansell **2** *c.*Ferrari **3** *b.*Renault **4** *b.*Alain Prost **5** *b.*Thierry Boutsen
6 *b.*Williams **7** *a.*Lamborghini **8** *b.*Gerhard Berger **9** *b.*Johnny Herbert
10 *a.*Emanuelle Pirro

QUIZ 27

Answers on page 244

1 **For which team did Alex Caffi drive in 1988?**
   a. Martini   b. Minardi   c. Dallara

2 **What was his nationality?**
   a. Spanish   b. Italian   c. Argentinian

3 **What nationality is Maurizio Gugelmin?**
   a. Italian   b. Brazilian   c. Colombian

4 **Where did he finish in the 1988 British Grand Prix?**
   a. Did not finish   b. Third   c. Fourth

5 **Where did the 1988 Portuguese Grand Prix take place?**
   a. Lisbon   b. Estoril   c. Oporto

6 **Which team managed to score just one point in the 1988 Constructors' Championship ?**
   a. March   b. Tyrrell   c. Minardi

7 **Which driver scored that point?**
   a. Pierluigi Martini   b. Piercarlo Ghinzani   c. Ivan Capelli

8 **How many Japanese drivers drove in the 1988 Japanese Grand Prix?**
   a. None   b. One   c. Two

9 **How many Australian drivers drove in the 1988 Australian Grand Prix?**
   a. None   b. One   c. Two

10 **What was the significance of Alain Prost's victory in the 1988 Australian Grand Prix?**
   a. He clinched the drivers' title.   b. He won the race in the pit lane
   c. His was the last victory for a turbo powered car.

Answers to page 240
1 *c.*Martin Brundle **2** *c.*Three **3** *b.*Nelson Piquet **4** *b.*Six **5** *b.*Five **6** *a.*Gerhard Berhger **7** *c.*Ferrari **8** *c.*Ayrton Senna **9** *c.*Six **10** *a.*Detroit

QUIZ 28

Answers on page 241

1 **Who won the first race of the 1989 season ?**
   a. Alain Prost   *b. Ayrton Senna*   *c. Nigel Mansell*

2 **In which car?**
   a. McLaren   *b. Williams*   *c. Ferrari*

3 **Which familiar Manufacturer's name appeared on the grid once more in 1989?**
   a. Dunlop   *b. Renault*   *c. Mercedes*

4 **Who won the 1989 World Drivers' Championship**
   a. Ayrton Senna   *b. Alain Prost*   *c. Gerhard Berger*

5 **Who won the 1989 Canadian Grand Prix?**
   a. Ayrton Senna   *b. Thierry Boutsen*   *c. Gerhard Berger*

6 **In which car?**
   a. Arrows   *b. Williams*   *c. Ferrari*

7 **Which engine supplier entered Formula One for the first time in their history in 1989 but withdrew at the end of the season?**
   a. Lamborghini   *b. Toyota*   *c. Honda*

8 **Who escaped from an horrendous fiery crash at Imola in 1989?**
   a. Derek Warwick   *b. Gerhard Berger*   *c. Alessandro Nannini*

9 **Which British driver finished fourth in Brazil in his first Grand Prix in 1989?**
   a. Derek Warwick   *b. Johnny Herbert*   *c. Johnny Dumfries*

10 **Who replaced him in the Benetton team later in the season?**
   a. Emanuelle Pirro   *b. Juha Piironen*   *c. Stefano Modena*

Answers to page 241

1 *b.*Enzo Ferrari 2 *c.*90 3 *b.*McLaren 4 *b.*McLaren 5 *a.*15 6 *a.*Lotus
7 *c.*Benetton 8 *c.*Illegal fuel 9 *c.*Martin Brundle 10 *a.*Ayrton Senna

QUIZ 29

Answers on page 240

1 **Who won the 1989 Japanese Grand Prix?**
   a. Ayrton Senna   *b.* Alessandro Nannini   *c.* Nigel Mansell

2 **Why was Nigel Mansell disqualified from the 1989 Portuguese Grand Prix?**
   a. Reversing in the pit lane   *b.* Illegal fuel   *c.* Ignoring a black flag

3 **Who won the race?**
   a. Ayrton Senna   *b.* Gerhard Berger   *c.* Nelson Piquet

4 **What happened to Mansell?**
   a. He received a three-race ban   *b.* He received a two -race ban
   c. He received a one-race ban

5 **Who finished third in Portugal?**
   a. Ayrton Senna   *b.* Stefan Johansson   *c.* Jonathan Palmer

6 **In which car?**
   a. McLaren   *b.* Onyx   *c.* Marble

7 **How many Italian drivers contested the 1989 Italian Grand Prix?**
   a. Six   *b.* Seven   *c.* Nine

8 **Where was the 1989 French Grand Prix held?**
   a. Paul Ricard   *b.* Le Mans   *c.* Dijon

9 **How many one-two finishes for McLaren did Prost and Senna score in 1989?**
   a. Four   *b.* Five   *c.* Six

10 **Who won the last race of the year in Adelaide?**
   a. Nelson Piquet   *b.* Riccardo Patrese   *c.* Thierry Boutsen

---

Answers to page 242
1 *c.*Dallara **2** *b.*Italian **3** *b.*Brazilian **4** *c.*Fourth **5** *b.*Estoril **6** *c.*Minardi
7 *a.*Pierluigi Martini **8** *b.*Two **9** *a.*None **10** *c.*His was the last victory for a turbo-powered car

---

Alan Jones continued his late season domination of 1979 in 1980.

He won five races and only failed to finish on the podium in four races during the 1980 season.

He became only the second Australian World Champion in the history of Formula One.

Sir Jack Brabham was the other.

He won the title three times. Was Jones going to repeat his feat?

Patrick Head designed a fabulous 'ground effect' new version of the Williams FWO7B for the year.

The Williams Team won the Constructors' title for the first time in their history, serving notice of what was to come in the future.

Carlos Reutemann joined the team from Ferrari at the start of the year, won in Monaco and finished third in the Drivers' Championship.

The tall, brooding Argentinian proved an enigma to many, seemingly to lack motivation if he thought his car was not handling.

Brazil's Nelson Piquet was the surprise of the season, winning his first Grand Prix at Long Beach and following it up with two more wins, at Zandvoort and Imola.

Brabham had switched from Alfa-Romeo engines to the doughty Ford Cosworth at the start of the year.

FACT FILE 2

Alfa Romeo returned as a manufacturer in 1980 with a new car, designed by former Ferrari engineer, Carlo Chitti.

Bruno Giacomelli qualified it on pole at Watkins Glen.

But the Alfa Team languished at the bottom of the Constructors' Championship at the end of 1980 because of its lack of reliability.

Arch-rivals Ferrari struggled too.

With 1979 World Drivers' Champion, Jody suffering the indignity of failing to qualify the wieldy car for the Canadian Grand Prix and only managing one top six finish all year.

Alfa's leading driver, Patrick Depailler, was tragically killed in a private testing accident at Hockenheim in mid-season.

He had joined the team at the start of the year after recovering from two badly broken legs, sustained in a hang gliding accident the previous season.

He was 35.

Renault were pouring huge sums into developing their turbo engines.

They, too, adopted sliding skirts for 1980.

But just three victories in the year would find them at fourth in the Championship, whilst arch-rivals, Ligier-Ford finished runner-up to Williams.

Jean-Pierre Jabouille, the driver, who had done so much of the development work for Renault, suffered severe leg injuries in an accident during the Canadian Grand Prix.

Politics and controversy dogged the sport once again in 1980.

Jean-Marie Balestre, the tyranical President of FISA (the sport's governing body) had decreed that sliding skirts would be banned from the start of 1981 and minimum weight limits would be sharply increased.

This obviously would favour the turbo-powered teams i.e. Renault,

Ferrari and Alfa Romeo. More weight meant more power and more power meant turbo-power.

The escallating expense of this caused great concern amongst the smaller teams, who did not having the backing of large manufacturers.

The once all-conquering McLaren and Tyrrell teams were struggling for finance.

Ballestre was also at loggerheads with the Formula One Constructors' Association (FOCA).

The autocratic Frenchman was determined to re-establish FISA as the sport's main player and he resented the lucrative television rights deals negotiated by the head of FOCA, Bernie Ecclestone, boss of the Brabham team.

The popular Swiss driver, Clay Regazzoni, crashed his Ensign into a parked car during the Long Beach Grand Prix. He was paralysed from the waist down.

His Grand Prix career was at an end but he would make a brave return to motor sport, learning to drive specially adapted cars with hand controls. And took a liking to competing in Paris-Dakar Rallye-Raids - in the truck section!

Alfred Neubauer, the famous Mercedes team-manger of the 1930s and 1950s, died at the age of 89.

FACT FILE 4

The FISA/FOCA row flared into full-scale confrontation at the 1980 Spanish Grand Prix.

A number of drivers had not paid fines imposed by FISA for not attending drivers' briefings at previous rounds.

Neither side would back down. FISA declared the race void, FOCA promptly endorsed it.

The race went ahead(although the three turbo teams boycotted it, Alan Jones won but the points were not valid for the Championship.

An uneasy peace was eventually reached after Goodyear threatened to pull out of the sport and FOCA threatened to pull their teams out and set up a rival World Championship.

Emerson Fittipaldi, whose Copersucar Team had not found great success, hung up his Grand Prix helmet to take up a managerial role. The team would struggle on until 1982, when it finally closed for good.

But Emerson's love of high speed motor sport continued to linger and his passion was rekindled when he took up racing once more in Indy Cars in the States where he has enjoyed phenomenal success.

He won the Indy 500 twice and the Overall Indy Car Championship twice, before having a huge accident at Michigan in 1996.

He finally decided that enough was enough after he was lucky to survive a light aircraft crash in 1997.

And former World Champion, Jody Scheckter, retired in disgust after his terrible 1980 season at Ferrari

Raymonds Mays, the founder of both ERA (English Racing Automobiles) and BRM (British Racing Motors) died in 1980 at the age of 81.

FACT FILE 5

The opening round of the 1981 season in Argentina was postponed, as the row between FISA and FOCA blazed on.

Pironi joined Gilles Villeneuve at Ferrari in what was to prove an ill-fated relationship.

Nigel Mansell, who had made his Grand Prix debut for Lotus, in Austria in 1980, took Mario Andretti's place in the team full-time in 1981.

Alain Prost joined Rene Arnoux at Renault and won his first ever Grand Prix in front of his adoring fans in Dijon

The 1981 French Grand Prix was run in two halves. The race and interrupted by rain after 58 laps and then re-started for the remaining 22 laps. Placings were given on aggregate times for both halves.

But, sadly, the racing on the track was very much overshadowed by the fighting off it.

FOCA were still threatening to form a breakaway World Championship series and FISA continued with their intransigence.

Eventually, in mid January what became famous as the 'Concorde Agreement' was drawn up.

FOCA agreed to acknowledge FISA's right to make the rules of the sport, whilst FISA acknowledged FOCA's rights to continue to negotiate the financial contracts with race organisers and television rights.

Bernie's empire was on its way!

VROOM VROOM!

FACT FILE 6

The Concorde Agreement wasn't ready in time to save the 1981 South African Grand Prix results (again only contested by FOCA-friendly teams)from exclusion in the World Championships.

Again poor old Alan Jones won.

Little did he know but had the race counted, he would have retained his World Drivers' crown at the end of the season!

FISA banned four-wheel-drive and six-wheelers from the Championships.

Nelson Piquet won the 1981 World Drivers' Championship for Brabham, giving Bernie something to smile about at the end of a troubled year.

It was the team's first title since Ecclestone took over the team from Sir Jack Brabham.

Piquet won by just one point from Carlos Reutemann.

The Argentinian driver had seemed poised to take the crown which he so much coveted when he set a blisteringly fast pole position for the final round of the year in Las Vegas.

Surely this would be Carlos' year.

But no, when the lights went green, he seemed totally outphased.

Jones won the race, Piquet was happy to settle for fifth, as Reutemann stuttered home eighth (reportedly suffering from a handling problem).

But Williams did take the Constructors' crown for an impressive second successive year.

The Ford-powered cars were still managing to stave off the charge of the turbo brigade but for how long?

Gilles Villeneuve put Ferrari back into contention by winning in Monaco and Spain in the new turbo-charged Ferrari 126.

McLaren too refound their winning ways in 1981.

Former Director, Teddy Mayer, sold part of the company to Ron Dennis, who was once mechanic for Jack Brabham!

Dennis brought in new designer, John Barnard, who produced what was to become a classic of Formula One - the carbon fibre McLaren MP4 chassis.

A delighted John Watson claimed the car's first victory in the 1981 British Grand Prix.

A new turbo-powered team, Toleman, financed by one of Britain's largest road-haulage contractors (and off-shore powerboat racer), Ted Toleman, joined the ranks in 1981.

Driven by two Brits Brian 'Super Hen' Henton and Derek Warwick, the wieldy cars struggled in their first season.

Henton brought the car home in 10th place in Italy.

But poor Warwick only managed to qualify for the final round!

Mike Hailwood, the former motorcycle World Champion, who had retired from Formula One after badly damaging his ankles when his McLaren crashed at the Nurburgring in 1974, was killed in a road accident with his little daughter. He was 41.

FACT FILE 8

The march of the turbos continued in 1982.

Of the 16 races,seven were won by turbo-charged cars and nine by normally-aspirated ones.

Ferrari took back what they considered to be their rightful place at the top of the Constructors' Championship.

But at a terrible price.

The mercurial Ferrari team-leader, Gilles Villeneuve was killed in a ghastly accident in practice for the Belgian Grand Prix at Zolder.

The little French Canadian was on a banzai lap when he clipped the rear wheel of a slower car. His seat belts tore from their mountings and he was hurled across the track and fatally injured.

The mood in the Ferrari camp was at a low ebb, as relationships between Villeneuve and his team-mate Didier were at an all-time low before the accident. For a while, they were not even on speaking terms.

The row between FISA and FOCA had errupted again after Piquet (Brabham) and Rosberg (Williams) were disqualified from first and second places in the second race of the year In Brazil for allegedly running underweight cars.

FISA teams boycotted the San Marino Grand Prix in protest

Just 13 FOCA cars took part.

Villeneuve's Ferrari led into the last lap, the team-leader assuming that Pironi would not try any deperate manouevre which might deprive the team of a famous one-two.

But the baby-faced Frenchman did just that, to Gilles utter disgust. Many think that his fury may just have got the better of him that fateful last day in Belgium.

FACT FILE 9

Alan Jones retired back to Australia 1t the end of 1981.

His place in the Williams team was taken by Finland's Keke Rosberg.

Back then, Keke was something of a novelty. Most of his fellow countrymen appeared to prefer to go rallying - and had a ream of world titles to show how good they were at it.

But Rosberg was a real flier in his chosen discipline, finishing a fine fifth in his first race for the team in South.

His second place in the next round in Brazil was even better. Then came that disqualification.

Designers of the normally aspirated cars knew that they needed every trick in the book to keep the weight down - and there were some very ingenious ploys used...

Both Brabham and Williams used a water-cooled braking system, which sprayed out the water during the race - then topped up the tanks before the cars were weighed at the end.

Brabham had a lot of engine problems with their new BMW turbo engines.

Reigning Champion,Nelson Piquet failed to qualify in Detroit.

The capital of the American car industry hosted a round of the Championship for the first time in 1982.

It was won by John Watson, who had only qualified 17th on the grid.

The drivers complained about the track surface -'like driving on a washboard' commented Wattie, afterwards.

Carlos Reutemann stunned the sport when he abruptly retired from Formula One after the first two rounds of the year.

He never lost his love of motor sport and finished third in the Argentine Rally for Audi.

Today, he is the Governor of Sante Fe Province and, rumour has it,may run for the Presidency of his beloved Argentina.

Ferrari suffered another severe blow in 1982 at Hockenheim.

Pironi qualified on pole in Friday's dry practice but, unsighted by driving rain' smashed into the back of Alain Prost's Renault in Saturday's session and sustained severe leg injuries which would spell the end of his Formula One career.

He died in an off-shore powerboat race off the Isle of Wight in 1987.

And there was more tragedy to come at the end of a sad, sad 1982 season.

Riccardo Paletti, the rookie, Osella driver sustained fatal injuries in a start line-accident in Canada

And then came news of the death at the age of 54 of Colin Chapman of a massive heart attack. One of the most innovative and brilliant designers in the business:the father of 'ground effect', 'Chunky' Chapman was an unmistakable figure in motor sport, a David Niven look-alike, with the same charisma. In latter years he had become increasingly disenchanted with the authorities and came under intense pressure when the de Lorean fraud was revealed.

1982 was the year of Finland's first World Drivers' Championship but many would prefer to forget it.

FACT FILE 11

The sport seemed to have gained its equilibrium after four years of bitter infighting amongst the authorities.

FISA banned 'ground-effect' for 1983. (Poor Colin Chapman must have turned in his grave).

The smaller non-turbo teams knew that they were in trouble and anxiously sought turbo-power.

Michele Alboreto gave the Ford Cosworth what would be the last victory for six years by a normally aspirated engine in Detroit.

But the turbo brigade dominated the Championships.

Nelson Piquet won his second Drivers' title at the final race of the year in a sun-soaked South African race.

His Brabham-BMW team-mate, Riccardo Patrese, won the race but Piquet cruised to third place, knowing his Championship was secure after arch-rival, Alain Prost, retired early on with engine failure.

Prost was strangely subdued during the weekend and was savaged by the French Press and the Renault team. after his failure to lift the crown.

Renault were furious that, after all the money they had poured into the development of the their turbos, the first Drivers' title had gone to one of the 'small' teams (and to a German engine manufacturer into the bargain!)

And what's more Ferrari won the Constructors' title.

FACT FILE 12

Niki Lauda, who had been lured out of retirement back to McLaren, won two Grands Prix in 1982. He struggled with the Ford engine for much of 1983 but had high hopes for the TAG turbo engine when it eventually arrived.

McLaren team boss Ron Dennis and the hundreds of special guests invited to the 1983 Monaco Grand Prix by title-sponsors, Marlboro, were mortified.

Neither Niki Lauda nor John Watson qualified for the famous race around the streets of the Principality.

Former Ligier designer Gerard Ducarouge had taken over at Lotus after the death of Colin Chapman.

Lotus tested a car with 'active suspension'- a computerised system devised to keep the car's undertray at an optimum angle.

Andrea de Cesaris had the best ever season of his career in 1983, with two second place finishes for the Alfa Romeo Turbo Team in Germany and South Africa.

He failed to win a single race in his career which spanned 15 seasons and comprised 208 Grands Prix!

The little Spirit team had Honda turbos for 1983 but failed to impress the Japanese and lost them to the Willliams team at the end of the year.

Former World motor-cycle Champion, Johnny Cecotto finished sixth at Long Beach in 1983.

He is the only Venezuelan driver to date to compete in the World Championship.

FACT FILE 13

The opening round of 1983 in Brazil was quite eventful.

Keke Rosberg finished second but was disqualified for receiving a push start after a pit stop.

Elio de Angelis finished 13th but was disqualified for running a Ford-powered Lotus instead of the Renault-powered car in which he qualifed.

Andrea de Cesaris was not allowed to start the race after failing to stop his Alfa Romeo at the weight-check.

Jacques Laffite rejoined Williams for 1983 but had a torrid time, failing to qualify for both Monza and the European Grand Prix at Brands Hatch.

Manfred Winkelhock's ATS-BMW was disqualified from the 1983 Dutch Grand Prix for overtaking on the parade lap (now who was that other German driver who had that problem recently?)

Doctor Jonathan Palmer made his debut in a third Williams at Brands Hatch. He finished 13th.

Jacques Villeneuve, uncle of 'Happy Jacques', he of the multi-coloured hair and the 1997 World Champion, was the younger brother of Gilles.

He failed to qualify a RAM-Ford in Montreal in 1983. His talents never matched those of his brother nor his nephew but he did win an Indy car race in 1985.

Patrick Tambay won an emotional race at Imola in 1983 and immediately dedicated his victory to the memory of the late Ferrari team-leader, Gilles Villeneuve.

Alain Prost had been fired by Renault for failing to win the Championship for them in 1983.

But Prost wasn't too unhappy and returned to team-up with Niki Lauda at McLaren, the team with whom Prost had begun his career in 1980.

The season was to provide rich pickings for the Woking-based team.

Prost won seven rounds, Niki won five but just squeezed home to his third World Drivers' title by 0.5 point!

McLaren finished with the amazing total of 143.5 points in the Constructors' Championship.

Nearest rivals Ferrari, scored just 57.5 points.

Only the Tyrrell team failed to run turbo engines in 1984. The funds just weren't there.

Both cars failed to qualify for the high-speed Austrian Grand Prix.

For the first time in Formula One history, the grid was composed solely of turbo-cars.

Renault, with their new drivers Tambay and Britain's Derek Warwick were desperate to win in front of their home fans in Dijon.

But it was Lauda's skill which managed to give the McLaren-TAG its fourth victory of the year, ahead of Tambay.

FACT FILE 15

The 1984 Monaco Grand Prix was a classic.

The Toleman-Hart team had signed Ayrton Senna, the young Brazilian protegé of Emerson Fittipaldi.

He had started the season well enough with two sixth place finishes.

But it was in the pouring rain at Monaco that he made everyone sit up and take notice.

There were accidents galore in the atrocious conditions both at the back and the front of the grid. French hopes were at a nadir as both Ligiers and both Renaults collided with each other.

Prost was on pole, with Nigel Mansell on the front row for the first time in his career in the much improved Lotus-Renault.

Prost and Mansell vied for the lead but, behind them, having started 13th was Senna, driving like a man possessed. Mansell spun into the Armco and Prost led. Senna in second place looked certain to pass him when the race was stopped because of the dangerous conditions.

Clerk of the Course was Jacky Ickx, himself once known as the 'Rain Master' found himself accused of favouring the TAG-Porsche powered McLaren.He was later fined by FISA for not following proper procedures for stopping the race.

Senna was philosophical: "For sure I would have overtaken him," he shrugged," but then I might have won or I might have spun off. I was on the limit too."

Who would have imagined the that Prost and Senna would become such bitter enemies in the future?

Poor Ken Tyrrell was in big trouble. An overjoyed Martin Brundle finished second in Detroit but the car was then disqualified for fuel irregularities.

Traces of lead shot were found in the water injection system, obviously some form of ballast.

FISA threw the little Surrey team out of the entire Championship.

They raced on under appeal but then were forced to sit out the last four races of the year when the governing body found against them and decreed that all points scored during the year should be nullified.

It was a bitter blow for the young Brundle who was just starting to establish himself and to his brilliant German team-mate, Stefan Bellof, who had finished third in Monaco, hard on Senna's heels

Downtown Dallas hosted a Grand Prix in 1984.

It was an organisational nightmare as the track surface broke up under the broiling Texas sun.

But one man had got the answer. Keke Rosber had bought himself a water-cooled skull cap to wear under his helmet. It had cost 2500 dollars.

It was worth every cent. Rosberg was untouchable but there were some hairy moments as he battled to get past Mansell's Lotus, whom he later accused of blocking tactics.

Mansell was in no fit state to argue. He had collapsed with heat exhaustion as he tried to push his crippled car across the line when its gearbox packed up on the last lap.

There were 14 accidents in the race - happily none serious.

FACT FILE 17

As the technical competition between the big names in the sport proceeded apace, many pondered on whether anyone would be able to keep up with the McLaren drivers in 1985.

The closed season had seen a number of major moves in the driver market.

Mansell had joined Rosberg in the Williams-Honda and the 'hot property' Ayrton Senna moved over to join the Lotus Renault brigade.

At last Alain Prost would win the Drivers' title but this time McLaren would just shade the Constructors' Championship by eight points from Ferrari.

Alfa Romeo carried the colours of Benetton for a second year but failed to score a point.

Michelin pulled out of Formula One, though Goodyear and Pirelli stayed on board.

This would be a season when new names would challenge the old order: When both Senna and Mansell would win their first Grand Prix; When the underfinanced Toleman team would be forced to miss the first three rounds of the year because of their lack of a tyre contract and when the Tyrrell Team would finally get their turbos.

It would also be a year in which the Tyrrell's brilliant young driver, Stefan Bellof, tipped by many as a future world beater would lose his life in a sports car accident at Spa.

And when Germany's Manfred Winkelhock would succumb to injuries received when his Porsche crashed at Mosport, Canada.

261

FACT FILE 18

Ayrton Senna's drive in Monaco in 1984 had shown the seeds of the greatness to come. The ability to drive in the wet is a sure sign of a driver's ability. Think of Stewart; think of Ickx; think of Schumacher. Then think of Senna.

It is fitting that his very first Grand Prix win should come on a rain-soaked track at Estoril. It was his 18th Grand Prix.

Starting from pole, in conditions better suited to powerboat racing than Formula One, he drove immaculately to lead from start to finish. It was hailed by many as the drive of the decade.

But not so for the ever-self-critical Brazilian.

"They all said I had made no mistakes, but that is not true, he commented. "At one point I had all four wheels on the grass, totally out of control but the car just came back onto the circuit. Everybody said it was fantastic car control. No way! It was pure luck."

Later he would a second time on the tricky, high-speed Spa circuit. He finished his second season in Formula One fourth overall in the Drivers' Championship.

And he lead more racing laps than any other driver during the year.

Later he would make a prophetic comment on his approach to racing: "The moments of joy in our life are very intense, but very short And they have to be overlaid very quickly by normal work if you want to continue to be successful."

FACT FILE 19

Elio de Angelis won the 1985 San Marino after Alain Prost, who had crossed the line first, was disqualified because his McLaren was found to be underweight at post-race scrutineering.

To the surprise of many it was the gifted young Italian who led the title table when the cars arrived in Monaco. Senna took pole but overcooked his engine on the start line.

Prost won the race after a great battle with Alboreto's Ferrari.

Only to run out of fuel on his victory lap!

But Elio's fighting third place kept him in the Championship lead.

Alboreto would be Prost's main rival until the end of the season but Alain's coolness in Monaco gave him the much needed points to continue towards his goal.

He finished fourth in the 1985 European Grand Prix on gloriously sunny day, a lowly placing for him but enough to assure him of becoming the first Frenchman to win the World title in the 35-year history of the sport.

But the biggest grin of all was on the face of the winner, Britain's Nigel Mansell.

It was his first Grand Prix victory ever in his 72nd race.

And to make it sweeter, he had passed Ayrton Senna to do it.

It was, quite amazingly, the first win by a British driver since 1977.

FACT FILE 20

The driver market was a fairly acrimonious place to be at the start of the 1986 season.

Elio de Angelis moved to Brabham because he felt that Senna was receiving preferrential treatment at Lotus.

Senna vetoed the appointment of Derek Warwick as his replacement, as he considered him too much of a rival. Instead, he insisted on young Johnny Dumfries, an inexperieced recent Formula 3 graduate.

Piquet moved to Williams to join Mansell and made it plain that he expected Nigel to bow to his superiority.

He had reckoned without the determination of the fiery Brit!

All was sweetness and light at McLaren, as Rosberg teamed with Prost for the year.

But McLaren designer John Barnard left to join Ferrari for a pot of gold.

He even persuaded Enzo Ferrari to allow him to set up his engineering workshop in Surrey, as he did not wish to move to Italy.

Incredibly, the'Old Man' agreed.

The sport was shocked to learn that Frank Williams had been critically injured after a road crash on his way back from a testing session at Paul Ricard.

He would remain in hospital for months and would be confined to a wheel chair for the rest of his life, severely paralysed from the waist down

FISA decreed that only turbo-charged engines were to be used in 1986.

And technology was on the march again, the cars carrying computerised links with their pits which enabled team managers to radio instructions to their drivers during the race concerning boost pressure and fuel consumption.

The Italian fashion house, Benetton, bought out the Toleman team and renamed the cars as Benettons. They ran BMW engines and signed the talented Austrian Gerhard Berger to drive for them.

He rewarded them with a win in Mexico, a first victory for both driver and team.

Nigel Mansell won five races for Williams and Piquet four.

In the Spanish Grand Prix Mansell finished just one hundreth of a second behind the Brazilian.

Senna took nine pole positions for Lotus during the season but only won twice.

At Adelaide,British hopes were high that Mansell could claim a fabulous first World Drivers' Championship. He only needed to finsish fourth, whilst both Piquet and Prost had to win to pip him to the post.

Mansell was lying second behind his team-mate, seemingly en route to the title.

With just a quarter of the race to go, his left rear tyre exploded in a shower of sparks and only Mansell's skill prevented a serious accident. But it was no comfort to the dejected driver.

Prost won the race (his 25th Grand Prix victory) and his second successive title, although Williams walked the Constructors Championship.

FACT FILE 22

The cost of running turbo engines was exhorbitant, so FISA decided to reintroduce normally aspirated power units in 1987.

Two new awards, the Jim Clark Cup and the Colin Chapman Tropy, were awarded to driver and team, respectively using normally aspirated 3.5 litre units in the season.

Britain's Jonathan Palmer won the Driver's Cup and his team, Tyrrell, the Constructors'. At last, Uncle Ken's smile returned!

Keke Rosberg had retired at the end of the 1986 season, so Sweden's affable Swede. Stefan Johansson joined Prost at McLaren.

Renault, instigators of the turbo revolution,decided they had enough of the sport and pulled out. Lotus turned to Honda power.

It was agreed that turbo engines would be phased out of Formula One over the next two years. Turbos would be banned completely from 1989 and for the sake of consistency, everyone concurred that there would be no more rule changes before 1991.

After 17 years with the Brabham team, South African-born designer,Gordon Murray switched allegiance to McLaren.

Senna again proved intransigent about his choice of team-mate, so Satoru Nakajima became the first Japanese driver to graduate to Formula One.

He surprised everyone by finishing an excellent fourth in the British Grand Prix, a source of much celebration back home in Okazaki City.

And everyone was delighted to see the return of Frank Williams to the pits, back to oversee yet another brilliant year for his team.

Mansell won six rounds and again looked good for the Championship.

But a practice accident before the 1987 Japanese Grand Prix caused bad back injuries which forced him to sit out the remaining two rounds.

The Drivers' title went to his team-mate Piquet for the third time, with Mansell second and Senna third.

Senna's forceful driving style wasn't exactly winning him many friends. Not that the Brazilian cared.

Mansell and Senna collided during the 1987 Belgian Grand Prix at Spa and the irate Englishman strode down the pits to confront the Lotus driver about the incident.

An angry scuffle followed!

Senna took the first of what would prove to be an all-time record six wins in Monaco.

Temperatures were rising between the team-mates in the Williams camp. Piquet, furious to have been beaten by Mansell in both France and Silverstone, announced that he would be looking for a new seat at the end of the season.

So intense was the rivalry between the two drivers that both spun off during practice for the British Grand Prix in an effort to outdo each other.

Nelson won the battle for pole by just 0.07seconds

But both Williams' drivers were outfumbled by Alain Prost who made a brilliant getaway from the second row to snatch the lead.

First Piquet, then Mansell bustled by and disappeared into the distance.

Much to the dismay of the 100,000 adoring fans at Silverstone, Mansell was forced to pit for new tyres.

He returned to the fray 28 seconds behind Piquet, with 29 laps remaining.

Surely the task was too much, even for Mansell in front of his home crowd?

But in a drive of typically, dogged determination, the British hero reeled in the Brazilian and pulled off a typically audacious overtaking manouevre at Stowe.

Mansell was so elated by his second successive British win that he stopped at Stowe corner and kissed the track. (Don't think Bernie would approve nowadays, Nigel!)

Frank Williams is reported to have radioed Mansell before the start: "I've only two words to say to you Nigel, 'brain power'. Have a good race!"

He did! And 'Mansell Mania' was born...

Although the hordes of supporters who invaded the track as he ran out of fuel on the slowing down lap gave other drivers, still racing to the finish, heart-attacks.

Almost unnoticed, Gerhard Berger had notched up back-to-back wins for Ferrari in Japan and Australia in 1987.

Senna, who could have snatched second place in the Drivers' Championship in Nigel's absence in Australia finished second in the race.

But his delight would be short-lived.

His Lotus-Honda was disqualified after scrutineering because of illegal brake ducts.

Michele Alboreto was promoted to second place, making it a Ferrari one-two.

Alain Prost broke Jackie Stewart's long-standing record of Grand Prix victories, his win in the Portuguese Grand Prix giving him a total of 28.

Williams won the 1987 Constructors' title with ease, scoring almost twice as many points as nearest rivals, McLaren.

FACT FILE 26

1988 would be the last year before the turbo cars were banned.

Piquet's strong affiliations with Honda saw him join Lotus in 1988.

Which left the way clear for Senna to join Prost at McLaren for whom Ron Dennis had also negociated a deal to run Honda engines during the year.

This left the Williams team struggling all season with a Judd power unit, which failed to produce any wins and saw the once dominant team finish a (for them) lowly seventh in the Constructors' Championship.

Bernie Ecclestone pulled the Brabham team out of the Championship, as their performances went into a decline.

The McLaren team dominated the year with 15 wins in 16 races.

Senna took 13 pole position, won eight races and his first World Drivers' Championship.

Thus, he became the third Brazilian to take the crown in the history of the World Championship.

Prost won seven races and finished runner-up.

The McLaren pair finished first and second in ten races.

Only Gerhard Berger interrupted a McLaren clean-sweep.

The battling Austrian took an emotional victory at Monza for Ferrari, just one month after the death of one of motor sport's icons, Enzo Ferrari, who died at the age of 90.

FACT FILE 27

The atmosphere between Prost and Senna at McLaren was bubbling.

There had been a clash of personalities from the start and 1989 would see it boil over onto a bitter rivalry both on and off the track.

Mansell and Piquet's relationship in 1987 was bad, but the Senna/Prost battle was to become worse and worse as the season progressed.

The Brazilian's supreme self-confidence in his ability, and often his forceful style of showing it did not impress the quieter, more affable French star.

Everything would come to a head in the final round of the year in Japan.

1989 marked the first year of the new formula for normally-aspirated cars.

McLaren continued their relationship with Honda, who duly obliged with a superb power unit.

Williams switched to Renault, who returned to the sport as major engine suppliers, having recovered from their turbo tantrums.

Nigel Mansell had moved over to Ferrari, after his poor 1988 season.

John Barnard's new car featured an innovative seven-speed gearbox which allowed the driver to change gear simply by flicking a paddle on the back of the steering wheel.

FACT FILE 28

Williams signed up one of the most experienced drivers in the business, Riccardo Patrese and Belgium's Thierry Boutsen for 1989.

Patrese would work closely with Patrick Head to bring the new Williams up to competitive form once more and was unlucky not to win two races.

Boutsen took the chequered flag for the first time in seven seasons - twice. A masterly display in torrential rain in Canada when he headed home a Williams one - two was followed by an equally impressive display in Australia.

Mansell thrilled his new team, Ferrari, by winning the first Grand Prix of the year in Brazil. He followed it up with another victory in Hungary.

And a win for his team-mate Berger in Portugal helped Ferrari to finish a highly respectable third in the 1989 Constructor's Championship.

But the gap between the big boys with the money to develop their cars and the 'minnows' of the sport, who did not, was never more evident.

There were no fewer than 20 teams and Pre-qualfying sessions had to be introduced to reduce the field down to the 30 who would attempt to qualify for the 26 places on the grid.

Brabham had been sold by Bernie Ecclestone and returned but were embarrasingly uncompetitive with the underpowered Judd engine.

And motor-cycle wizzards Yamaha came up with a power unit for Zakspeed which didn't exactly set the tracks alight.

Once again, the season was all about McLaren.

The boys in red and white won 10 of the year's 16 races.

Senna won six; Prost four.

You could have cut the atmosphere with a knife as the pair arrived in Japan for the penultimate round. Prost needed to win one of the last two rounds to clinch a third title - Senna needed to win both.

Qualified on the front row of the grid, the two hurtled towards the chicane. Neither would give quarter and they locked wheels and slid off in an embarrasing tangle for team boss, Ron Dennis.

The title was Prost's -or was it. Senna got a push start from the marshalls past the chicane, returned to the pits for a new nose cone and 'won' the race.

But he was later disqualified in a rage by the stewards for having missed out part of the circuit when he restarted.

He was fined 100,000 dollars and given a suspended ban on his racing licence for the next six months.

Benetton's young Italian Alessandro Nannini, who had finished in second place was awarded the victory - and Prost won this World title.

And Nannini went on to prove his prowess in the final race of the year by finishing in a fine second place.

The Benetton team would finish fourth in the Constructors' Championship and they had something else to smile about. Ferrari designer John Barnard decided not to renew his contract with Maranello and joined Benetton in October.

1980s

RESULTS

RESULTS 1980

1980 What a difference a year makes! The 1979 World Drivers' Champion, Jody Scheckter would retire at the end of 1980 with just two points to his name. He even failed to qualify in Montreal, much to his chagrin! And the all-conquering Ferrari team finished the year in 10th place in the Constructors' table. Another former World Champion to hang up his helmet at the end of the year was Emerson Fittipaldi. But he would return to racing - and how! - in CART racing in the USA a few years later. Alan Jones won five races and, with the help of new team-mate, Reutemann, gave Williams their very first Constructors' title. The sport was robbed of the plucky little Frenchman Depailler when he died in a high-speed testing accident at Hockenheim in mid-season. Clay Regazzoni was paralysed for life after a massive "Off" at Long Beach. And Jean-Pierre Jabouille, the leading light of the Renault Turbo onslaught, suffered severe leg injuries in an accident during the Canadian Grand Prix which would effectively end his Grand Prix career. McLaren, too, had little to smile about. Although some French chap named Prost did finish sixth in his first ever Formula One race in Argentina...Ligier proved to be Williams' nearest rivals and a certain Brazilian called Piquet finished runner-up to Jones in the Drivers' Championship. There were 14 rounds. Best five results from first half of the season, best five from seven in second half for Drivers' title. All cars finishing in top six places took Constructors' points. Points: 9-6-4-3-2-1 for first six places.

ROUND 1/ARGENTINE GRAND PRIX

BUENOS AIRES, 13 JANUARY

1. JONES(AUS)	WILLIAMS-FORD	1HR 43MIN 24.38SEC
2. PIQUET(BRA)	BRABHAM-FORD	1HR 43MIN 48.97SEC
3. ROSBERG(FIN)	FITTIPALDI-FORD	1HR 44MIN 43.02SEC
4. DALY(IRL)	TYRRELL-FORD	1HR 44MIN 47.86SEC
5. GIACOMELLI(ITA)	ALFA ROMEO	52 LAPS
6. PROST(FRA)	MCLAREN-FORD	52 LAPS

Race: 53 laps of 3.71mile/5.97km (196 miles/316.41kms)
Fastest lap: Jones, 1min 50.45sec, 120.87mph/194.53kph
Pole position: Jones, 1min 44.17sec 24 starters, 7 classified finishers

ROUND 2/BRAZILIAN GRAND PRIX

INTERLAGOS, 27 JANUARY

1. ARNOUX(FRA)	RENAULT TURBO	1HR 40MIN 01.33SEC
2. DE ANGELIS(ITA)	LOTUS-FORD	1HR 40MIN 23.19SEC
3. JONES(AUS)	WILLIAMS-FORD	1HR 41MIN 07.44SEC
4. PIRONI(FRA)	LIGIER-FORD	1HR 41MIN 41.46SEC
5. PROST(FRA)	MCLAREN-FORD	1HR 42MIN 26.74SEC
6. PATRESE(ITA)	ARROWS-FORD	39 LAPS

Race: 40 laps of 4.89mile/7.87km (195.6miles/314.8kms)
Fastest lap: Arnoux, 2min 27.31sec, 119.57mph/ 192.42kph
Pole position: Jabouille(FRA)Renault Turbo, 2min 21.4sec 24 starters, 16 class. finishers

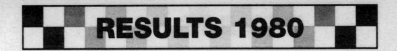

RESULTS 1980

ROUND 3/ SOUTH AFRICAN GRAND PRIX
KYALAMI, 1 MARCH

1. ARNOUX(FRA)	RENAULT TURBO	1HR 36MIN 52.54SEC
2. LAFFITE(FRA)	LIGIER-FORD	1HR 37MIN 26.61SEC
3. PIRONI(FRA)	LIGIER-FORD	1HR 37MIN 45.03SEC
4. PIQUET(BRA)	BRABHAM-FORD	1HR 37MIN 53.56SEC
5. REUTEMANN(ARG)	WILLIAMS-FORD	77 LAPS
6. MASS(GER)	ARROWS-FORD	77 LAPS

Race: 78 laps of 2.55mile/4.1km (198.9miles/319.8kms)
Fastest lap: Arnoux, 1min 13.15sec, 125.49mph/201.96
Pole position: Jabouille(FRA) Renault Turbo, 1min 10.00sec 24 starters, 13 class. finishers

ROUND 4/US GRAND PRIX (WEST)
LONG BEACH, CALIFORNIA, 30 MARCH

1. PIQUET(BRA)	BRABHAM-FORD	1HR 50MIN 18.55SEC
2. PATRESE(ITA)	ARROWS-FORD	1HR 51MIN 07.76SEC
3. E. FITTIPALDI(BRA)	FITTIPALDI-FORD	1HR 51MIN 37.11SEC
4. WATSON(GB)	MCLAREN-FORD	79 LAPS
5. J. SCHECKTER(SA)	FERRARI	79 LAPS
6. PIRONI(FRA)	LIGIER-FORD	79 LAPS

Race: 80.5 laps of 2.02mile/3.25km (162.61miles/261.63km)
Fastest lap: Piquet, 1min 19.83sec, 91.09mph/146.33kph
Pole position: Piquet, 1min 17.69sec 24 starters, 10 classified finishers

ROUND 5/BELGIAN GRAND PRIX
ZOLDER, 4 MAY

1. PIRONI(FRA)	LIGIER-FORD	1HR 38MIN 46.51SEC
2. JONES(AUS)	WILLIAMS-FORD	1HR 39MIN 33.88SEC
3. REUTEMANN(ARG)	WILLIAMS-FORD	1HR 40MIN 10.63SEC
4. ARNOUX (FRA)	RENAULT TURBO	71 LAPS
5. JARIER(FRA)	TYRRELL-FORD	71 LAPS
6. G. VILLENEUVE(CAN)	FERRARI	71 LAPS

Race: 72 laps of 2.65mile/4.26km (190.8miles/306kms)
Fastest lap: Laffite(FRA), Ligier-Ford, 1min 20.88sec, 117.88mph/189.70kph
Pole position: Jones, 1min 19.12sec 24 starters, 11 classified finishers

ROUND 6/MONACO GRAND PRIX
MONTE CARLO, 18 MAY

1. REUTEMANN(ARG)	WILLIAMS-FORD	1HR 55MIN 34.37SEC
2. LAFFITE(FRA)	LIGIER-FORD	1HR 56MIN 47,99SEC
3. PIQUET(BRA)	BRABHAM-FORD	1HR 56MIN 52.09SEC
4. MASS(GER)	ARROWS-FORD	75 LAPS
5. G. VILLENEUVE(CAN)	FERRARI	75 LAPS
6. E. FITTIPALDI(BRA)	FITTIPALDI-FORD	74 LAPS

Race: 76 laps of 2.06mile/3.31km (156.56miles/251.56kms)
Fastest lap: Patrese(ITA), Arrows-Ford, 1min 26.06sec, 86.09mph/138.55kph
Pole position: Pironi(FRA), Ligier-Ford, 1min 24.81sec 20 starters, 8 classified finishers

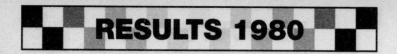
RESULTS 1980

ROUND 7/FRENCH GRAND PRIX
PAUL RICARD, 29 JUNE

1. JONES(AUS)	WILLIAMS-FORD	1HR 32MIN 43.42SEC
2. PIRONI(FRA)	LIGIER-FORD	1HR 32MIN 47.94SEC
3. LAFFITE(FRA)	LIGIER-FORD	1HR 33MIN 13.68SEC
4. PIQUET(BRA)	BRABHAM-FORD	1HR 33MIN 58.30SEC
5. ARNOUX(FRA)	RENAULT TURBO	1HR 33MIN 59.57SEC
6. REUTEMANN(ARG)	WILLIAMS-FORD	1HR 34MIN 00.16SEC

Race: 54 laps of 3.61mile/5.81km (194.94miles/313.74miles)
Fastest lap: Jones, 1min 41.45sec,128.11mph/206.17kph
Pole position: Laffite, 1min 38.88sec 24 starters, 14 classified finishers

ROUND 8/BRITISH GRAND PRIX
BRANDS HATCH, 13 JULY

1. JONES(AUS)	WILLIAMS-FORD	1HR 34MIN 49.23SEC
2. PIQUET(BRA)	BRABHAM-FORD	1HR 35MIN 00.24SEC
3. REUTEMANN(ARG)	WILLIAMS-FORD	1HR 35MIN 02.51SEC
4. DALY(IRL)	TYRRELL-FORD	75 LAPS
5. JARIER(FRA)	TYRRELL-FORD	75 LAPS
6. PROST(FRA)	MCLAREN-FORD	75 LAPS

Race: 76 laps of 2.61mile/4.21km (198.36miles/320kms)
Fastest lap: Pironi(FRA), Ligier-Ford, 1min 12.37sec,130.02mph/209.24kph
Pole position: Pironi, 1min 11.01sec 24 starters, 13 classified finishers

ROUND 9/GERMAN GRAND PRIX
HOCKENHEIM, 10 AUGUST

1. LAFFITE(FRA)	LIGIER-FORD	1HR 22MIN 59.73SEC
2. REUTEMANN(ARG)	WILLIAMS-FORD	1HR 23MIN 02.92SEC
3. JONES(AUS)	WILLIAMS-FORD	1HR 23MIN 43.26SEC
4. PIQUET(BRA)	BRABHAM-FORD	1HR 23MIN 44.21SEC
5. GIACOMELLI(ITA)	ALFA ROMEO	1HR 24MIN 16.22SEC
6. G. VILLENEUVE(CAN)	FERRARI	1HR 24MIN 28.45SEC

Race: 45 laps of 4.22mile/6.79km (189.91miles/305.6kms)
Fastest lap: Jones, 1 min 48.49sec, 139.9mph/225.25kph
Pole position: Jones, 1min 45.85sec 24 starters, 16 classified finishers

ROUND 10/AUSTRIAN GRAND PRIX
OSTERREICHRING, 17 AUGUST

1. JABOUILLE(FRA)	RENAULT TURBO	1HR 26MIN 15.73SEC
2. JONES(AUS)	WILLIAMS-FORD	1HR 26MIN 16.55SEC
3. REUTEMANN(ARG)	WILLIAMS-FORD	1HR 26MIN 35.09SEC
4. LAFFITE(FRA)	LIGIER-FORD	1HR 26MIN 57.75SEC
5. PIQUET(BRA)	BRABHAM-FORD	1HR 27MIN 18.54SEC
6. DE ANGELIS(ITA)	LOTUS-FORD	1HR 27MIN 30.70SEC

Race: 54 laps of 3.69mile/5.94km (199.26 miles/320.76kms)
Fastest lap: Arnoux(FRA), Renault Turbo, 1min 32.53ec, 143.66mph/231.20kph
Pole position: Arnoux, 1min 30.27sec 24 starters, 16 classified finishers

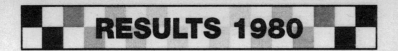
RESULTS 1980

ROUND 11/DUTCH GRAND PRIX
ZANDVOORT, 31 AUGUST

1. PIQUET(BRA)	BRABHAM-FORD	1HR 38MIN 13.87SEC
2. ARNOUX(FRA)	RENAULT	1HR 38MIN 26.76SEC
3. LAFFITE(FRA)	LIGIER-FORD	1HR 38MIN 27.26SEC
4. REUTEMANN(ARG)	WILLIAMS-FORD	1HR 38MIN 29.12SEC
5. JARIER(FRA)	TYRRELL-FORD	1HR 39MIN 13.85SEC
6. PROST(FRA)	MCLAREN-FORD	1HR 39MIN 36.45SEC

Race: 72 laps of 2.64mile/4.25km (190.08miles/306kms)
Fastest lap: Arnoux, 1min 19.35sec,119.87mph/192.91kph
Pole position: Arnoux, 1 min 17.44sec 24 starters, 11 classified finishers

ROUND 12/ITALIAN GRAND PRIX
IMOLA, 14 SEPTEMBER

1. PIQUET(BRA)	BRABHAM-FORD	1HR 38MIN 07.52SEC
2. JONES(AUS)	WILLIAMS-FORD	1HR 38MIN 36.45SEC
3. REUTEMANN(ARG)	WILLIAMS-FORD	1HR 39MIN 21.19SEC
4. DE ANGELIS(ITA)	LOTUS-FORD	59 LAPS
5. ROSBERG(FIN)	FITTIPALDI-FORD	59 LAPS
6. PIRONI(FRA)	LIGIER-FORD	59 LAPS

Race: 60 laps of 3.11mile/5km (186.6 miles/300kms)
Fastest lap: Jones, 1min 36.10sec, 116.4mph/ 187.33kph
Pole position: Arnoux(FRA), Renault Turbo, 1min 33.99sec 24 starters, 13 class. finishers

ROUND 13/CANADIAN GRAND PRIX
MONTREAL, 28 SEPTEMBER

1. JONES(AUS)	WILLIAMS-FORD	1HR 46MIN 45.53SEC
2. REUTEMANN(ARG)	WILLIAMS-FORD	1HR 47MIN 01.07SEC
3. PIRONI(FRA)	LIGIER-FORD	1HR 47MIN 04.60SEC
4. WATSON(GB)	MCLAREN-FORD	1HR 47MIN 16.51SEC
5. G.VILLENEUVE(CAN)	FERRARI	1HR 47MIN 40.76SEC
6. REBAQUE(MEX)	BRABHAM-FORD	69 LAPS

Race: 70 laps of 2.74 mile/4.41km (197.28miles/317.52kms)
Fastest lap: Pironi, 1min 28.77sec, 113.4mph/182.5kph
Pole position: Piquet(BRA), Brabham-Ford, 1min 27.32sec 24 starters 12 class.finishers

ROUND 14/US GRAND PRIX(EAST)
WATKINS GLEN, 5 OCTOBER

1. JONES(AUS)	WILLIAMS-FORD	1HR 34MIN 36.05SEC
2. REUTEMANN(ARG)	WILLIAMS-FORD	1HR 34MIN 40.26SEC
3. PIRONI(FRA)	LIGIER-FORD	1HR 34MIN 48.62SEC
4. DE ANGELIS(ITA)	LOTUS-FORD	1HR 35MIN 05.74SEC
5. LAFFITE(FRA)	LIGIER-FORD	58 LAPS
6. ANDRETTI(USA)	LOTUS-FORD	58 LAPS

Race: 59 laps of 3.38mile/5.44km (199.42miles/320.96kms)
Fastest lap: Jones, 1min 34.07sec, 129.24mph/207.99kph
Pole position: Giacomelli(ITA) Alfa Romeo, 1min 3.29sec 24 starters, 11 class. finishers

RESULTS 1980

DRIVERS' WORLD CHAMPIONSHIP 1980

1.	JONES	67 points	4.	LAFFITE	34 points
2.	PIQUET	54 points	5.	PIRONI	32 points
3.	REUTEMANN	42 points	6.	ARNOUX	29 points

CONSTRUCTORS' WORLD CHAMPIONSHIP 1980

1.	WILLIAMS-FORD	120 points	4.	RENAULT	38 points
2.	LIGIER-FORD	66 points	5.	LOTUS-FORD	14 points
3.	BRABHAM-FORD	55 points	6.	TYRRELL-FORD	12 points

1981 This should have been Reutemann's year. The Drivers' title chase went down to the wire at the final race - held in the car park of Caesars Palace Las Vegas. The Argentinian took pole but seemed to lose heart in the race and Piquet, gleefully, took the Championship by just one point. Prost moved to Renault and won his first Grand Prix. Pironi replaced Scheckter at Ferrari. Watson brought joy to McLaren by winning the British Grand Prix.

Mansell scored his first podium finish, third in Belgium. Williams dominated the Constructors' Championship again. The political wrangling between the teams and the authorities continued. Italy hosted two Grands Prix for the first time since 1957. There were 15 official rounds. Best 11 results counted for the Drivers' Championship. All races counted for the Constructors' Championship, with points awarded to every car in top six. Points: 9-6-4-3-2-1.

ROUND 1/US GRAND PRIX (WEST)
LONG BEACH, 15 MARCH

1. JONES(AUS)	WILLIAMS-FORD	1HR 50MIN 41.33SEC
2. REUTEMANN(ARG)	WILLIAMS-FORD	1HR 50MIN 50.52SEC
3. PIQUET(BRA)	BRABHAM-FORD	1HR 51MIN 16.25SEC
4. ANDRETTI(USA)	ALFA ROMEO	1HR 51MIN 30.64SEC
5. CHEEVER(USA)	TYRRELL-FORD	1HR 51MIN 48.03SEC
6. TAMBAY(FRA)	THEODORE-FORD	1HR 51MIN 48.03SEC

Race: 80.5 laps of 2.02mile/3.25km (162.61miles/261.63kms)
Fastest lap: Jones, 1min 20.90sec, 89.89mph/144.66kph
Pole position: Patrese(ITA), Arrows-Ford, 1min 19.4sec 24 starters, 8 classified finishers

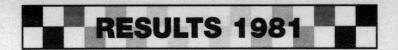

RESULTS 1981

ROUND 2/BRAZILIAN GRAND PRIX
RIO DE JANEIRO, 29 MARCH

1. REUTEMANN(ARG)	WILLIAMS-FORD	2HR 00MIN 23.66SEC
2. JONES(AUS)	WILLIAMS-FORD	2HR 00MIN 28.10SEC
3. PATRESE(ITA)	ARROWS-FORD	2HR 01MIN 26.74SEC
4. SURER(SWISS)	ENSIGN-FORD	2HR 01MIN 40.69SEC
5. DE ANGELIS(ITA)	LOTUS-FORD	2HR 01MIN 50.08SEC
6. LAFFITE(FRA)	LIGIER-MATRA	2HR 01MIN 50.49SEC

Race: 62 laps of 3.13mile/5.03km (194.06miles/311.86kms)
Fastest lap: Surer, 1min 54.30sec, 98.46mph/158.45kph
Pole position: Piquet(BRA), Brabham-Ford,1min 35.07sec 24 starters, 13 class. finishers

ROUND 3/ARGENTINE GRAND PRIX
BUENOS AIRES, 12 APRIL

1. PIQUET(BRA)	BRABHAM-FORD	1HR 34MIN 32.74SEC
2. REUTEMANN(ARG)	WILLIAMS-FORD	1HR 34MIN 59.35SEC
3. PROST(FRA)	RENAULT TURBO	1HR 35MIN 22.72SEC
4. JONES(AUS)	WILLIAMS-FORD	1HR 35MIN 40.62SEC
5. ARNOUX(FRA)	RENAULT-TURBO	1HR 36MIN 04.59SEC
6. DE ANGELIS(ITA)	LOTUS-FORD	52 LAPS

Race: 53 laps of 3.71mile/5.97km (196.63kms/316.41kms)
Fastest lap: Piquet, 1min 45.29sec, 126.80mph/204.07kph
Pole position: Piquet, 1min 42.66sec 24 starters, 13 classified finishers

ROUND 4/SAN MARINO GRAND PRIX
IMOLA, 3 MAY

1. PIQUET(BRA)	BRABHAM-FORD	1HR 51MIN 23.97SEC
2. PATRESE(ITA)	ARROWS-FORD	1HR 51MIN 28.55SEC
3. REUTEMANN(ARG)	WILLIAMS-FORD	1HR 51MIN 30.31SEC
4. REBAQUE(MEX)	BRABHAM-FORD	1HR 51MIN 46.86SEC
5. PIRONI(FRA)	FERRARI TURBO	1HR 51MIN 49.84SEC
6. DE CESARIS(ITA)	MCLAREN-FORD	1HR 52MIN 30.58SEC

Race: 60 laps of 3.13mile/5.04km (187.8miles/302.4kms)
Fastest lap: G. Villeneuve, Ferrari Turbo, 1min 48.06sec, 104.33mph/167.90kph
Pole position: G. Villeneuve, 1min 34.52sec 24 starters, 13 classified finishers

ROUND 5/BELGIAN GRAND PRIX
ZOLDER 17 MAY 1981

1. REUTEMANN(ARG)	WILLIAMS-FORD	1HR 16MIN 31.61SEC
2. LAFFITE(FRA)	LIGIER-MATRA	1HR 17MIN 07.67SEC
3. MANSELL(GB)	LOTUS-FORD	1HR 17MIN 15.30SEC
4. G.VILLENEUVE(CAN)	FERRARI TURBO	1HR 17MIN 19.25SEC
5. DE ANGELIS(ITA)	LOTUS-FORD	1HR 17MIN 20.81SEC
6. CHEEVER(USA)	TYRRELL-FORD	1HR 17MIN 24.12SEC

Race: *54 laps of 2.65mile/4.26km (143miles/230.04kms)
Fastest lap: Reutemann, 1min 23.30sec, 114.45mph/184.19kph
Pole position: Reutemann, 1min 22.28sec 24 starters, 13 classified finishers
*Race distance reduced from 70 laps due to rain

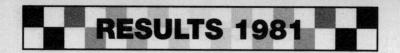

RESULTS 1981

ROUND 6/MONACO GRAND PRIX
MONTE CARLO, 31 MAY

1. G. VILLENEUVE(CAN)	FERRARI TURBO	1HR 54MIN 23.38SEC
2. JONES(AUS)	WILLIAMS-FORD	1HR 55MIN 03.29SEC
3. LAFFITE(FRA)	LIGIER-MATRA	1HR 55MIN 52.62SEC
4. PIRONI(FRA)	FERRARI TURBO	75 LAPS
5. CHEEVER(USA)	TYRRELL-FORD	74 LAPS
6. SURER(SWISS)	ENSIGN-FORD	74 LAPS

Race: 76 laps of 2.06mile/3.31km (156.56miles/251.56kms)
Fastest lap: Jones, 1min 27.47sec, 84.70mph/136.31kph
Pole position: Piquet(BRA), Brabham-Ford,1min 25.71sec 20 starters, 7 class. finishers

ROUND 7/SPANISH GRAND PRIX
JARAMA, 21 JUNE

1. G.VILLENEUVE(CAN)	FERRARI TURBO	1HR 46MIN 35.01SEC
2. LAFFITE(FRA)	LIGIER-MATRA	1HR 46MIN 35.23SEC
3. WATSON(GB)	MCLAREN-FORD	1HR 46MIN 35.59SEC
4. REUTEMANN(ARG)	WILLIAMS-FORD	1HR 46MIN 36.02SEC
5. DE ANGELIS(ITA)	LOTUS-FORD	1HR 46MIN 36.25SEC
6. MANSELL(GB)	LOTUS-FORD	1HR 47MIN 03.59SEC

Race: 80 laps of 2.06mile/3.31km (164.8miles/246.8kms)
Fastest lap: Jones(AUS), Williams-Ford,1min 17.82sec, 95.21mph/153.22kph
Pole position: Laffite, 1min 13.75sec 24 starters 16 classified finishers

ROUND 8/FRENCH GRAND PRIX
DIJON/PRENOIS, 5 JULY

1. PROST(FRA)	RENAULT TURBO	1HR 35MIN 48.13SEC
2. WATSON(GB)	MCLAREN-FORD	1HR 35MIN 50.42SEC
3. PIQUET(BRA)	BRABHAM-FORD	1HR 36MIN 12.35SEC
4. ARNOUX(FRA)	RENAULT TURBO	1HR 36MIN 30.43SEC
5. PIRONI(FRA)	FERRARI	79 LAPS
6. DE ANGELIS(ITA)	LOTUS-FORD	79 LAPS

Race: *80 laps of 2.36mile/3.8km (188.8miles/304kms)
Fastest lap: Prost, 1min 09.14sec, 122.94mph/197.86kph
Pole position: Arnoux, 1min 05.95sec 24 starters, 17 classified finishers
*Race interrupted by rain. Places awarded on aggregate of two halves.

ROUND 9/BRITISH GRAND PRIX
SILVERSTONE, 18 JULY

1. WATSON(GB)	MCLAREN-FORD	1HR 26MIN 54.80SEC
2. REUTEMANN(ARG)	WILLIAMS-FORD	1HR 27MIN 35.45SEC
3. LAFFITE(FRA)	LIGIER-MATRA	67 LAPS
4. CHEEVER(USA)	TYRRELL-FORD	67 LAPS
5. REBAQUE(MEX)	BRABHAM-FORD	67 LAPS
6. BORGUDD(SWE)	ATS-FORD	

Race: 68 laps of 2.93mile/4.72km (199.24miles/320.96kms)
Fastest lap: Arnoux(FRA), Renault Turbo, 1min 15.07sec, 140.61mph/226.29kph
Pole position: Arnoux, 1min 11.00sec 24 starters, 11 classified finishers

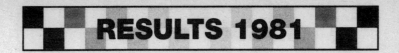

RESULTS 1981

ROUND 10/GERMAN GRAND PRIX
HOCKENHEIM, 2 AUGUST

1. PIQUET(BRA)	BRABHAM-FORD	1HR 25MIN 55.60SEC
2. PROST(FRA)	RENAULT TURBO	1HR 26MIN 07.12SEC
3. LAFFITE(FRA)	LIGIER-MATRA	1HR 27MIN 00.20SEC
4. REBAQUE(MEX)	BRABHAM-FORD	1HR 27MIN 35.29SEC
5. CHEEVER(USA)	TYRRELL-FORD	1HR 27MIN 35.29SEC
6. WATSON (GB)	MCLAREN-FORD	44 LAPS

Race: 45 laps of 4.22mile/6.79km (189.91miles/305.6kms)
Fastest lap: Jones(AUS), Williams-Ford, 1min 52.42sec, 135.07mph/217.37kph
Pole position: Prost, 1min 47.5sec 24 starters, 15 classified finishers

ROUND 11/AUSTRIAN GRAND PRIX
OSTERREICHRING, 16 AUGUST

1. LAFFITE(FRA)	LIGIER-MATRA	1HR 27MIN 36.47SEC
2. ARNOUX(FRA)	RENAULT TURBO	1HR 27MIN 41.64SEC
3. PIQUET(BRA)	BRABHAM-FORD	1HR 27MIN 43.81SEC
4. JONES(AUS)	WILLIAMS-FORD	1HR 27MIN 48.51SEC
5. REUTEMANN(ARG)	WILLIAMS-FORD	1HR 28MIN 08.32SEC
6. WATSON (GB)	MCLAREN-FORD	1HR 29MIN 07.61SEC

Race: 53 laps of 3.69mile/5.94km (199.26miles/320.76kms)
Fastest lap: Laffite, 1min 37.62sec, 136.17mph/320.76kph
*Pole position:*Arnoux, 1min 32.01sec 24 starters, 11 classified finishers

ROUND 12/DUTCH GRAND PRIX
ZANDVOORT, 30 AUGUST

1. PROST(FRA)	RENAULT TURBO	1HR 40MIN 22.43SEC
2. PIQUET(BRA)	BRABHAM-FORD	1HR 40MIN 30.67SEC
3. JONES(AUS)	WILLIAMS-FORD	1HR 40MIN 57.93SEC
4. REBAQUE(MEX)	BRABHAM-FORD	71 LAPS
5. DE ANGELIS(ITA)	LOTUS-FORD	71 LAPS
6. SALAZAR(CHILE)	ENSIGN-FORD	70 LAPS

Race: 72 laps of 2.64mile/4.25km (190.8miles/306kms)
Fastest lap: Jones, 1min 21.83sec, 116.24mph/187.06kph
Pole position: Prost, 1min 18.18sec 24 starters, 10 classified finishers

ROUND 13/ITALIAN GRAND PRIX
MONZA, 13 SEPTEMBER

1. PROST(FRA)	RENAULT TURBO	1HR 26MIN 33.90SEC
2. JONES(AUS)	WILLIAMS-FORD	1HR 26MIN 56.07SEC
3. REUTEMANN(ARG)	WILLIAMS-FORD	1HR 27MIN 24.48SEC
4. DE ANGELIS(ITA)	LOTUS-FORD	1HR 28MIN 06.80SEC
5. PIRONI(FRA)	FERRARI TURBO	1HR 28MIN 08.42SEC
6. PIQUET(BRA)	BRABHAM-FORD	51 LAPS

Race: 52 laps of 3.6mile/5.8km (180miles/290kms)
Fastest lap: Reutemann, 1min 37.53sec, 133.03mph/214.09kph
Pole position: Arnoux(FRA), Renault Turbo, 1min 33.46sec 24 starters, 10 class. finishers

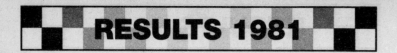

RESULTS 1981

ROUND 14/CANADIAN GRAND PRIX
MONTREAL, 27 SEPTEMBER

1. LAFFITE(FRA)	LIGIER-MATRA	2HR 01MIN 25.21SEC
2. WATSON(GB)	MCLAREN-FORD	2HR 01MIN 31.44SEC
3. G.VILLENEUVE(CAN)	FERRARI TURBO	2HR 03MIN 15.48SEC
4. GIACOMELLI(ITA)	ALFA ROMEO	62 LAPS
5. PIQUET(BRA)	BRABHAM-FORD	62 LAPS
6. DE ANGELIS(ITA)	LOTUS-FORD	62 LAPS

Race: *63 laps of 2.74mile/4.41km (172.62miles/277kms)
Fastest lap: Watson, 1min 49.48sec, 90.11mph/145.02kph
Pole position: Piquet, 1min 29.21sec 24 starters, 12 classified finishers
*Wet race, finished after two hours, 7 laps short of scheduled distance.

ROUND 15/US GRAND PRIX
LAS VEGAS, 17 OCTOBER

1. JONES(AUS)	WILLIAMS-FORD	1HR 44MIN 09.08SEC
2. PROST(FRA)	RENAULT-TURBO	1HR 44MIN 29.13SEC
3. GIACOMELLI(ITA)	ALFA ROMEO	1HR 44MIN 29.51SEC
4. MANSELL(GB)	LOTUS-FORD	1HR 44MIN 56.55SEC
5. PIQUET(BRA)	BRABHAM-FORD	1HR 45MIN 25.52SEC
6. LAFFITE(FRA)	LIGIER-MATRA	1HR 45MIN 27.25SEC

Race: 75 laps of 2.27mile/3.65km (170miles/273.75kms)
Fastest lap: Pironi(FRA),Ferrari Turbo, 1min 20.16sec, 101.86mph/163.93kph
Pole position: Reutemann(ARG) Williams-Ford, 1min 17.82sec
24 starters, 12 classified finishers

DRIVERS' WORLD CHAMPIONSHIP 1981

1. PIQUET	50 *points*	4. LAFFITE	44 *points*
2. REUTEMANN	49 *points*	5. PROST	43 *points*
3. JONES	46 *points*	6. WATSON	27 *points*

CONSTRUCTORS' WORLD CHAMPIONSHIP 1981

1. WILLIAMS-FORD	98 *points*	4. LIGIER-MATRA	44 *points*
2. BRABHAM-FORD	61 *points*	5. FERRARI	34 *points*
3. RENAULT	54 *points*	6. MCLAREN-FORD	28 *points*

RESULTS 1982

1982 Once more, a year of great sadness clouded the sport. The brilliant Gilles Villeneuve died in an horrific practice accident in Belgium and his team-mate Didier Pironi suffered terrible leg injuries in impossible practice conditions at Hockenheim. The baby-faced Frenchman would later lose his life in an off-shore powerboat race in Britain in 1987, his thirst for speed unquenchable. A shell-shocked Patrick Tambay took the laurels for Ferrari in Germany after a very brave drive. Rookie Riccardo Paletti died in a start-line accident in Canada. And the sport lost one of its greatest innovators in December when Lotus team-boss, Colin Chapman, died of a heart attack. Alan Jones left Williams to return home to Oz. Finland's Rosberg took his place and clinched the Drivers' title, despite only winning one race! Reutemann lasted only two rounds.The enegmatic Argentinian quitting for good to return home to Santa Fe. Niki Lauda was lured back from retirement by McLaren to win two races and spurred on team-mate Watson to equal his tally. Brabham harnessed the BMW turbo to great effect to claim victory in Canada. Elio de Angelis won his first Grand Prix, as did Riccardo Patrese, in Monaco. Mario Andretti hung up his Formula One helmet at the end of the season to return to a formidable Indy Car record in the States. The drivers went on strike before the South African race, thanks to an ongoing row with the autocratic FIA. There were THREE Grands Prix in the USA! There were 16 rounds, including the 'Swiss' Grand Prix at Dijon. Best 11 results counted for Drivers' title. Best six cars in every race for Constructors'. Points: 9-6-4-2-1.

ROUND 1/SOUTH AFRICAN GRAND PRIX
KYALAMI,23 JANUARY

1. PROST(FRA)	RENAULT TURBO	1HR 32MIN 08.40SEC
2. REUTEMANN(ARG)	WILLIAMS-FORD	1HR 32MIN 23.35SEC
3. ARNOUX(FRA)	RENAULT TURBO	1HR 32MIN 36.30SEC
4. LAUDA(AUT)	MCLAREN-FORD	1HR 32MIN 40.51SEC
5. ROSBERG(FIN)	WILLIAMS-FORD	1HR 32MIN 54.54SEC
6. WATSON(GB)	MCLAREN-FORD	1HR 32MIN 59.39SEC

Race: 77 laps of 2.55mile/4.1km (196.35miles/315.7kms)
Fastest lap: Prost, 1min 08.28sec, 134.46mph/216kph
Pole position: Arnoux, 1min 06.35sec 26 starters, 18 classified finishers

RESULTS 1982

ROUND 2/BRAZILIAN GRAND PRIX
RIO DE JANEIRO, 21 MARCH

1.PROST(FRA)	RENAULT TURBO	1HR 44MIN 33.13SEC
2.WATSON (GB)	MCLAREN-FORD	1HR 44MIN 36.12SEC
3.MANSELL(GB)	LOTUS-FORD	1HR 45MIN 10.00SEC
4.ALBORETO(ITA)	TYRRELL-FORD	1HR 45MIN 23.90SEC
5.WINKELHOCK(GER)	ATS-FORD	62 LAPS
6.PIRONI(FRA)	FERRARI	62 LAPS

Race: 63 laps of 3.13 mile/5.03km (197.19miles/316.89kms)
Fastest lap: Prost, 1min 37.02sec, 116mph/186.69kph
Pole position: Prost,1min 28.81sec 26 starters, 10 classified finishers*
*Piquet(BRA)Brabham-Ford and Rosberg(FIN) Williams-Ford finished 1st and 2nd but
were disqualified for running underweight.

ROUND 3/US GRAND PRIX (WEST)
LONG BEACH, 4 APRIL

1. LAUDA(AUT)	MCLAREN-FORD	1HR 58MIN 25.32SEC
2. ROSBERG(FIN)	WILLIAMS-FORD	1HR 58MIN 39.98SEC
3.*PATRESE (ITA)	BRABHAM-FORD	1HR 59MIN 44.46SEC
4. ALBORETO(ITA)	TYRRELL-FORD	1HR 59MIN 46.27SEC
5. DE ANGELIS(ITA)	LOTUS-FORD	74 LAPS
6. WATSON (GB)	MCLAREN-FORD	74 LAPS

Race: 75.5 laps of 2.13mile/3.43km (160.82miles/258.97kms)
Fastest lap: Lauda, 1min 30,83sec, 84.42mph/135.86kph
Pole position: de Cesaris(ITA)Alfa Romeo, 1min 27.31sec 26 starters, 10 class. finishers*
*G.Villeneuve(CAN) Ferrari Turbo,finished third but disqualified for illegal rear wing.

ROUND 4/SAN MARINO GRAND PRIX*
IMOLA, 25 APRIL

1. PIRONI(FRA)	FERRARI TURBO	1HR 36MIN 38.89SEC
2. G.VILLENEUVE(CAN)	FERRARI TURBO	1HR 36MIN 39.25SEC
3. ALBORETO(ITA)	TYRRELL-FORD	1HR 37MIN 46.57SEC
4. JARIER(FRA)	OSELLA-FORD	59 LAPS
5. SALAZAR(CHILE)	ATS-FORD	57 LAPS

Race: 60 laps of 3.13mile/5.04km (187.8miles/302.4kms)
Fastest lap: Pironi, 1min 35.04sec, 119.63mph/190.92kph
Pole position: Arnoux(FRA),Renault Turbo 1min 29.77sec 14 starters, 5 class finishers
*Race boycotted by many of the major teams

RESULTS 1982

ROUND 5/BELGIAN GRAND PRIX
ZOLDER, 9 MAY

1. WATSON (GB)	MCLAREN-FORD	1HR 35MIN 42.00SEC
2. ROSBERG(FIN)	WILLIAMS-FORD	1HR 35MIN 49.26SEC
3.*CHEEVER(USA)	LIGIER-MATRA	69 LAPS
4. DE ANGELIS(ITA)	LOTUS-FORD	68 LAPS
5. PIQUET(BRA)	BRABHAM-BMW TURBO	67 LAPS
6. SERRA(BRA)	FITTIPALDI-FORD	67 LAPS

Race: 70 laps of 2.65mile/4.26km (143.1miles/230.14kms)
Fastest lap: Watson, 1min 20.21sec, 118.86mph/191.28kph
Pole position: Prost(FRA), Renault Turbo, 1min 15.70sec 26 starters, 9 class. finishers
*Ferrari withdrew after the death of Gilles Villeneuve in practice. Lauda(McLaren),
finished third, but was disqualified for having an underweight car.

ROUND 6/MONACO GRAND PRIX
MONTE CARLO,23 MAY

1. PATRESE(ITA)	BRABHAM-FORD	1HR 54MIN 11.26SEC
2. PIRONI(FRA)	FERRARI TURBO	75 LAPS
3. DE CESARIS(ITA)	ALFA ROMEO	75 LAPS
4. MANSELL(GB)	LOTUS-FORD	75 LAPS
5. DE ANGELIS(ITA)	LOTUS-FORD	75 LAPS
6. DALY(IRL)	WILLIAMS-FORD	74 LAPS

Race: 76 laps of 2.06mile/3.31km (156.56miles/251.56kms)
Fastest lap: Patrese, 1min 26.35sec, 85.8mph/138.07kph
Pole position: Arnoux(FRA), Renault Turbo, 1min 23.3sec 20 starters, 9 classified finishers

ROUND 7/US GRAND PRIX (EAST)
DETROIT, 6 JUNE

1. WATSON(GB)	MCLAREN-FORD	1HR 58MIN 41.04SEC
2. CHEEVER(USA)	LIGIER-MATRA	1HR 58MIN 56.77SEC
3. PIRONI(FRA)	FERRARI TURBO	1HR 59MIN 09.12SEC
4. ROSBERG(FIN)	WILLIAMS-FORD	1HR 59MIN 53.02SEC
5. DALY(IRL)	WILLIAMS-FORD	2HR 00MIN 04.80SEC
6. LAFFITE(FRA)	LIGIER-MATRA	61 LAPS

Race: 62 laps of 2.49mile/4.01km (154.38miles/248.62kms)
Fastest lap: Prost(FRA),Renault Turbo, 1min 50.44sec,81.27mph/130.8kph
Pole position: Prost(FRA),Renault Turbo,1min 48.54sec 25 starters, 11 class. finishers

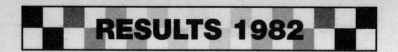

RESULTS 1982

ROUND 8/CANADIAN GRAND PRIX
MONTREAL, 13 JUNE

1. PIQUET(BRA)	BRABHAM-BMW TURBO	1HR 46MIN 39.58SEC
2. PATRESE (ITA)	BRABHAM-FORD	1HR 46MIN 53.38SEC
3. WATSON(GB)	MCLAREN-FORD	1HR 47MIN 41.41SEC
4. DE ANGELIS(ITA)	LOTUS-FORD	69 LAPS
5. SURER(SWISS)	ARROWS-FORD	69 LAPS
6. DE CESARIS(ITA)	ALFA ROMEO	68 LAPS

Race: 70 laps of 2.74mile/4.41km (191.9miles/308.7kms)
Fastest lap: Pironi(FRA), Ferrari, 1min 28min 32sec, 111.69mph/179.75kph
Pole position: Pironi(FRA), Ferrari Turbo, 1min 27.51sec 26 starters, 11 class. finshers

ROUND 9/DUTCH GRAND PRIX
ZANDVOORT, 3 JULY

1. PIRONI(FRA)	FERRARI TURBO	1HR 38MIN 03.25SEC
2. PIQUET(BRA)	BRABHAM-BMW TURBO	1HR 38MIN 24.90SEC
3. ROSBERG(FIN)	WILLIAMS-FORD	1HR 38MIN 25.62SEC
4. LAUDA(AUT)	MCLAREN-FORD	71 LAPS
5. DALY(IRL)	WILLIAMS-FORD	71 LAPS
6. BALDI(ITA)	ARROWS-FORD	71 LAPS

Race: 72 laps of 2.64mile/4.25km (190.8miles/306kms)
Fastest lap: Warwick(GB), Toleman-Hart Turbo, 1min 19.78sec, 119.22mph, 191.87kph
Pole position: Arnoux(FRA), Renault Turbo, 1min 14.23sec 26 starters, 15 class. finishers

ROUND 10/BRITISH GRAND PRIX
BRANDS HATCH, 18 JULY

1. LAUDA(AUT)	MCLAREN-FORD	1HR 35MIN 33.81SEC
2. PIRONI(FRA)	FERRARI TURBO	1HR 35MIN 59.54SEC
3. TAMBAY(FRA)	FERRARI TURBO	1HR 36MIN 12.25SEC
4. DE ANGELIS(ITA)	LOTUS-FORD	1HR 36MIN 15.05SEC
5. DALY(IRL)	WILLIAMS-FORD	1HR 36MIN 15.24SEC
6. PROST(FRA)	RENAULT TURBO	1HR 36MIN 15.45SEC

Race: 76 laps of 2.61mile/4.21km (198.36miles/320kms)
Fastest lap: Henton(GB), Tyrrell-Ford, 1min 13.03sec, 128.86mph/207.35kph
Pole position: Rosberg(FIN), Williams-Ford, 1min 09.54sec 26 starters, 10 class. finishers

ROUND 11/FRENCH GRAND PRIX
PAUL RICARD, 25 JULY

1. ARNOUX(FRA)	RENAULT TURBO	1HR 33MIN 33.22SEC
2. PROST(FRA)	RENAULT TURBO	1HR 33MIN 50.53SEC
3. PIRONI(FRA)	FERRARI TURBO	1HR 34MIN 15.35SEC
4. TAMBAY(FRA)	FERRARI TURBO	1HR 34MIN 49.46SEC
5. ROSBERG(FIN)	WILLIAMS-FORD	1HR 35MIN 04.21SEC
6. ALBORETO(ITA)	TYRRELL-FORD	1HR 35MIN 05.56SEC

Race: 54 laps of 3.61mile/5.81km (194.94miles/313.74kms)
Fastest lap: Patrese(ITA), Brabham BMW Turbo, 1min 40.08sec, 129.87mph/209.00kph
Pole position: Arnoux, 1min 34.41sec 26 starters, 16 classified finishers

RESULTS 1982

ROUND 12/GERMAN GRAND PRIX
HOCKENHEIM. 8 AUGUST

1. TAMBAY(FRA)	FERRARI TURBO	1HR 27MIN 25.18SEC
2. ARNOUX(FRA)	RENAULT TURBO	1HR 27MIN 41.56SEC
3. ROSBERG(FIN)	WILLIAMS-FORD	44 LAPS
4. ALBORETO(ITA)	TYRRELL-FORD	44 LAPS
5. GIACOMELLI(ITA)	ALFA ROMEO	44 LAPS
6. SURER(SWISS)	ARROWS-FORD	44 LAPS

Race: 45 laps of 4.22mile/6.79km (189.91miles/305.6kms)
Fastest lap: Piquet(BRA), Brabham-BMW Turbo, 1min 54.04sec, 133.33 mph/214.58kph
Pole position: *Pironi(FRA), Ferrari Turbo 1min 47.95sec 25 starters, 11 class. finishers
*Pironi suffered severe injuries in accident after setting fastest time. Race pole position was left vacant.

ROUND 13/AUSTRIAN GRAND PRIX
OSTERREICHRING, 15 AUGUST

1. DE ANGELIS(ITA)	LOTUS-FORD	1HR 25MIN 02.12SEC
2. ROSBERG(FIN)	WILLIAMS-FORD	1HR 25MIN 02.34SEC
3. LAFFITE(FRA)	LIGIER-MATRA	52 LAPS
4. TAMBAY(FRA)	FERRARI TURBO	52 LAPS
5. LAUDA (AUT)	MCLAREN-FORD	52 LAPS
6. BALDI(ITA)	ARROWS-FORD	52 LAPS

Race: 53 laps of 3.69mile/5.94km (199.26miles/320.76kms)
Fastest lap: Piquet(BRA),Brabham-BMW Turbo, 1min 33.7sec, 141.86mph/228.30kph
*Pole position:*Piquet, 1min 27.61sec 26 starters,8 classified finishers

ROUND 14/SWISS GRAND PRIX
DIJON-PRENOIS, 29 AUGUST

1. ROSBERG(FIN)	WILLIAMS-FORD	1HR 32MIN 41.09SEC
2. PROST(FRA)	RENAULT TURBO	1HR 32MIN 45.53SEC
3. LAUDA(AUT)	MCLAREN-FORD	1HR 33MIN 41.43SEC
4. PIQUET(BRA)	BRABHAM-BMW TURBO	79 LAPS
5. PATRESE(ITA)	BRABHAM-BMW TURBO	79 LAPS
6. DE ANGELIS(ITA)	LOTUS-FORD	79 LAPS

Race: 80 laps of 2.36mile/3.8km (188.8miles/304kms)
Fastest lap: Prost,1min 07.48sec, 125.97mph/202.74kph
Pole position: Prost, 1min 01.38sec 25 starters, 15 classified finishers

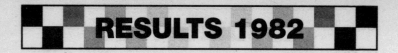

RESULTS 1982

ROUND 15 ITALIAN GRAND PRIX

MONZA, 12 SEPTEMBER

1. ARNOUX(FRA)	RENAULT TURBO	1HR 22MIN 25.73SEC
2. TAMBAY(FRA)	RENAULT TURBO	1HR 22MIN 39.80SEC
3. ANDRETTI(USA)	FERRARI TURBO	1HR 23MIN 14.19SEC
4. WATSON(GB)	MCLAREN-FORD	1HR 23MIN 53.58SEC
5. ALBORETO(ITA)	TYRRELL-FORD	51 LAPS
6. CHEEVER(USA)	LIGIER-MATRA	51 LAPS

Race: 52 laps of 3.6mile/5.8km (180miles/290kms)
Fastest lap: Arnoux, 1min 33.62sec, 138.59mph/223.03kph
Pole position: Andretti, 1min 28.47sec 26 starters, 12 classified finishers

ROUND 16/US GRAND PRIX

LAS VEGAS, CAESARS PALACE, 25 SEPTEMBER

1. ALBORETO (ITA)	TYRRELL-FORD	1HR 41MIN 56.89SEC
2. WATSON (GB)	MCLAREN-FORD	1HR 42MIN 24.18SEC
3. CHEEVER(USA)	LIGIER-MATRA	1HR 42MIN 53.34SEC
4. PROST(FRA)	RENAULT TURBO	1HR 43MIN 05.54SEC
5. ROSBERG(FIN)	WILLIAMS-FORD	1HR 43MIN 08.26SEC
6. DALY(IRL)	WILLIAMS-FORD	74 LAPS

Race: 75 laps of 2.27 mile/3.65km (170.25miles/273.75kms)
Fastest lap: Alboreto, 1min 19.64sec, 102.52mph/164.99kph
Pole position: Prost, 1min 16.36sec 24 starters, 13 classified finishers

DRIVERS' WORLD CHAMPIONSHIP 1982

1. ROSBERG	44 points	4. PROST	34 points
2. PIRONI	39 points	5. LAUDA	30 points
2. WATSON	39 points	6. ARNOUX	28 points

CONSTRUCTORS' WORLD CHAMPIONSHIP 1982

1. FERRARI	74 points	4. WILLIAMS-FORD	58 points
2. MCLAREN-FORD	69 points	5. LOTUS-FORD	30 points
3. RENAULT	62 points	6. TYRRELL-FORD	25 points

RESULTS 1983

1983 This was the start of the turbo age. Renault had lead the way, Ferrari had followed. Now all of the leading contenders were queuing up for turbo power. Lotus acquired Renault engines midway through the season; McLaren were to use Porsche power; Williams joined up with Honda; Alfa developed their own effective unit. Alboreto scored the 155th and last victory for the normally-aspirated Ford Cosworth unit in Motown itself, Detroit.

Arnoux joined Tambay at Ferrari, and Cheever joined Prost at Renault. Prost lost out to Piquet in the final round of the year in South Africa and was subject to unjustified vilification by the French press. If only the Renault had been more reliable.

Ferrari won the Constructors' Championship. There were 15 rounds.

Britain hosted two Grands Prix, the Brands Hatch event nominated for European Grand Prix status. Best 11 results counted for Drivers' title, best six finishers for Constructors'. Points: 9-6-4-3-2-1 for first six places.

ROUND 1/BRAZILIAN GRAND PRIX
RIO DE JANEIRO, 13 MARCH

1. PIQUET(BRA)	BRABHAM-BMW TURBO	1HR 48MIN 27.73SEC
2.*ROSBERG(FIN)	WILLIAMS-FORD	DISQUALIFIED
3. LAUDA(AUT)	MCLAREN-FORD	1HR 49MIN 19.61SEC
4. LAFFITE(FRA)	WILLIAMS-FORD	1HR 49MIN 41.70SEC
5. TAMBAY(FRA)	FERRARI TURBO	1HR 49MIN 45.85SEC
6. SURER(SWISS)	ARROWS-FORD	1HR 49MIN 45.94SEC

Race: 63 laps of 3.13mile/5.03km (197.19miles/316.89kms)
Fastest lap: Piquet, 1min 39.83sec, 112.73mph/181.43kph
Pole position: Rosberg, 1min 34.53sec 26 starters, 14 classified finishers

ROUND 2/US GRAND PRIX (WEST)
LONG BEACH, CALIFORNIA, 27 MARCH

1. WATSON(GB)	MCLAREN-FORD	1HR 53MIN 34.90SEC
2. LAUDA(AUT)	MCLAREN-FORD	1HR 54MIN 02.90SEC
3. ARNOUX(FRA)	FERRARI TURBO	1HR 54MIN 48.50SEC
4. LAFFITE(FRA)	WILLIAMS-FORD	74 LAPS
5. SURER(SWISS)	ARROWS-FORD	74 LAPS
6. CECOTTO(VEN)	THEODORE-FORD	74 LAPS

Race: 75 laps of 2.04mile/3.28km (153miles/246kms)
Fastest lap: Lauda, 1min 28.33sec, 82.94mph/133.48kph
Pole position: Tambay(FRA), Ferrari Turbo, 1min26.12sec 26 starters, 12 class. finishers

RESULTS 1983

ROUND 3/FRENCH GRAND PRIX
PAUL RICARD, 17 APRIL

1. PROST(FRA)	RENAULT TURBO	1HR 34MIN 13.90SEC
2. PIQUET(BRA)	BRABHAM-BMW TURBO	1HR 34MIN 43.60SEC
3. CHEEVER(USA)	RENAULT TURBO	1HR 34MIN 54.20SEC
4. TAMBAY(FRA)	FERRARI TURBO	1HR 35MIN 20.8SEC
5. ROSBERG(FIN)	WILLIAMS-FORD	53 LAPS
6. LAFFITE(FRA)	WILLIAMS-FORD	53 LAPS

Race: 54 laps of 3.61mile/5.81km (194.94miles/313.74kms)
Fastest lap: Prost, 1min 42.70sec, 126.56mph/203.67kph
Pole position: Prost, 1min 36.67sec 26 starters, 13 classified finishers

ROUND 4/SAN MARINO GRAND PRIX
IMOLA, 1 MAY

1. TAMBAY(FRA)	FERRARI TURBO	1HR 37MIN 52.50SEC
2. PROST (FRA)	RENAULT TURBO	1HR 38MIN 41.20SEC
3. ARNOUX(FRA)	FERRARI TURBO	59 LAPS
4. ROSBERG(FIN)	WILLIAMS-FORD	59 LAPS
5. WATSON(GB)	MCLAREN-FORD	59 LAPS
6. SURER(SWISS)	ARROWS-FORD	59 LAPS

Race: 60 laps of 3.13mile/5.04km (187.8miles/302.4kms)
Fastest lap: Patrese(ITA), Brabham-BMW Turbo, 1min 34.44sec, 119.38mph/192.13kph
Pole position: Arnoux, 1min 31.24sec 26 starters, 13 classified finishers

ROUND 5/MONACO GRAND PRIX
MONTE CARLO, 15 MAY

1. ROSBERG(FIN)	WILLIAMS-FORD	1HR 56MIN 38.10SEC
2. PIQUET(BRA)	BRABHAM-BMW TURBO	1HR 56MIN 56.60SEC
3. PROST(FRA)	RENAULT TURBO	1HR 57MIN 09.50SEC
4. TAMBAY(FRA)	FERRARI TURBO	1HR 57MIN 42.40SEC
5. SULLIVAN(USA)	TYRRELL-FORD	74 LAPS
6. BALDI(ITA)	ALFA ROMEO TURBO	74 LAPS

Race: 76 laps of 2.06mile/3.31km (156.56miles/251.56kms)
Fastest lap: Piquet, 1min 27.3sec, 84.88mph/136.60kph
Pole position: Prost, 1min 24.84sec 20 starters, 7 classified finishers

ROUND 6/ BELGIAN GRAND PRIX
SPA-FRANCORCHAMPS, 22 MAY

1. PROST(FRA)	RENAULT TURBO	1HR 27MIN 11.50SEC
2. TAMBAY(FRA)	FERRARI TURBO	1HR 27MIN 34.70SEC
3. CHEEVER(USA)	RENAULT TURBO	1HR 27MIN 51.40SEC
4. PIQUET(BRA)	BRABHAM-BMW TURBO	1HR 27MIN 53.80SEC
5. ROSBERG(FIN)	WILLIAMS-FORD	1HR 28MIN 02.00SEC
6. LAFFITE(FRA)	WILLIAMS-FORD	1H28MIN44.60SEC

Race: 40 laps of 4.32mile/6.95km (172.8miles/278.0kms)
Fastest lap: de Cesaris(ITA),Alfa Romeo Turbo, 2min 07.50sec, 121.92mph/196.22kph
Pole position: Prost, 2min 04.62sec 26 starters, 14 classified finishers

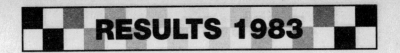

RESULTS 1983

ROUND 7/US GRAND PRIX(EAST)
DETROIT, 5 JUNE

1. ALBORETO(ITA)	TYRRELL-FORD	1HR 50MIN 53.70SEC
2. ROSBERG(FIN)	WILLIAMS-FORD	1HR 51MIN 01.40SEC
3. WATSON(GB)	MCLAREN-FORD	1HR 51MIN 03.00SEC
4. PIQUET(BRA)	BRABHAM-BMW TURBO	1HR 52MIN 05.90SEC
5. LAFFITE(FRA)	WILLIAMS-FORD	1HR 52MIN 26.30SEC
6. MANSELL(GB)	LOTUS-FORD	59 LAPS

Race: 60 laps of 2.5mile/4.02km (150miles/241.2kms)
Fastest lap: Watson, 1min 47.67sec, 83.59mph/134.53kph
Pole position: Arnoux(FRA) Ferrari Turbo, 1min 44.74sec 26 starters, 12 class. finishers

ROUND 8/CANADIAN GRAND PRIX
MONTREAL, 12 JUNE

1. ARNOUX(FRA)	FERRARI TURBO	1HR 48MIN 31.8SEC
2. CHEEVER(USA)	RENAULT TURBO	1HR 49MIN 13.9SEC
3. TAMBAY(FRA)	FERRARI TURBO	1HR 49MIN 24.5SEC
4. ROSBERG(FIN)	WILLIAMS-FORD	1HR 49MIN 48.9SEC
5. PROST(FRA)	RENAULT TURBO	69 LAPS
6. WATSON(GB)	MCLAREN-FORD	69 LAPS

Race: 70 laps of 2.74mile/4.41km (191.8miles/308.7kms)
Fastest lap: Tambay, 1min 30.85sec, 108.58mph/174.75kph
Pole position: Arnoux, 1min 28.73sec 26 starters, 10 classified finishers

ROUND 9/BRITISH GRAND PRIX
SILVERSTONE, 16 JULY

1. PROST(FRA)	RENAULT TURBO	1HR 24MIN 39.8SEC
2. PIQUET(BRA)	BRABHAM-BMW TURBO	1HR 24MIN 58.9SEC
3. TAMBAY(FRA)	FERRARI TURBO	1HR 25MIN 06.0SEC
4. MANSELL(GB)	LOTUS-RENAULT TURBO	1HR 25MIN 18.7SEC
5. ARNOUX(FRA)	FERRARI TURBO	1HR 25MIN 38.7SEC
6. LAUDA(AUT)	MCLAREN-FORD	66 LAPS

Race: 67 laps of 2.93mile/4.72km (196.31miles/316.24kms)
Fastest lap: Prost, 1min 14.21sec, 142.23mph/228.9kph
Pole position: Arnoux, 1min 09.46sec 26 starters, 17 classified finishers

ROUND 10/GERMAN GRAND PRIX
HOCKENHEIM, 7 AUGUST

1. ARNOUX(FRA)	FERRARI TURBO	1HR 27MIN 10.30SEC
2. DE CESARIS(ITA)	ALFA ROMEO TURBO	1HR 28MIN 20.90SEC
3. PATRESE(ITA)	BRABHAM-BMW TURBO	1HR 28MIN 54.40SEC
4. PROST(FRA)	RENAULT TURBO	1HR 29MIN 11.10SEC
5*.WATSON(GB)	MCLAREN-FORD	44 LAPS
6. LAFFITE(FRA)	WILLIAMS-FORD	44 LAPS

Race: 45 laps of 4.22mile/6.8km (189.91miles/305.6kms)
Fastest lap: Arnoux, 1min 53.94sec, 133.44mph, 214.76kph
Pole position: Tambay(FRA),Ferrari Turbo, 1min 49.33sec 26 starters, 13 class. finishers
*Lauda(AUT)McLaren-Ford, finished 5th but disqualified for push start in pits.

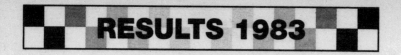

RESULTS 1983

ROUND 11/AUSTRIAN GRAND PRIX
OSTERREICHRING, 14 AUGUST

1. PROST (FRA)	RENAULT TURBO	1HR 24MIN 2.80SEC
2. ARNOUX(FRA)	FERRARI TURBO	1HR 24MIN 39.60SEC
3. PIQUET(BRA)	BRABHAM-BMW TURBO	1HR 25MIN 00.40SEC
4. CHEEVER(USA)	RENAULT TURBO	1HR 25MIN 01.10SEC
5. MANSELL(GB)	LOTUS-RENAULT TURBO	52 LAPS
6. LAUDA(AUT)	MCLAREN-FORD	51 LAPS

Race: 53 laps of 3.69mile/5.94km (199.26miles/320.76kms)
Fastest lap: Prost, 1min 33.96sec, 141.46mph/227.66kph
Pole position: Tambay(FRA) Ferrari Turbo, 1min 29.87sec 26 starters, 13 class. finishers

ROUND 12/DUTCH GRAND PRIX
ZANDVOORT, 28 AUGUST

1. ARNOUX(FRA)	FERRARI TURBO	1HR 38MIN 42.00SEC
2. TAMBAY(FRA)	FERRARI TURBO	1HR 39MIN 02.80SEC
3. WATSON(GB)	MCLAREN-FORD	1HR 39MIN 25.70SEC
4. WARWICK(GB)	TOLEMAN-HART TURBO	1HR 39MIN 58.80SEC
5. BALDI(ITA)	ALFA ROMEO TURBO	1HR 40MIN 06.20SEC
6. ALBORETO(ITA)	TYRRELL-FORD	71 LAPS

Race: 72 laps of 2.64mile/4.25km (190.8miles/306kms)
Fastest lap: Arnoux, 1min 19.86sec, 119.10mph/191.67kph
Pole position: Piquet(BRA), Brabham-BMW Turbo, 1min 15.63sec 26 starters, 14 classified finishers

ROUND 13/ITALIAN GRAND PRIX
MONZA, 11 SEPTEMBER

1. PIQUET(BRA)	BRABHAM-BMW TURBO	1HR 23MIN 10.90SEC
2. ARNOUX(FRA)	FERRARI TURBO	1HR 23MIN 21.10SEC
3. CHEEVER(USA)	RENAULT TURBO	1HR 23MIN 29.50SEC
4. TAMBAY(FRA)	FERRARI TURBO	1HR 23MIN 39.90SEC
5. DE ANGELIS(ITA)	LOTUS-RENAULT TURBO	1HR 24MIN 04.60SEC
6. WARWICK(GB)	TOLEMAN-HART TURBO	1HR 24MIN 24.30SEC

Race: 52 laps of 3.6mile/5.8km (180miles/290kms)
Fastest lap: Piquet, 1min 34.43sec, 137.39mph/221.11 kph
Pole position: Patrese(ITA), Brabham-BMW Turbo, 1min 29.12sec 26 starters, 13 classified finishers

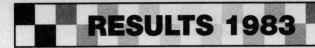

RESULTS 1983

EUROPEAN GRAND PRIX
BRANDS HATCH, 25 SEPTEMBER

1. PIQUET(BRA)	BRABHAM-BMW TURBO	1HR 36MIN 45.90SEC
2. PROST(FRA)	RENAULT TURBO	1HR 36MIN 52.40SEC
3. MANSELL(GB)	LOTUS-RENAULT TURBO	1HR 37MIN 16.20SEC
4. DE CESARIS(ITA)	ALFA ROMEO TURBO	1HR 37MIN 20.30SEC
5. WARWICK(GB)	TOLEMAN-HART TURBO	1HR 37MIN 30.80SEC
6. GIACOMELLI(ITA)	TOLEMAN-HART TURBO	1HR 37MIN 38.10SEC

Race: 76 laps of 2.61mile/4.21km (198.36miles/320kms)
Fastest lap: Mansell, 1min 14.34sec, 126.56mph/203.68kph
Pole position: de Angelis(ITA), Lotus Renault Turbo, 1min 12.09sec 26 starters, 15
classified finishers

ROUND 15/SOUTH AFRICAN GRAND PRIX
KYALAMI, 15 OCTOBER

1. PATRESE(ITA)	BRABHAM-BMW TURBO	1HR 33MIN 25.70SEC
2. DE CESARIS(ITA)	ALFA ROMEO TURBO	1HR 33MIN 35.00SEC
3. PIQUET(BRA)	BRABHAM-BMW TURBO	1HR 33MIN 47.70SEC
4. WARWICK(GB)	TOLEMAN-HART TURBO	76 LAPS
5. ROSBERG(FIN)	WILLIAMS-HONDA TURBO	76 LAPS
6. CHEEVER(USA)	RENAULT TURBO	76 LAPS

Race: 77 laps of 2.55mile/4.1km (196.35miles/315kms)
Fastest lap: Piquet, 1min 09.95sec, 131.25mph, 211.22kph
Pole position: Tambay(FRA)Ferrari Turbo, 1min 06.55sec 26 starters, 12 class. finishers

DRIVERS' WORLD CHAMPIONSHIP 1983

1. PIQUET	59 *points*	5. ROSBERG	27 *points*
2. PROST	57 *points*	6. CHEEVER	22 *points*
3. ARNOUX	49 *points*	6. WATSON	22 *points*
4. TAMBAY	40 *points*		

CONSTRUCTORS' WORLD CHAMPIONSHIP 1983

1. FERRARI	89 *points*	4. WILLIAMS-FORD	36 *points*
2. RENAULT	79 *points*	5. MCLAREN-FORD	36 *points*
3. BRABHAM-BMW	72 *points*	6. ALFA ROMEO	18 *points*

RESULTS 1984

1984 Mclaren monopolised the season, thanks to their TAG-badged Porsche power unit. Lauda won his third World Drivers' Championship from team-mate Prost by just half a point. Prost had fled from Renault after the end of season nasties to rejoin the English team. A 24-year-old Brazilian called Ayrton Senna arrived on the scene with Toleman and nearly won in Monaco. Britain's Martin Brundle joined the supremely talented young German Stefan Bellof in the Tyrrell team. But it was to be an ugly year for 'Uncle Ken'. All results were nullified at the end of the season, when the Authorities found the team responsible for car-weight irregularities. Tamby was hoofed out by Ferrari but snapped up by Renault, who also took on Britain's favourite, Derek Warwick. Alboreto joined the 'Prancing Horse'equipe. Turbo power was the only way to go... Long Beach was dropped from the calendar and Downtown Dallas hosted its one and only Grand Prix to date. Portugal saw its first round since 1960. There were 16 rounds, best eleven results counted. Top six cars scored points for Constructors' title. Points: 9-6-4-3-2-1. Half points awarded in Monaco because rain halted race before half distance.

ROUND 1/ BRAZILIAN GRAND PRIX

RIO DE JANEIRO, 25 MARCH

1. PROST(FRA)	MCLAREN-TAG PORSCHE	1HR 42MIN 34.50SEC
2. ROSBERG(FIN)	WILLIAMS-HONDA TURBO	1HR 43MIN 15.00SEC
3. DE ANGELIS'ITA)	LOTUS-RENAULT TURBO	1HR 43MIN 33.60SEC
4. CHEEVER(USA)	ALFA ROMEO TURBO	60 LAPS
5. TAMBAY(FRA)	RENAULT TURBO	59 LAPS
6. BOUTSEN(BEL)	ARROWS-FORD	59 LAPS

Race: 61 laps of 3.13mile/5.03km (197.19miles/316.89kms)
Fastest lap: Prost, 1min 36.50sec, 116.62mph/187.70kph
Pole position: de Angelis. 1min 28.39sec 26 starters, 8 classified finishers

ROUND 2/SOUTH AFRICAN GRAND PRIX

KYALAMI, 7 APRIL

1. LAUDA(AUT)	MCLAREN-TAG PORSCHE	1HR 29MIN 23.40SEC
2. PROST(FRA)	MCLAREN-TAG PORSCHE	1HR 30MIN 29.40SEC
3. WARWICK (GB)	RENAULT TURBO	74 LAPS
4. PATRESE(ITA)	ALFA ROMEO TURBO	73 LAPS
5. DE CESARIS(ITA)	LIGIER-RENAULT TURBO	73 LAPS
6. SENNA(BRA)	TOLEMAN-HART TURBO	72 LAPS

Race: 75 laps of 2.55mile/4.1km (191.25miles/307.50kms)
Fastest lap: Tambay(FRA) Renault Turbo,1min 08.88sec, 133.28mph/214.49kph
Pole position: Piquet(BRA) Brabham-BMW Turbo,1min 04.87sec 26 starters, 12 classified finishers

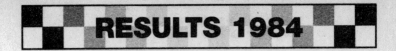

RESULTS 1984

ROUND 3/BELGIAN GRAND PRIX
ZOLDER, 29 APRIL

1. ALBORETO(ITA)	FERRARI TURBO	1HR 36MIN 32.05SEC
2. WARWICK(GB)	RENAULT TURBO	1HR 37MIN 14.43SEC
3. ARNOUX(FRA)	FERRARI TURBO	1HR 37MIN 41.85SEC
4. ROSBERG(FIN)	WILLIAMS-HONDA TURBO	69 LAPS
5. DE ANGELIS(ITA)	LOTUS-RENAULT TURBO	69 LAPS
6. SENNA(BRA)	TOLEMAN-HART TURBO	68 LAPS

Race: 70 laps of 2.65mile/4.26km (143miles/230.14kms)
Fastest lap: Arnoux, 1min 19.29sec, 120.23mph/ 193.50kph
Pole position: Alboreto, 1min 14.85sec 26 starters, 10 classified finishers

ROUND 4/SAN MARINO GRAND PRIX
IMOLA, 6 MAY

1. PROST(FRA)	MCLAREN-TAG PORSCHE	1HR 36MIN 53.68SEC
2. ARNOUX(FRA)	FERRARI TURBO	1HR 37MIN 07.10SEC
3. DE ANGELIS(ITA)	LOTUS-RENAULT	59 LAPS
4. WARWICK(GB)	RENAULT TURBO	59 LAPS
5. BOUTSEN(BEL)	ARROWS-FORD	59 LAPS
6. DE CESARIS(ITA)	LIGIER-RENAULT	58 LAPS

Race: 60 laps of 3.13mile/5.04km (187.8miles/302.4kms)
Fastest lap: Piquet(BRA), Brabham-BMW,1min 33.28sec, 120.87mph/194.52kph
Pole position: Piquet, 1min 28.52sec 26 starters, 9 classified finishers

ROUND 5/FRENCH GRAND PRIX
DIJON-PRENOIS, 20 MAY

1. LAUDA (AUT)	MCLAREN-TAG PORSCHE	1HR 31MIN 11.95SEC
2. TAMBAY(FRA)	RENAULT TURBO	1HR 31MIN 19.11SEC
3. MANSELL(GB)	LOTUS-RENAULT TURBO	1HR 31MIN 35.92SEC
4. ARNOUX (FRA)	FERRARI TURBO	1HR 31MIN 55.66SEC
5. DE ANGELIS(ITA)	LOTUS-RENAULT TURBO	1HR 32MIN 18.08SEC
6. ROSBERG(FIN)	WILLIAMS-HONDA TURBO	78 LAPS

Race: 79 laps of 2.42mile/3.89km (191.18miles/307.31kms)
Fastest lap: Prost(FRA)McLaren-TAG Turbo, 1min 05.26sec, 13.24mph, 133.24mph/214.43kph
Pole position: Tambay, 1min 02.20sec 26 starters, 13 classified finishers

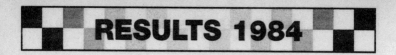

RESULTS 1984

ROUND 6/MONACO GRAND PRIX

MONTE CARLO, 3 JUNE

1. PROST(FRA)	MCLAREN-TAG PORSCHE	1HR 01MIN 07.74SEC
2. SENNA(BRA)	TOLEMAN-HART TURBO	1HR 01MIN 15.19SEC
3. ARNOUX(FRA)	FERRARI TURBO	1HR 01MIN 36.82SEC
4. ROSBERG(FIN)	WILLIAMS-HONDA TURBO	1HR 01MIN 42.99SEC
5. DE ANGELIS(ITA)	LOTUS-RENAULT TURBO	1HR 01MIN 52.18SEC
6. ALBORETO(ITA)	FERRARI TURBO	30 LAPS

Race: 31 laps of 2.06mile/3.31km (63miles/102.61kms)
Fastest lap: Senna, lmin 54.33sec, 64.80mph/104.28kph
Pole position: Prost, 1min 22.66sec 20 starters, 8 classified finishers
*Race scheduled for 77 laps but halted because of torrential rain after 31 laps.
Bellof(Tyrrell) finished third on the track but lost result in team's post-season
disqualification.

ROUND 7/ CANADIAN GRAND PRIX

MONTREAL, 17 JUNE

1. PIQUET(BRA)	BRABHAM-BMW TURBO	1HR 46MIN 23.75SEC
2. LAUDA(AUT)	MCLAREN-TAG PORSCHE	1HR 46MIN 26.36SEC
3. PROST(FRA)	MCLAREN-TAG PORSCHE	1HR 47MIN 51.78SEC
4. DE ANGELIS(ITA)	LOTUS-RENAULT TURBO	69 LAPS
5. ARNOUX(FRA)	FERRARI TURBO	68 LAPS
6. MANSELL(GB)	LOTUS-RENAULT TURBO	68 LAPS

Race: 70 laps of 2.74mile/4.41km (191miles/ 308.7kms)
Fastest lap: Piquet 1min 28.76sec, 111.69mph/178.86kph
Pole position: Piquet, 1min 25.44sec 26 starters, 11 classified finishers

ROUND 8/US GRAND PRIX (EAST)

DETROIT, 24 JUNE

1.PIQUET(BRA)	BRABHAM-BMW TURBO	1HR 55MIN 41.84SEC
2.DE ANGELIS(ITA)	LOTUS-RENAULT TURBO	1HR 56MIN 14.48SEC
3.T.FABI(ITA)	BRABHAM-BMW TURBO	1HR 57MIN 08.37SEC
4.PROST(FRA)	MCLAREN-TAG PORSCHE	1HR 57MIN 37.10SEC
5.LAFFITE(FRA)	WILLIAMS-HONDA TURBO	62 LAPS

Race: 63 laps of 2.5mile/4.02mile (157.5miles/253.26kms)
Fastest lap: Warwick(GB)Renault Turbo, 1min 46.22sec, 84.73mph/136.36kph
Pole position: Piquet, 1min 40.98sec 26 starters, 5 classified finishers*
*Race re-started after first lap pile-up

RESULTS 1984

ROUND 9/US GRAND PRIX
DALLAS, 8 JULY

1. ROSBERG(FIN)	WILLIAMS-HONDA TURBO	2HR 01MIN 22.62SEC
2. ARNOUX(FRA)	FERRARI TURBO	2HR 01MIN 45.08SEC
3. DE ANGELIS(ITA)	LOTUS-RENAULT TURBO	66 LAPS
4. LAFFITE(FRA)	WILLIAMS-HONDA TURBO	65 LAPS
5. GHINZANI(ITA)	OSELLA-ALFA TURBO	65 LAPS
6. MANSELL(GB)	LOTUS-RENAULT TURBO	64 LAPS

Race: 67 laps of 2.42mile/3.9km (162.14miles/261.30kms)
Fastest lap: Lauda(AUT),McLaren-TAG Porsche, 1min 45.35sec, 82.83mph/133.3kph
Pole position: Mansell(GB) Lotus-Renault Turbo 1min 37.04sec 25 starters, 8 class. finishers

ROUND 10/BRITISH GRAND PRIX
BRANDS HATCH, 22 JULY

1. LAUDA(AUT)	MCLAREN-TAG PORSCHE	1HR 29MIN 28.53SEC
2. WARWICK(GB)	RENAULT TURBO	1HR 30MIN 10.66SEC
3. SENNA(BRA)	TOLEMAN-HART	1HR 30MIN 31.86SEC
4. DE ANGELIS(ITA)	LOTUS-RENAULT TURBO	70 LAPS
5. ALBORETO(ITA)	FERRARI TURBO	70 LAPS
6. ARNOUX(FRA)	FERRARI TURBO	70 LAPS

Race: 71 laps of 2.61mile/4.21km (185.31miles/298.91kms)
Fastest lap: Lauda, 1min 13.19sec, 128mph/206.84kph
Pole position: Piquet(BRA),Brabham-BMW Turbo, 1min 10.87sec 27 starters, 12 classified finishers

ROUND 11/GERMAN GRAND PRIX
HOCKENHEIM, 5 AUGUST

1. PROST(FRA)	MCLAREN-TAG PORSCHE	1HR 24MIN 43.21SEC
2. LAUDA(AUT)	MCLAREN-TAG PORSCHE	1HR 24MIN 46.36SEC
3. WARWICK(GB)	RENAULT TURBO	1HR 25MIN 19.63SEC
4. MANSELL(GB)	LOTUS-RENAULT TURBO	1HR 25MIN 34.87SEC
5. TAMBAY(FRA)	RENAULT TURBO	1HR 25MIN 55.16SEC
6. ARNOUX(FRA)	FERRARI TURBO	43 LAPS

Race: 44 laps of 4.22mile/6.8km (185.68miles/299.2kms)
Fastest lap: Prost, 1min 53.54sec, 13.92mph/215.52kph
Pole position: Prost, 1min 47.01sec 26 starters, 9 classified finishers

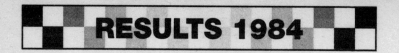

RESULTS 1984

ROUND 12/AUSTRIAN GRAND PRIX
OSTERREICHRING, 19 AUGUST

1. LAUDA(AUT)	MCLAREN-TAG PORSCHE	1HR 21MIN 12.85SEC
2. PIQUET(BRA)	BRABHAM-BMW TURBO	1HR 21MIN 36.38SEC
3. ALBORETO(ITA)	FERRARI TURBO	1HR 22MIN 01.85SEC
4. T.FABI(ITA)	BRABHAM-BMW TURBO	1HR 22MIN 09.16SEC
5. BOUTSEN(BEL)	ARROWS-BMW TURBO	50 LAPS
6. SURER(SWISS)	ARROWS-BMW TURBO	50 LAPS

Race: 51 laps of 3.69mile/5.94km (188.19miles/302.94kms)
Fastest lap: Lauda, 1min 32.88sec, 143.11mph,230.31kph
Pole position: Piquet, 1min 26.17sec 25 starters, 12 classified finishers

ROUND 13/ DUTCH GRAND PRIX
ZANDVOORT, 26 AUGUST

1. PROST(FRA)	MCLAREN-TAG PORSCHE	1HR 37MIN 21.47SEC
2. LAUDA(AUT)	MCLAREN-TAG PORSCHE	1HR 37MIN 31.75SEC
3. MANSELL(GB)	LOTUS-RENAULT TURBO	1HR 38MIN 41.01SEC
4. DE ANGELIS(ITA)	LOTUS-RENAULT TURBO	70 LAPS
5. T.FABI(ITA)	BRABHAM-BMW TURBO	70 LAPS
6. TAMBAY(FRA)	RENAULT TURBO	70 LAPS

Race: 71 laps of 2.64mile/4.25km (190.8miles/306kms)
Fastest lap: Arnoux, 1min 19.47sec. 119.69mph/192.63kph
Pole position: Prost, 1min 13.57sec 27 starters, 13 classified finishers

ROUND 14/ITALIAN GRAND PRIX
MONZA, 9 SEPTEMBER

1. LAUDA(AUT)	MCLAREN-TAG PORSCHE	1HR 20MIN 29.07SEC
2. ALBORETO(ITA)	FERRARI TURBO	1HR 20MIN 53.31SEC
3. PATRESE(ITA)	ALFA ROMEO TURBO	50 LAPS
4. JOHANSSON(SWE)	TOLEMAN-HART TURBO	49 LAPS
5. GARTNER(AUT)	OSELLA-ALFA TURBO	49 LAPS
6. BERGER(AUT)	ATS-BMW TURBO	49 LAPS

Race: 51 laps of 3.6mile/5.8km (183.6miles/295.8kms)
Fastest lap: Lauda, 1min 31.91sec, 141.16mph/227.17kph
Pole position: Piquet(BRA)Brabham-BMW Turbo 1min 26.58sec 25 starters, 10 classified finishers

ROUND 15/EUROPEAN GRAND PRIX
NURBURGRING, 7 OCTOBER

1. PROST(FRA)	MCLAREN-TAG PORSCHE	1HR 35MIN 13.28SEC
2. ALBORETO(ITA)	FERRARI TURBO	1HR 35MIN 37.19SEC
3. PIQUET(BRA)	BRABHAM-BMW TURBO	1HR 35MIN 38.21SEC
4. LAUDA(AUT)	MCLAREN-TAG PORSCHE	1HR 35MIN 56.37SEC
5. ARNOUX(FRA)	FERRARI TURBO	1HR 36MIN 14.71SEC
6. PATRESE(ITA)	ALFA ROMEO TURBO	66 LAPS

Race: 67 laps of 2.82mile/4.54km (188.94miles/304.18kms)
Fastest lap: Piquet/Alboreto, 1min 23.15sec, 122.2mph/196.66kph
Pole position: Piquet, 1min 18.87sec 26 starters, 11 classified finishers

RESULTS 1984

ROUND 16/PORTUGUESE GRAND PRIX
ESTORIL, 21 OCTOBER

1. PROST(FRA)	MCLAREN-TAG PORSCHE 1HR 41MIN 11.75SEC
2. LAUDA(AUT)	MCLAREN-TAG PORSCHE 1HR 41MIN 25.18SEC
3. SENNA(BRA)	TOLEMAN-HART TURBO 1HR 41MIN 31.79SEC
4. ALBORETO(ITA)	FERRARI TURBO 1HR 41MIN 32.07SEC
5. DE ANGELIS(IA)	LOTUS-RENAULT TURBO 1HR 42MIN 43.92SEC
6. PIQUET(BRA)	BRABHAM-BMW TURBO 69 LAPS

Race: 70 laps of 2.7mile/4.35km (189.0miles/304.5kms)
Fastest lap: Lauda, 1min 23.0sec, 117.24mph/188.68kph
Pole position: Piquet, 1min 21.70sec 27 starters, 17 classified finishers

DRIVERS' WORLD CHAMPIONSHIP 1984

1. LAUDA	72 points	4. ALBORETO 30.5 points
2. PROST	71.5 points	5. PIQUET 29 points
3. DE ANGELIS 34 points		6. ARNOUX 27 points

CONSTRUCTORS' WORLD CHAMPIONSHIP 1984

1. MCLAREN-TAG PORSCHE	143.5	4. BRABHAM-BMW 38 points
2. FERRARI	57.5 points	5. RENAULT 34 points
3. LOTUS-RENAULT	47 points	6. WILLIAMS-HONDA 25.5 points

1985 Alain Prost won the first of his outstanding four World titles - and Ayrton Senna won his very first Grand Prix. The combination of the Frenchman and his McLaren-TAG Porsche were simply the best.Senna joined Lotus and Mansell moved to Williams, where he sent the British fans into ecstasy by claiming his first Grand Prix victory at Brands Hatch. The brilliant German, Stefan Bellof, died in a sports car accident at Spa and fellow-countryman, Manfred Winkelhock succumbed after his Porsche left the track at Mosport. Lauda retired for good at the end of the year and Ulsterman John Watson also hung up his Formula One helmet. Alan Jones returned to the scene in the uncompetitive Haas Lola at the end of the season. The series went 'Down Under' for the first time, with a final round at the fabulous Adelaide circuit. There were 16 rounds. Best 11 counted for Drivers' title. Top six cars for Constructors' Championship. Points: 9-6-4-3-2-1.

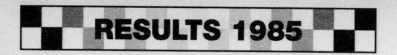
RESULTS 1985

ROUND 1/BRAZILIAN GRAND PRIX
RIO DE JANEIRO, 7 APRIL

1. PROST(FRA)	MCLAREN-TAG PORSCHE	1HR 41MIN 26.10SEC
2. ALBORETO(ITA)	FERRARI TURBO	1HR 41MIN 29.40SEC
3. DE ANGELIS(ITA)	LOTUS-RENAULT TURBO	60 LAPS
4. ARNOUX(FRA)	FERRARI TURBO	59 LAPS
5. TAMBAY(FRA)	RENAULT TURBO	59 LAPS
6. LAFFITE(FRA)	LIGIER-RENAULT TURBOT	59 LAPS

Race: 61 laps of 3.13mile/5.03km (197.19miles/316.89kms)
Fastest lap: Prost, 1min 36.7sec, 116.38mph/187.29kph
Pole position: Alboreto, 1min 27.77sec 25 starters, 13 classified finishers

ROUND 2/PORTUGUESE GRAND PRIX
ESTORIL, 21 APRIL

1. SENNA(BRA)	LOTUS-RENAULT TURBO	2HR 00MIN 28.0SEC
2. ALBORETO(ITA)	FERRARI TURBO	2HR 01MIN 31.0SEC
3. TAMBAY(FRA)	RENAULT TURBO	66 LAPS
4. DE ANGELIS(ITA)	LOTUS-RENAULT TURBO	66 LAPS
5. MANSELL(GB)	WILLIAMS-HONDA TURBO	65 LAPS
6. BELLOF(GER)	TYRRELL-FORD	65 LAPS

Race: 67 laps of 2.7mile/4.35km (180.9miles/291.45kms)
Fastest lap: Senna, 1min 44.12sec, 93.40mph/150.40kph
Pole position: Senna, 1min 21.00sec 26 starters, 9 classified finishers

ROUND 3/SAN MARINO GRAND PRIX
IMOLA, 5 MAY

1. DE ANGELIS(ITA)	LOTUS-RENAULT TURBO	1HR 34MIN 35.96SEC
2. BOUTSEN(BEL)	ARROWS-BMW TURBO	59 LAPS
3. TAMBAY(FRA)	RENAULT TURBO	59 LAPS
4. LAUDA(AUT)	MCLAREN-TAG PORSCHE	59 LAPS
5. MANSELL(GB)	WILLIAMS-HONDA TURBO	58 LAPS
6. JOHANSSON(SWE)	FERRARI TURBO	57 LAPS

Race: 60 laps of 3.13mile/5.04km (187.8miles/302.4kms)
Fastest lap: Alboreto(ITA) Ferrari Turbo,1min 30.96sec, 123.95mph/199.47kph
Pole position: Senna(BRA),Lotus-Renault Turbo, 1min 27.33sec 26 starters, 10 class. finishers

ROUND 4/MONACO GRAND PRIX
MONTE CARLO, 19 MAY

1. PROST(FRA)	MCLAREN-TAG PORSCHE	1HR 51MIN 58.03SEC
2. ALBORETO(ITA)	FERRARI TURBO	1HR 52MIN 05.60SEC
3. DE ANGELIS(ITA)	LOTUS-RENAULT TURBO	1HR 53MIN 25.20SEC
4. DE CESARIS(ITA)	LIGIER-RENAULT TURBO	77 LAPS
5. WARWICK(GB)	RENAULT TURBO	77 LAPS
6. LAFFITE(FRA)	LIGIER-RENAULT TURBO	77 LAPS

Race: 78 laps of 2.06mile/3.31km (160.68miles/258.18kms)
Fastest lap: Alboreto, 1min 22.64sec, 89.65mph/144.28kph
Pole position: Senna(BRA), Lotus-Renault Turbo, 1min 20.45sec 20 starters, 11 class. finishers

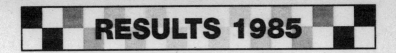
RESULTS 1985

ROUND 5/CANADIAN GRAND PRIX
MONTREAL, 16 JUNE

1. ALBORETO(ITA)   FERRARI TURBO   1HR 46MIN 01.8SEC
2. JOHANSSON(SWE)   FERRARI TURBO   1HR 46MIN 03.8SEC
3. PROST(FRA)   MCLAREN-TAG PORSCHE   1HR 46MIN 06.2SEC
4. ROSBERG(FIN)   WILLIAMS-HONDA TURBO   1HR 46MIN 29.6SEC
5. DE ANGELIS(ITA)   LOTUS-RENAULT TURBO   1HR 46MIN 45.2SEC
6. MANSELL(GB)   WILLIAMS-HONDA TURBO   1HR 47MIN 19.7SEC

Race: 70 laps of 2.74 mile/4.41km (191.8 miles/ 308.7 kms)
Fastest lap: Senna(BRA) Lotus-Renault Turbo, 1min 27.45sec, 112.81mph/181.55 kph
Pole position: de Angelis, 1min 24.57sec 25 starters, 17 classified finishers

ROUND 6/US GRAND PRIX (EAST)
DETROIT, 23 JUNE

1. ROSBERG(FIN)   WILLIAMS-HONDA TURBO   1HR 55MIN 39.9SEC
2. JOHANSSON(SWE)   FERRARI TURBO   1HR 56MIN 37.4SEC
3. ALBORETO(ITA)   FERRARI TURBO   1HR 56MIN 43.0SEC
4. BELLOF(GER)   TYRRELL-FORD   1HR 56MIN 46.1SEC
5. DE ANGELIS(ITA)   LOTUS-RENAULT TURBO   1HR 57MIN 06.8SEC
6. PIQUET(BRA)   BRABHAM-BMW TURBO   62 LAPS

Race: 63 laps of 2.5mile/4.02km (157.50 miles/253.26 kms)
Fastest lap: Senna(BRA), Lotus-Renault Turbo, 1min 45.61sec, 85.22mph, 137.14kph
Pole position: Senna, 1min 42.05sec 25 starters, 12 classified finishers

ROUND 7/FRENCH GRAND PRIX
PAUL RICARD, 7 JULY

1. PIQUET(BRA)   BRABHAM-BMW TURBO   1HR 31MIN 46.3SEC
2. ROSBERG(FIN)   WILLIAMS-HONDA TURBO   1HR 31MIN 52.9SEC
3. PROST(FRA)   MCLAREN-TAG PORSCHE   1HR 31MIN 55.6SEC
4. JOHANSSON(SWE)   FERRARI TURBO   1HR 32MIN 39.8SEC
5. DE ANGELIS(ITA)   LOTUS-RENAULT TURBO   1HR 32MIN 40.0SEC
6. TAMBAY(FRA)   RENAULT TURBO   1HR 33MIN 01.4SEC

Race: 53 laps of 3.61mile/5.81km (191.33 miles/307.93 kms)
Fastest lap: Rosberg, 1min 39.91sec, 130.08mph/209.3kph
Pole position: Rosberg, 1min 32.46sec 25 starters, 15 classified finishers

ROUND 8/BRITISH GRAND PRIX
SILVERSTONE, 21 JULY

1. PROST(FRA)   MCLAREN-TAG PORSCHE   1HR 18MIN 10.44SEC
2. ALBORETO(ITA)   FERRARI TURBO   64 LAPS
3. LAFFITE(FRA)   LIGIER-RENAULT TURBO   64 LAPS
4. PIQUET(BRA)   BRABHAM-BMW TURBO   64 LAPS
5. WARWICK(GB)   RENAULT TURBO   64 LAPS
6. SURER(SWISS)   BRABHAM-BMW TURBO   63 LAPS

Race: 65 laps of 2.93mile/4.72km (190.45 miles/306.8kms)
Fastest lap: Prost, 1min 09.89sec, 151.04mph/243.07kph
Pole position: Rosberg(FIN), Williams-Honda Turbo,1min 05.59sec 26 starters, 11 class. finishers

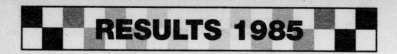

RESULTS 1985

ROUND 9/GERMAN GRAND PRIX

NURBURGRING, 4 AUGUST

1. ALBORETO(ITA)	FERRARI TURBO	1HR 35MIN 31.3SEC
2. PROST(FRA)	MCLAREN-TAG PORSCHE	1HR 35MIN 43.0SEC
3. LAFFITE(FRA)	LIGIER-RENAULT TURBO	1HR 36MIN 22.5SEC
4. BOUTSEN(BEL)	ARROWS-BMW TURBO	1HR 36MIN 26.6SEC
5. LAUDA(AUT)	MCLAREN-TAG PORSCHE	1HR 36MIN 45.3SEC
6. MANSELL(GB)	WILLIAMS-HONDA TURBO	1HR 36MIN 48.2SEC

Race: 67 laps of 2.82 mile/4.54km (188.94 miles/304.18kms)
Fastest lap: Lauda, 1min 22.81sec, 122.70mph/197.46kph
Pole position: T. Fabi(ITA)Toleman-Hart Turbo, 1min 17.43sec 27 starters, 12 class. finishers

ROUND 10/AUSTRIAN GRAND PRIX

OSTERREICHRING, 18 AUGUST

1. PROST(FRA)	MCLAREN-TAG PORSCHE	1HR 20MIN 12.6SEC
2. SENNA(BRA)	LOTUS-RENAULT TURBO	1HR 20MIN 42.6SEC
3. ALBORETO(ITA)	FERRARI TURBO	1HR 20MIN 47.0SEC
4. JOHANSSON(SWE)	FERRARI TURBO	1HR 20MIN 51.7SEC
5. DE ANGELIS(ITA)	LOTUS-RENAULT TURBO	1HR 21MIN 34.7SEC
6. SURER(SWISS)	BRABHAM-BMW TURBO	51 LAPS

Race: 52 laps of 3.69 mile/5.94km (191.88 miles/308.88kms)
Fastest lap: Prost, 1min 29.24sec, 148.94mph/239.7kph
Pole position: Prost, 1min 25.49sec 25 starters, 10 classified finishers

ROUND 11/DUTCH GRAND PRIX

ZANDVOORT, 25 AUGUST

1. LAUDA(AUT)	MCLAREN-TAG PORSCHE	1HR 32MIN 29.26SEC
2. PROST(FRA)	MCLAREN-TAG PORSCHE	1HR 32MIN 29.50SEC
3. SENNA(BRA)	LOTUS-RENAULT TURBO	1HR 33MIN 17.85SEC
4. ALBORETO(ITA)	FERRARI TURBO	1HR 33MIN 18.10SEC
5. DE ANGELIS(ITA)	LOTUS-RENAULT TURBO	69 LAPS
6. MANSELL(GB)	WILLIAMS-HONDA TURBO	69 LAPS

Race: 70 laps of 2.64mile/4.25km (184.8 miles/297.8kms)
Fastest lap: Prost, 1min 16.54sec, 124.27mph/200.00kph
Pole position: Piquet(BRA), Brabham-BMW Turbo, 1min 11.07sec 26 starters, 10 class. finishers

ROUND 12/ITALIAN GRAND PRIX

MONZA, 8 SEPTEMBER

1. PROST(FRA)	MCLAREN-TAG PORSCHE	1HR 17MIN 59.5SEC
2. PIQUET(BRA)	BRABHAM-BMW TURBO	1HR 18MIN 51.1SEC
3. SENNA(BRA)	LOTUS-RENAULT TURBO	1HR 18MIN 59.8SEC
4. SURER(SWISS)	BRABHAM-BMW TURBO	1HR 19MIN 00.1SEC
5. JOHANSSON(SWE)	FERRARI TURBO	50 LAPS
6. DE ANGELIS(ITA)	LOTUS-RENAULT TURBO	50 LAPS

Race: 51 laps of 3.6 mile/5.81km (183.6 miles/295.8kms)
Fastest lap: Mansell(GB) Williams-Honda Turbo, 1min 28.28sec, 149.96 mph/236.51kph
Pole position: Senna, 1min 25.08sec 26 starters, 13 classified finishers

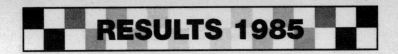
RESULTS 1985

ROUND 13/BELGIAN GRAND PRIX
SPA, 15 SEPTEMBER

1. SENNA(BRA)	LOTUS-RENAULT TURBO	1HR 34MIN 19.9SEC
2. MANSELL(GB)	WILLIAMS-HONDA TURBO	1HR 34MIN 48.3SEC
3. PROST(FRA)	MCLAREN-TAG PORSCHE	1HR 35MIN 15.0SEC
4. ROSBERG(FIN)	WILLIAMS-HONDA TURBO	1HR 35MIN 35.2SEC
5. PIQUET(BRA)	BRABHAM-BMW TURBO	42 LAPS
6. WARWICK(GB)	RENAULT TURBO	42 LAPS

Race: 43 laps of 4.32mile/6.95km (185.76miles/298.85kms)
Fastest lap: Prost, 2min 01.73sec, 127.53mph/205.24kph
Pole position: Prost, 1min 55.31sec 24 starters, 13 classified finishers

ROUND 14/EUROPEAN GRAND PRIX
BRANDS HATCH, 6 OCTOBER

1. MANSELL(GB)	WILLIAMS-HONDA TURBO	1HR 32MIN 58.10SEC
2. SENNA(BRA)	LOTUS-RENAULT TURBO	1HR 33MIN 19.50SEC
3. ROSBERG(FIN)	WILLIAMS-HONDA TURBO	1HR 33MIN 56.60SEC
4. PROST(FRA)	MCLAREN-TAG PORSCHE	1HR 34MIN 04.20SEC
5. DE ANGELIS(ITA)	LOTUS-RENAULT TURBO	74 LAPS
6. BOUTSEN(BEL)	ARROWS-BMW TURBO	73 LAPS

Race: 75 laps of 2.61mile/4.21km (195.75 miles/315.75 kms)
Fastest lap: Laffite(FRA),Ligier-Renault Turbo, 1min 11.53sec, 131.57mph/211.73kph
Pole position: Senna, 1min 07.17sec 26 starters, 12 classified finishers

ROUND 15/SOUTH AFRICAN GRAND PRIX
KYALAMI, 19 OCTOBER

1. MANSELL(GB)	WILLIAMS-HONDA TURBO	1HR 28MIN 22.90SEC
2. ROSBERG(FIN)	WILLIAMS-HONDA TURBO	1HR 28MIN 30.40SEC
3. PROST(FRA)	MCLAREN-TAG PORSCHE	1HR 30MIN 14.70SEC
4. JOHANSSON(SWE)	FERRARI TURBO	74 LAPS
5. BERGER(AUT)	ARROWS-BMW TURBO	74 LAPS
6. BOUTSEN(BEL)	ARROWS-BMW TURBO	74 LAPS

Race: 75 laps of 2.55mile/4.1km (191.25miles/307.50kms)
Fastest lap: Rosberg, 1min 08.15sec, 134.71mph/216.80kph
Pole position: Mansell, 1min 02.37sec 20 starters, 7 classified finishers

ROUND 16/AUSTRALIAN GRAND PRIX
ADELAIDE, 3 NOVEMBER

1. ROSBERG(FIN)	WILLIAMS-HONDA TURBO	2HR 00MIN 40.10SEC
2. LAFFITE(FRA)	LIGIER-RENAULT TURBO	2HR 01MIN 26.60SEC
3. STREIFF(FRA)	LIGIER-RENAULT TURBO	2HR 02MIN 09.00SEC
4. CAPELLI(ITA)	TYRRELL-RENAULT TURBO	81 LAPS
5. JOHANSSON(SWE)	FERRARI TURBO	81 LAPS
6. BERGER(AUT)	ARROWS-BMW TURBO	81 LAPS

Race: 82 laps of 2.35mile/3.78km (192.70 miles/309.96kms)
Fastest lap: Rosberg, 1min 23.70sec, 100.90mph/162.38kph
Pole position: Senna(BRA),Lotus-Renault Turbo, 1min 19.84sec 25 starters, 8 class. finishers

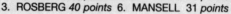

RESULTS 1985/6

DRIVERS' WORLD CHAMPIONSHIP 1985

1. PROST	73 points	4. SENNA	38 points
2. ALBORETO	53 points	5. DE ANGELIS	33 points
3. ROSBERG	40 points	6. MANSELL	31 points

CONSTRUCTORS' WORLD CHAMPIONSHIP 1985

1. MCLAREN-TAG	90 points	3. WILLIAMS-HONDA	71 points
2. FERRARI	82 points	5. BRABHAM-BMW	26 points
3. LOTUS-RENAULT	71 points	5. LIGIER-RENAULT	23 points

1986 This should have been Mansell's year. The Englishman claimed five victories to team-mate Piquet's four and reigning Champion Prost's four. But it was the little Frenchman who took the honours at the end of the season, to become the first driver to win back-to-back titles since Fangio in the 'fifties (and, back then, the great man won *four* in a row!) How many times have we seen the replay of that tyre exploding on Mansell's Williams in Adelaide? The sport lost one of its most gifted artists when the delightful Elio de Angelis was killed, testing for his new Brabham team at Paul Ricard. And the Grand Prix career of France's popular and impudent Jacques Laffite was ended by a start-line pile-up at Brands Hatch in which he broke both legs. The Renault team quit the sport at the end of 1985 and Senna refused to accept Britain's redundant Derek Warwick as his team-mate at Lotus. He got the Earl of Dumfries instead - no contest! Warwick joined Brabham after the death of de Angelis. Keke Rosberg decided to hang up his Formula One helmet at the end of a season when he was simply unable to match the genius of Prost at McLaren. And Ferrari struggled all season. Toleman became Benetton and Paddock prankster Gerhard Berger gave the team its first victory in Mexico. There were 16 rounds. Hungary hosted its first Grand Prix and Mexico returned to the calendar for the first time since 1970. Best eleven results counted for the Drivers' title. Top six places counted for Constructors'. Points:9-6-4-3-2-1.

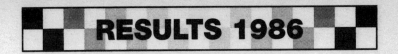
RESULTS 1986

ROUND 1/BRAZILIAN GRAND PRIX
RIO DE JANEIRO, 23 MARCH

1. PIQUET(BRA)	WILLIAMS-HONDA TURBO	1HR 39MIN 32.58SEC
2. SENNA(BRA)	LOTUS-RENAULT TURBO	1HR 40MIN 07.41SEC
3. LAFFITE(FRA)	LIGIER-RENAULT TURBO	1HR 40MIN 32.34SEC
4. ARNOUX(FRA)	LIGIER-RENAULT TURBO	1HR 41MIN 01.01SEC
5. BRUNDLE(GB)	TYRRELL-RENAULT TURBO	60 LAPS
6. BERGER(AUT)	BENETTON-BMW TURBO	59 LAPS

Race: 61 laps of 3.13mile/5.03km (197.19miles/316.89kms)
Fastest lap: Piquet, 1min 33.55sec, 120.31mph/193.61kph
Pole position: Senna, 1min 25.50sec 25 starters, 10 classified finishers

ROUND 2/SPANISH GRAND PRIX
JEREZ, 13 APRIL

1. SENNA(BRA)	LOTUS-RENAULT TURBO	1HR 48MIN 47.74SEC
2. MANSELL(GB)	WILLIAMS-HONDA TURBO	1HR 48MIN 47.75SEC
3. PROST(FRA)	MCLAREN-TAG PORSCHE	1HR 49MIN 09.29SEC
4. ROSBERG(FIN)	MCLAREN-TAG PORSCHE	71 LAPS
5. T.FABI(ITA)	BENETTON-BMW TURBO	71 LAPS
6. BERGER(AUT)	BENETTON-BMW TURBO	71 LAPS

Race: 72 laps of 2.62mile/4.22km (188.64miles/303.84kms)
Fastest lap: Mansell, 1min 27.18sec, 108.23mph/174.19kph
Pole position: Senna, 1min 21.60sec 25 starters, 8 classified finishers

ROUND 3/SAN MARINO GRAND PRIX
IMOLA, 27 APRIL

1. PROST(FRA)	MCLAREN-TAG PORSCHE	1HR 32MIN 28.41SEC
2. PIQUET(BRA)	WILLIAMS-HONDA TURBO	1HR 32MIN 36.05SEC
3. BERGER(AUT)	BENETTON-BMW TURBO	59 LAPS
4. JOHANSSON(SWE)	FERRARI TURBO	59 LAPS
5. ROSBERG(FIN)	MCLAREN-TAG PORSCHE	58 LAPS
6. PATRESE(ITA)	BRABHAM-BMW TURBO	58 LAPS

Race: 60 laps of 3.13mile/5.04km (187.8 miles/302.4kms)
Fastest lap: Piquet, 1min 28.67sec, 127.15mph/204.63kph
Pole position: Senna(BRA)Lotus-Renault Turbo, 1min 25.05sec 26 starters, 10 class. finishers

ROUND 4/MONACO GRAND PRIX
MONTE CARLO, 11 MAY

1. PROST(FRA)	MCLAREN-TAG PORSCHE	1HR 55MIN 41.06SEC
2. ROSBERG(FIN)	MCLAREN-TAG PORSCHE	1HR 56MIN 06.08SEC
3. SENNA(BRA)	LOTUS-RENAULT TURBO	1HR 56MIN 34.71SEC
4. MANSELL(GB)	WILLIAMS-HONDA TURBO	1HR 56MIN 52.46SEC
5. ARNOUX(FRA)	LIGIER-RENAULT TURBO	77 LAPS
6. LAFFITE(FRA)	LIGIER-RENAULT TURBO	77 LAPS

Race: 78 laps of 2.07mile/3.33km (161.46 miles/259.74 kms)
Fastest lap: Prost, 1min 26.62sec, 85.96mph/138.24kph
Pole position: Prost, 1min 22.63sec 20 starters, 12 classified finishers

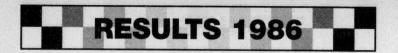

RESULTS 1986

ROUND 5/BELGIAN GRAND PRIX

SPA, 25 MAY

1. MANSELL(GB)	WILLIAMS-HONDA TURBO	1HR 27MIN 57.93SEC
2. SENNA(BRA)	LOTUS-RENAULT TURBO	1HR 28MIN 17.75SEC
3. JOHANSSON(SWE)	FERRARI TURBO	1HR 28MIN 24.52SEC
4. ALBORETO(ITA)	FERRARI TURBO	1HR 28MIN 27.56SEC
5. LAFFITE(FRA)	LIGIER-RENAULT TURBO	1HR 29MIN 08.62SEC
6. PROST(FRA)	MCLAREN-TAG PORSCHE	1HR 30MIN 15.70SEC

Race: 43 laps of 4.31mile/6.94km (185.33miles/298.42kms)
Fastest lap: Prost, 1min 59.28sec, 130.15mph/209.45kph
Pole position: Piquet(BRA),Williams-Honda Turbo,1min 54.33sec 25 starters, 12 class. finishers

ROUND 6/CANADIAN GRAND PRIX

MONTREAL, 15 JUNE

1. MANSELL(GB)	WILLIAMS-HONDA TURBO	1HR 42MIN 26.42SEC
2. PROST(FRA)	MCLAREN-TAG PORSCHE	1HR 42MIN 47.07SEC
3. PIQUET(BRA)	WILLIAMS-HONDA TURBO	1HR 43MIN 02.68SEC
4. ROSBERG(FIN)	MCLAREN-TAG PORSCHE	1HR 44MIN 02.09SEC
5. SENNA(BRA)	LOTUS-RENAULT TURBO	68 LAPS
6. ARNOUX(FRA)	LIGIER-RENAULT TURBO	68 LAPS

Race: 69 laps of 2.74mile/4.41km (189.06miles/304.29kms)
Fastest lap: Piquet, 1min 25.44sec, 115.46mph/185.81kph
Pole position: Mansell, 1min 24.19sec 24 starters, 12 classified finishers

ROUND 7/US GRAND PRIX

DETROIT, 22 JUNE

1. SENNA(BRA)	LOTUS-RENAULT TURBO	1HR 51MIN 12.85SEC
2. LAFFITE(FRA)	LIGIER-RENAULT TURBO	1HR 51MIN 43.86SEC
3. PROST(FRA)	MCLAREN-TAG PORSCHE	1HR 51MIN 44.67SEC
4. ALBORETO(ITA)	FERRARI TURBO	1HR 52MIN 43.78SEC
5. MANSELL(GB)	WILLIAMS-HONDA TURBO	62 LAPS
6. PATRESE(ITA)	BRABHAM-BMW TURBO	62 LAPS

Race: 63 laps of 2.5mile/4.02km (157.50miles/253.26kms)
Fastest lap: Piquet(BRA),Williams-Honda Turbo, 1min 41.23sec, 88.90mph/143.10kph
Pole position: Senna,1min 38.30sec 26 starters, 10 classified finishers

ROUND 8/FRENCH GRAND PRIX

PAUL RICARD,6 JULY

1. MANSELL(GB)	WILLIAMS-HONDA	1HR 37MIN 19.27SEC
2. PROST(FRA)	MCLAREN-TAG PORSCHE	1HR 37MIN 36.40SEC
3. PIQUET(BRA)	WILLIAMS-HONDA TURBO	1HR 37MIN 56.82SEC
4. ROSBERG(FIN)	MCLAREN-TAG PORSCHE	1HR 38MIN 08.00SEC
5. ARNOUX(FRA)	LIGIER-RENAULT TURBO	79 LAPS
6. LAFFITE(FRA)	LIGIER-RENAULT TURBO	79 LAPS

Race: 80 laps of 2.37mile/3.81km (189.60miles/304.8kms)
Fastest lap: Mansell,1min 09.99sec,121.86mph/196.12kph
Pole position: Senna(BRA)Lotus-Renault Turbo,1min 06.53sec 26 starters, 11 class. finishers

RESULTS 1986

ROUND 9/BRITISH GRAND PRIX
BRANDS HATCH, 13 JULY

1. MANSELL(GB)	WILLIAMS-HONDA TURBO	1HR 30MIN 38.5SEC
2. PIQUET(BRA)	WILLIAMS-HONDA TURBO	1HR 30MIN 44.1SEC
3. PROST(FRA)	MCLAREN-TAG PORSCHE	74 LAPS
4. ARNOUX(FRA)	LIGIER-RENAULT TURBO	73 LAPS
5. BRUNDLE(GB)	TYRRELL-RENAULT TURBO	72 LAPS
6. STREIFF(FRA)	TYRRELL-RENAULT TURBO	72 LAPS

Race: 75 laps of 2.61mile/4.21km (195.75miles/ 315.75kms)
Fastest lap: Mansell, 1min 09.59sec, 131.57mph/211.74kph
Pole position: Piquet, Williams-Honda Turbo, 1min 06.96sec
*26 starters, 9 classified finishers. Race re-started after first lap incident

ROUND 10/GERMAN GRAND PRIX
HOCKENHEIM, 27 JULY

1.PIQUET(BRA)	WILLIAMS-HONDA TURBO	1HR 22MIN 08.26SEC
2.SENNA(BRA)	LOTUS-RENAULT TURBO	1HR 22MIN 23.70SEC
3.MANSELL(GB)	WILLIAMS-HONDA TURBO	1HR 22MIN 52.84SEC
4.ARNOUX(FRA)	LIGIER-RENAULT TURBO	1HR 23MIN 23.44SEC
5.ROSBERG(FIN)	MCLAREN-TAG PORSCHE	43 LAPS
6.PROST(FRA)	MCLAREN-TAG PORSCHE	43 LAPS

Race: 44 laps of 4.22mile/ 6.8km (185.68 miles/299.20kms)
Fastest lap: Berger(AUT),Benetton-BMW, 1min 46.6sec, 142.63mph/229.53kph
Pole position: Rosberg, 1min 42.01sec 26 starters, 12 classified finishers

ROUND 11/HUNGARIAN GRAND PRIX
HUNGARORING, 10 AUGUST

1. PIQUET(BRA)	WILLIAMS-HONDA TURBO	2HR 00MIN 34.51SEC
2. SENNA(BRA)	LOTUS-RENAULT TURBO	2HR 00MIN 52.20SEC
3. MANSELL(GB)	WILLIAMS-HONDA TURBO	75 LAPS
4. JOHANSSON(SWE)	FERRARI TURBO	75 LAPS
5. DUMFRIES(GB)	LOTUS-RENAULT TURBO	74 LAPS
6. BRUNDLE(GB)	TYRRELL-RENAULT TURBO	74 LAPS

Race: 76 laps of 2.49mile/4.01km (189.24miles/304.76kms)
Fastest lap: Piquet,1min 31.00sec; 98.67mph/ 158.79kph
Pole position: Senna, 1min 29.45sec 26 starters, 10 classified finishers

ROUND 12/AUSTRIAN GRAND PRIX
OSTERREICHRING, 17 AUGUST

1. PROST(FRA)	MCLAREN-TAG PORSCHE	1HR 21MIN 22.5SEC
2. ALBORETO(ITA)	FERRARI TURBO	51 LAPS
3. JOHANSSON(SWE)	FERRARI TURBO	50 LAPS
4. JONES(AUS)	LOLA-FORD TURBO	50 LAPS
5. TAMBAY(FRA)	LOLA-FORD TURBO	50 LAPS
6. DANNER(GER)	ARROWS-BMW TURBO	49 LAPS

Race: 52 laps of 3.7mile/5.9km (192.4miles/306.8kms)
Fastest lap: Berger(AUT), Benetton-BMW Turbo, 1min 29.44sec, 148.61sec, 239.16kph
Pole position: Fabi(ITA)Benetton-BMW Turbo, 1min 23.55sec 25 starters, 11 class. finishers

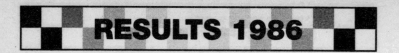
RESULTS 1986

ROUND 13/ITALIAN GRAND PRIX
MONZA, 7 SEPTEMBER

1. PIQUET(BRA)	WILLIAMS-HONDA TURBO	1HR 17MIN 42.9SEC
2. MANSELL(GB)	WILLIAMS-HONDA TURBO	1HR 17MIN 52.7SEC
3. JOHANSSON(SWE)	FERRARI TURBO	1HR 18MIN 05.8SEC
4. ROSBERG(FIN)	MCLAREN-TAG PORSCHE	1HR 18MIN 36.7SEC
5. BERGER(AUT)	BENETTON-BMW TURBO	50 LAPS
6. JONES(AUS)	LOLA-FORD TURBO	49 LAPS

Race: 51 laps of 3.6mile/5.8km (183.6miles/295.8kms)
Fastest lap: T. Fabi(ITA),Benetton-BMW Turbo, 1min 28.1sec,147.27mph/237.0kph
Pole position: T. Fabi, 1min 24.08sec 27 starters, 11 classified finishers

ROUND 14/PORTUGUESE GRAND PRIX,
ESTORIL, 21 SEPTEMBER

1. MANSELL(GB)	WILLIAMS-HONDA TURBO	1HR 37MIN 21.9SEC
2. PROST(FRA)	MCLAREN-TAG PORSCHE	1HR 37MIN 40.7SEC
3. PIQUET(BRA)	WILLIAMS-HONDA TURBO	1HR 38MIN 11.2SEC
4. SENNA(BRA)	LOTUS-RENAULT TURBO	69 LAPS
5. ALBORETO(ITA)	FERRARI TURBO	69 LAPS
6. JOHANSSON(SWE)	FERRARI TURBO	69 LAPS

Race: 70 laps of 2.7mile/4.35km (189.0miles/304.5kms)
Fastest lap: Mansell, 1min 20.94sec, 120.22mph/193.47kph
Pole position: Senna, 1min 16.67sec 27 starters, 13 classified finishers

ROUND 15/MEXICAN GRAND PRIX
MEXICO CITY, 12 OCTOBER 1986

1. BERGER(AUT)	BENETTON-BMW TURBO	1HR 33MIN 18.7SEC
2. PROST(FRA)	MCLAREN-TAG PORSCHE	1HR 33MIN 44.1SEC
3. SENNA(BRA)	LOTUS-RENAULT TURBO	1HR 34MIN 11.2SEC
4. PIQUET(BRA)	WILLIAMS-HONDA TURBO	67 LAPS
5. MANSELL(GB)	WILLIAMS-HONDA TURBO	67 LAPS
6. ALLIOT(FRA)	LIGIER-RENAULT TURBO	67 LAPS

Race: 68 laps of 2.75mile/4.42km (187.0miles/300.56kms)
Fastest lap: Piquet, 1min 19.36sec, 124.62mph/200.55kph
Pole position: Senna, 1min 16.99sec 25 starters, 16 classified finishers

ROUND 16/AUSTRALIAN GRAND PRIX
ADELAIDE, 26 OCTOBER

1. PROST(FRA)	MCLAREN-TAG PORSCHE	1HR 54MIN 20.39SEC
2. PIQUET(BRA)	WILLIAMS-HONDA TURBO	1HR 54MIN 24.59SEC
3. JOHANSSON(SWE)	FERRARI TURBO	81 LAPS
4. BRUNDLE(GB)	TYRRELL-RENAULT TURBO	80 LAPS
5. STREIFF(FRA)	TYRRELL-RENAULT TURBO	80 LAPS
6. DUMFRIES(GB)	LOTUS-RENAULT TURBO	80 LAPS

Race: 82 laps of 2.35mile/3.78km (192.70miles/309.96kms)
Fastest lap: Piquet, 1min 20.79sec, 104.64mph/168.4kph
Pole position: Mansell(GB),Williams-Honda Turbo, 1min 18.4sec 26 starters, 10 class. finishers

RESULTS 1986/7

DRIVERS' WORLD CHAMPIONSHIP 1986

1. PROST	72 points	4.	SENNA	55 points
2. MANSELL	70 points	5.	JOHANSSON	23 points
3. PIQUET	69 points	6.	ROSBERG	22 points

CONSTRUCTORS' WORLD CHAMPIONSHIP 1986

1. WILLIAMS-HONDA	141 points	4.	FERRARI	37 points
2. MCLAREN-TAG	96 points	5.	LIGIER-RENAULT	29 points
3. LOTUS-RENAULT	60 points	5.	BENETTON-BMW	19 points

1987 Once again the motor sporting Gods did not smile on Mansell. Despite winning six races, he had to watch the title go to his team-mate Piquet (who only won three). It was the Brazilian's third title in seven years. The Brit suffered a back injury in a practice accident in Japan and was unable to contest the last two rounds of the year. Senna notched up the first of what was to be his record-breaking six-victory haul in Monaco. His luckless Lotus team-mate this time was Honda-favourite, Nakajima, who startled the pundits by finishing fourth at Silverstone! Alan Jones quit Formula One for good this time. Gerhard Berger joined Alboreto at Ferrari and won in Japan and Australia. Johansson joined Prost at McLaren but often struggled in qualifying. Normally-aspirated cars returned to the Championship - the turbo cars' days were numbered. There were 16 races. Best 11 results counted for Drivers' Championship (poor Mansell!). Top six cars scored points for Constructors' title (which proved yet another Williams' walkover). Points: 9-6-4-3-2-1.

ROUND 1/BRAZILIAN GRAND PRIX

RIO DE JANEIRO, 12 APRIL

1. PROST(FRA)	MCLAREN-TAG PORSCHE	1HR 39MIN 45.14SEC
2. PIQUET(BRA)	WILLIAMS-HONDA TURBO	1HR 40MIN 25.69SEC
3. JOHANSSON(SWE)	MCLAREN-TAG PORSCHE	1HR 40MIN 41.90SEC
4. BERGER(AUT)	FERRARI TURBO	1HR 41MIN 24.38SEC
5. BOUTSEN(BEL)	BENETTON-FORD TURBO	60 LAPS
6. MANSELL(GB)	WILLIAMS-HONDA TURBO	60 LAPS

Race: 61 laps of 3.13mile/5.03km (197.19miles/316.89kms)
Fastest lap: Piquet, 1min 33.86sec,119.9mph/192.96kph
Pole position: Mansell, 1min 26.13sec 22 starters, 12 classified finishers

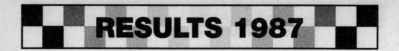
RESULTS 1987

ROUND 2/SAN MARINO GRAND PRIX
IMOLA, 3 MAY 1987

1. MANSELL(GB)	WILLIAMS-HONDA TURBO	1HR 31MIN 24.08SEC
2. SENNA(BRA)	LOTUS-HONDA TURBO	1HR 31MIN 51.62SEC
3. ALBORETO(ITA)	FERRARI- TURBO	1HR 32MIN 03.22SEC
4. JOHANSSON(SWE)	MCLAREN-TAG PORSCHE	1HR 32MIN 24.66SEC
5. BRUNDLE(GB)	ZAKSPEED-TURBO	57 LAPS
6. NAKAJIMA(JAP)	LOTUS-HONDA TURBO	57 LAPS

Race: 59 laps of 3.13mile/5.04km (184.67miles/297.36kms)
Fastest lap: T.Fabi(ITA)Benetton-Ford Turbo,1min29.25sec,125.44mph/201.85kph
Pole position: Senna, 1min 25.83sec   25 starters, 13 classified finishers

ROUND 3/BELGIAN GRAND PRIX
SPA-FRANCORCHAMPS, 17 MAY

1. PROST(FRA)	MCLAREN-TAG PORSCHE	1HR 27MIN 03.22SEC
2. JOHANSSON(SWE)	MCLAREN-TAG PORSCHE	1HR 27MIN 27.98SEC
3. DE CESARIS(ITA)	BRABHAM-BMW TURBO	42 LAPS
4. CHEEVER(USA)	ARROWS-MEGATRON	42 LAPS
5. NAKAJIMA(JAP)	LOTUS-HONDA TURBO	42 LAPS
6. ARNOUX(FRA)	LIGIER-MEGATRON	41 LAPS

Race: 43 laps of 4.31mile/6.94km (185.33miles/298.42kms)
Fastest lap: Prost, 1min 57.15sec, 132.51mph/213.26kph
Pole position: Mansell(GB) Williams-Honda Turbo, 1min 52.03sec 26 starters, 10 class. finishers

ROUND 4/MONACO GRAND PRIX
MONTE CARLO, 30 MAY

1. SENNA(BRA)	LOTUS-HONDA TURBO	1HR 57MIN 54.09SEC
2. PIQUET(BRA)	WILLIAMS-HONDA TURBO	1HR 58MIN 27.30SEC
3. ALBORETO(ITA)	FERRARI-TURBO	1HR 59MIN 06.92SEC
4. BERGER(AUT)	FERRARI-TURBO	77 LAPS
5. PALMER(GB)	TYRRELL-FORD	76 LAPS
6. CAPELLI(ITA)	MARCH-FORD	76 LAPS

Race: 78 laps of 2.07mile/3.33km (161.46miles/259.74kms)
Fastest lap: Senna, 1min 27.69sec, 84.9mph/136.64kph
Pole position: Mansell(GB), Williams-Honda Turbo, 1min 23.04sec 24 starters, 13 class. finishers

ROUND 4/US GRAND PRIX(EAST)
DETROIT, 21 JUNE

1. SENNA(BRA)	LOTUS-HONDA TURBO	1HR 50MIN 16.36SEC
2. PIQUET(BRA)	WILLIAMS-HONDA TURBO	1HR 50MIN 50.18SEC
3. PROST(FRA)	MCLAREN-TAG PORSCHE	1HR 51MIN 01.69SEC
4. BERGER(AUT)	FERRARI-TURBO	1HR 51MIN 18.96SEC
5. MANSELL(GB)	WILLIAMS-HONDA TURBO	62 LAPS
6. CHEEVER(USA)	ARROWS-MEGATRON	60 LAPS

Race: 63 laps of 2.5mile/4.02km (157.50miles/253.26kms)
Fastest lap: Senna, 1min 40.46sec, 89.58mph/144.17kph
Pole position: Mansell, 1min 39.26sec 26 starters, 12 classified finishers

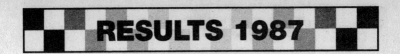

RESULTS 1987

ROUND 6/FRENCH GRAND PRIX
PAUL RICARD, 5 JULY

1. MANSELL(GB)	WILLIAMS-HONDA TURBO	1HR 37MIN 03.84SEC
2. PIQUET(BRA)	WILLIAMS-HONDA TURBO	1HR 37MIN 11.55SEC
3. PROST(FRA)	MCLAREN-TAG PORSCHE	1HR 37MIN 59.09SEC
4. SENNA(BRA)	LOTUS-HONDA TURBO	79 LAPS
5. T. FABI(ITA)	BENETTON-FORD TURBO	77 LAPS
6. STREIFF(FRA)	TYRRELL-FORD	76 LAPS

Race: 80 laps of 2.37mile/3.81km (189.60miles/304.80kms)
Fastest lap: Piquet, 1min 09.55sec, 122.64mph/197.37kph
Pole position: Mansell, 1min 06.45sec 26 starters, 9 classified finishers

ROUND 7/BRITISH GRAND PRIX
SILVERSTONE, 12 JULY

1. MANSELL(GB)	WILLIAMS-HONDA TURBO	1HR 19MIN 11.78SEC
2. PIQUET(BRA)	WILLIAMS-HONDA TURBO	1HR 19MIN 13.70SEC
3. SENNA(BRA)	LOTUS-HONDA TURBO	64 LAPS
4. NAKAJIMA(JAP)	LOTUS-HONDA TURBO	63 LAPS
5. WARWICK (GB)	ARROWS-MEGATRON	63 LAPS
6. T.FABI(ITA)	BENETTON-FORD TURBO	63 LAPS

Race: 65 laps of 2.97mile/4.78km (193.05miles/301.70kms)
Fastest lap: Mansell, 1min 09.83sec, 153.06mph/246.32kph
Pole position: Piquet, 1min 07.11sec 25 starters, 9 classified finishers

ROUND 8/GERMAN GRAND PRIX
HOCKENHEIM, 26 JULY 1987

1.PIQUET(BRA)	WILLIAMS-HONDA TURBO	1HR 21MIN 25.09SEC
2.JOHANSSON (SWE)	MCLAREN-TAG PORSCHE	1HR 23MIN 04.68SEC
3.SENNA(BRA)	LOTUS-HONDA TURBO	43 LAPS
4.STREIFF(FRA)	TYRRELL-FORD	43 LAPS
5.PALMER(GB)	TYRRELL-FORD	43 LAPS
6.ALLIOT(FRA)	LOLA-FORD	42 LAPS

Race: 44 laps of 4.22mile/6.8km (185.68miles/299.20kms)
Fastest lap: Mansell(GB), Williams-Honda Turbo, 1min 45.72sec, 143.82mph/231.46kph
Pole position: Mansell, 1min 42.62sec 26 starters, 7 classified finishers

ROUND 9/HUNGARIAN GRAND PRIX
HUNGARORING, 9 AUGUST

1.PIQUET(BRA)	WILLIAMS-HONDA TURBO	1HR 59MIN 26.79SEC
2 SENNA(BRA)	LOTUS-HONDA TURBO	2HR 00MIN 04.52SEC
3.PROST(FRA)	MCLAREN-TAG PORSCHE	2HR 00MIN 54.25SEC
4.BOUTSEN(BEL)	BENETTON-FORD TURBO	75 LAPS
5.PATRESE(BRA)	BRABHAM-BMW TURBO	75 LAPS
6.WARWICK(GB)	ARROWS-MEGATRON TURBO	74 LAPS

Race: 76 laps of 2.49 mile/4.01km (189.24miles/304.76kms)
Fastest lap: Piquet, 1min 30.15sec, 99.6mph/160.30kph
Pole position: Mansell, 1min 28.05sec 26 starters, 14 classified finishers

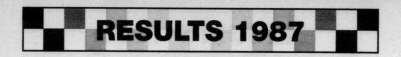

RESULTS 1987

ROUND 10/AUSTRIAN GRAND PRIX
OSTERREICHRING, 16 AUGUST

1. MANSELL(GB)	WILLIAMS-HONDA TURBO	1HR 18MIN 44.90SEC
2. PIQUET(BRA)	WILLIAMS-HONDA TURBO	1HR 19MIN 40.60SEC
3. T.FABI(ITA)	BENETTON-FORD TURBO	51 LAPS
4. BOUTSEN(BEL)	BENETTON-FORD TURBO	51 LAPS
5. SENNA(BRA)	LOTUS-HONDA TURBO	50 LAPS
6. PROST(FRA)	MCLAREN-TAG PORSCHE	50 LAPS

Race: 52 laps of 3.69mile/5.94km (191.88miles/308.88kms)
Fastest lap: Mansell, 1min 28.32sec, 150.50mph/242.21kph
Pole position: Piquet, 1min 23. 36sec 26 starters, 15 classified finishers

ROUND 11/ITALIAN GRAND PRIX
MONZA, 6 SEPTEMBER

1. PIQUET(BRA)	WILLIAMS-HONDA TURBO	1HR 14MIN 47.71SEC
2. SENNA(BRA)	LOTUS-HONDA TURBO	1HR 14MIN 49.51SEC
3. MANSELL(GB)	WILLIAMS-HONDA TURBO	1HR 15MIN 36.74SEC
4. BERGER(AUT)	FERRARI TURBO	1HR 15MIN 45.69SEC
5. BOUTSEN(BEL)	BENETTON-FORD TURBO	1HR 16MIN 09.03SEC
6. JOHANSSON(SWE)	MCLAREN-TAG PORSCHE	1HR 16MIN 16.49SEC

Race: 50 laps of 3.6mile/5.8km (180.0miles/290.0kms)
Fastest lap: Senna, 1min 26.8sec, 149.48mph/240.56kph
Pole position: Piquet, 1min 23.46sec 26 starters, 16 classified finishers

ROUND 12 PORTUGUESE GRAND PRIX
ESTORIL, 20 SEPTEMBER

1. PROST(FRA)	MCLAREN-TAG TURBO	1HR 37MIN 03.91SEC
2. BERGER(AUT)	FERRARI TURBO	1HR 37MIN 24.40SEC
3. PIQUET(BRA)	WILLIAMS-HONDA TURBO	1HR 38MIN 07.20SEC
4. T.FABI(ITA)	BENETTON-FORD TURBO	69 LAPS
5. JOHANSSON(SWE)	MCLAREN-TAG PORSCHE	69 LAPS
6. CHEEVER(USA)	ARROWS-MEGATRON	68 LAPS

Race: 70 laps of 2.7mile/4.35km (189.0 miles/304.5kms)
Fastest lap: Berger, 1min 19.28sec, 122.74mph/197.52kph
Pole position: Berger, 1min 17.62sec 26 starters, 14 classified finishers

ROUND 13/SPANISH GRAND PRIX
JEREZ, 27 SEPTEMBER

1. MANSELL(GB)	WILLIAMS-HONDA TURBO	1HR 49MIN 12.69SEC
2. PROST(FRA)	MCLAREN-TAG TURBO	1HR 49MIN 34.92SEC
3. JOHANSSON(SWE)	MCLAREN-TAG TURBO	1HR 49MIN 43.51SEC
4. PIQUET(BRA)	WILLIAMS-HONDA TURBO	1HR 49MIN 44.14SEC
5. SENNA(BRA)	LOTUS-HONDA TURBO	1HR 50MIN 26.20SEC
6. ALLIOT(FRA)	LOLA-FORD	71 LAPS

Race: 72 laps of 2.62mile/4.22km (188.64miles/303.84kms)
Fastest lap: Berger(AUT)Ferrari Turbo, 1min 26.99sec,108.47mph/174.57kph
Pole position: Piquet, 1min 22.46sec 26 starters, 16 classified finishers

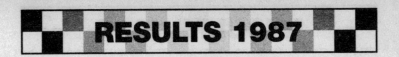

RESULTS 1987

ROUND 14/MEXICAN GRAND PRIX
MEXICO CITY, 18 OCTOBER

1. MANSELL(GB)	WILLIAMS-HONDA TURBO	1HR 26MIN 24.21SEC
2. PIQUET(BRA)	WILLIAMS-HONDA TURBO	1HR 26MIN 50.38SEC
3. PATRESE(ITA)	BRABHAM-BMW TURBO	1HR 27MIN 51.09SEC
4. CHEEVER(USA)	ARROWS-MEGATRON TURBO	1HR 28MIN 05.56SEC
5. T.FABI(ITA)	BENETTON-FORD TURBO	61 LAPS
6. ALLIOT(FRA)	LOLA-FORD	60 LAPS

Race: 63 laps of 2.75 mile/4.42km (173.25 miles/278.46 kms)
Fastest lap: Piquet, 1min 19.13sec, 124.97mph/201.13kph
Pole position: Mansell, 1min 18.38sec 26 starters, 9 classified finishers

ROUND 15 JAPANESE GRAND PRIX
SUZUKA, 1 NOVEMBER

1. BERGER(AUT)	FERRARI TURBO	1HR 32MIN 58.07SEC
2. SENNA(BRA)	LOTUS-HONDA TURBO	1HR 33MIN 15.46SEC
3. JOHANSSON(SWE)	MCLAREN-TAG TURBO	1HR 33MIN 15.77SEC
4. ALBORETO(ITA)	FERRARI TURBO	1HR 34MIN 18.51SEC
5. BOUTSEN(BEL)	BENETTON-FORD TURBO	1HR 34MIN 23.65SEC
6. NAKAJIMA(JAP)	LOTUS-HONDA TURBO	1HR 34MIN 34.55SEC

Race: 51 laps of 3.64 mile/5.86 km (185.64 miles/ 298.86kms)
Fastest lap: Prost(FRA), McLaren-TAG Porsche,1min 43.84sec, 126.21mph/203.12kph
Pole position: Berger, 1min 40.04sec 26 starters, 15 classified finishers

ROUND 16/AUSTRALIAN GRAND PRIX
ADELAIDE, 15 NOVEMBER

1. BERGER(AUT)	FERRARI TURBO	1HR 52MIN 56.14SEC
2* ALBORETO(ITA)	FERRARI TURBO	1HR 54MIN 04.03SEC
3. BOUTSEN(BEL)	BENETTON-FORD TURBO	81 LAPS
4. PALMER(GB)	TYRRELL-FORD	80 LAPS
5. DALMAS(FRA)	LOLA-FORD	79 LAPS
6. MORENO(BRA)	AGS-FORD	79 LAPS

Race: 82 laps of 2.35 mile/3.78 km (192.70miles/309.96kms)
Fastest lap: Berger, 1min 20.42sec, 105.12mph/169.18kph
Pole position: Berger, 1min 17.27sec 26 starters, 9 classified finishers*
*Senna finished second but disqualified for illegal brakes.

 DRIVERS' WORLD CHAMPIONSHIP 1987

1. PIQUET	73 *points*	4. PROST	46 *points*
2. MANSELL	61 *points*	5. BERGER	36 *points*
3. SENNA	57 *points*	6. JOHANSSON	30 *points*

CONSTRUCTORS' WORLD CHAMPIONSHIP 1987

1. WILLIAMS-HONDA	137 *points*	5. BENETTON-FORD	28 *points*
2. MCLAREN-TAG	76 *points*	6. ARROWS-MEGATRON	11 *points*
3. LOTUS-HONDA	64 *points*	6. TYRRELL-FORD	11 *points*
4. FERRARI	53 *points*		

RESULTS 1988

1988 McLaren dominated the season. Senna joined from Lotus, won eight races and the Championship. Prost won seven and finished runner-up.The Grand Old Man of Motor Racing, Enzo Ferrari, died at the age of 90 and Berger and Alboreto finished one-two at Monza a month later in a sentiment-charged tribute for Ferrari. This was the last year for Turbo engines. Williams struggled with the Judd engine and Ferrari floundered. Piquet joined Lotus for big bucks and the patient Patrese teamed with Mansell at Williams. There were 16 rounds. The best eleven results counted for the Drivers' title, top six cars for Constructors' Championship. Points: 9-6-4-3-2-1 for first six places.

ROUND 1/BRAZILIAN GRAND PRIX
RIO DE JANEIRO, 3 APRIL

1. PROST(FRA)	MCLAREN-HONDA TURBO	1HR 36MIN 06.90SEC
2. BERGER(AUT)	FERRARI TURBO	1HR 36MIN 16.70SEC
3. PIQUET(BRA)	LOTUS-HONDA TURBO	1HR 37MIN 15.40SEC
4. WARWICK(GB)	ARROWS-MEGATRON	1HR 37MIN 20.20SEC
5. ALBORETO(ITA)	FERRARI TURBO	1HR 37MIN 21.40SEC
6. NAKAJIMA(JAP)	LOTUS-HONDA TURBO	59 LAPS

Race: 60 laps of 3.13mile/5.03km (187.8miles/301.8kms)
Fastest lap: Berger, 1min 32.94sec. 121.09mph,194.87kph
Pole position: Senna(BRA),McLaren-Honda Turbo,1min 28.10sec 26 starters, 9 classified finishers

ROUND 2/SAN MARINO GRAND PRIX
IMOLA, 1 MAY

1.SENNA(BRA)	MCLAREN-HONDA TURBO	1HR 32MIN 41.30SEC
2.PROST(FRA)	MCLAREN-HONDA TURBO	1HR 32MIN 43.60SEC
3.PIQUET(BRA)	LOTUS-HONDA TURBO	59 LAPS
4.BOUTSEN(BEL)	BENETTON-FORD	59 LAPS
5.NANNINI(ITA)	BENETTON-FORD	59 LAPS
6.CHEEVER(USA)	ARROWS-MEGATRON	59 LAPS

Race: 60 laps of 3.13mile/5.04km (187.8miles/302.4kms)
Fastest lap: Prost, 1min 29.68sec, 125.7mph/202.30kph
Pole position: Senna, 1min 27.15sec 26 starters, 18 classified finishers

ROUND 3/MONACO GRAND PRIX
MONTE CARLO,15 MAY

1.PROST(FRA)	MCLAREN-HONDA TURBO	1HR 57MIN 17.10SEC
2.BERGER(AUT)	FERRARI TURBO	1HR 57MIN 37.50SEC
3.ALBORETO(ITA)	FERRARI TURBO	1HR 57MIN 58.30SEC
4.WARWICK(GB)	ARROWS-MEGATRON	77 LAPS
5.PALMER(GB)	TYRRELL-FORD	77 LAPS
6.PATRESE(ITA)	WILLIAMS-JUDD	77 LAPS

Race: 78 laps of 2.07mile/3.33km (161 miles/259.74kms)
Fastest lap: Senna(BRA), McLaren-Honda, 1min 26.32sec, 86.3mph/138.8kph
Pole position: Senna: 1min 24.00mph 26 starters, 10 classified finishers

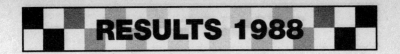
RESULTS 1988

ROUND 4/ MEXICAN GRAND PRIX
MEXICO CITY, 29 MAY

1. PROST(FRA)	MCLAREN-HONDA TURBO	1HR 30MIN 15.7SEC
2. SENNA(BRA)	MCLAREN-HONDA TURBO	1HR 30MIN 22.8SEC
3. BERGER(AUT)	FERRARI TURBO	1HR 31MIN 13.1SEC
4. ALBORETO(ITA)	FERRARI TURBO	66 LAPS
5. WARWICK(GB)	ARROWS-MEGATRON	66 LAPS
6. CHEEVER(USA)	ARROWS-MEGATRON	66 LAPS

Race: 67 laps of 2.75mile/4.42km (184 miles/ 296.14kms)
Fastest lap: Prost, 1min 18.61sec, 125.81mph/202.47kph
Pole position: Senna, 1min 17.47sec 26 starters, 16 classified finishers

ROUND 5/CANADIAN GRAND PRIX
MONTREAL, 12 JUNE

1. SENNA(BRA)	MCLAREN-HONDA TURBO	1HR 39MIN 46.6SEC
2. PROST(FRA)	MCLAREN-HONDA TURBO	1HR 39MIN 52.6SEC
3. BOUTSEN(BEL)	BENETTON-FORD TURBO	1HR 40MIN 38.0SEC
4. PIQUET(BRA)	LOTUS-HONDA TURBO	68 LAPS
5. CAPELLI(ITA)	MARCH-JUDD	68 LAPS
6. PALMER(GB)	TYRRELL-FORD	67 LAPS

Race: 69 laps of 2.73mile/4.39km (188.37miles/ 302kms)
Fastest lap: Senna, 1min 24.97sec, 115.57mph/185.99kph
Pole position: Senna, 1min 21.68sec 26 starters, 14 classified finishers

ROUND 6/ US GRAND PRIX (EAST)
DETROIT, 19 JUNE

1. SENNA(BRA)	MCLAREN-HONDA TURBO	1HR 54MIN 56.0SEC
2. PROST(FRA)	MCLAREN-HONDA TURBO	1HR 55MIN 34.8SEC
3. BOUTSEN(BEL)	BENETTON-FORD TURBO	62 LAPS
4. DE CESARIS(ITA)	RIAL-FORD	62 LAPS
5. PALMER(GB)	TYRRELL-FORD	62 LAPS
6. MARTINI(ITA)	MINARDI-FORD	62 LAPS

Race: 63 laps of 2.5 mile/ 4.02km (157.50 miles/253.26 kms)
Fastest lap: Prost,1min 44.84sec, 85.85mph/138.16kph
Pole position: Senna, 1min 40.61sec 16 starters, 9 classified finishers

ROUND 7/FRENCH GRAND PRIX
PAUL RICARD, 3 JULY

1. PROST(FRA)	MCLAREN-HONDA TURBO	1HR 37MIN 37.30SEC
2. SENNA(BRA)	MCLAREN-HONDA TURBO	1HR 38MIN 09.10SEC
3. ALBORETO(ITA)	FERRARI TURBO	1HR 38MIN 43.80SEC
4. BERGER(AUT)	FERRARI TURBO	79 LAPS
5. PIQUET(BRA)	LOTUS-HONDA TURBO	79 LAPS
6. NANNINI(ITA)	BENETTON-FORD TURBO	79 LAPS

Race: 80 laps of 2.37 mile/3.81 km (189.60 miles/ 304.80 kms)
Fastest lap: Prost, 1min 11.74sec, 119.00mph/191.35kph
Pole position: Prost, 1min 07.59sec 26 starters, 15 classified finishers

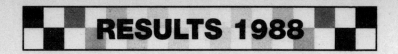

RESULTS 1988

ROUND 8/BRITISH GRAND PRIX
SILVERSTONE, 10 JULY

1. SENNA(BRA)	MCLAREN-HONDA TURBO	1HR 33MIN 16.4SEC
2. MANSELL(GB)	WILLIAMS-JUDD	1HR 33MIN 39.7SEC
3. NANNINI(ITA)	BENETTON-FORD	1HR 34MIN 07.6SEC
4. GUGELMIN (BRA)	MARCH-JUDD	1HR 34MIN 27.8SEC
5. PIQUET(BRA)	LOTUS-HONDA TURBO	1HR 34MIN 37.2SEC
6. WARWICK(GB)	ARROWS-MEGATRON	64 LAPS

Race: 65 laps of 2.97 mile/4.78 km (193.05 miles/ 301.70kms)
Fastest lap: Mansell, 1min 23.31sec, 128.3mph/206.48kph
Pole position: Berger(AUT) Ferrari Turbo, 1min 10.13sec 26 starters, 19 class. finishers

ROUND 9/GERMAN GRAND PRIX
HOCKENHEIM, 24 JULY

1. SENNA(BRA)	MCLAREN-HONDA TURBO	1HR 32MIN 54.20SEC
2. PROST(FRA)	MCLAREN-HONDA TURBO	1HR 33MIN 07.80SEC
3. BERGER(AUT)	FERRARI TURBO	1HR 33MIN 46.30SEC
4. ALBORETO(ITA)	FERRARI TURBO	1HR 34MIN 35.10SEC
5. CAPELLI(ITA)	MARCH-JUDD	1HR 34MIN 43.80SEC
6. BOUTSEN(BEL)	BENETTON-FORD	43 LAPS

Race: 44 laps of 4.22 mile/6.8 km (185.68 miles/ 299.20 kms)
*Fastest lap:*Nannini(ITA), BenettonFord,2min03.03sec,123.58sec/198.89kph
Pole position: Senna, 1min 44.60sec 26 starters, 19 classified finishers

ROUND 10/ HUNGARIAN GRAND PRIX
HUNGARORING, 7 AUGUST

1. SENNA(BRA)	MCLAREN-HONDA TURBO	1HR 57MIN 47.10SEC
2. PROST(FRA)	MCLAREN-HONDA TURBO	1HR 57MIN 47.60SEC
3. BOUTSEN(BEL)	BENETTON-FORD	1HR 58MIN 18.50SEC
4. BERGER(AUT)	FERRARI TURBO	1HR 59MIN 15.80SEC
5. GUGELMIN(BRA)	MARCH-JUDD	75 LAPS
6. PATRESE(ITA)	WILLIAMS-JUDD	75 LAPS

Race: 76 laps of 2.49mile/4.01km (189.24miles/304.76kms)
Fastest lap: Prost, 1min 30.64sec, 99.06mph/159.43kph
Pole position: Senna, 1min 27.64sec 26 starters, 13 classified finishers

ROUND 11/BELGIAN GRAND PRIX
SPA-FRANCORCHAMPS, 28 AUGUST

1. SENNA(BRA)	MCLAREN-HONDA TURBO	1HR 28MIN 00.60SEC
2. PROST(FRA)	MCLAREN-HONDA TURBO	1HR 28MIN 31.00SEC
3. CAPELLI(ITA)	MARCH-JUDD	1HR 29MIN 16.30SEC
4. PIQUET(BRA)	LOTUS-HONDA TURBO	1HR 29MIN 24.20SEC
5. WARWICK(GB)	ARROWS-MEGATRON	1HR 29MIN 25.90SEC
6. CHEEVER(USA)	ARROWS-MEGATRON	42 LAPS

Race: 43 laps of 4.31 mile/6.94km (185.33miles/ 298.42kms)
Fastest lap: Berger(AUT), Ferrari Turbo, 2min 00.77sec, 128.54mph/206.87kph
Pole position: 1min 53.72sec 26 starters, 15 classified finishers*
*Boutsen and Nannini(Benetton) finished third and fourth but were disqualified for illegal fuel.

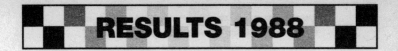

RESULTS 1988

ROUND 12/ITALIAN GRAND PRIX
MONZA, 11 SEPTEMBER

1. BERGER(AUT)	FERRARI TURBO	1HR 17MIN 39.70SEC
2. ALBORETO(ITA)	FERRARI TURBO	1HR 17MIN 40.30SEC
3. CHEEVER(USA)	ARROWS-MEGATRON	1HR 18MIN 15.20SEC
4. WARWICK(GB)	ARROWS-MEGATRON	1HR 18MIN 15.90SEC
5. CAPELLI(ITA)	MARCH-JUDD	1HR 18MIN 32.30SEC
6. BOUTSEN(BEL)	BENETTON-FORD	1HR 18MIN 39.60SEC

Race: 51 laps of 3.6mile/5.8km (183.6iles/284.58kms)
Fastest lap: Alboreto, 1min 29.07sec, 145.70mhp/ 234.4kph
Pole position: Senna(BRA),McLaren-Honda,1min 25.97sec 26 starters, 13 class. finishers

ROUND 13/ PORTUGUESE GRAND PRIX
ESTORIL, 25 SEPTEMBER

1. PROST(FRA)	MCLAREN-HONDA TURBO	1HR 37MIN 41.00SEC
2. CAPELLI(ITA)	MARCH-JUDD	1HR 37MIN 50.50SEC
3. BOUTSEN(BEL)	BENETTON-FORD	1HR 38MIN 25.60SEC
4. WARWICK(GB)	ARROWS-MEGATRON	1HR 38MIN 48.40SEC
5. ALBORETO(ITA)	FERRARI TURBO	1HR 38MIN 52.80SEC
6. SENNA(BRA)	MCLAREN-HONDA TURBO	1HR 38MIN 59.30SEC

Race: 70 laps of 2.7mile/4.35km (189.0 miles/ 304.5kms)
Fastest lap: Berger(AUT) Ferrari Turbo,1min 21.96sec, 118.7mph/191.1kph
Pole position: Prost, 1min 17.41sec 26 starters, 12 classified finishers

ROUND 14/SPANISH GRAND PRIX
JEREZ, 2 OCTOBER

1. PROST(FRA)	MCLAREN-HONDA TURBO	1HR 48MIN 43.90SEC
2. MANSELL(GB)	WILLIAMS-JUDD	1HR 49MIN 10.10SEC
3. NANNINI (ITA)	BENETTON-FORD	1HR 49MIN 19.30SEC
4. SENNA(BRA)	MCLAREN-HONDA	1HR 49MIN 30.70SEC
5. PATRESE (ITA)	WILLIAMS-JUDD	1HR 49MIN 31.30SEC
6. BERGER(AUT)	FERRARI TURBO	1HR 49MIN 35.70SEC

Race: 72 laps of 2.62mile/ 4.22 km (188.64 miles/303.84kms)
Fastest lap: Prost, 1min 27.85sec, 107.4mph/172.86kph
Pole position: Senna, 1min 24.07sec 26 starters, 14 classified finishers

ROUND 15/JAPANESE GRAND PRIX
SUZUKA, 30 OCTOBER

1. SENNA(BRA)	MCLAREN-HONDA TURBO	1HR 33MIN 26.2SEC
2. PROST(FRA)	MCLAREN-HONDA TURBO	1HR 33MIN 39.5SEC
3. BOUTSEN(BEL)	BENETTON-FORD	1HR 34MIN 02.3SEC
4. BERGER(AUT)	FERRARI TURBO	1HR 34MIN 52.9SEC
5. NANNINI(ITA)	BENETTON-FORD	1HR 34MIN 56.8SEC
6. PATRESE(ITA)	WILLIAMS-JUDD	1HR 35MIN 03.8SEC

Race: 51 laps of 3.64mile/5.86km (185.64 miles/ 298.86 kms)
Fastest lap: Senna, 1min 46.33sec, 123.26mph/198.38kph
Pole position: Senna, 1min 41.85sec 26 starters, 17 classified finishers

RESULTS 1988/9

ROUND 16 AUSTRALIAN GRAND PRIX
ADELAIDE, 13 NOVEMBER

1. PROST(FRA)	MCLAREN-HONDA TURBO	1HR 53MIN 14.7SEC
2. SENNA(BRA)	MCLAREN-HONDA TURBO	1HR 53MIN 51.5SEC
3. PIQUET(BRA)	LOTUS-HONDA TURBO	1HR 54MIN 02.2SEC
4. PATRESE(ITA)	WILLIAMS-JUDD	1HR 54MIN 34.8SEC
5. BOUTSEN(BEL)	BENETTON-FORD	81 LAPS
6. CAPELLI(ITA)	MARCH-JUDD	81 LAPS

Race: 82 laps of 2.35 mile/3.78 km (192.70 miles/ 309.96kms)
Fastest lap: Prost, 1min 21.2sec, 104.10mph/167.60kph
Pole position: Senna, 1min 17.75sec 26 starters, 11 classified finishers

DRIVERS' WORLD CHAMPIONSHIP 1988

1. SENNA	*90 points*	4.	BOUTSEN	*27 points*
2. PROST	*87 points*	5.	ALBORETO	*24 points*
3. BERGER	*41 points*	6.	PIQUET	*22 points*

CONSTRUCTORS' WORLD CHAMPIONSHIP 1988

1. MCLAREN-HONDA	*199 points*	4.	ARROWS-MEGATRON	*23 points*
2. FERRARI	*65 points*	4.	LOTUS-HONDA	*23 points*
3. BENETTON-FORD	*39 points*	6.	MARCH-JUDD	*22 points*

1989 The bitter rivalry between McLaren team-mates, Senna and Prost became ridiculous. The two were not even on speaking terms when they collided in Japan. Senna, eventually lost out to the Frenchman, who took his third Drivers' title. Mansell joined Ferrari and became a legend in Italy by winning his very first Grand Prix for the team in Brazil. Alessandro Nannini led the Benetton attack in impressive style. Britain's Johnny Herbert began the year alongside, in the wake of his horrific Brands accident, but did not last the season. Jean Alesi scored his first points in France. Turbos had been phased out.Williams began their historic association with Renault, with their V10s. McLaren walked away with the Constructors' title again with their Honda V10, winning 10 of the 16 Grands Prix. A total of 20 Grands Prix teams led to the introduction of pre-qualifying. Best 11 results counted for Drivers' Championship. Top six cars from all rounds for Constructors'. Points: 9-6-4-3-2-1.

ROUND 1/BRAZILIAN GRAND PRIX
RIO DE JANEIRO, 26 MARCH

1. MANSELL(GB)	FERRARI	1HR 38MIN 58.74SEC
2. PROST(FRA)	MCLAREN-HONDA	1HR 39MIN 06.55SEC
3. GUGELMIN(BRA)	MARCH-JUDD	1HR 39MIN 08.11SEC
4. HERBERT(GB)	BENETTON-FORD	1HR 39MIN 09.24SEC
5. WARWICK(GB)	ARROWS-FORD	1HR 39MIN 16.61SEC
6. NANNINI(ITA)	BENETTON-FORD	1HR 39MIN 16.99SEC

Race: 61 laps of 3.13mile/5.03km (190.93miles/306.83kms)
Fastest lap: Patrese(ITA), Williams-Renault,1min 32.51sec,121.66mph/195.79kph
Pole position: Senna(BRA), McLaren-Honda, 1min 25.30sec 26 starters, 14 class. finishers

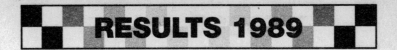
RESULTS 1989

ROUND 2/SAN MARINO GRAND PRIX
IMOLA, 23 APRIL

1. SENNA(BRA)	MCLAREN-HONDA	1HR 26MIN 51.25SEC
2. PROST(FRA)	MCLAREN-HONDA	1HR 27MIN 31.47SEC
3. NANNINI(ITA)	BENETTON-FORD	57 LAPS
4. BOUTSEN(BEL)	WILLIAMS-RENAULT	57 LAPS
5. WARWICK(GB)	ARROWS-FORD	57 LAPS
6. PALMER(GB)	TYRRELL-FORD	57 LAPS

Race: 58 laps of 3.13 mile/5.04km (181.54 miles/292.32kms)
Fastest lap: Prost, 1min 26.79sec, 129.9mph/209.04kph
Pole position: Senna, 1min 26.01sec 26 starters, 12 classified finishers

ROUND 3/MONACO GRAND PRIX
MONTE CARLO, 7 MAY

1. SENNA(BRA)	MCLAREN-HONDA	1HR 53MIN 33.25SEC
2. PROST(FRA)	MCLAREN-HONDA	1HR 54MIN 23.78SEC
3. MODENA(ITA)	BRABHAM-JUDD	76 LAPS
4. CAFFI(ITA)	DALLARA-FORD	75 LAPS
5. ALBORETO(ITA)	TYRRELL-FORD	75 LAPS
6. BRUNDLE(GB)	BRABHAM-JUDD	75 LAPS

Race: 77 laps of 2.07 mile/3.33km (159.39 miles/256.41kms)
Fastest lap: Prost, 1min 25.50sec, 87.1mph/140.1kph
Pole position: Senna, 1min 22.31sec 26 starters, 15 classified finishers

ROUND 4/MEXICAN GRAND PRIX
MEXICO CITY, 28 MAY

1. SENNA(BRA)	MCLAREN-HONDA	1HR 35MIN 21.43SEC
2. PATRESE(ITA)	WILLIAMS-RENAULT	1HR 35MIN 36.99SEC
3. ALBORETO(ITA)	TYRRELL-FORD	1HR 35MIN 52.69SEC
4. NANNINI(ITA)	BENETTON-FORD	1HR 36MIN 06.93SEC
5. PROST (FRA)	MCLAREN-FORD	1HR 36MIN 17.54SEC
6. TARQUINI(ITA)	AGS-FORD	68SEC

Race: 69 laps of 2.75mile/4.42km (187.0miles/300.56kms)
Fastest lap: Mansell(GB), Ferrari, 1min 20.42sec, 122.97mph/197.91kph
Pole position: Senna, 1min 17.85sec 26 starters, 15 classified finishers

ROUND 5/US GRAND PRIX
PHOENIX, 4 JUNE

1. PROST(FRA)	MCLAREN-HONDA	2HR 01MIN 33.13SEC
2. PATRESE(ITA)	WILLIAMS-RENAULT	2HR 02MIN 12.83SEC
3. CHEEVER(USA)	ARROWS-FORD	2HR 02MIN 16.34SEC
4. DANNER(GER)	RIAL-FORD	74 LAPS
5. HERBERT(GB)	BENETTON-FORD	74 LAPS
6. BOUTSEN(BEL)	WILLIAMS-RENAULT	74 LAPS

Race: 75 laps of 2.36mile/3.8km (177 miles/285kms)
Fastest lap: Senna(BRA)McLaren-Honda, 1min 33.97sec, 90.41mph/145.51kph
Pole position: Senna, 1min 30.11sec 26 starters, 9 classified finishers

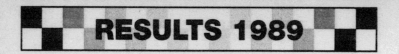

RESULTS 1989

ROUND 6/CANADIAN GRAND PRIX
MONTREAL, 18 JUNE

1. BOUTSEN(BEL)	WILLIAMS-RENAULT	2HR 01MIN 24.07SEC
2. PATRESE(ITA)	WILLIAMS-RENAULT	2HR 01MIN 54.08SEC
3. DE CESARIS(ITA)	DALLARA-FORD	2HR 03MIN 00.72SEC
4. PIQUET(BRA)	LOTUS-JUDD	2HR 03MIN 05.56SEC
5. ARNOUX(FRA)	LIGIER-FORD	68 LAPS
6. CAFFI(ITA)	DALLARA-FORD	67 LAPS

Race: 69 laps of 2.73mile/4.39km (188.37 miles/302.91kms)
Fastest lap: Palmer(GB) Tyrrell-Ford,1min 31.93sec, 106.83mph/171.92kph
Pole position: Senna(BRA)McLaren-Honda, 1min 20.97sec 26 starters, 8 class. finishers

ROUND 7/FRENCH GRAND PRIX
PAUL RICARD, 9 JULY

1. PROST(FRA)	MCLAREN-HONDA	1HR 38MIN 29.41SEC
2. MANSELL(GB)	FERRARI	1HR 39MIN 13.43SEC
3. PATRESE(ITA)	WILLIAMS-RENAULT	1HR 39MIN 36.33SEC
4. ALESI(FRA)	TYRRELL-FORD	1HR 39MIN 42.64SEC
5. JOHANSSON(SWE)	ONYX-FORD	79 LAPS
6. GROUILLARD(FRA)	LIGIER-FORD	79 LAPS

Race: 80 laps of 2.37mile/3.81km (189.60 miles/304.80kms)
Fastest lap: Gugelmin(BRA), March-Judd,1min 12.09sec,118.32mph/190kph
Pole position: Prost, 1min 07.20sec 26 starters, 13 classified finishers

ROUND 18/BRITISH GRAND PRIX
SILVERSTONE, 16 JULY

1. PROST(FRA)	MCLAREN-HONDA	1HR 19MIN 22.13SEC
2. MANSELL(GB)	FERRARI	1HR 19MIN 41.50SEC
3. NANNINI(ITA)	BENETTON-FORD	1HR 20MIN 10.15SEC
4. PIQUET(BRA)	LOTUS-JUDD	1HR 20MIN 28.87SEC
5. MARTINI(ITA)	MINARDI-FORD	63 LAPS
6. SALA(SPA)	MINARDI-FORD	63 LAPS

Race: 64 laps of 2.97 mile/4.78km (190.08 miles/305.92kms)
Fastest lap: Mansell, 1min 12.02sec, 148.47mph/238.93kph
Pole position: Senna(GB)McLaren-Honda,1min 09.1sec 26 starters, 12 class. finishers

ROUND 9/GERMAN GRAND PRIX
HOCKENHEIM, 30 JULY

1. SENNA(BRA)	MCLAREN-HONDA	1HR 21MIN 43.30SEC
2. PROST(FRA)	MCLAREN-HONDA	1HR 22MIN 01.45SEC
3. MANSELL(GB)	FERRARI	1HR 23MIN 06.56SEC
4. PATRESE(ITA)	WILLIAMS-RENAULT	44 LAPS
5. PIQUET(BRA)	LOTUS-JUDD	44 LAPS
6. WARWICK(GB)	ARROWS-FORD	44 LAPS

Race: 45 laps of 4.22mile/6.8km (189.9 miles/306kms)
Fastest lap: Senna,1min 45.90sec,143.60mph/231.10kph
Pole position: Senna,1min 42.30sec 26 starters, 12 classified finishers

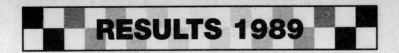

RESULTS 1989

ROUND 10/HUNGARIAN GRAND PRIX
HUNGARORING, 13 AUGUST

1. MANSELL(GB)	FERRARI	1HR 49MIN 38.65SEC
2. SENNA(BRA)	MCLAREN-HONDA	1HR 50MIN 04.62SEC
3. BOUTSEN(BEL)	WILLIAMS-RENAULT	1HR 50MIN 17.00SEC
4. PROST(FRA)	MCLAREN-HONDA	1HR 50MIN 22.83SEC
5. CHEEVER(USA)	ARROWS-FORD	1HR 50MIN 23.76SEC
6. PIQUET(BRA)	LOTUS-JUDD	1HR 50MIN 50.69SEC

Race: 77 laps of 2.47 mile/ 3.97 km - 190.19 miles/305.69 kms)
Fastest lap: Mansell,1min 22.64sec,107.41 mph/ 172.86 kph
Pole position: Patrese(ITA)Williams-Renault, 1min 19.73sec 26 starters, 13 class. finishers

ROUND 11/BELGIAN GRAND PRIX
SPA-FRANCORCHAMPS, 27 AUGUST

1. SENNA(BRA)	MCLAREN-HONDA	1HR 40MIN 54.20SEC
2. PROST(FRA)	MCLAREN-HONDA	1HR 40MIN 55.50SEC
3. MANSELL(GB)	FERRARI	1HR 40MIN 56.02SEC
4. BOUTSEN(BEL)	WILLIAMS-RENAULT	1HR 41MIN 48.61SEC
5. NANNINI(ITA)	BENETTON-FORD	1HR 42MIN 03.00SEC
6. WARWICK(GB)	ARROWS-FORD	1HR 42MIN 12.51SEC

Race: 44 laps of 4.31mile/6.94km (189.64 miles/ 305.36 kms)
*Fastest lap:*Prost, 2min 11.57sec, 117.99mph/189.89kph
Pole position: Senna, 1min 50.87sec 26 starters, 16 classified finishers

ROUND 12/ITALIAN GRAND PRIX
MONZA, 10 SEPTEMBER

1. PROST(FRA)	MCLAREN-HONDA	1HR 19MIN 27.55SEC
2. BERGER(AUT)	FERRARI	1HR 19MIN 34.88SEC
3. BOUTSEN(BEL)	WILLIAMS-RENAULT	1HR 19MIN 42.53SEC
4. PATRESE(ITA)	WILLIAMS-RENAULT	1HR 20MIN 06.27SEC
5. ALESI(FRA)	TYRRELL-FORD	52 LAPS
6. BRUNDLE(GB)	BRABHAM-JUDD	52 LAPS

Race: 53 laps of 3.6 mile/5.8 km (190.8 miles /307.4kms)
Fastest lap: Prost, 1min 28.11sec, 147.26mph/ 236.99 kph
Pole position: Senna(BRA)McLaren-Honda, 1min 23.72sec 26 starters, 11 class. finishers

ROUND 13 PORTUGUESE GRAND PRIX
ESTORIL, 24 SEPTEMBER

1. BERGER(AUT)	FERRARI	1HR 36MIN 48.55SEC
2. PROST(FRA)	MCLAREN-HONDA	1HR 37MIN 21.18SEC
3. JOHANSSON(SWE)	ONYX-FORD	1HR 37MIN 43.87SEC
4. NANNINI(ITA)	BENETTON-FORD	1HR 38MIN 10.92SEC
5. MARTINI(ITA)	MINARDI-FORD	70 LAPS
6. PALMER(GB)	TYRRELL-FORD	70 LAPS

Race: 71 laps of 2.7 mile/4.35 km (191.7 miles/ 308.85 kms)
Fastest lap: Berger, 1min 18.99sec, 123.19mph/198.26kph
*Pole position:*Senna(BRA),McLaren-Honda, 1min 15.47sec 26 starters, 14 class. finishers

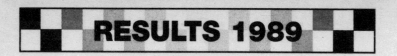

RESULTS 1989

ROUND 14/SPANISH GRAND PRIX
JEREZ, 1 OCTOBER

1. SENNA(BRA)	MCLAREN-HONDA	1HR 47MIN 48.26SEC
2. BERGER(AUT)	FERRARI	1HR 48MIN 15.32SEC
3. PROST(FRA)	MCLAREN-HONDA	1HR 48MIN 42.05SEC
4. ALESI(FRA)	TYRRELL-FORD	72 LAPS
5. PATRESE(ITA)	WILLIAMS-RENAULT	72 LAPS
6. ALLIOT(FRA)	LOLA-LAMBORGHINI	72 LAPS

Race: 73 laps of 2.62 mile/4.22km (191.26 miles/308.06 kms)
Fastest lap: Senna,1min 25.78sec, 109.99mph/177.02kph
Pole position: Senna, 1min 20.29sec 26 starters, 10 classified finishers

ROUND 15/JAPANESE GRAND PRIX
SUZUKA, 22 OCTOBER

1* NANNINI(ITA)	BENETTON-FORD	1HR 35MIN 06.28SEC
2. PATRESE (ITA)	WILLIAMS-RENAULT	1HR 35MIN 18.18SEC
3. BOUTSEN(BEL)	WILLIAMS-RENAULT	1HR 35MIN 19.72SEC
4. PIQUET(BRA)	LOTUS-JUDD	1HR 36MIN 50.50SEC
5. BRUNDLE(GB)	BRABHAM-JUDD	52 LAPS
6. WARWICK(GB)	ARROWS-FORD	52 LAPS

Race: 53 laps of 3.64 mile/5.86km (192.92 miles/310.58 kms)
Fastest lap: Prost, 1min 43.51sec, 126.62mph/203.78kph
Pole position: Senna,1min 38.04sec 26 starters, 10 classified finishers
*Senna disqualified after taking short cut after clash with Prost

ROUND 16 AUSTRALIAN GRAND PRIX
ADELAIDE, 5 NOVEMBER

1. BOUTSEN(BEL)	WILLIAMS-RENAULT	2HR 00MIN 17.42SEC
2. NANNINI(ITA)	BENETTON-FORD	2HR 00MIN 46.08SEC
3. PATRESE(ITA)	WILLIAMS-RENAULT	2HR 00MIN 55.10SEC
4. NAKAJIMA(JAP)	LOTUS-JUDD	2HR 00MIN 59.75SEC
5. PIRRO(ITA)	BENETTON-FORD	68 LAPS
6. MARTINI(ITA)	MINARDI-FORD	67 LAPS

Race: *70 laps of 2.35 mile/ 3.78 km (164.5 miles/264.6 kms)
Fastest lap: Nakajima, 1min 38.48sec, 86.48mph/139.18kph
Pole position: Senna, 1min 16.66sec 26 starters, 8 classified finishers
*Stopped after two hours because of rain

DRIVERS' WORLD CHAMPIONSHIP 1989

1. PROST	76 points	4.	MANSELL	38 points	
2. SENNA	60 points	5.	BOUTSEN	37 points	
3. PATRESE	40 points	5.	NANNINI	32 points	

CONSTRUCTORS' WORLD CHAMPIONSHIP 1989

1. MCLAREN-HONDA	141 points	4. BENETTON-FORD	39 points
2. WILLIAMS-RENAULT	77 points	5. TYRRELL-FORD	16 points
3. FERRARI	59 points	6. LOTUS-JUDD	15 points

1990s

QUIZ & FACT

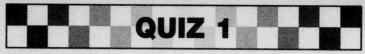

QUIZ 1

Answers on page 328

1 **Who won the first round of the 1990 Championship?**
   a. Alain Prost   b. Ayrton Senna   c. Nigel Mansell

2 **On which circuit was the race held?**
   a. Kyalami   b. Monaco   c. Phoenix

3 **Who finished second?**
   a. Saturo Nakajima   b. Jean Alesi   c. Alain Prost

4 **Who partnered Jean Alesi in the 1990 Tyrrell team?**
   a. Saturo Nakajima   b. Martin Brundle   c. Aguri Suzuki

5 **On which circuit did the 1990 Brazilian Grand Prix take place?**
   a. Buenos Aires   b. Sao Paulo   c. Interlagos

6 **Who won the race?**
   a. Andrea de Cesaris   b. Alain Prost   c. Andrea Moda

7 **Which car was he driving?**
   a. McLaren   b. Arrows   c. Ferrari

8 **Which engine powered the Lotus team in 1990?**
   a. Ford   b. Lamborghini   c. Ferrari

9 **Who was Derek Warwick's team-mate at Lotus?**
   a. Ayrton Senna   b. Martin Connelly   c. Martin Donnelly

10 **Who was the boss of Benetton in 1990?**
   a. David Richards   b. Ricco Benetton   c. Flavio Briatore

Answers to page 328
1 *a.*Andrea de Cesaris **2** *a.*Alain Prost **3** *c.*Ferrari **4** *b.*it was Ferrari's 100th
Grand Prix win **5** *c.*Riccardo Patrese **6** *b.*Italian **7** *c.*Camel **8** *a.*Three **9** *a.*None
finished **10** *a.*Aguri Suzuki

QUIZ 2

Answers on page 329

1 Who became the first son of a World Champion ever to qualify for a Grand Prix in 1990?
  a. Damon Hill *b.* David Brabham *c.* Paul Stewart

2 With which car?
  a. Brabham *b.* Hill *c.* Lotus

3 In which race?
  a. British Grand Prix *b.* San Marino Grand Prix
  c. Monaco Grand Prix

4 Which son of a famous father failed to prequalify for the first two rounds of the year?
  a. Christian Fittipaldi *b.* Geoff Brabham *c.* Gary Brabham

5 Who won the 1990 Grand Prix at Imola?
  a. Gerhard Berger *b.* Riccardo Patrese *c.* Robert Moreno

6 Why was it an emotional win?
  a. He had a bad crash there in 1989 *b.* It was his birthday
  c. had not won a race for seven years

7 Who finished second?
  a. Alain Prost *b.* Gerhard Berger *c.* Riccardo Patrese

8 In which car?
  a. Benetton *b.* Ferrari *c.* McLaren Honda

9 Who won the Monaco Grand Prix for the third time in 1990?
  a. Alain Prost *b.* Ayrton Senna *c.* Nigel Mansell

10 Which Ferrari test driver finished sixth at Monaco?
  a. Nicola Larini *b.* JJ Lehto *c.* Andrea de Cesaris

Answers to page 329
1 *a.*On pole **2***c.*Thierry Boutsen **3** *c.*Derek Warwick **4** *a.*He ran back to the pits and jumped into the spare car for the restart **5** *a.*Martin Donnelly **6** *b.*Alessandro Nannini **7** *b.*Benetton **8** *b.*Ayrton Senna **9** *c.*They both spun off into the gravel trap **10** *b.*Ayrton Senna

327

QUIZ 3

Answers on page 326

1 **Who was disqualified for having an underweight car after finishing 16th in the 1990 French Grand Prix?**
   a. Ayrton Senna   *b.* Jean Alesi   *c.* Andrea de Cesaris

2 **Who won the race?**
   a. Alain Prost   *b.* Ayrton Senna   *c.* Jean Alesi

3 **In which car?**
   a. Williams   *b.* McLaren   *c.* Ferrari

4 **What was the significance of the victory?**
   a. It was his 40th Grand Prix win   *b.* It was Ferrari's 100th Grand Prix win   *c.* It was Ron Dennis' birthday

5 **Which driver notched up his 200th Grand Prix at Silverstone in 1990?**
   a. Alain Prost   *b.* Derek Warwick   *c.* Riccardo Patrese

6 **What is his nationality?**
   a. Brazilian   *b.* Italian   *c.* Mexican

7 **Which branding did Lotus carry in 1990?**
   a. JPS   *b.* United Colours of Benetton   *c.* Camel

8 **How many British drivers took part in the 1990 British Grand Prix?**
   a. Three   *b.* Four   *c.* Five

9 **Where did the best placed Brit finish in the race?**
   a. None finished   *b.* Third   *c.* Fourth

10 **Which Japanese driver finished sixth in Britain?**
   a. Aguri Suzuki   *b.* Saturo Nakjima   *c.* Toshio Suzuki

---

Answers to page 326
1 *b.*Ayrton Senna 2 *c.*Phoenix 3 *b.*Jean Alesi 4 *a.*Saturo Nakajima 5 *c.*Interlagos
6 *b.*Alain Prost 7 *c.*Ferrari 8 *b.*Lamborghini 9 *c.*Martin Donnelly 10 *c.*Flavio
Briatore.

QUIZ 4

Answers on page 327

1 **Where did Nigel Mansell qualify for the British Grand Prix in 1990?**
   a. On pole *b. Second* *c. Did not qualify*

2 **Who won the 1990 Hungarian Grand Prix?**
   a. Derek Warwick *b. Ayrton Senna* *c. Thierry Boutsen*

3 **Which British driver was involved in an horrendous accident at the start of the 1990 Italian Grand Prix?**
   a. Nigel Mansell *b. Martin Brundle* *c. Derek Warwick*

4 **What happened to him?**
   a. He ran back to the pits and took the spare car for the restart
   b. He was knocked unconscious
   c. He retired from racing immediately

5 **Who received near fatal injuries in practice for the Spanish Grand Prix in 1990?**
   a. Martin Donnelly *b. Martin Brundle* *c. Pierluigi Mmartini*

6 **Which up-and-coming young Italian driver had his arm severed in a helicopter accident in 1990?**
   a. Andrea de Cesaris *b. Alessandro Nannini* *c. Alex Caffi*

7 **For whom did he drive?**
   a. Minardi *b. Benetton* *c. Dallara*

8 **Who deliberately ran into the back of Alain Prost at the start of the 1990 Japanese Grand Prix?**
   a. Nigel Mansell *b. Ayrton Senna* *c. Nelson Piquet*

9 **What happened next?**
   a. They had a punch-up *b. Senna went on to win the race*
   c. They both ended up in the gravel trap

10 **Who won the 1990 World Drivers' Championship?**
   a. Nelson Piquet *b. Ayrton Senna* *c. Alain Prost*

Answers to page 327

1 *b.*David Brabham **2** *a.*Brabham **3** *c.*Monaco **4** *c.*Gary Brabham **5** *b.*Riccardo Patrese **6** *c.*He had not won a race for seven years **7** *b.*Gerhard **8** *c.*McLaren **9***b.*Ayrton Senna **10** *b.*JJ Lehto

---

QUIZ 5

Answers on page 332

1 **Who became only the second driver to have competed in 200 Grands Prix in 1991?**
   a. Andrea de Cesaris   b. Nigel Mansell   c. Nelson Piquet

2 **For which team did he drive in 1991?**
   a. Williams   b. Benetton   c. Leyton House

3 **How many races did he win in 1991?**
   a. None   b. One   c. Two

4 **Which ebullient young team based at Silverstone made its Formula One debut in 1991?**
   a. Coloni   b. Lambo   c. Jordan

5 **Who was their team boss?**
   a. Peter Collins   b. Eddie Jordan   c. Ron Dennis

6 **Which driver that he would retire at the end of 1990 was lured back to Formula One for 1991?**
   a. Alain Prost   b. Gerhard Berger   c. Nigel Mansell

7 **Who persuaded him?**
   a. Ron Dennis   b. Flavio Briatore   c. Frank Williams

8 **What did he insist upon?**
   a. Number One status   b. A personal motorhome
   c. An appartment in Monaco

9 **Which driver who was to become the darling of the 'tifosi' took the second seat at Ferrari?**
   a. Jean Alesi   b. Gerhard Berger   c. Alex Zanardi

10 **Which future World Champion drove for Lotus in 1991?**
   a. Nigel Mansell   b. Mika Hakkinen   c. Michael Schumacher

Answers to page 332
1 *a.*JJ Lehto 2 *a.*Mikka Hakkinen 3 *b.*Jean-Marie Balestre 4 *b.*Max Moseley
5 *c.*Nigel Mansell 6 *b.*He broke down 7 *c.*Did not finish 8 *b.*Riccardo Patrese
9 *a.*Nigel Mansell 10 *b.*Five

QUIZ 6

Answers on page 333

1 **Which future World Champion made his debut in the 1991 Belgian Grand Prix?**
a. Damon Hill   *b.* Mika Hakkinen   *c.* Michael Schumacher

2 **For which team?**
a. Benetton   *b.* Jordan   *c.* Lotus

3 **Which multi World Champion retired from Formula One completely at the end of 1991?**
a. Alain Prost   *b.* Nelson Piquet   *c.* Riccardo Patrese

4 **Which multi World Champion decided to 'take a sabatical' at the end of 1991?**
a. Alain Prost   *b.* Nelson Piquet   *c.* Riccardo Patrese

5 **Who won the first four races of 1991?**
a. Alain Prost   *b.* Nigel Mansell   *c.* Ayrton Senna

6 **Where was the 1991 US Grand Prix held?**
a. Dallas   *b.* Detroit   *c.* Phoenix

7 **How many Japanese drivers finished in the top six in the race?**
a. None   *b.* One   *c.* Two

8 **For whom did Martin Brundle drive in 1991?**
a. Jordan   *b.* Brabham   *c.* Tyrrell

9 **Where did the Jordan team finish in their first season in Formula One in the Constructors' Championship?**
a. Third   *b.* Fifth   *c.* Seventh

10 **What is the name of their then PR who is now the ITV pits reporter?**
a. James Allen   *b.* Martin Brundle   *c.* Louise Goodman

Answers to page 333

1 *b.*He ran out of fuel **2** *b.*Michael Bartels **3** *b.*Bertrand Gachot **4** *b.*He collided with Alesi **5** *b.*He had his own accident and slid off into the gravel trap **6** *a.*Gerhard Berger **7** *c.*Ayrton Senna **8** *a.*He was sacked by Ferrari **9** *b.*Gianni Morbidelli **10** *b.*14

QUIZ 7

Answers on page 330

1 **Which Ferrari test driver finished third in the 1991 San Marino Grand Prix?**
   a. JJ Lehto   *b.* Gianni Morbidelli   *c.* Jean Alesi

2 **Which future World Champion scored his first World Championship points in San Marino?**
   a. Mika Hakkinen   *b.* Damon Hill   *c.* Michael Schumacher

3 **Who was ousted as President of FISA in 1991?**
   a. Bernie Ecclestone   *b.* Jean-Marie Balestre
   c. Bernard Consten

4 **Who replaced him?**
   a. Oswald Moseley   *b.* Max Moseley   *c.* Ron Dennis

5 **Who thought he was about to win in Canada and waved to the crowd at the beginning of the last lap ?**
   a. Nelson Piquet   *b.* Gerhard Berger   *c.* Nigel Mansell

6 **What happened next?**
   a. He hit a hare on the circuit   *b.* He broke down
   c. He crashed out on somebody's engine oil

7 **Where did the McLarens finish?**
   a. First and second   *b.* Second and third   *c.* Did not finish

8 **Who gave Williams their first win of the 1991 season?**
   a. Nigel Mansell   *b.* Riccardo Patrese   *c.* Jonathan Palmer

9 **Who won the 1991 British Grand Prix?**
   a. Nigel Mansell   *b.* Ayrton Senna   *c.* Alain Prost

10 **How many Grands Prix did Mansell win in 1991?**
   a. Four   *b.* Five   *c.* Six

Answers to page 330
1 *c.*Nelson Piquet 2 *b.*Benetton 3 *b.*One 4 *c.*Jordan 5 *b.*Eddie Jordan 6 *c.*Nigel Mansell 7 *c.*Frank Williams 8 *a.*Number One status 9 *a.*Jean Alesi 10 *b.*Mika Hakkinen

---

QUIZ 8

Answers on page 331

1 **What happened to Ayrton Senna in the 1991 German Grand Prix?**
   a. He collided with a back marker   *b.* He ran out of fuel
   c. He collided with his team-mate

2 **Steffi Graf's boyfriend at the time failed to qualify a Lotus for the German race. Who was he?**
   a. Michael Schumacher   *b.* Michael Bartels   *c.* Mikka Hakkinen

3 **Who finished sixth for Jordan in the 1991 British Grand Prix?**
   a. Eddie Jordan   *b.* Betrand Gachot   *c.* Michael Schumacher

4 **What happened to Michael Schumacher in the 1991 Australian Grand Prix?**
   a. He finished sixth   *b.* He collided with Jean Alesi
   c. He was disqualified for ignoring a black flag?

5 **What happened to Nigel Mansell in the 1991 Japanese Grand Prix?**
   a. He collided with Senna   *b.* He had his own accident and slid into the gravel trap   *c.* He suffered from heat exhaustion

6 **Who won the race?**
   a. Gerhard Berger   *b.* Riccardo Patrese   *c.* Alain Prost

7 **And who won the Championship?**
   a. Nigel Mansell   *b.* Alain Prost   *c.* Ayrton Senna

8 **Why did Alain Prost not take part in the 1991 Australian Grand Prix?**
   a. Ferrari had sacked him   *b.* He refused to race because of torrential rain   *c.* He was suffering from sinusitis

9 **Who replaced him in the race?**
   a. JJ Lehto   *b.* Gianni Morbidelli   *c.* Nicola Larini

10 **The Australian race was one of the shortest ever in the history of Formula One due to the wet conditions. How many laps were there?**
   a. 10   *b.* 14   *c.* 20

Answers to page 331

1 *c.*Michael Schumacher **2** *b.*Jordan **3** *b.*Nelson Piquet **4** *a.*Alain Prost
5 *c.*Ayrton Senna **6** *c.*Phoenix **7** *c.*Two **8** *b.*Brabham **9** *b.*Fifth **10** *c.*Louise
Goodman

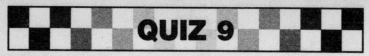

QUIZ 9

Answers on page 336

1. **Which practical joker once threw Senna's briefcase out of a helicopter?**
   a. Alain Prost   *b.* Gerhard Berger   *c.* Michael Schumacher

2. **What is the name of Nigel Mansell's wife?**
   a. Jane   *b.* Rosemary   *c.* Rosanne

3. **Who won the first five races of 1992?**
   a. Ayrton Senna   *b.* Nigel Mansell   *c.* Alain Prost

4. **Where did Michael Schumacher score his first podium finish?**
   a. South Africa 1992   *b.* Mexico 1992   *c.* Brazilian 1992.

5. **What is signifcant about the 1992 Mexican Grand Prix?**
   a. It was the last one to be held in the country   *b.* The President waved the chequered flag   *c.* A donkey was spotted on the track before first practice

6. **Which lady driver tried to qualify a Brabham in 1992?**
   a. Davina Galica   *b.* Giovana Amati   *c.* Desire Wilson

7. **Who failed to qualify his Brabham six times in 1992?**
   a. David Brabham   *b.* Damon Hill   *c.* Perry McCarthy

8. **For which team was he the test driver?**
   a. McLaren   *b.* Jordan   *c.* Williams

9. **How many races did Nigel Mansell win in 1992?**
   a. Eight   *b.* Nine   *c.* Ten

10. **How many times did he and team-mate Patrese finish first and second in the season?**
    a. Six   *b.* Seven   *c.* Eight

Answers to page 336
1 *b.*Belgium 2 *c.*Nigel Mansell 3 *b.*Renault 4 *c.*Four 5 *c.*Four 6 *b.*Ayrton Senna
7 *a.*Newman Haas 8 *b.* Ayrton Senna 9 *a.*Alain Prost 10 *c.*Damon Hill

---

334

QUIZ 10

Answers on page 337

1 **Which famous film star's son competed in Formula One in 1992?**
   a. Paul Newman's   b. Steve McQueen's
   c. Jean Paul Belmondo's

2 **For which team did he drive?**
   a. Brabham   b. March   c. Jordan

3 **Who was Michael Schumacher's team-mate in 1992?**
   a. Johnny Herbert   b. Martin Brundle   c. Roberto Moreno

4 **In which team?**
   a. Jordan   b. Benetton   c. Ferrari

5 **Where did he finish in the British Grand Prix?**
   a. Second   b. Third   c. Fourth

6 **Where did Michael Schumacher finish in the same race?**
   a. Second   b. Third   c. Fourth

7 **How many times did Nigel Mansell win the British Grand Prix in his career? (careful!)**
   a. Three   b. Four   c. Five

8 **How many points did the Jordan Team score in the 1992 Constructors' Championship?**
   a. None   b. One   c. Ten

9 **Which young driver made his Formula One debut in 1992 for the Minardi team?**
   a. Christian Fittipaldi   b. Paul Stewart   c. Ukyo Katayama

10 **Who is his famous uncle?**
   a. Ayrton Senna   b. Wilson Fittipaldi   c. Emerson Fittipaldi

---

Answers to page 337

1 *b.*Jordan   **2** *b.*McLaren   **3** *c.*Mario Andretti   **4** *b.*He was fired   **5** *c.*Alain Prost
6 *b.*Donington   **7** *c.*Ayrton Senna   **8** *b.*James Hunt   **9** *c.*Gerhard Berger   **10** *b.*Keke
Rosberg

QUIZ 11

Answers on page 334

1 **Where did Michael Shumacher win his first Grand Prix?**
   a. Hungary   *b.* Belgium   *c.* Hungary

2 **Who finished second?**
   a. Martin Brundle   *b.* Ayrton Senna   *c.* Nigel Mansell.

3 **Which engine manufacturer won the title for the first time in 1992?**
   a. Mercedes   *b.* Renault   *c.* Lamborghini

4 **How many British drivers took part in the 1992 British Grand Prix?**
   a. Two   *b.* Three   *c.* Four

5 **How many French drivers took part in the 1992 French Grand Prix?**
   a. Two   *b.* Three   *c.* Four

6 **Who was banned from driving in Britain for 28 days after being caught doing 121 mph on the M25?**
   a. Damon Hill   *b.* Ayrton Senna   *c.* Nigel Mansell

7 **Which team gained Nigel Mansell's signature for the 1983 season?**
   a. Newman Haas   *b.* Roger Penske   *c.* Team Green

8 **Who offered to drive for Williams for nothing in 1983?**
   a. Nigel Mansell   *b.* Ayrton Senna   *c.* Alain Prost

9 **Who signed as Williams team leader for 1983?**
   a. Alain Prost   *b.* Martin Brundle   *c.* Riccardo Patrese

10 **Which young hopeful was eventually signed to drive the second Williams in 1983?**
   a. Christian Fittipaldi   *b.* Mika Hakkinen   *c.* Damon Hill

Answers to page 334
1 *b.*Gerhard Berger 2 *c.*Rosanne 3 *b.*Nigel Mansell 4*a.*South Africa 5 *a.*It was the last to be held in the country 6 *b.*Giovana Amati 7 *b.*Damon Hill 8 *c.*Williams 9 *b.*Nine 10 *a.*Six

QUIZ 12

Answers on page 335

1 **Which team fielded no less than six different drivers during 1993?**
   a. McLaren   *b.* Jordan   *c.* Minardi

2 **Which team ran an American in the series for the first time since 1989?**
   a. Jordan   *b.* McLaren   *c.* Ligier

3 **Who is the driver's famous father?**
   a. Phil Hill   *b.* Dan Gurney   *c.* Mario Andretti

4 **What happened to him at the end of the season?**
   a. He went back to the States because he was home-sick
   b. He was fired   *c.* He crashed and wrote off the car

5 **Who was hauled up in front of a FISA tribunal in March 1993 for allegedly bringing the sport into disrepute?**
   a. Ayrton Senna   *b.* Eddie Irvine   *c.* Alain Prost

6 **Which British circuit hosted a Grand Prix for the first time since 1938?**
   a. Goodwood   *b.* Donington   *c.* Brooklands

7 **Who drove on a race-by-race basis for the opening rounds of the 1993 Championship?**
   a. Damon Hill   *b.* Michael Schumacher   *c.* Ayrton Senna

8 **Which former World Champion died suddenly of a heart attack in June 1993?**
   a. John Surtees   *b.* James Hunt   *c.* Denny Hulme

9 **Who weighed in the heaviest before the first round of the season?**
   a. Derek Warwick   *b.* Johnny Herbert   *c.* Gerhard Berger

10 **Who commented laconically: "He must have been sitting on his wallet!"**
   a. Nigel Mansell   *b.* Keke Rosberg   *c.* James Hunt

Answers to page 335

1 *c.*Jean-Paul Belmondo **2** *b.*March **3** *c.*Brundle **4** *b.*Benetton **5** *b.*Third
6 *c.*Fourth **7** *b.*Four **8** *b.*One **9** *a.*Christian Fittipaldi **10** *c.*Emerson Fittipaldi

---

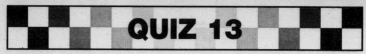

QUIZ 13

Answers on page 340

1 **Whose 1993 budget was estimated to be three times greater than any other team's?**
   a. McLaren *b.* Williams *c.* Ferrari

2 **Which 'foreign' team employed two British drivers in 1993?**
   a. Minardi *b.* Sauber *c.* Ligier

3 **Who said: "I genuinely don't know how quick he is. I mean how quick he could be, if he had to be..."**
   a. Ron Dennis *b.* Patrick Head *c.* Luca Montezemolo

4 **Of whom was he speaking?**
   a. Michael Andretti *b.* Michael Schumacher *c.* Alain Prost

5 **Who said: "Senna? Why should I want Senna? I've got..."**
   a. Frank Williams *b.* Tom Walkinshaw *c.* Eddie Jordan

6 **Of whom was he speaking?**
   a. Alain Prost *b.* Eddie Irvine *c.* Michael Schumacher

7 **Which new team finished fifth in its very first Formula One outing in South Africa in 1993?**
   a. Footwork *b.* Sauber *c.* Stewart

8 **Who was driving?**
   a. Rubens Barrichello *b.* JJ Lehto *c.* Aguri Suzuki

9 **Who scored his first victory in 18 months in South Africa?**
   a. Gerhard Berger *b.* Alain Prost *c.* Thierry Boutsen

10 **Where did Damon Hill qualify on his debut for Williams in South Africa?**
   a. Did not qualify *b.* Third *c.* Sixth

Answers to page 340
1 *a.*Ford 2 *b.*Mika Hakkinen 3 *a.*None 4 *b.*Christian Fittipaldi 5 *b.*Japan
6 *c.*Alessandro Zanardi 7 *a.*Pedro Lamy 8 *a.* None 9 *b.*Niki Lauda 10 *b.*Williams

QUIZ 14

Answers on page 341

1 **Who won three times in a row in 1993? (careful!)**
   a. Alain Prost   *b.* Damon Hill   *c.* Michael Schumacher

2 **At which circuit did Damon Hill score his maiden Grand Prix victory?**
   a. Silverstone   *b.* Spa   *c.* Hungaroring

3. **How many wins did Alain Prost score in 1993?**
   a. Six   *b.* Seven   *c.* Eight

4 **And how many wins did Ayrton Senna notch up in 1993?**
   a. Three   *b.* Four   *c.* Five

5 **Where did Michael Schumacher score his second Grand Prix victory?**
   a. Spa   *b.* Portugal   *c.* Germany

6 **Who tried to thump Eddie Irvine in 1993?**
   a. Michael Schumacher   *b.* Rubens Barrichello   *c.* Ayrton Senna

7 **Why?**
   a. He had stolen his girl-friend   *b.* He had repassed him after being lapped   *c.* He had been rude to him

8 **Which Italian finished sixth for Minardi in the 1993 San Marino Grand Prix?**
   a. Fabrizio Barbazza   *b.* Pierluigi Martini   *c.* Andrea de Cesaris

9 **Which British driver scored his first point in three years when he finished sixth at Silverstone in 1993?**
   a. Johnny Herbert   *b.* Derek Warwick   *c.* Mark Blundell

10 **Where did Michael Andretti score his first World Championship points?**
   a. Monza   *b.* Spain   *c.* Monaco

Answers to page 341
1 *c.*Eddie Irvine 2 *b.*Martin Brundle 3 *c.*Andrea de Cesaris 4 *a.*Jos Verstappen 5 *b.*Williams 6 *b.*Simtek 7 *c.*Sir Jack Brabham 8 *c.*Martin Brundle 9 *c.*Martin Brundle 10 *c.*Damon Hill.

QUIZ 15

Answers on page 338

1 **Which engine did the McLaren team use in 1993?**
   a. Ford   *b. Honda*   *c. Peugeot*

2 **Who outqualified his team-mate Senna in a McLaren in 1993?**
   a. Michael Andretti   *b. Mika Hakkinen*   *c. Gerhard Berger*

3 **How many races did Ferrari win in 1993?**
   a. None   *b. One*   *c. Two*

4 **Who was launched into the air at the very end of the 1993 Italian Grand Prix?**
   a. Michael Andretti   *b. Christian Fittipaldi*   *c. Martin Brundle*

5 **Where did Eddie Irvine make his Grand Prix debut in 1993?**
   a. Monza   *b. Japan*   *c. Australia*

6 **Who nearly killed himself at Spa in a huge accident in a Lotus?**
   a. Johnny Herbert   *b. Mika Hakkinen*   *c. Alessandro Zanardi*

7 **Who replaced him for the last four races of the year?**
   a. Pedro Lamy   *b. Martin Brundle*   *c. Jean-Marc Gounon*

8 **How many points did the Tyrrell team score in 1993?**
   a. None   *b. One*   *c. Two*

9 **Which former World Champion returned to the Ferrari fold as a consultant in 1993?**
   a. Jody Scheckter   *b. Niki Lauda*   *c. Jacky Ickx*

10 **Who won the 1993 Constructors' Championship by a country mile?**
   a. McLaren   *b. Williams*   *c. Benetton*

Answers to page 338
1 *c.*Ferrari 2 *c.*Ligier 3 *b.*Patrick Head 4 *c.*Alain Prost 5 *b.*Tom Walkinshaw
6 *c.*Michael Schumacher 7 *b.*Sauber 8 *b.*JJ Lehto 9 *b.*Alain Prost 10 *b.*Third

QUIZ 16

Answers on page 339

1 **Who was given a three-race ban after being found responsible for causing a major accident in the Brazilian Grand Prix in 1994?**
   a. Michael Schumacher   *b.* Mika Hakkinen   *c.* Eddie Irvine

2 **Who was knocked unconscious in the incident?**
   a. Rubens Barrichello   *b.* Martin Brundle   *c.* Eric Bernard

3 **Who replaced Irvine at Jordan in the Monaco Grand Prix?**
   a. Johnny Herbert   *b.* Aguri Suzuki   *c.* Andrea de Cesaris

4 **Which young hopeful made his Grand Prix debut for the Benetton team in 1994?**
   a. Jos Verstappen   *b.* Heinz-Harald Frentzen
   c. Roland Ratzenberger

5 **Which team did Ayrton Senna join for the 1994 season?**
   a. Benetton   *b.* Williams   *c.* Ferrari

6 **Which brand new Formula One team did Nick Wirth found in 1994?**
   a. Pacific   *b.* Sauber   *c.* Simtek

7 **Which former World Champion owned shares in the company?**
   a. Niki Lauda   *b.* Alain Prost   *c.* Sir Jack Brabham

8 **Which British driver joined McLaren in 1994?**
   a. Derek Warwick   *b.* David Coulthard   *c.* Martin Brundle

9 **Who was the first driver ever to refuel under the new regulations in Brazil?**
   a. Ayrton Senna   *b.* Michael Schumacher   *c.* Martin Brundle

10 **Who said: "No pun intended, but we are playing with fire".**
   a. Jos Verstappen   *b.* Martin Brundle   *c.* Damon Hill

Answers to page 339

1 *b.*Damon Hill 2 *c.*Hungaroring 3 *b.*Seven 4 *c.*Five 5 *b.*Portugal 6 *c.*Ayrton
Senna 7 *b.*He had repassed him after being lapped 8 *a.* Fabrizio Barbazza
9 *b.*Derek Warwick 10 *b.*Spain

QUIZ 17

Answers on page 344

1 Who was punted off at the start at the Pacific Grand Prix in Aida in 1994?
   a. Damon Hill   *b.* Ayrton Senna   *c.* Martin Brundle

2 Who won the first four races of the 1994 season?
   a. Damon Hill   *b.* Gerhard Berger   *c.* Michael Schumacher

3 Who replaced Jos Verstappen at Benetton at Imola in 1994?
   a. Johnny Herbert   *b.* Gerhard Berger   *c.* JJ Lehto

4 Who was knocked unconscious in a practice accident at Imola in 1994?
   a. Pedro Lamy   *b.* Rubens Barrichello   *c.* Mika Hakkinen

5 What was the nationality of Roland Ratzenberger who died so tragically at Imola?
   a. German   *b.* Swiss   *c.* Austrian

6 Which car was he driving?
   a. Simtek   *b.* Pacific   *c.* Sauber

7 What was the name of the corner where the great Ayrton Senna lost his life on the Imola circuit?
   a. Variente Bassa   *b.* Villeneuve   *c.* Tamburello

8 Who collided with Damon Hill at the start of the 1994 Monaco Grand Prix?
   a. Eddie Irvine   *b.* Pedro Lamy   *c.* Mika Hakkinen

9 Karl Wendlinger was critically injured in a practice accident at Monaco. For which team was he driving?.
   a. Lotus   *b.* Sauber   *c.* Benetton

10 Who finished a fine second in Monaco in 1994?
   a. Rubens Barrichello   *b.* Martin Brundle   *c.* Olivier Panis

Answers to page 344
1 *b.*Rubens Barrichello 2 *c.*His skid block plank. had worn too thin 3 *c.*Eddie Irvine 4 *c.*David Coulthard 5 *a.*One 6 *c.*Nigel Mansell 7 *b.*Nigel Mansell 8 *c.*Michael Schumacher 9 *b.*Williams 10 *c.*Ayrton Senna

QUIZ 18

Answers on page 345

1 **Who was lucky to escape with his life after an horrific crash whilst testing at Silverstone?**
   a. Pedro Lamy   *b. David Brabham*   *c. Johnny Herbert*

2 **And which replacement Italian driver was lucky to escape a high speed shunt in practice for the Spanish Grand Prix?**
   a. Gianni Morbidelli   *b. Andrea Montermini*
   c. Alessandro Zanardi

3 **Who was drafted into the second Williams for the Spanish race?**
   a. Nigel Mansell   *b. Heinz-Harald Frentzen*   *c. David Coulthard*

4 **Who made a guest appearance for Williams in the 1994 French Grand Prix?**
   a. Alain Prost   *b. Nigel Mansell*   *c. Alan Jones*

5 **Who received a two race suspension after the 1994 British Grand Prix?**
   a. Mika Hakkinen   *b. Jean Alesi*   *c. Michael Schumacher*

6 **Why?**
   a. He ignored a black flag   *b. He collided with Damon Hill*
   c. He failed to attend the pot race Press Conference

7 **Who was given a one race ban after causing an almighty accident at the beginning of the 1994 German Grand Prix?**
   a. Eddie Irvine   *b. Mika Hakkinen*   *c. David Coulthard*

8 **Who had a miraculous escape when his car caught fire during a refuelling stop in Germany?**
   a. Heinz-Harald Frentzen   *b. Jos Verstappen*
   c. Rubens Barrichello

9 **How many of the 26 starters failed to finish the first lap of the 1994 German Grand Prix?**
   a. 10   *b. 11*   *c. 12*

10 **Which team's two cars eliminated each other on the first lap of the 1994 Hungarian Grand Prix?**
   a. McLaren   *b. Ferrari*   *c. Jordan*

Answers to page 345
1 *a.*Lotus **2** *b.*Nigel Mansell **3** *b.*Two **4** *b.*Mark Blundell **5** *c.*Mercedes **6** *a.*None
7 *b.*Jean Alesi **8** *c.*Ferrari **9** *c.*Renault **10** *c.*32 points.

QUIZ 19

Answers on page 342

1 **Who claimed the first ever pole position for himself and his team in Belgium?**
   a. Gianni Morbidelli *b.* Rubens Barrichello *c.* David Brabham

2 **Michael Schumacher won the race with ease but was later disqualified. Why?**
   a. He overtook under waved yellow flags; *b.* He punched Bernie Ecclestone *c.* His skid block (or plank) had worn too thin.

3 **Who caused the accident at the start of the Italian Grand Prix in 1994?**
   a. Mika Hakkinen *b.* David Coulthard *c.* Eddie Irvine

4 **Who claimed the first podium finish of his career in Portugal in 1994?**
   a. Rubens Barrichello *b.* Eddie Irvine *c.* David Coulthard

5 **How many points separated Damon Hill and Michael Schumacher after the 1994 Japanese Grand Prix?**
   a. One *b.* Two *c.* Three

6 **Who drove for Williams in the last three races of 1994?**
   a. David Coulthard *b.* Alain Prost *c.* Nigel Mansell

7 **Who won the Australian Grand Prix?**
   a. Gerhard Berger *b.* Nigel Mansell *c.* Mika Hakkinen

8 **Who won the 1994 World Drivers' Championship?**
   a. Nigel Mansell *b.* Damon Hill *c.* Michael Schumacher

9 **Who won the 1994 Constructors' Championship?**
   a. Benetton *b.* Williams *c.* Ferrari

10 **To whom did Schumacher dedicate his Championship?**
   a. His mother *b.* His wife *c.* Ayrton Senna

Answers to page 342
1 *b.*Ayrton Senna 2 *c.*Michael Schumacher 3 *c.*JJ Lehto 4 *b.*Rubens Barrichello
5 *c.*Austrian 6 *a.*Simtek 7 *c.*Tamburello 8 *c.*Mika Hakkinen 9 *b.*Sauber
10 *b.*Martin Brundle

QUIZ 20

Answers on page 343

1 **Which famous name was missing from the 1995 season?**
   a. Lotus   b. Ferrari   c. Tyrrell

2 **Who was too hefty to fit into his McLaren at the start of the year?**
   a. Gerhard Berger   b. Nigel Mansell   c. Mika Hakkinen

3 **How many races did he eventually contest in 1995?**
   a. One   b. Two   c. Three

4 **Who replaced him in the team for the rest of the season?**
   a. Martin Brundle   b. Mark Blundell   c. Jos Verstappen

5 **Who was the McLaren engine supplier in 1995?**
   a. Peugeot   b. Ford   c. Mercedes

6 **How many races did they win?**
   a. None   b. One c. Two

7 **Who won his first and to date his only Grand Prix in Canada?**
   a. Rubens Barrichello   b. Jean Alesi   c. Martin Brundle

8 **In which car?**
   a. Benetton   b. McLaren   c. Ferrari

9 **Which engines did Benetton use in 1995?**
   a. Ford   b. Peugeot   c. Renault

10 **What was Michael Schumacher's winning points margin over Damon Hill at the end of the season?**
   a. Twenty points   b. 25 points   c. 32 points

Answers to page 343
1 *a.*Pedro Lamy 2 *b.*Andrea Montermini 3 *c.*David Coulthard 4 *b.*Nigel Mansell
5 *c.*Michael Schumacher 6 *a.*He ignored a black flag 7 *b.*Mika Hakkinen 8 *b.*Jos
Verstappen 9 *b.*11 10 *c.*Jordan.

QUIZ 21

Answers on page 348

1 **Who clashed with Michael Schumacher's Benetton whilst battling for the lead in the 1995 British Grand Prix?**
   a. Jean Alesi   *b. Eddie Irvine*   *c. Damon Hill*

2 **Who won the first Grand Prix of his career at Silverstone in 1995?**
   a. David Coulthard   *b. Martin Brundle*   *c. Johnny Herbert*

3 **How many races had he contested before he tasted the victory champagne?**
   a. 64   *b. 74*   *c. 84*

4 **Who claimed his very first Formula One pole position in Argentina in 1995.**
   a. Johnny Herbert   *b. Martin Brundle*   *c. David Coulthard*

5 **What happened to the first and second finishers in the 1995 Brazilian Grand Prix?**
   a. They were disqualified   *b. They were disqualified but later reinstated*   *c. They were fined for not attending the pre-event Press Conference.*

6 **Which great former World Champion died in 1995?**
   a. Juan Manuel Fangio   *b. Guiseppe Farina*   *c. Luigi Fagioli*

7 **How many races were there in 1995?**
   a. 16   *b. 17*   *c. 18*

8 **Which team closed its doors after the 1995 Monaco Grand Prix?**
   a. Pacific   *b. Larousse*   *c. Simtek*

9 **Which engines did the Jordan team run in 1995?**
   a. Ford   *b. Hart*   *c. Peugeot*

10 **In which race did the Jordans finish second and third in 1995?**
   a. Monaco   *b. Canada*   *c. Japan*

Answers to page 348
1 *a.*Aida 2 *a.*Third 3 *b.*Harvey Postlethwaite 4 *a.*David Coulthard 5 *b.*David Coulthard 6 *c.*David Coulthard 7 *c.*Patrick Head 8 *b.*Ukyo Katayama 9 *b.*Tyrrell 10 *b.*Mika Hakkinen

---

QUIZ 22

Answers on page 349

1. Who collided with Michael Schumacher at Adelaide in 1995?
   a. Damon Hill   *b.* Eddie Irvine   *c.* Jean Alesi

2. Who said: "After the Monza crash, I was angry with a capital A"?
   a. Damon Hill   *b.* Roberto Moreno   *c.* Michael Schumacher

3. Which car was described as 'a moving chicane' in 1995?
   a. Pacific   *b.* Ferrari   *c.* Forti

4. Who had to share his drive for Ligier in 1995 with Aguri Suzuki?
   a. Olivier Panis   *b.* Ukyo Katayama   *c.* Martin Brundle

5. Who won his second ever Grand Prix at Monza in 1995?
   a. Jean Alesi   *b.* Johnny Herbert   *c.* Heinz-Harald Frentzen

6. And who won the very first Grand Prix of his career in Portugal?
   a. David Coulthard   *b.* Mark Blundell   *c.* Martin Brundle

7. How many races did Michael Schumacher win in 1995?
   a. Eight   *b.* Nine   *c.* Ten

8. Why did Mika Hakkinen miss out on the 1995 Pacific Grand Prix at Aida?
   a. He was getting married   *b.* He had an apendectomy
   c. He was suspended

9. Who replaced him in the McLaren?
   a. Nigel Mansell   *b.* Jan Magnussen   *c.* Mika Salo

10. What is his nationality?
    a. Swedish   *b.* Finnish   *c.* Danish

Answers to page 349

1 *b.*Eddie Irvine   2 *b.*Jacques Villeneuve   3 *c.*Martin Brundle   4 *b.*Johnny Herbert
5 *b.*Three   6 *b.*Mika Hakkinen   7 *a.*None   8 *b.*Barry Green   9 *b.*Jacques Villeneuve
10 *b.*Third

QUIZ 23

Answers on page 346

1 **At which race did Michael Schumacher clinch his second World Championship?**
a. Aida *b.* Suzuka *c.* Adelaide

2 **Where did David Coulthard finish in the 1995 World Drivers' Championship?**
a. Third *b.* Fourth *c.* Sixth

3 **Who was design Director at Tyrrell in 1995?**
a. Derek Gardner *b.* John Barnard *c.* Harvey Postlethwaite

4 **Who received a ten second stop-go penalty for speeding in the pit lane at the 1995 British Grand Prix whilst in the lead?**
a. David Coulthard *b.* Michael Schumacher *c.* Eddie Irvine

5 **Who had to have his tonsils removed in 1995?**
a. Mika Salonen *b.* David Coulthard *c.* Gerhard Berger

6 **Who embarrassed himself by sliding into the wall on the pit lane entry at Adelaide in 1955?**
a. Johnny Herbert *b.* Eddie Irvine *c.* David Coulthard

7 **Who described the Williams' team's lack of reliability in 1995 as 'grisly and unforgiveable'?**
a. Damon Hill *b.* Frank Williams *c.* Patrick Head

8 **Who was lucky to escape from an enormous start-line accident in Portugal in 1995?**
a. Pedro Diniz *b.* Ukyo Katayama *c.* Pedro Lamy

9 **Mika Salo scored his first World Championship points in Italy in 1995. In which car?**
a. Arrows *b.* Tyrrell *c.* Lotus

10 **Which other Finn almost lost his life in an horrific accident in practice for the 1995 Grand Prix in Adelaide?**
a. JJ Lehto *b.* Mika Hakkinen *c.* Jan Magnussen

Answers to page 346
1 *c.*Damon Hill 2 *c.*Johnny Herbert 3 *b.* 74 4 *c.*David Coulthard 5 *b.*They were disqualified but later reinstated 6 *a.*Juan-Manuel Fangio 7 *b.*17 8 *c.*Simtek 9 *c.*Peugeot 10 *b.*Canada

QUIZ 24

Answers on page 347

1 **Who joined Ferrari as number two to Michael Schumacher in 1996?**
   a. Rubens Barrichello   *b. Eddie Irvine*   *c. Pedro Lamy*

2 **Who became only the fourth driver in history to take pole position in his first ever Grand Prix in 1996?**
   a. Ginacarlo Fisichella   *b. Jacques Villeneuve*
   c. Ricardo Rosset

3 **Who 'returned to his roots' at Jordan for 1996?**
   a. Ivan Capelli   *b. Maurizio Gugelmin*   *c. Martin Brundle*

4 **Who drove the second Sauber in 1996?**
   a. Jean-Christophe Bouillon   *b. Johnny Herbert*
   c. Giancarlo Fisichella

5 **How many races did Michael Schumacher win in 1996?**
   a. One   *b. Three*   *c. Four*

6 **Which driver made an amazing recovery from serious injury to make the start line in Adelaide in 1996?**
   a. Pedro Diniz   *b. Mika Hakkinen*   *c. Johnny Herbert*

7 **How many races did Benetton win in 1996?**
   a. None   *b. One*   *c. Two*

8 **Who said:"If he gets a sniff of the title, believe me watch out."**
   a. Jean Todt   *b. Barry Green*   *c. Patrick Head*

9 **Of whom?**
   a. Michael Schumacher   *b. Jacques Villeneuve*   *c. Damon Hill*

10 **Where did Eddie Irvine finish in his first outing for Ferrari?**
   a. Did not finish   *b. Third*   *c. Sixth*

Answers to page 347

1 *c.*Jean Alesi **2** *c.*Michael Schumacher **3** *c.*Forti **4** *c.*Brundle **5** *b.*Johnny Herbert **6** *a.*David Coulthard **7** *b.*Nine **8** *b.*He had an apendectomy **9** *b.*Jan Magnussen **10** *c.*Danish

QUIZ 25

Answers on page 352

1 **Who won the 1996 Monaco Grand Prix?**
   a. Damon Hill   *b.* Jacques Villeneuve   *c.* Olivier Panis

2 **Which British driver finished third?**
   a. Damon Hill   *b.* David Coulthard   *c.* Johnny Herbert

3 **Who was the Benetton test driver in 1996?**
   a. Dario Franchitti   *b.* Vicenzo Sospiri   *c.* Jarno Trulli

4 **How many one-two finishes did the Williams 'twins' score in 1996?**
   a. Six   *b.* Seven   *c.* Eight

5 **Which team withdrew from racing during the 1996 season?**
   a. Minardi   *b.* Forti   *c.* Ligier

6 **Who suffered engine failure whilst in the lead of the 1996 German Grand Prix?**
   a. Michael Schumacher   *b.* Jacques Villeneuve
   c. Gerhard Berger

7 **In which car?**
   a. McLaren   *b.* Benetton   *c.* Ferrari

8 **Who suffered an embarrassing moment when his engine blew up on the parade lap of the 1996 French Grand Prix?**
   a. David Coulthard   *b.* Michael Schumacher   *c.* Jos Verstappen

9 **Where was the 1996 French Grand Prix held?**
   a. Dijon-Prenois   *b.* Paul Ricard   *c.* Magny Cours

10 **Who won his very first Grand Prix at the Nurburgring in 1996?**
   a. Jacques Villenuve   *b.* Olivier Panis   *c.* Heinz-Harald Frentzen

---

Answers to page 352
1 *c.*Arrows 2 a and *b.*Prost and Stewart 3 *c.*Ralf Schumacher 4 *a.*Lola 5 *b.* and *c.* Ricardo Rosset and Vicenzo Sospiri 6 *c.*Bridgestone 7 *b.*Austria 8 *c.*David Richards 9 *b.*Nick Heidfeld 10 *a.*Jan Magnussen.

QUIZ 26

Answers on page 353

1 Who was lucky to escape with minor burns when his car
   caught fire with a vengeance in Argentina 1996?
   a. Jos Verstappen   *b. Eddie Irvine*   *c. Pedro Diniz*

2 Who said: "The two most important drivers in the Paddock are
   Michael Schumacher because he's the best and Pedro Diniz
   because he's the richest."
   a. Jackie Stewart   *b. Flavio Briatore*   *c. Niki Lauda*

3 Who pushed Jacques Villeuve into the armco during practice
   for the 1996 Italian Grand Prix?
   a. Pedro Diniz   *b. Pedro Lamy*   *c. Ricardo Rosset*

4 How many Grands Prix did Damon Hill win on his way to his
   first World Drivers' title?
   a. Seven   *b. Eight c. Nine*

5 Who hit the wall on the opening lap of the 1996 Monaco
   Grand Prix?
   a. Eddie Irvine   *b. Mika Hakkinen*   *c. Michael Schumacher*

6 Who said: "When I get the winning car, I am ready to win"?
   a. Michael Schumacher   *b. Eddie Irvine*   *c. Mika Hakkinen*

7 What was the Williams team's winning points margin over
   Ferrari in the 1996 Constructors' Championship?
   a. 95 points   *b. 105 points*   *c. 115 points*

8 Who said: "Racing is more than just going quick through a
   corner. It's the whole package"?
   a. Michael Schumacher   *b. Jacques Villeneuve*
   c. Gerhard Berger

9 Who was suffering from the after-effects of pneumonia at the
   start of the 1996 season?
   a. David Coulthard   *b. Gerhard Berger*   *c. Damon Hill*

10 Who said: "Last year was the worst of my racing career"?
   a. Johnny Herbert   *b. Olivier Panis*   *c. Eddie Irvine*

Answers to page 353

1 *c.*Damon Hill **2** *c.*Rubens Barrichello **3** *b.*Eddie Irvine **4** *c.*Melbourne **5** *b.*David
Coulthard **6** *c.*Ralf Schumacher **7** *b.*Third **8** *c.*Jacques Villeneuve **9** *b.*Heinz-
Harald Frentzen **10** *b.*One

QUIZ 27

Answers on page 350

1 **For which team did reigning World Champion, Damon Hill, drive in 1997?**
   a. Williams   *b.* Jordan   *c.* Arrows

2 **Which two famous names returned to the grid in 1997?**
   a. Prost   *b.* Stewart   *c.* Brabham

3 **Which young charger with a famous name joined the Jordan line-up for the season?**
   a. Christian Jones   *b.* Christian Fittipaldi   c.Ralf Schumacher

4 **Which new team went bust after only one race in 1997?**
   a. Prost   *b.* Lola   *c.* Stewart

5 **Who were the team's unlucky drivers?**
   a. Jos Verstappen   *b.* Ricardo Rosset   *c.* Vicenzo Sospiri

6 **Which new tyre company entered the fray in 1997?**
   a. Continental   *b.* Pirelli   *c.* Bridgestone

7 **Which country hosted a Grand Prix for the first time in 10 years in 1997?**
   a. Mexico   *b.* Austria   *c.* USA

8 **Who replaced Flavio Briatore at Benetton during 1997?**
   a. Rocco Benetton   *b.* Peter Collins   *c.* David Richards

9 **Who was McLaren's test driver in 1997?**
   a. Dario Franchitti   *b.* Nick Heidfeld   *c.* Alan McNish

10 **Who was number two driver for the Stewart team in 1997?**
   a. Jan Magnussen   *b.* Alan McNish   *c.* Shinji Nakano

Answers to page 350
1 *c.*Olivier Panis   2 *c.*Johnny Herbert   3 *b.*Vicenzo Sospiri   4 *a.*Six   5 *b.*Forti
6 *c.*Gerhard Berger   7 *b.*Benetton   8 *b.* Michael Schumacher   9 *c.*Magny Cours
10 *a.*Jacques Villeneuve

QUIZ 28

Answers on page 351

1 **Who did Jackie Stewart try to sign up for 1997?**
   a. David Coulthard   *b.* Heinz-Harald Frentzen   *c.* Damon Hill

2 **Who brought tears to the Scot's eyes by finishing second at Monaco?**
   a. Jan Magnussen   *b.* Jos Verstappen   *c.* Rubens Barrichello

3 **Who triggered a first corner accident in the opening round of the season in Australia which elminated both Johnny Herbert and Jacques Villeneuve?**
   a. Mika Hakkinen   *b.* Eddie Irvine   *c.* Ralf Schumacher

4 **Where was the race held?**
   a. Adelaide   *b.* Perth   *c.* Melbourne

5 **Who won the race?**
   a. Michael Schumacher   *b.* David Coulthard   *c.* Mika Hakkinen

6 **Who punted his team-mate off in Brazil?**
   a. Pedro Diniz   *b.* Jos Verstappen   *c.* Ralf Schumacher

7 **Where did he finish in the race?**
   a. Did not Finish   *b.* Third   *c.* Sixth

8 **Who won the 1997 World Drivers' Championship?**
   a. Michael Schumacher   *b.* Damon Hill   *c.* Jacques Villeneuve

9 **Who officially finished second?**
   a. Michael Schumacher   *b.* Heinz-Harald Frentzen
   c. Jacques Villeneuve.

10 **How many races did Benetton win in 1997?**
   a. None   *b.* One   *c.* Two

Answers to page 351

1 *c.*Pedro Diniz **2** *b.*Flavio Briatore **3** *b.*Pedro Diniz **4** *b.* Eight **5** *c.*Michael Schumacher **6** *c.*Mika Hakkinen **7** *b.*105 points **8** *c.*Gerhard Berger **9** *b.*Gerhard Berger **10** *c.*Eddie Irvine.

QUIZ 29

Answers on page 356

1 **Who won the 1997 San Marino Grand Prix?**
   a. Michael Schumacher   b. Heinz-Harald Frentzen
   c. Jacques Villeneuve

2 **Where did Mika Hakkinen win the first Grand Prix of his career?**
   a. Japan   b. Jerez   c. Austria

3 **Who were the McLaren team title-sponsors in 1997?**
   a. Marlboro   b. Mild Seven   c. West

4 **Who finished third for Benetton in the 1997 British Grand Prix?**
   a. Jean Alesi   b. Gerhard Berger   c. Alexander Wurz

5 **Who broke both legs in a nasty accident in the 1997 Canadian Grand Prix.**
   a. Olivier Panis   b. Gerhard Berger   c. Gianni Morbidelli

6 **Which young newcomer to Formula One led for up to half-distance in the 1997 Austrian Grand Prix?**
   a. Alexander Wurz   b. Giancarlo Fisichella   c. Jarno Trulli

7 **In which car?**
   a. Jordan   b. Prost   c. Benetton

8 **Who tried to knock Jacques Villeneuve off the track in the final race of the year in Jerez?**
   a. Michael Schumacher   b. Eddie Irvine   c. Ralf Schumacher

9 **Who came off second best?**
   a. Michael Schumacher   b. Eddie Irvine   c. Ralf Schumacher

10 **Who hung up his Formula One helmet at the end of the 1997 season after 210 Grands Prix?**
   a. Johnny Herbert   b. Gerhard Berger   c. Jean Alesi

Answers to page 356
1 *b.*Two **2** *c.*Alesi and Herbert **3** *c.*Michael Schumacher **4** *b.*Jacques Villeneuve
5 *b.*Giancarlo Fisichella **6** *c.*Michael Schumacher **7** *a.*None **8** *c.*Alexander Wurz
9 *b.*Alexander Wurz **10** *c.*Jarno Trulli.

354

QUIZ 30

Answers on page 357

1 **How many Grand Prix teams were there at the start of the 1998 seaon?**
   a. 11 b 12   *c.* 13

2 **And how many were there at the end of the season?**
   a. 10   *b.* 11   *c.* 12

3 **How many teams retained their 1997 driver line-up at the start of 1998?**
   a. Three   *b.* Four   *c.* Five

4 **Which engines did the Jordan team run in 1998?**
   a. Peugeot   *b.* Mecachrome   *c.* Mugen-Honda

5 **Who became the baby of the pack, making his Formula One debut at the tender age of 19?**
   a. Jarno Trulli   *b.* Ricardo Rosset   *c.* Esteban Tuero

6 **What was his nationality?**
   a. Brazilian   *b.* Argentinian   *c.* Italian

7 **Where did he qualify for his very first Grand Prix?**
   a. a 17th   *b.* 20th   *c.* 22nd

8 **Which designer had joined the McLaren team ?**
   a. Patrick Head   *b.* Adrian Newey   *c.* John Barnard

9 **Which team's cars had not passed the crash test when they arrived for the first round in Australia?**
   a. Stewart   *b.* Tyrrell c.Prost

10 **Who suffered his only mechanical failure of the year after only five laps of the race?**
   a. Jacques Villeneuve   *b.* Michael Schumacher   *c.* Damon Hill

Answers to page 359
1 *c.*Tyrrell 2 *b.*Four 3 *b.*Three 4 *c.*Mika Salo 5 *b.*Esteban Tuero 6 *b.*BAR
7 *c.*Jordan 8 *b.*Jean Alesi 9 *b.*Marc Gene 10 *b.*Gary Anderson

QUIZ 31

Answers on page 354

1 **How many Japanese drivers started in the 1998 season?**
   a. One   *b.* Two   *c.* Three

2 **Which team-mates collided with each other on the first lap of practice for the 1998 Argentine Grand Prix?**
   a. Hill and Schumacher   *b.* Fisichella and Wurz
   c. Alesi and Herbert

3 **Who had David Coulthard in a spin early in the race?**
   a. Eddie Irvine   *b.* Jacques Villeneuve   *c.* Michael Schumacher

4 **And who tangled with DC later in the race and eliminated himself in the process?**
   a. Esteban Tuero   *b.* Jacques Villeneuve   *c.* Johnny Herbert

5 **Who nearly came to blows with Eddie Irvine after they both ended up in the kitty litter in Spain in 1998?**
   a. Ralf Schumacher   *b.* Giancarlo Fisichella   *c.* Jean Alesi

6 **Who collected a stop-go penalty for speeding in the pit lane in Spain but still managed to finish third?**
   a. Jacques Villeneuve   *b.* Heinz-Harald Frentzen
   c. Michael Schumacher

7 **How many races did the Williams team win in 1998?**
   a. None   *b.* One   *c.* Two

8 **Who refused to give best to Michael Schumacher round the Loews Hairpin at Monaco in 1998?**
   a. Eddie Irvine   *b.* Giancarlo Fisichella   *c.* Alexander Wurz

9 **Who had what appeared to be an horrendous accident at the start of the Canadian Grand Prix?**
   a. Eddie Irvine   *b.* Alexander Wurz   *c.* Giancarlo Fisichella

10 **Who landed on top of Jean Alesi's Sauber in the first corner at the restart?**
   a. Giancarlo Fisichalla   *b.* Jarno Trulli   *c.* Esteban Tuero

---

Answers to page 354
1 *b.*Heinz-Harald Frentzen **2** *b.*Jerez **3** *c.*West **4** *c.*Alexander Wurz **5** *a.*Olivier Panis **6** *c.*Jarno Trulli **7** *b.*Alain Prost **8** *a.*Michael Schumacher **9** *a.*Michael Schumacher **10** *b.*Gerhard Berger.

Answers on page 359

1 **Whom did Michael Schumacher force off the road during the Canadian Grand Prix in 1998?**
   a. Alexander Wurz   *b. Heinz-Harald Frentzen*
   c. Jacques Villeneuve

2 **Who finally won this eventful afternoon's entertainment?**
   a. Mika Hakkinen   *b. Jacques Villeneuve*   *c. Michael Schumacher*

3 **Who took Jan Magnussen's place at Tyrrell mid-way through the 1998 season?**
   a. Esteban Tuero   *b. Jos Verstappen*   *c. Alan McNish*

4 **Ferrari finished first and second in France. How many years was it since Ferrari last scored a one-two finish?**
   a. Six   *b. Eight*   *c. Ten*

5 **Which Grand Prix Team introduce a two-seater version for promotional purposes in 1998?**
   a. Stewart   *b. McLaren*   *c. Benetton*

6 **Who gave Murray 'Talker' the ride of his septugenarian life in it at Silverstone?**
   a. Ron Denis   *b. Mika Hakkinen*   *c. Martin Brundle*

7 **Where was Michael Schumacher when he won the 1998 British Grand Prix?**
   a. In the armco   *b. In the pits*   *c. In the lead*

8 **Who labelled Damon Hill a 'sad old man' after the race?**
   a. Michael Schumacher   *b. Jacques Villeneuve c. Eddie Irvine*

9 **Who splashed home sixth at Silverstone?**
   a. Ralf Schumacher   *b Jean Alesi*   *c. Olivier Panis*

10 **How many British drivers took part in the 1998 British Grand Prix?**
   a. Three   *b. Four*   *c. Five*

Answers to page 355

1 *a.Alexander Wurz* *b.*11 3 *b.*Four 4 *c.*Mugen-Honda 5 *c.*Esteban Tuero
6 *b.*Argentinian 7 *a.*17th 8 *b.*Adrian Newey 9 *c.*Prost 10*b.*Michael Schumacher.

QUIZ 33

Answers on page 360

1 **Who claimed the first pole of his Formula One career in Austria in 1998?**
   a. Eddie Irvine *b. Jean Alesi* *c. Ginacarlo Fisichella*

2 **Who drove through the field from last to second place in Austria?**
   a. Michael Schumacher *b. David Coulthard* *c. Eddie Irvine*

3 **Mika Hakkinen and David Coulthard gave Mercedes a one-two victory in its home race at Hockenheim. When was the last time the 'Silver Arrows' won in Germany?**
   a. 1934 *b. 1954* *c. 1964*

4 **Which team finished first and second in the 1998 Belgian Grand Prix at Spa?**
   a. Ferrari *b. McLaren* *c. Jordan*

5 **Who ran into the back of David Coulthard on the rain-soaked track at Spa?**
   a. Eddie Irvine *b. Michael Schumacher* *c. Jean Alesi*

6 **Why will the race go down in the history books?**
   a. It was one of the wettest ever *b. It witnessed one of the biggest first lap shunts ever* *c. It was one of the slowest ever*

7 **What was unique about the victory podium at Monza (apart from it being Michael Schumacher's first win in a Ferrari in front of the tifosi)?**
   a. It was Ferrari's first one-two finish *b. It was the first time two brother had appeared on the same podium* *c. It was the first time two German drivers had appeared on the same podium*

8 **What was the points' difference between Mika Hakkinen and Michael Schumacher after Monza 1998?**
   a. They were level; *b. Hakkinen had a one-point advantage*
   c. Michael Schumacher had a one-point advantage.

9 **How many races did Hakkinen win in his Championship year?**
   a. Eight *b. Nine* *c. Ten*

10 **And how many pole positions?**
   a. Nine *b. Ten* *c. Eleven*

Answers to page 360
1 *c.*BAR 2 *b.*Argentina 3 *c.*Malaysia 4 *a.*Mika Hakkinen 5 *b.*Stewart 6 *b.*Michael Schumacher 7 *c.*Rubens Barrichello 8 *c.*Eddie Irvine 9 *b.*Heinz-Harald Frentzen 10 *c.*Pedro de la Rosa

---

QUIZ 34

Answers on page 355

1 **Which famous name will be missing from the Grand Prix Grid in 1999 for the first time since 1970?**
   a. McLaren   *b. Stewart*   *c. Tyrrell*

2 **How many teams have retained the same driver line-up in 1999 as they had in 1998?**
   a. Three   *b. Four*   *c. Five*

3 **How many drivers will be competing in their first season of Formula One in 1999?**
   a. Two   *b. Three*   *c. Four*

4 **Who got booted out of his team at the last minute to make way for Tora Takagi?**
   a. Jos Verstappen   *b. Jan Magnussen*   *c. Mika Salo*

5 **Who surprisingly retired from Grand Prix racing after only one season?**
   a. Jarno Trulli   *b. Esteban Tuero*   *c. Pedro Diniz*

6 **For which team is Jacques Villeneuve racing in 1999?**
   a. Williams   *b. BAR*   *c. Sauber*

7 **For which team was Pedro de la Rosa test driver in 1998?**
   a. Williams   *b. McLaren*   *c. Jordan*

8 **Who will be the most experienced Grand Prix driver on the grid in 1999?**
   a. Johnny Herbert   *b. Jean Alesi*   *c. Michael Schumacher*

9 **Who is the only driver on the 1999 Grand Prix grid to hold a University degree in economics?**
   a. Jacques Villeneuve   *b. Marc Gene*   *c. Michael Schumacher*

10 **Which designer masterminds the Stewart team challenge in 1999?**
   a. Rory Byrne   *b. Gary Anderson*   *c. John Barnard*

Answers to page 357

1 *b.*Heinz-Harald Frentzen 2 *c.*Michael Schumacher 3 *b.*Jos Verstappen 4 *b.*Eight 5 *b.*McLaren 6 *c.*Martin Brundle 7 *b.*In the pits 8 *c.*Eddie Irvine 9 *a.*Ralph Schumacher 10 *b.*Four

359

QUIZ 35

Answers on page 358

1 **Which team had to change its livery before the start of the 1999 season?**
   a. Williams *b.* Prost *c.* BAR2.

2 **Which Grand Prix was not included in the 1999 calendar, despite an appeal from its country's President?**
   a. Hungary *b.* Argentina *c.* Brazil

3 **Which Far Eastern country will host its first Grand Prix in 1999?**
   a. China *b.* Indonesia *c.* Malaysia

4 **Who claimed pole position for the first round of 1999 in Australia?**
   a. Mika Hakkinen *b.* David Coulthard *c.* Michael Schumacher

5 **Which team's cars suffered identical fires on the grid?**
   a. McLaren *b.* Stewart *c.* Minardi

6 **Who could not get into gear on the grid and had to start from the back?**
   a. Johnny Herbert *b.* Michael Schumacher *c.* Marc Gene

7 **Who started from the pit lane?**
   a. Johnny Herbert *b.* Michael Schumacher
   c. Rubens Barrichello

8 **Who won the 1999 Australian Grand Prix?**
   a. Mika Hakkinen *b.* Jacques Villeneuve *c.* Eddie Irvine

9 **Who finished second for his new team?**
   a. Ralf Schumacher *b.* Heinz-Harald Frentzen *c.* Pedro Diniz

10 **Who scored a point in the very first Grand Prix drive of his career in Australia?**
   a. Marc Gene *b.* Ricardo Zonta *c.* Pedro de la Rosa

Answers to page 358
1 *c.*Giancarlo Fisichella 2 *b.*David Coulthard 3 *b.*1954 4 *a.*Jordan 5 *b.*Michael Schumacher 6 *b.*It witnessed one of the biggest first lap shunts ever 7 *b.*It was the first time two brothers had appeared on the same podium 8 *a.*They were level 9 *b.*Nine 10 *a.*Nine

---

FACT FILE 1

There were no fewer than 19 teams trying to qualify *and* prequalify for the grid in 1990.

Hands up those of you who remember Life Racing; Coloni or Eurobrun!

The season started on a sadly all-too familiar note of discord and bitterness.

Senna was still smarting from the exclusion in Japan, which had not only cost him the race but the Drivers' title.

And cost him 100,000 dollars..Pocket money maybe for the Brazilian - but a severe dent in the ego of a very proud man.

His angry words fuelled the fires all winter. Senna criticised FISA. FISA refused to renew his racing licence. Ron Dennis was caught in the crossfire.

However, at least the dreaded Prost had left for Ferrari. He was replaced by the less contentious figure of Gerhard Berger, who would over the years become one of Ayrton's greatest friends in the sport.

But a state of open warfare still raged between Senna and Prost.

Senna eventually capitulated before the opening round of the year in Phoenix, Arizona.

The brilliant Brazilian overcame the grumps and drove to a magnificent victory.

But it was Berger who put his McLaren on pole.

Alongside him on the front row was the surprise package of the weekend: Pierluigi Martini in his Minardi.

Martini had already given the Minardi fans something to cheer the previous year, when he had actually led the Portuguese Grand Prix for one glorious lap (the only time in history that a Minardi has led a Grand Prix!)

Martini was the nephew of the Italian racer of the seventies, Giancarlo Martini.

FACT FILE 2

Gary Brabham, second son of Sir Jack, became the first son of a former World Champion to attempt to qualify for a Grand Prix in Phoenix.

He failed even to pre-qualify the terrible Life Racing car in either the USA or Brazil and gave up Grand Prix racing there and then.

No one could blame him. Bruno Giacomelli, who bought into the team (goodness knows why!) was a driver of vast experience. He had qualified his Alfa Romeo on Pole at Watkins Glen ten years earlier. But he hadn't raced in Formula One for seven years.

Even he failed to pre-qualify the apology for a racing car that was the Life once in 12 attempts.

Needless to say, the team folded at the end of 1990.

Another team to fold even before the end of the year was Eurobrun.

Italy's Claudio Langes did not pre-qualify once in 1990 and Brazil's Roberto Moreno's 13th place in Phoenix was the team's only finish of the year.

The Coloni team refused to accept reality, however, and would soldier on into 1991, despite the fact that their driver Betrand Gachot failed to qualify for any of the 16 rounds (and failed to pre-qualify on ten occasions!).

David Brabham, youngest of Sir Jack's three sons, became the first son of a former World Champion to qualify for a Grand Prix in Monaco in 1990 - in a Brabham.

He managed to finish just once in the season in the highly uncompetitive car - 15th in France - but found himself disqualified because the car was underweight!

The team dispensed with his services at the end of the year.

FACT FILE 3

Passions were high as the teams arrived at Interlagos.

The Brazilian fans left little room for doubt about their feelings for FISA's Jean-Marie Balestre's treatment of their idol.

The choleric 'President' spent the weekend in the close company of a number of burly bodyguards...

But, to add insult to injury, the much-vilified Alain Prost won the race!

Senna had set pole and set off like a rocket. But he tangled with a back-marker and had to pit for a new nose. He finished a furious third.

The two chief protagonists arrived at Silverstone with three victories apiece, neck-a-neck in the title battle.

Only Riccardo Patrese had been able to break their stranglehold, with a fighting win in San Marino. It was his first victory in seven years; seven years since he had been leading the very same race for Brabham and spun it all away.

The relationship between Prost and Mansell at Ferrari was in the doldrums. Mansell felt the Frenchman was receiving preferrential treatment.

It all boiled over at Silverstone, where random drug testing was introduced for the first time in Grand Prix racing.

Mansell, in search of his third British victory, took pole, although unhappy with his Ferrari.

He took pole, had to give best to Senna, then overtook him at Stowe to the delirium of the crowd. But his Ferrari's gearbox broke.

In a fit of petulance, 'Our Nige' announced his intention to retire at the end of the season (new readers, start here...)

Prost won the race - but Mansell hogged the headlines.

FACT FILE 4

Prost claimed Ferrari's 100th Grand Prix victory in France in 1990, whilst Patrese became the first driver ever to enter 200 Grands Prix at Silverstone.

Derek Warwick had a heart-stopping accident on the first lap at Monza, when his Lotus barrel-rolled in the middle of the track and disintegrated. The brave Brit, coolly jogged back to the pits and, after a medical check, took the re-start in the spare.

Team-mate, Martin Donnelly, was not so lucky in practice for the Spanish Grand Prix. A high-speed impact with the armco, saw the luckless Ulsterman thrown into the middle of the track, still strapped to his seat.

Only prompt trackside medical attention saved his life. Thankfully he has made a miraculous recovery and today runs his own team, guiding young hopefuls in the Junior Formulae.

Meanwhile the Senna-Prost battle rumbled on.

The pair arrived in Japan with Senna ahead on points - with six wins to Prost's five.

Prost had to win to keep Ferrari hopes alive.

Side by side on the front row and into the first corner - the motor sport world held its breath... And, almost unbelievably, history repeated itself.

The pair ended up in the gravel trap, wheels locked.

Some years later, Senna admitted that he had deliberately run Prost off the road.

But the tactic secured the Brazilian's first Drivers' Championship and McLaren secured the 1990 Constructors' crown.

It all left a sour taste in the mouth and a row which would yet again run and run throughout the closed season.

FACT FILE 5

There were 18 teams scrapping for the 26 grid place in the 1991 Championship.

Coloni yet again refused to throw in the towel until the end of the season by which time poor Claudio Langes' confidence was wrecked. He failed to prequalify for any of the 13 races he entered!

But one team which certainly wasn't around just to make up the numbers was the new Jordan team. The ebullient EJ had enjoyed success at all levels of the sport, and the Irishman with the gift of the gab was determined to make his mark in the top rank.

Unfortunately, the team saw itself in the headlines for all the *wrong* reasons in mid-summer...The promising Belgian Bertrand Gachot ('Bert' to his friends) found himself spending time at Her Majesty's Pleasure after a stupid 'road rage' incident.

It seems he had taken exception to a London cabbie cutting him up and had used a CS gas spray to indicate his displeasure!! The long arm of the law was not impressed, even if he was a racing driver. And neither was EJ.

A replacement had to be found pretty sharpish for the Belgian Grand Prix.

So, EJ, drafted in a young German hopeful called Michael Schumacher...

A stunning fifth place on the grid in his first Grand Prix came to naught when he cooked the clutch.

And then, that greedy Mr Briatore over at Benetton, poached Eddie's latest asset from under his nose.

The wrangling continued but Michael was ensconced at Benetton and Jordan eventually signed another up-and-coming talent for the last three races of the year, Alessandro Zanardi (yes, the 1999 Williams team leader was an EJ 'find' too...)

FACT FILE 6

To no-one's surprise, Nigel Mansell had been persuaded not to retire by Frank Williams.

He lined up alongside Riccardo Patrese at Williams, on the strict understanding that he would have the unchallenged Number One status in the team.

Riccardo seemed happy enough to rub along, particularly when he was the one to take Williams' first victory of the year in Mexico...

Jean Alesi had had a Williams' contract in his brief-case at the start of the year but, to the delight of the tifosi, as the politics unwound, the Frenchman of Sicilian origins joined Prost at Ferrari.

There was a commentators' nightmare at Brabham, as Britain's Martin Brundle and Mark Blundell teamed up in the sadly uncompetitive Brabham Yamaha.

Meanwhile, Lotus, little did they know it, had signed yet another future World Champion in Mika Hakkinen (who used to have the beating of one M. Schumacher in Formula Three.)

The Finn had benefitted from the best advice, even in his early Euroseries days, when one James Hunt took more than a passing interest in his career.

And another former World Champion, his fellow-countryman, Keke Rosberg, was to become his close friend and mentor.

Mika soon showed his mettle by scoring points in only his third Grand Prix, with fifth place at Monaco in the uncompetitive Lotus-Judd.

FACT FILE 7

The combination of Senna and the McLaren MP4 won all of the first four races of the 1991 season.

The Brazilian started from pole position on each occasion and simply drove away from the opposition.

The authorities were starting to express concern that such dominance would alienate the fans if racing became too predictable.

Williams were struggling with their six-speed semi-automatic gearbox. And Ferrari were never in the hunt.

The men from Maranello didn't win a race all season for the first time since 1987.

Fortunately for the fans, the McLaren magic deserted the team in the middle of the season and the title fight took off.

Nelson Piquet became only the second driver in history to compete in over 200 Grands Prix in 1991.

And he took what would be the last of his 23 career victories in Canada for Benetton, destined to disappear from the Grand Prix scene at the end of the year, with three World Championship titles to his credit.

Lacking a Formula One drive in 1992, he would accept the chance to tackle the Indy 500. But an horrific practice accident, the worst of his long career, left him with severe feet and leg injuries. However, he bravely returned to the Brickyard in 1993 and then turned his hand to long distance sports car racing, including Le Mans.

FACT FILE 8

The autocratic, choleric, Jean-Marie Balestre found himself on the wrong end of a re-election attempt as President of FISA in mid-summer.

In his place came, the silky-tongued, former lawyer (and founder Director of March Engineering and Simtek) Max Moseley.

The Moseley / Ecclestone axis was literally in the driving seat...

Back on the track, Williams and Mansell had got their act together and the British driver reeled off three victories in succession to challenge Senna and McLaren's supremacy.

By the end of the year, the Championship was down to the wire once more.

Everyone held their breath at the first corner in Japan but nothing happened. Instead, Mansell had an accident on lap nine, all by himself, ended up in the kitty litter, and handed Senna his second successive World Championship.

Berger happily took his first win for McLaren, whilst Senna's victory in the final round in Australia assured them of yet another Constructors' Championship.

Meanwhile, over at Ferrari, a disillusioned Alain Prost had been ignominiously sacked before the last race in Australia.

He had been openly critical of the Ferrari team and was replaced by Gianni Morbidelli for the final round.

Prost decided to take a sabatical - although he did find time to test a Ligier in 1992 (perhaps with an eye to the future?). But he would be back in 1993.

Yet another no-hoper joined the fray in 1992 - Andrea Moda (an major Italian shoe manufucturer).

Brazil's Roberto Moreno worked wonders to qualify the car for Monaco, the one and only time it made the grid. But the team was eventually chucked out of the Championship.

The hapless Gachot finished sixth at Monaco for the Larrousse team and was left to rue what might have been but for a moment of madness at Hyde Park Corner the previous summer.

Jordan, full of hope, after their wonderful fifth place in the 1991 Constructors Championship, struggled all year. They finished up bottom of the pile, with only a solitary point to their name.

For the first time in 12 years, a lady driver attempted to qualify for a Grand Prix.

But Italy's Giovanna Amati was unable to follow the example of her fellow countrywoman, Lella Lombardi and failed to make the grid at any of her three attempts.

Sadly, Lombardi, the only woman ever to score points in a Grand Prix, died of cancer, at the age of 48, in March 1992.

With Prost's departure , the way was open for Jean Alesi to make a name for himself as Ferrari team-leader in 1992.

But Ferrari's fortunes were on the slide.

They finished the year without a single podium finish, fourth in the Championship, 70 points behind third-placed Benetton and a massive 143 points behind title winners, Williams.

FACT FILE 10

There were some famous family names in the entry lists in 1992.

And not all from the world of Formula One.

Paul Belmondo, son of the French mega-film star, Jean-Paul, shrugged off the play-boy label, and did a good job of bringing his uncompetitive March home in one piece on a number of occasions to silence those who scoffed. His best result, a creditable ninth in Hungary.

Christian Fittipaldi boasted not only a famous father in Wilson but an even more famous uncle in double world title holder and Indycar star, Emerson.

The 21-year-old, was sidelined by a back injury for three races, after a practice crash in France. But he showed all the family bounce and confidence to come back to score his first Championship point in Japan for the little Minardi team.

The man with the major task on his hands though, was Damon Hill, son of one of Britain's greatest and best loved drivers, Graham.

It was certainly fortunate for Damon that he had signed as Williams' test driver in 1991, for he had little chance to shine in the uncompetitive Brabham in the latter part of the 1992 season.

Unlike his peers, Hakkinen and Schumacher, Damon found himself with a dog of a car in which to try to make an impression on the Formula One scene.

He only managed to qualify for two races out of eight.

Happily for him, his testing prowess would sufficiently impress Williams designer Patrick Head for him to fight his corner for 1993.

The rest, as they say, is history.

Although 1992 belonged to Nigel Mansell, there was little doubt about the coming man for the next decade.

The buzz word in the Paddock was Schumacher.

After scoring points in three of his five appearances for Benetton in 1991, team boss, Flavio Briatore had decided to build his team around the shining talent of the young German.

Out went John Barnard and in came Ross Brawne and Rory Byrne to provide the right mount for the young pretender.

Michael took his first podium in only the second race of 1992, with third in Mexico.

His first Formula One victory came at Spa, his 17th Grand Prix.

He only failed to score four times in 16 races.

And he was not afraid of anyone as his brush with Senna in France proved.

He finished his first full season third in the Drivers' Championship, three points ahead of Senna.

Team-mate, Martin Brundle, was the first of many to learn just what it is like to play second fiddle to Germany's finest.

Brundle's season started disastrously with four retirements, but after that he gave a very good account of himself, failing to finish only once.

He claimed five podium finishes and finished six overall in the Drivers' table.

Martin was very unlucky indeed to lose his seat for 1993 to Riccardo Patrese.

After all the disappointments and near-misses of the past, **Nigel Mansell got his just reward in 1992.**

But again, his year would end in mystifying anger and controversy.

Quite why he and Frank Williams parted company at the end of such a glorious year for both driver and team, we shall never know.

But then Frank (or Sir Frank, as he now is), has always proved unfathomable.

Mansell's season was a personal triumph.

His nine wins eclipsed Senna's record of eight in one season.

He won the first five races of the year and fought the Brazilian tooth-and-nail to try to claim that Monaco victory which would eventually elude him.

Senna was not ready to relinquish his Monaco crown and took his fifth win in the Principality.

But Mansell did give his adoring home fans something to cheer about at Silverstone, with his third British Grand Prix victory, his fourth Grand Prix win on home territory.

The Championship was all sewn up in Hungary, despite a scare when Mansell had to pit for a puncture.

Second place to Senna was all he needed for the Championship, which he dedicated to his wife, Rosanne.

And he won the Sports' Personality of the year award for the second time at the end of 1992...

But he was off across the 'Pond' to join the Newman Haas Indycar team for 1993.

And more glory lay in store.

FACT FILE 13

Both Brabham and March had bid Formula One farewell, as had Dallara and Fondmetal.

New kids on the block in 1993 were Sauber, with their Ilmor (Mercedes)engines and Michael Schumacher's old sparring partner, Karl Wendlinger as team-leader.

Ligier ran a couple of 'rosbifs' Martin Brundle and Mark Blundell. The pair managed three podium finishes between them, Blundell particularly impressive in only his second season in Formula One, and Ligier finished fifth in the Championship.

Christian Fittipaldi continued to impress with Minardi, despite a potentially nast accident when he was launched into the air after colliding with the rear of his team-mate's car within sight of the finish line at Monza.

Eddie Jordan seemed to be playing 'musical seats' with no less than five drivers vying for the second car alongside Brazil's Runbens Barrichello.

Jordan 'New boy' Eddie Irvine incurred the wrath of Senna when he unlapped himself during the race.

The irate Brazilian (after an unaccustomed glass of schnapps, and a Gerhard Berger wind-up!) marched into the Jordan garage and punched the rookie Irishman on the nose for his temerity!

Jordan ran their third different engine in three years - a neat unit from Brian Hart.

But McLaren were in the dumps. After Honda's withdrawal, Ron Denis had tried hard to get Renault V10s for his team but had to settle for customer Ford V8s. And, to make matters worse, he had to _pay_ for them.

It was just another problem for his much vaunted new driver, America's Michael Andretti, son of the legendary Mario, and already a super star himself in Indycars.

Swingeing rule changes had limited the number of practice laps and eliminated testing at most circuits.

The reforms militated against Andretti Jnr. "If I'd known all these things were going to change, I wouldn't have done the deal," he said.

Many criticised him for commuting back and forth to the USA, instead of moving to Europe. But Formula One can be a hostile environment, totally unlike the warm cameraderie of Indy Cars.

Andretti managed just four laps in his first three Grands Prix.
Driving errors compounded by bad luck eroded his confidence as the season progressed. And the Press wolves tore him to pieces.

His season ended with a fine third place finish at Monza, spiritual motor sport home for the Andretti family. But the writing was on the wall and he was told that his services would not be required for the last three races. Period.

Despite entreaties to go testing, Michael found that this task was entrusted to Mika Hakkinen.

The Finn was more familiar with the McLaren than either Andretti or Senna. He put his knowledge to good use on his first outing for the team.

He jumped into the car in Portugal - and outqualified Senna!

Mika took his first podium finish for McLaren in the next race in Japan, finishing third behind his team-leader.

Gerhard Berger joined Alesi at Ferrari for 1993 but again, Maranello were without a win all year. Alesi's second place finish at Monza was the best that they could muster to keep the tifosi happy.

Michael Schumacher notched up the second Grand Prix victory of his career in Portugal for Benetton. He managed to tangle with Senna at Kyalami (but didn't get punched in the nose!).

Although Senna won five races, it was Schumacher's Benetton which was the greatest threat to the all-conquering Williams cars in 1993.

FACT FILE 15

Politics reared its ugly head major style in 1993. The atmosphere was worse than the FISA/FOCA wars of 1980/81.

Quite simply, the 'Max/Bernie' axis wanted to ban all 'electronic gizmos' or 'driver aids'(such as active suspension and traction control)which had proliferated in the last couple of years for 1994.

Only problem was, according to the 'Concorde Agreement', they left it too late to tell the teams.

Arguments raged. Frank Williams and Ron Dennis refused to comply.

So the 'powers-that-be' applied strong-arm tactics, and the teams, eventually, had to climb down.

It was all rather pathetic and spiteful.

Alain Prost was the victim of politics too on his return to Formula One after his sabbatical.

He was hauled up in front of the FIA for allegedly bringing the sport into disrepute for making criticisms in the Press. How petty can you get!

Senna, too, was not above his own political gestures.

He wanted to join Williams for 1993, but Prost's watertight contract precluded that.

So, Senna, agreed to drive for McLaren on a race-by-race basis.
Not until the French Grand Prix did the Brazilian deign to sign his contract.

At Imola, he arrive five minutes before the first session, straight off a flight from Brazil.

He finished the season runner-up to Prost, with five wins to his name but looking over his shoulder at the young lions, Hill, Schumacher and Hakkinen, nipping at his heels.

Alain Prost won his fourth World Drivers' title in 1993 for Williams.

He qualified on the front row for each and every one of the 16 Grand Prix in the year, claimed 13 pole positions and seven wins.

He won the first round of the year in South Africa after an 18-month lay-off.

And he refused to be intimidated when his old rival, Senna, challenged him at the chicane at Hockenheim. It was Senna who spun in what Patrick Head described as 'a tasty moment'!

Prost's professionalism helped his young team-mate Damon Hill throughout the year.

It was the first time in 15 years that Williams had changed both team drivers at the start of a season.

And former test driver ,Hill silenced his critics by finishing a fine second behind Senna in only his second outing for the team in Brazil.

Hill's first pole was in France, when he outqualified his illustrious team-mate.

His career first victory in the 1993 Hungarian Grand Prix was the first ever to be recorded by the son of a Grand Prix winner.

It was 31 years since his late father, Graham Hill, had scored his maiden Grand Prix victory in the Dutch Grand Prix at Zandvoort at the wheel of a BRM.

To prove it was no flash in the pan, Damon went on to win at Spa and at Monza.

He finished the year third overall in the Drivers' table - ahead of one Michael Schumacher...

FACT FILE 17

The new rules for 1994 caused much consternation at the beginning of the year.

How would passive suspension and lack of traction control affect the cars?

And would there be any repercussions from the introduction of compulsory refuelling stops.

A drop of 12.5 per cent in TV viewing figures had worried the powers-that-be. Obviously, they hoped that these rule changes would bring back the audience.

Two new teams joined the fray: Simtek which had grown from Simtek Research, which had been founded by Max Moseley, and Pacific Racing.

Moseley had sold his 50per cent interest in Simtek to 22-year-old Nick Wirth after he became FISA President. And thrice World Champion, Sir Jack Brabham had an interest in the team.

Small wonder that his youngest son, David, was driving in his second Formula One season.

Pacific lined up the once-promising Gachot with film-star Jean Paul Belmondo's son for his second crack at Formula One.

It would prove a tragic and torrid year for these minnows.

After 147 Grands Prix without a win, Britain's popular Derek Warwick had hung up his Grand Prix gloves at the start of 1994.

And with only 23 points in 127 Grands Prix starts, the French Larrousse team would disappear at the end of the 1994 season.

It would also prove to be the last season for the once all-conquering Lotus team, who began the season without a victory for six years and failed to score a point all season.

Ferrari fielded the most experienced driver line-up for 1994 in Alesi and Berger, the pair having competed in no fewer than 250 Grands Prix between them.

McLaren had a new engine - Peugeot.

And a very un-McLaren driver line-up in that Hakkinen and Brundle could not boast one pole position nor win between them!

They had a hard act to follow. McLaren had only finished outside the top two in the Constructors' Championship once in the past 11 years.

McLaren would be Brundle's seventh different team since he made his Formula One debut for Tyrrell in 1984.

Tyrrell were anxious. They had failed to score a single point in 1993 for the first time in their history. They had high hopes of British driver Mark Blundell and he would not let them down.

His third place in Spain in 1994 would be the team's first podium finish in four years.

The Minardi twins, Christian Fittipaldi and Gianni Morbidelli had transferred to Footwork (Arrows).

Fittipaldi scored two fourth places and starred in Monaco, qualifying sixth and running in fourth place until his gearbox broke.

Sauber had signed up Germany's Heinz-Harald Frentzen to join his former Mercedes Junior Sports Car team-mate Karl Wendlinger (third member of the Mercede triumvirate was one Schumacher. M)

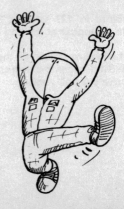

Goodyear Racing boss, Leo Mehl, threatened to halt the supply of tyres to the teams if Formula One supremo Bernie Ecclestone didn't come up with the necessary allocation of passes in Brazil.

He did...

Senna, now the Williams team-leader, delighted the home fans at Interlagos by qualifying in pole position for the 63rd time in his career - and found himself lining up alongside the Benetton of Michael Schumacher.

Pit crews were apprehensive about the first unaccustomed refuelling stops to come in the race.

And, an omen for the future, Michael Schumacher overtook Senna in the pits during his stop in the race.

Schumacher went on to take the first of what would prove to be four consecutive victories in the first four races of 1994.

Senna spun and stalled much to the Brazilian crowd's dismay and it was left to Hill to salvage Williams' pride with second place.

Jordan's Eddie Irvine got himself into hot water on lap 35.

He collided with young Jos Verstappen in the second Benetton as the pair tried to avoid a rapidly slowing Martin Brundle. The Dutchman was launched skywards and virtually landed on Brundle.

Martin's helmet was cracked and he was momentarily knocked out. Fortunately, he did not suffer more than a big headache.

Irvine was blamed for the incident and given a one-race ban.

He appealed.

And was given a three-race ban by FISA...

FACT FILE 20

The weekend of May 1, 1994 is deeply etched in the memory of all followers of motor sport worldwide.

Rubens Barrichello had an enormous accident in Friday qualifying at the Variante Bassa chicane. His car clipped a kerb and was launched towards the wall, grazed the tyre wall and rolled.

Rubens was knocked unconscious and needed track-side medical assistance to clear his airways.

When he came round in the track's medical unit, he found his fellow countryman, Ayrton Senna, anxiously waiting by his bedside.

Rubens would make a full recovery, although he would take no further part in the meeting.

Saturday morning provided another blow, this time of tragic proportions.

Austria's young Roland Ratzenberger, who had finished a pleasing 11th in Aida in his Simtek in the previous round, was killed outright when he was catapulted into the wall at nearly 200mph,after bodywork failure .

He was 31.

Senna was devastated.

Williams, Benetton and Sauber packed up and left the circuit for the day.

Senna had qualified on pole. But somehow it didn't seem important and he discussed his distress at length with Grand Prix Medical Supremo, Professor Sid Watkins.

Should he race on 1 May or not?

FACT FILE 21

The 1994 San Marino Grand Prix was the most tragic in recent history.

JJ Lehto, who had just returned from a serious neck injury, stalled his Benetton on the grid and an unsighted Pedro Lamy ploughed into the back of him in his Lotus.

A wheel and debris flew into the crowd, four spectators were taken to hospital. Sadly, one 28-year-old later died.

The race was not stopped. Instead of red flags, the safety car came out for four laps, whilst the track was cleared.

Senna headed the pack as the safety car peeled off on lap five.

One lap later, came the moment watched in horror on television screens the world over.

Senna's Williams speered straight on at the notorious Tamburello corner and hurtled into the wall at 180 mph.

The brilliant Brazilian died in hospital several hours later.

Part of the front suspension had been forced back and pierced the familiar bright yellow helmet.

Senna had started 164 Grands Prix; qualified on the front row 87 times; qualified on pole 65 times and won 41 Grands Prix.

Amazingly , the race was re-started but the motor sport gods were not finished yet.

Berger stopped, his heart not in the racing. His thoughts with his friend.

On lap 49, Michele Alboreto's Minardi shed a wheel as he was exiting the pit lane and he careered through a number of waiting mechanics.

Schumacher won the race but nobody really cared who won the 1994 San Marino Grand Prix.

Drivers observed a minute's silence on the grid in Monaco in memory of Senna and Ratzenberger.

But they had had even more food for thought after Thursday's Practice session.

Karl Wendlinger's life hung in the balance after his Sauber smashed into the armco at the exit from the tunnel.

The German was kept in a controlled coma until the swelling in his brain had subsided. Happily, he would eventually recover and return to drive in Formula One again.

The FIA announced sweeping new regulations in reaction to the terrible accidents of the last two events.

Williams' test driver, David Coulthard, was given the impossible task of driving in the Williams' seat left vacant by Senna's death.

The young Scot rose to the occasion and finished fifth on his second Grand Prix outing in Canada (thus emulating another great Scot, the late Jim Clark).

Schumacher took his sixth win in seven starts in France.

Williams invited Nigel Mansell back from the States as a 'guest' driver at Magny Cours. He qualified second but retired with broken transmission.

The season appeared to be going all Schumacher's way.

But the second half of the year would prove to be as contentious as the first half was tragic.

FACT FILE 23

Michael Schumacher overtook Damon Hill on the parade lap at the 1994 British Grand Prix; was given a 10-second stop-go penalty; black-flagged when he ignored it and fined $17,000.

Damon Hill achieved a feat which had eluded his late father, Graham, when he won his home Grand Prix at Silverstone.

Two young chargers, Rubens Barrichello and Mika Hakkinen collided on the very last corner and earned themselves suspended one race bans.

But Schumacher was in bigger trouble, two weeks later, the FIA announced that he had been disqualified from the British race and his second-place points deducted; a two-race ban had been issued and Benetton were fined $330,000 for failing to bring him into the pits.

100mm x 300mm wooden planks were fitted to the bottom of the cars for the next round in Germany, aimed at reducing downforce and thus cornering speeds.

Schumacher was allowed to start in front of his home fans at Hockenheim.

The front row was an all-Ferrari affair for the first time since the 1990 Portuguese Grand Prix, with Gerhard Berger claiming his ninth pole position.

The start was shambolic; Hakkinen nerfed Coulthard into Blundell's Tyrrell, who in turn took out both Jordans and Frentzen's Sauber at the front of the pack. Whilst four back markers took each other out. Johnny Herbert lost out to Martin Brundle in a dispute over the same piece of track.

Altogether 11 cars failed to complete the opening lap!

Hakkinen was given a one race ban.

Jos Verstappen was the luckiest man on the circuit when he escaped with minor burns when his Benetton burst into flames during his refuelling stop.

383

FACT FILE 24

Berger's victory in Germany was Ferrari's first since the 1990 Spanish Grand Prix.

Neither Hill nor Schumacher had scored points, so the gap remained at 27 points.

With his two-race ban looming Michael Schumacher knew he had to score as many points as possible in Hungary and in Belgium.

He won at the Hungaroring, then drove sublimely to victory at Spa, only to be disqualified hours later because the 'plank' had worn down below the admitted tolerance margin!

Rubens Barrichello brought the smile back to Eddie Jordan's face by becoming the youngest driver to take a Grand Prix pole position in Belgium at the age of 22.

With Schumacher on his extended 'vacation' Hill took maximum points in Italy and in Portugal.

But the German ace struck back on his return, to win in Jerez.

And Nigel Mansell ousted Coulthard from the second Williams for the final three races of the year.

Damon drove a blinder in the rain in Japan to set up a nail-biting finish with Schumacher in Australia. The gap - one point.

Whether or not Schumacher deliberately drove into Hill in Adelaide will long remain a subject of conjecture. Only Michael himself knows the truth.

However, the facts are: both failed to finish; Schumacher won the Drivers' title by just one point; Nigel Mansell won the race, the 31st and last of his Grand Prix career, and Williams won the Constructors' Championship by 118 points to Benetton's 103.

The controversies of Adelaide 1994 rumbled on over the closed season.

The atmosphere between Hill and Schumacher remained chilly to say the least , particularly as Michael had branded Damon as 'not a number one driver'.

Sir Jack Brabham's interest in Simtek had waned. Son David was replaced by Holland's Jos Verstappen, who gave a good account of himself in the difficult circumstances.

But the team closed its doors after the 1995 Monaco Grand Prix, where Schiattarella and Verstappen contrived to take each other out at the start.

Pacific soldiered on with pay-as-you-go drivers. Gachot scored their best result - eighth in Australia before they too decided it was time to wring the curtain down at the end of 1994.

Brazilian zillionaire Pedro Diniz did himself no favours at all by taking to the wheel of the clumsy. labouring Forti. His reputation suffered as a consequence and he would spend the next few seasons trying to re-establish his competence in the eyes of his peers.

At Sauber, poor Karl Wendlinger made a brave return after his horrific Monaco accident. But, sadly, the spark was gone, and he was replaced by young Jean-Christophe Bouillon.

Nigel Mansell staggered everybody by attempting to make a come-back with McLaren in 1994.

The 'return' bore the elements of farce, as he proved too hefty to fit into the regular cockpit.

A new chassis was built to accommodate him but his season lasted just 1.3 races before he called it quits and walked away from Formula One to pursue his golfing interests and contest Pro-Am events with his great chum,Greg Norman.

No-one doubted that the Williams FW 17 was the best car of 1995 but it proved unreliable and the Benetton, now with Renault power, and Schumacher were the class act.

Williams had 12 pole positions and 5 wins; Benetton 4 pole positions and 11 wins. And that sums up the season.

In the wake of the Imola tragedies, engine sizes were reduced from 3.5 to 3 litres. And Williams' Adrian Newey estimated that downforce was reduced by 40 percent with the new regulations.

Driver finesse was at a premium.

And Benetton held the trump card in Schumacher.

He rattled off a record nine wins in the year and clinched his second successive title at Aida.

Meanwhile, team-mate Johnny Herbert was busy scoring his first ever World Championship win before the home crowds at Silverstone, after Hill and Schumacher took each other out.

Johnny played tambourine at Eddie Jordan's annual post Grand Prix bash, whilst Damon strutted his stuff on guitar. The song was 'Johnny Be Good' - and nobody was more deserving of the accolade than the chirpy electrician's son from Essex!

And Johnny would take a second win at Monza, when Hill and Schumacher took each other out once again, in September.

His determined battling would help bring the Constructors' title home to Benetton for the first time in the team's history.

And would bring him a career-best fourth in the Drivers' table.

Whilst the Hill/Schumacher battle dominated the headlines, there were other performances of note in the 1995 season.

Ferrari's Jean Alesi at long, long last took the chequered flag in a Grand Prix in Canada.

After taking the flag he stood up in the cockpit to acknowledge the fans - and stalled the car.

He hitched a lift back to the pits with Schumacher's Benetton!

Britain's David Coulthard had a miserable start to the season, suffering with persistent tonsillitis. However, once the offending tonsils had been removed, DC came into his own.

He took his maiden Grand Prix victory in Portugal and reeled off four consecutive pole positions.

McLaren, now with Mercedes power, were still looking for their first win in two seasons.

Mika Hakkinen was forced to miss the Pacific Grand Prix at Aida for an apendectomy.

McLaren's young Danish test driver, Jan Magnussen, aquitted himself well as stand-in.

But Mika was back with an astounding second place just two weeks later in Suzuka.

Then came that awful accident in practice in Adelaide.
The Finn's McLaren hurtled into the armco and he suffered severe head injuries when his head hit the steering wheel.

Only prompt action by the trackside medical staff saved his life.

Happily, the Finn would make a full recovery.

FACT FILE 28

For the first time in the history of the sport, one team fielded two sons of famous Grand Prix winners in 1996.

Damon Hill, son of twice World Champion, Graham, was joined in the Williams team by Indycar Champion, Jacques Villeneuve, son of Gilles.

And what a combination they proved to be. They won 12 of the 16 rounds; claimed 12 pole positions, six one-two finishes, and assured Williams of the Constructors' Championship with four rounds remaining.

Damon Hill made no mistake about claiming the Drivers' title for his own - the first son of a World Champion to follow in his father's footsteps to date. He won eight races.

But the Championship went down to the wire in Japan yet again! This time, it was his own team-mate who was the challenger.

The wiry, unconventional, little Villeneuve, in his baggy racing overalls was a revelation from the very first practice session in the opening round of the season at the new circuit in Melbourne.

He became one of the elite cast of three (four if you count Farina in the very first Grand Prix at Silverstone in 1950) to qualify in pole position for their very first Formula One race.

Carlos Reutemann and Mario Andretti were the other two - and they didn't do too badly...

He led the race until five laps from the end, when engine problems forced him to slow and let his team-leader Hill past.

It was a case of 'all-the-fours' for Jacques in 1996.

He won fourth time out, at the Nurburgring. And he wracked up a total of four wins in the season - a record for a Grand Prix rookie.

FACT FILE 29

Michael Schumacher had joined Ferrari for a rumoured 25 million dollars in 1996.

And his surprise new team-mate was Eddie Irvine. Cynics wondered how the bucolic Irishman would fit in with the fastidious German.
But you know what they say about opposites...

The Ferrari was 'difficult' to put it mildly but Schumacher wrung its neck and took three classic victories.

His self-confessed favourite was in Monza, his first for Ferrari in front of the adoring tifosi; but the pundits rank his drive to victory in a rain-soaked Barcelona, where he quite simply drove away from the opposition at the rate of four seconds a lap as one of *the* great drives.

Stirling Moss commented: "In my opinion, there isn't a top three at the moment, there's a top one".

The season had its low points too.

Schuey claimed a brilliant pole position in Monaco, then drove into the wall on the first lap, much to everyone's disbelief. Then, in France, his engine blew up on the *parade lap*; at Silverstone it lasted just three laps.

The 'Big Three' shared the 16 pole positions between them and they won all but one of the races.

Olivier Panis spoiled the party by taking Ligier's first victory in 15 years in the rain-sodden Monaco Grand Prix in 1996. Just three cars were running at the finish. But Olivier deserved his first Grand Prix win.

His team-mate, Pedro Diniz, had had a lucky escape earlier in the year, when his car burst into flames out on the circuit in Argentina after an oil leak.

The Brazilian scrambled free with minor burns - and the photos made *all* the papers!

FACT FILE 30

The Ferrari twins, Alesi and Berger had joined the reigning Champions, Benetton for 1996. But there were to be no wins for the team this season.

The 'nervous' car suited Alesi's driving style better and he collected four second place finishes.

But his Sicilian blood continued to boil over from time to time and, rumour has it, that the Benetton,mechanics locked him in the transporter to cool down during one Silverstone test...

Berger, suffered from the after effects of pneumonia for the first half of the 1996 season. The affable Austrian was leading in Germany until his engine let him down just three laps from the finish.

Elsewhere, everyone was struggling to make the podium.

Coulthard finished second in Monaco - the high spot of McLaren's season - whilst Hakkinen managed third on four occasions.

Johnny Herbert - very much much number two to Frentzen at Sauber -claimed his only top six finish all season in Monaco, when he finished third of the three classified finishers!

Martin Brundle, in what would prove to be his last season, of Formula One, struggled for points at Jordan.

The good news is that he has the opportunity to repeat his 1990 Le Mans victory for Jaguar now, with the superfast Toyota sports car.

And he makes a great TV commentator - very much in the mould of the late James Hunt.

FACT FILE 31

Yet again controversy marred the end of a fantastic see-saw Championship in 1997.

Michael Schumacher's desperate attempt to take Jacques Villeneuve out of the final round of the 1997 season at Jerez saw the German villified around the world. Even the Italian Press demanded that he be fired by Ferrari.

The strength of condemnation and public outcry certainly took the German by surprise and gave him food for thought during the closed season.

The FIA stripped him of his second place in the Championship and ordered him to do seven days work on behalf of the European Commission's Safety Campaign in 1998...

Fortunately for Villeneuve, unlike the hapless Hill in 1995, he finished the race in Jerez in third (allowing Mika Hakkinen to score his first ever Grand Prix victory in the process - another bone of contention, when the mists of anger at the Schumacher incident had cleared).

Jacques claimed the title which his late father Gilles so coveted, with 10 pole positions, seven wins and three fastest laps to his credit.

Schumacher M. won five rounds, three poles and set three fastest laps.

A surprise statistic of the season is that Heinz-Harald Frentzen set six fastest laps in 1997.

The German only won one race for his new team, Williams, but inherited second place in the Drivers' Championship after Schumacher's disqualification (albeit with half as many points as team-leader Villeneuve)

FACT FILE 32

John Barnard was replaced at Ferrari for the 1997 season by Rory Byrne(who had intended to retire from Formula One and start a new life in Thailand!) and Ross Brawne.

Nick Wirth, previously of Simtek, took over at Benetton and later in the season, David Richards, the Pro-drive supremo and mastermind behind the Subaru World Rally Championship winning team, took over from Falvio Briatore.

Relations between Briatore and his drivers, Alesi and Berger deteriorated throughout the season.

Alesi made a terrible blunder in the opening round in Melbourne when he neglected to come in for his fuel stop and ran out of gas out on the track.

Berger had a horrid season, suffering from a bad sinus condition, which necessitated two operations and deeply affected by the death of his father in a light aircraft accident.

The Austrian's drive to victory at Hockenheim was probably the most popular win of the year in the Paddock and, in true style,
he rounded off his 210-race career with a flying fourth place
in the final Grand Prix of 1997 at Jerez.

Stand-in for Berger for three races, Germany's young Alexander Wurz did an excellent job.

He outqualified Alesi and came home third at Silverstone in only his third Grand Prix.

1997 was the year of the young pretenders, with Fisichella and Ralf Schumacher (younger brother of Michael) at Jordan, Wurz test driver at Benetton, and Jarno Trulli, replacing the injured Panis at Prost and leading the Austrian Grand Prix up to half distance.

FACT FILE 33

Young Ralf Schumacher finished a bright third in Argentina, his second Grand Prix, but he felt the sharp side of EJ'S tongue when he returned to the pits. He had punted his team-mate, Fisichella off the track in the process (now I wonder where he learned that trick...?)

But he was in deeper hot water later in the year when his over-exuberance at the start of the European Grand Prix at the Nurburgring saw him eliminate big brother Michael at the first corner.

Rumour has it that young Ralf wasn't invited to the family Christmas party that year...

Fisichella showed plenty of promise, though he sometimes seemed to go to sleep in the second half of races. But his second place finish at Spa behind Schumacher Snr was a gem.

Hakkinen's victory at Jerez, after 91 attempts, although contentious, was rightly acclaimed. The Finn's recovery from his Adelaide accident in 1995 little less than miraculous.

And Scotland's David Coulthard had every reason to smile.

DC won the opening round of the year in Melbourne - his very first victory for the newly-liveried West McLaren Mercedes team.

And his victory in front of the Ferrari faithful at Monza later in the year was equally sweet.

Lola returned to Grand Prix racing at the beginning of the year with major sponsorship from Master Card.

Their cars failed to qualify for the first round in Australia and the team went broke, leaving drivers, Sospiri and Rosset in the lurch.

FACT FILE 34

Schumacher wasn't the only one to be hauled in front of the authorities in 1997.

The refreshingly non-politically correct, Jaccques Villeneuve was forced to interrupt his preparations for Canada mid-season to return to Paris to face the music for allegedly 'bringing the sport into disrepute' for his outspoken criticisms.

His indiscretions *on* the track, however, nearly cost him his title.

He raced under appeal in Japan, after being cited for overtaking under a waved yellow during practice (after a couple of early season warnings). He was later docked two points for his fifth-place finish.

1997 saw the return of two illustrious name to the Grand Prix Grid: Prost and Stewart.

Prost bought out Ligier and campaigned Olivier Panis and Saturo Nakano (in deference to Honda). Panis impressed in the early part of the year, an excellent second in Spain.

But he suffered two badly broken legs in a bad accident during the Canadian Grand Prix and finished sixth on a very brave return just three months later at the Nurburgring.

Stewart Racing returned with all the professionalism one would expect of Formula One's first truly professinal driver.

Jackie (and son, Paul) had the backing of Ford. But, unlike Prost, they started from scratch, with a brand new team.

Rubens Barrichello moved over from Jordan and young Danish hot-shoe, Jan Magnussen, was given a proper chance at last.

The team was plagued with gearbox problems during the early part of the season.

But, in Monaco, their were tears of joy in the Stewart pit as Barrichello finished a brilliant second in only the team's fifth Grand Prix.

FACT FILE 35

Coulthard won the prize for 'Best of the Brits' in 1997.

But 1996 World Driver's Champion, Damon Hill plummeted to the depths.

Turfed out of Williams in favour of Heinz-Harald Frentzen, Damon surprised many (including Eddie Jordan) by joining Arrows for the 1997 season.

He stopped on the parade lap in the opening race of the year - throttle problem...

Mechanical problems and an underpowered engine blighted his season and not even the arrival of designer John Barnard could provide the cure.

There was one bright spot in the season at the Hungaroring - a tight, twisty circuit, at which top-end speed counted for less.

To everyone's amazement (including a hoarse Murray Walker) Damon was leading right up to the last lap, when a hydraulic leak forced him to give best to Jacques Villeneuve.

Team-mate Pedro Diniz proved that he was no slouch during the year, even outqualifying the reigning World Champion on three occasions.

Emerson Fittipaldi, former double World Champion and mega Indy racing star, was a guest in the Paddock at Hockenheim: "Why are Gerhard and I the only ones smiling?" he asked.

If your name was Denis, Tyrrell or Williams, you did not have too much to smile about in the back room.

The political shenanigans rumbled on, with these three, refusing to sign Max and Bernie's 'Concorde Agreement'.

There was much talk of Bernie's desire to float Formula One - and many suggestions that maybe it would be better for FISA to put its own house in order before the 'For Sale' signs were put up.

FACT FILE 36

The 1998 season began with the news of the buy-out of Tyrrell by BAR, British American Racing - the new team, headed up by Jacques Villeneuve's manager, Craig Pollock.

The buy-out meant that BAR would be guaranteed to receive all its multi-million pound TV revenue and prize money from the start of its racing career in 1999.

Originally, Ken Tyrrell was to remain nominally in charge, but he had soon had enough and walked away from a Formula One scene which he had graced with such dignity since 1970.

Whilst Williams, Ferrari and McLaren retained their driver line-up for 1998, there were new faces in strange places in the other teams.

The 'Benetton Babes' of Alexander Wurz and Giancarlo Fisichella came under David Richards' wing at Benetton, after Gerhard Berger's retirement and Jean Alesi's defection to Sauber.

And Alain Prost offered young Jarno Trulli the second seat at Prost after his impressive performances in 1997 (Jarno is named after the late great Finnish motor-cycle racer, Jarno Saarinen).

And Damon Hill had found a new home for himself after his unhappy 1997 season with Arrows.

Eddie Jordan had, at last, got his man.

Damon would bring joy to the team and, let's be honest, to everyone in the Paddock, by winning the Belgian Grand Prix at a rain-soaked Spa.

It was Jordan's first Grand Prix win after seven seasons of trying.

And young Ralf Schumacher did his bit too, finishing in a fine second place.

At the end of the year, EJ achieved another ambition, when Hill's fighting fourth place in Japan saw Jordan edge out Benetton for fourth place in the Constructors' Championship.

The 1998 season belonged to the 'Silver Arrows' of McLaren, as any motor racing fan will tell you.

But the result of the first race was the subject of bitter controversy (and this time it did not include Michael Schumacher).

Hakkinen and Coulthard dominated the field but Coulthard moved over to give the Finn victory. Why? Because the drivers had a pre-race pact that whoever made it to the first corner first would win.

The punters were livid. DC had thrown away the win, in their eyes - and Mika had won his second Grand Prix again, in dubious circumstances.

Mika would go on to win seven more races and the 1998 World Drivers' title, whilst DC would play rear-gunner, with six second places in the second half of the season.

Once again, the title would go down to the wire between Hakkinen and you-know-who at Ferrari.

But a clutch problem, saw Schumacher Senior relegated to the back of the grid and his charge through the field came to naught when he ran over debris on the track.

But the brilliant German had garnered six impressive wins for Ferrari in the season.

And side-kick, Eddie Irvine, had eight podiums to his name.

The pair nearly set the Monza Autodrome alight when they finished one-two for Ferrari in September!

Goodyear had hoped to make their exit from the sport on a winning note - sadly, it was not to be.

FACT FILE 38

The 1998 season was something of a shock for reigning Champion Jacques Villeneuve and team-mate Heinz Harald Frentzen.

The Williams cars did not win a race during the year - for the first time in 10 years.

Adrian Newey's departure to McLaren had caught the normally alert Williams' design department napping.

Three third-place finishes were all that 'Happy Jacques' pink hair and all, and 'Harry-Heinz' could muster.

Stewart too, were in the doldrums.

Barrichello managed to scrape two fifth-place finishes and, with their Ford Masters looking over their shoulder, the Stewarts had to dispense with the services of young Magnussen.

Holland's Jos Verstappen was the replacement but he too would struggle with the car and find his P45 on the shelf at the end of the season.

Happily for Jos, he would find employment with the much-vaunted, multi-million, Yamaha project under the watchful eye of the astute brilliance of Harvey Postlethwaite for 1999 and beyond...

The 'Benetton Babes' shone.

And they showed no respect for their elders.

Fisichella finished in a fine second place in Monaco, whilst team-mate Wurz was busy giving Schumacher Senior a right seeing-to at the Loews hairpin.

Young Wurz was lucky to emerge unscathed from an accident in the tunnel - whilst Schuey headed for an unscheduled pit stop which would ruin his day!

David Richards was replaced by Rocco Benetton as team manager during the season.

Argentina's 19-year-old, Esteban Tuero, acquitted himself well during the season in the Minardi and it was sad to see him decide to quit Formula One for 1999.

FACT FILE 39

The new all-singing and dancing BAR team found themselves in hot water before the 1999 season even started.

The powers-that-be were less than impressed by their launch of two cars in different livery.

And yet again, someone would be hauled in front of 'the beak' for 'bringing the sport into disrepute'. Yawn.

Villeneuve had joined his mate Craig Pollock in the over-hyped team.

Williams had an all-new driver line-up for the first time since 1993: Twice Indy car Champ Alessandro Zanardi (making his return to Formula One) and young Schumacher Junior, Ralf, a surprise selection.

Johnny Herbert teamed up with Barrichello in a happy Stewart line-up. Unfortunately, both cars caught fire on the grid!

Heinz-Harald Frentzen sought refuge in the bossom of the Jordan team, alongside Damon Hill

There were three new kids on the block:Spain's Pedro de la Rosa at Arrows; Spanish Economics Graduate, Marc Gene at Minardi, and Brazil's Ricardo Zonta at BAR

The 1999 season got off to a fantastic start in Melbourne.

The 'Silver Arrows' dominated practice but collapsed during the race.

'Irv the Swerve' (Eddie Irvine) took his first Grand Prix victory as Schumacher Senior suffered numerous problems.

Schumacher Junior was third, and Heinz-Harald Frentzen a happy second for his new team, Jordan.

Damon Hill, starting his 100th Grand Prix, ended up in the gravel trap at the second corner.

And Pedro de la Rosa was welcomed home by King Carlos of Spain after scoring one point for sixth place in his very first Grand Prix.

1990s

RESULTS

RESULTS 1990

1990 Prost joined Mansell at Ferrari in a straight swap with Berger. Senna and Prost continued to tangle (literally) on and off the track. The Brazilian triumphed, six wins to five and the pair ended up in the gravel on the first corner in Japan for the second successive year. Piquet gave Benetton back-to-back wins in Japan and Australia. Mansell threw a wobbly when his car let him down at Silverstone, threatened to retire at the end of the year - and didn't...Poor Nannini's Grand Prix career ended when his arm was severed in a helicopter accident. And Ireland's Martin Donnelly was terribly injured in a practice crash in Spain. Prost gave Ferrari their 100th GP win in France but McLaren pipped them to the Constructors' Championship. There were 16 Grands Prix. For the last time, best 11 results counted and points were 9-6-4-3-2-1 for top six places.

ROUND 1/US GRAND PRIX
PHOENIX, 11 MARCH

1. SENNA(BRA)	MCLAREN-HONDA	1HR 52MIN 32.8SEC
2. ALESI (FRA)	TYRRELL-FORD	1HR 52MIN 41.5SEC
3. BOUTSEN(BEL)	WILLIAMS-RENAULT	1HR 53MIN 26.9SEC
4. PIQUET(BRA)	BENETTON-FORD	1HR 53MIN 41.2SEC
5. MODENA(ITA)	BRABHAM-JUDD	1HR 53MIN 42.3SEC
6. NAKAJIMA(JAP)	TYRRELL-FORD	71 LAPS

Race: 70 laps of 2.36 mile/3.8km (165.2 miles/ 266 kms)
Fastest lap: Berger(AUT) McLaren-Honda, 1min 31.05sec,93.31mph/150.14kph
Pole position: Berger, 1min 28.66sec 26 starters, 14 classified finishers

ROUND 2/BRAZILIAN GRAND PRIX
INTERLAGOS, 25 MARCH

1. PROST(FRA)	FERRARI	1HR 37MIN 21.3SEC
2. BERGER(AUT)	MCLAREN-HONDA	1HR 37MIN 34.8SEC
3. SENNA(BRA)	MCLAREN-HONDA	1HR 37MIN 59.0SEC
4. MANSELL(GB)	FERRARI	1HR 38MIN 08.5SEC
5. BOUTSEN(BEL)	WILLIAMS-RENAULT	70 LAPS
6. PIQUET(BRA)	BENETTON-FORD	70 LAPS

Race: 71 laps of 2.69 mile/4.33km (190.99 miles/307.43kms)
Fastest lap: Berger, 1min 19.9sec,121.09mph/194.87kph
Pole position: Senna, 1min 17.28sec 26 starters, 14 classified finishers

ROUND 3/SAN MARINO
IMOLA, 13 MAY

1. PATRESE(ITA)	WILLIAMS-RENAULT	1HR 30MIN 55.05SEC
2. BERGER(AUT)	MCLAREN-HONDA	1HR 31MIN 00.06SEC
3. NANNINI(ITA)	BENETTON-FORD	1HR 31MIN 01.08SEC
4. PROST(FRA)	FERRARI	1HR 31MIN 01.14SEC
5. PIQUET(BRA)	BENETTON-FORD	1HR 31MIN 48.6SEC
6. ALESI(FRA)	TYRRELL-FORD	60 LAPS

Race: 61 laps of 3.13 mile/5.04km - 190.93 miles/ 307.44 kms)
Fastest lap: Senn(BRA), Mclaren-Honda, 1min 27.16sec, 129.36mph/208.18kph
Pole position: Senna, 1min 23.22sec 26 starters, 13 classified finishers

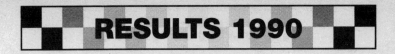

RESULTS 1990

ROUND 4/MONACO GRAND PRIX
MONTE CARLO, 27 MAY

1. SENNA(BRA)	MCLAREN-HONDA	1HR 52MIN 46.9SEC
2. ALESI(FRA)	TYRRELL-FORD	1HR 52MIN 48.1SEC
3. BERGER(AUT)	MCLAREN-HONDA	1HR 52MIN 49.1SEC
4. BOUTSEN(BEL)	WILLIAMS-RENAULT	77 LAPS
5. CAFFI(ITA)	ARROWS-FORD	76 LAPS
6. BERNARD(FRA)	LOLA-LAMBORGHINI	76 LAPS

Race: 78 laps of 2.07 mile/3.33km (161.46 miles/259.74kms)
Fastest lap: Senna, 1min 24.47sec, 88.13mph/141.84kph
Pole position: Senna, 1min 21.31sec 26 starters, 7 classified finishers

ROUND 5/CANADIAN GRAND PRIX
MONTREAL, 10 JUNE

1. SENNA(BRA)	MCLAREN-HONDA	1HR 42MIN 56.4SEC
2. PIQUET(BRA)	BENETTON-FORD	1HR 43MIN 06.9SEC
3. MANSELL(GB)	FERRARI	1HR 43MIN 09.8SEC
4. BERGER(AUT)	MCLAREN-HONDA	1HR 43MIN 11.3SEC
5. PROST(FRA)	FERRARI	1HR 43MIN 12.2SEC
6. WARWICK(GB)	LOTUS-LAMBORGHINI	68 LAPS

Race: 70 laps of 2.73mile/4.4km (191.1 miles/308kms)
Fastest lap: Berger, 1min 22.08sec, 119.65mph/192.55kph
Pole position: Senna, 1min 20.40sec 26 starters, 13 classified finishers

ROUND 6/MEXICAN GRAND PRIX
MEXICO CITY, 24 JUNE

1. PROST(FRA)	FERRARI	1HR 32MIN 35.78SEC
2. MANSELL(GB)	FERRARI	1HR 33MIN 01.13SEC
3. BERGER(AUT)	MCLAREN-HONDA	1HR 33MIN 01.31SEC
4. NANNINI(ITA)	BENETTON-FORD	1HR 33MIN 16.88SEC
5. BOUTSEN(BEL)	WILLIAMS-RENAULT	1HR 33MIN 22.45SEC
6. PIQUET(BRA)	BENETTON-FORD	1HR 33MIN 22.73SEC

Race: 69 laps of 2.75 mile/4.42km (187.0 miles/300.56 kms)
Fastest lap: Prost, 1min 17.96sec, 126.85mph/204.25kph
Pole position: Berger, 1min 17.23sec 26 starters, 20 classified finishers

ROUND 7/FRENCH GRAND PRIX
PAUL RICARD, 8 JULY

1. PROST(FRA)	FERRARI	1HR 33MIN 29.6SEC
2. CAPELLI(ITA)	LEYTON HOUSE-JUDD	1HR 33MIN 38.2SEC
3. SENNA(BRA)	MCLAREN-HONDA	1HR 33MIN 41.2SEC
4. PIQUET(BRA)	BENETTON-FORD	1HR 34MIN 10.8SEC
5. BERGER(AUT)	MCLAREN-HONDA	1HR 34MIN 11.8SEC
6. PATRESE(ITA)	WILLIAMS-RENAULT	1HR 34MIN 38.9SEC

Race: 80 laps of 2.4mile/3.8km - 192 miles/ 304 kms)
Fastest lap: Mansell(GB), Ferrari, 1min 08.01sec, 125.44mph/201.83kph
Pole position: Mansell, 1min 04.40sec 26 starters, 19 classified finishers

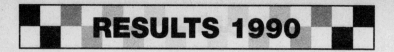

RESULTS 1990

ROUND 8/BRITISH GRAND PRIX
SILVERSTONE, 15 JULY

1. PROST(FRA)	FERRARI	1HR 18MIN 30.9SEC
2. BOUTSEN(BEL)	WILLIAMS-RENAULT	1HR 19MIN 10.1SEC
3. SENNA(BRA)	MCLAREN-HONDA	1HR 19MIN 14.1SEC
4. BERNARD(FRA)	LOLA-LAMBORGHINI	1HR 19MIN 46.3SEC
5. PIQUET(BRA)	BENETTON-FORD	1HR 19MIN 55.0SEC
6. SUZUKI(JAP)	LOLA-LAMBORGHINI	63 LAPS

Race: 64 laps of 2.97mile/4.78km (190.08 miles/305.92 kms)
Fastest lap: Mansell(GB) Ferrari, 1min 11.29sec, 149.98mph/241.38kph
Pole position: Mansell,1min 07.43sec 26 starters, 14 classified finishers

ROUND 9/GERMAN GRAND PRIX
HOCKENHEIM, 29 JULY

1. SENNA(BRA)	MCLAREN-HONDA	1HR 20MIN 47.2SEC
2. NANNINI(ITA)	BENETTON-FORD	1HR 20MIN 53.7SEC
3. BERGER(AUT)	MCLAREN-HONDA	1HR 20MIN 55.7SEC
4. PROST(FRA)	FERRARI	1HR 21MIN 32.4SEC
5. PATRESE(ITA)	WILLIAMS-HONDA	1HR 21MIN 35.2SEC
6. BOUTSEN(BEL)	WILLIAMS-HONDA	1HR 22MIN 08.7SEC

Race: 45 laps of 4.22 mile/6.8 km (189.9 miles/306 kms)
Fastest lap: Boutsen,1min 45.6sec, 144.08mph/231.88kph
Pole position: Senna, 1min 40.20sec 26 starters, 11 classified finishers

ROUND 10/HUNGARIAN GRAND PRIX
HUNGARORING, 12 AUGUST

1. BOUTSEN(BEL)	WILLIAMS-RENAULT	1HR 49MIN 30.6SEC
2. SENNA(BRA)	MCLAREN-HONDA	1HR 49MIN 30.9SEC
3. PIQUET(BRA)	BENETTON-FORD	1HR 49MIN 58.5SEC
4. PATRESE(ITA)	WILLIAMS-RENAULT	1HR 50MIN 02.4SEC
5. WARWICK(GB)	LOTUS-LAMBORGHINI	1HR 50MIN 44.8SEC
6. BERNARD(FRA)	LOTUS-LAMBORGHINI	1HR 50MIN 54.9SEC

Race: 77 laps of 2.47 mile/3.97 km (190.19 miles /305.69 kms)
Fastest lap: Patrese,1min 22.06sec, 106.08mph/174.08kph
Pole position: Boutsen,1min 17.91sec 26 starters, 17 classified finishers

ROUND 11/BELGIAN GRAND PRIX
SPA-FRANCORCHAMPS, 26 AUGUST

1. SENNA(BRA)	MCLAREN-HONDA	1HR 26MIN 31.2SEC
2. PROST(FRA)	FERRARI	1HR 26MIN 35.6SEC
3. BERGER(AUT)	MCLAREN-HONDA	1HR 27MIN 00.5SEC
4. NANNINI(ITA)	BENETTON-FORD	1HR 27MIN 21.3SEC
5. PIQUET(BRA)	BENETTON-FORD	1HR 28MIN 01.7SEC
6. GUGELMIN (BRA)	LEYTON HOUSE-JUDD	1HR 28MIN 20.9SEC

Race: 44 laps of 4.31 mile/6.94 km (189.64 miles/305 kms)
Fastest lap: Prost, 1min 55.1sec, 134.89mph/217.09kph
Pole position: Senna,1min 50.37sec 26 starters, 17 classified finishers

RESULTS 1990

ROUND 12/ITALIAN GRAND PRIX
MONZA, 9 SEPTEMBER

1. SENNA(BRA)	MCLAREN-HONDA	1HR 17MIN 57.9SEC
2. PROST(FRA)	FERRARI	1HR 18MIN 03.9SEC
3. BERGER(AUT)	MCLAREN-HONDA	1HR 18MIN 05.3SEC
4. MANSELL(GB)	FERRARI	1HR 18MIN 54.1SEC
5. PATRESE(ITA)	WILLIAMS-RENAULT	1HR 19MIN 23.2SEC
6. NAKAJIMA(JAP)	TYRRELL-FORD	52 LAPS

Race: 53 laps of 3.6 mile/ 5.8 km (190.8 miles/ 307.4 kms)
Fastest lap: Senna, 1min 26.25sec, 150.42mph/242.08kph
Pole position: Senna, 1min 22.53sec 26 starters*, 13 classified finishers
*Race started three times due to first lap accidents.

ROUND 13/PORTUGUESE GRAND PRIX
ESTORIL, 23 SEPTEMBER

1. MANSELL(GB)	FERRARI	1HR 22MIN 11.0SEC
2. SENNA(BRA)	MCLAREN-HONDA	1HR 22MIN 13.8SEC
3. PROST(FRA)	FERRARI	1HR 22MIN 15.2SEC
4. BERGER(AUT)	MCLAREN-HONDA	1HR 22MIN 16.9SEC
5. PIQUET(BRA)	BENETTON-FORD	1HR 23MIN 08.4SEC
6. NANNINI(ITA)	BENETTON-FORD	1HR 23MIN 09.3SEC

Race: 61* laps of 2.7 mile/4.35 km (164.7 miles/ 265.35kms)
Fastest lap: Patrese(ITA),Williams-Renault,1min 18.31sec, 124.26mph/199.93kph
Pole position: Mansell, 1min 13.56sec 25 starters, 15 classified finishers
*Race halted after 61 of 71 laps due to accident

ROUND 14/SPANISH GRAND PRIX
JEREZ, 30 SEPTEMBER

1. PROST(FRA)	FERRARI	1HR 48MIN 01.5SEC
2. MANSELL(GB)	FERRARI	1HR 48MIN 23.5SEC
3. NANNINI(ITA)	BENETTON-FORD	1HR 48MIN 36.3SEC
4. BOUTSEN(BEL)	WILLIAMS-RENAULT	1HR 48MIN 44.8SEC
5. PATRESE(ITA)	WILLIAMS-RENAULT	1HR 48MIN 58.9SEC
6. SUZUKI(JAP)	LOLA-LAMBORGHINI	1HR 49MIN 05.2SEC

Race: 73 laps of 2.62 mile/4.22km (191.26 miles/308.06 kms)
Fastest lap: Patrese, 1min 24.51sec, 111.64mph/179.63kph
*Pole position:*Senna(BRA),McLaren-Honda, 1min 18.39sec 25 starters* 10 classified finishers
*Martin Donnelly qualified but dns after practice accident

ROUND 15/JAPANESE GRAND PRIX
SUZUKA, 21 OCTOBER

1. PIQUET(BRA)	BENETTON-FORD	1HR 34MIN 36.8SEC
2. MORENO(BRA)	BENETTON-FORD	1HR 34MIN 44.0SEC
3. SUZUKI(JAP)	LOLA-LAMBORGHINI	1HR 34MIN 59.3SEC
4. PATRESE(ITA)	WILLIAMS-RENAULT	1HR 35MIN 13.1SEC
5. BOUTSEN(BEL)	WILLIAMS-RENAULT	1HR 35MIN 23.7SEC
6. NAKAJIMA(JAP)	TYRRELL-FORD	1HR 35MIN 49.2SEC

Race: 53 laps of 3.64 mile/5.86 km (192.92 mph/ 310.58 kms)
Fastest lap: Patrese, 1min 44.23sec, 125.74mph/202.31sec
Pole position: Senna(BRA)McLaren-Honda, 1min 36.99sec 25 starters, 10 classified finishers

RESULTS 1990/1

ROUND 16/ AUSTRALIAN GRAND PRIX
ADELAIDE, 4 NOVEMBER

1. PIQUET(BRA)	BENETTON-FORD	1HR 49MIN 44.6SEC
2. MANSELL(GB)	FERRARI	1HR 49MIN 47.7SEC
3. PROST(FRA)	FERRARI	1HR 50MIN 21.8SEC
4. BERGER(AUT)	MCLAREN-HONDA	1HR 50MIN 31.4SEC
5. BOUTSEN(BEL)	WILLIAMS-HONDA	1HR 51MIN 35.7SEC
6. PATRESE(ITA)	WILLIAMS-HONDA	80 LAPS

Race: 81 laps of 2.35 mile/3.78 km (190.35 miles/306.18kms)
Fastest lap: Mansell, 1min 18.2sec, 108.12mph/173.97kph
Pole position: Senna(BRA), McLaren-Honda,1min 15.70sec 26 starters, 13 class. finishers

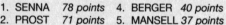

DRIVERS' WORLD CHAMPIONSHIP 1990

1. SENNA	*78 points*	4. BERGER	*40 points*
2. PROST	*71 points*	5. MANSELL	*37 points*
3. PIQUET	*43 points*	6. BOUTSEN	*34 points*

CONSTRUCTORS' WORLD CHAMPIONSHIP 1990

1. MCLAREN-HONDA	*121 points*	4. WILLIAMS-RENAULT	*57 points*
2. FERRARI	*110 points*	5. TYRRELL-FORD	*16 points*
3. BENETTON-FORD	*71 points*	6. LOLA-LAMBORGHINI	*11 points*

1991 Little did anyone realise that the sport was about to witness the emergence of two future World Champions. One Schumacher M. made his Grand Prix debut for Eddie Jordan's fledgling team, and a shy Finn, Hakkinen M. joined Lotus. Both scored points in their first year. and Jordan finished fifth in the Constructors' Championship. But it was the 'old order' who reigned, with Senna taking his third world title, and the 'unretired' Mansell pushing him hard. Jean Alesi's impressive 1990 performances, earned the French-born Sicilian a dream-drive alongside Prost at Ferrari. The season would prove difficult for the men from Maranello and triple World Champion Prost was eventually fired for airing his views! Quite simply, the Prancing Horse had lost its competitive edge. Triple Drivers' Champion, Piquet,had one win for Benetton in Canada but abdicated when Schumacher joined the team. Without a competitive seat at the end of the season, the Brazilian would look to the USA for 1992, with disastrous results. He, like Patrese, had competed in 200 Grands Prix. Phoenix was the last US Grand Prix on the calendar to date. There were 16 Grands Prix. All races counted for the Championship. Points: 10-6-4-3-2-1, for the first time for the Drivers' title. Top six cars scored for Constructors'.

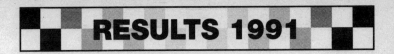

RESULTS 1991

ROUND 1/US GRAND PRIX
PHOENIX, 10 MARCH

1. SENNA(BRA)	MCLAREN-HONDA	2HR 00MIN 47.63SEC
2. PROST(FRA)	FERRARI	2HR 01MIN 04.15SEC
3. PIQUET(BRA)	BENETTON-FORD	2HR 01MIN 05.20SEC
4. MODENA(ITA)	TYRRELL-FORD	81 LAPS
5. NAKAJIMA(JAP)	TYRRELL-FORD	80 LAPS
6. SUZUKI(JAP)	LOLA-FORD	79 LAPS

Race: 81 laps of 2.32mile/3.72km (187.92 miles/301.32kms)
Fastest lap: Alesi(FRA), Ferrari,1min 36.76sec,95.94mph/154.4kph
Pole position: Senna, 1min 21.43sec 26 starters, 12 classified finishers

ROUND 2/BRAZILIAN GRAND PRIX
INTERLAGOS, 24 MARCH

1. SENNA(BRA)	MCLAREN-HONDA	1HR 38MIN 28.13SEC
2. PATRESE(ITA)	WILLIAMS-RENAULT	1HR 38MIN 31.12SEC
3. BERGER(AUT)	MCLAREN-HONDA	1HR 38MIN 33.54SEC
4. PROST(FRA)	FERRARI	1HR 38MIN 47.50MIN
5. PIQUET(BRA)	BENETTON-FORD	1HR 38MIN 50.09SEC
6. ALESI(FRA)	FERRARI	1HR 38MIN 51.77SEC

Race: 71 laps of 2.69 mile/ 4.33km (190.99 miles/307.43kms)
Fastest lap: Mansell(GB), Williams-Ford,1min 20.44sec, 120.28mph/193.65kph
Pole position: Senna, 1min 16.40sec 25 starters, 13 classified finishers

ROUND 3/SAN MARINO GRAND PRIX
IMOLA, 28 APRIL

1. SENNA(BRA)	MCLAREN-HONDA	1HR 35MIN 14.75SEC
2. BERGER(AUT)	MCLAREN-HONDA	1HR 35MIN 16.43SEC
3. LEHTO(FIN)	DALLARA-JUDD	60 LAPS
4. MARTINI(ITA)	MINARDI-FERRARI	59 LAPS
5. HAKKINEN(FIN)	LOTUS-JUDD	58 LAPS
6. BAILEY(GB)	LOTUS-JUDD	58 LAPS

Race: 61 laps of 3.13 mile/5.04 km (190.93 miles/307.44miles)
Fastest lap: Berger, 1min 26.53sec, 130.29mph/209.77kph
Pole position: Senna, 1min 21.88sec 25* starters, 13 classified finishers
*Prost spun on warm-up lap and did not start

ROUND 4/MONACO GRAND PRIX
MONTE CARLO, 12 MAY

1. SENNA(BRA)	MCLAREN-HONDA	1HR 53MIN 02.34SEC
2. MANSELL(GB)	WILLIAMS-RENAULT	1HR 53MIN 20.68SEC
3. ALESI(FRA)	FERRARI	1HR 53MIN 49.79SEC
4. MORENO(BRA)	BENETTON-FORD	77 LAPS
5. PROST(FRA)	FERRARI	77 LAPS
6. PIRRO(ITA)	DALLARA-JUDD	77 LAPS

Race: 78 laps of 2.07mile/3.33km (161.46 miles/259.74 kms)
Fastest lap: Prost, 1min 24.37sec,88.24mph/142.07kph
Pole position: Senna, 1min 20.34sec 26 starters, 12 classified finishers

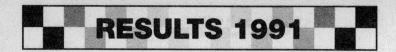

RESULTS 1991

ROUND 5/CANADIAN GRAND PRIX
MONTREAL, 2 JUNE

1. PIQUET(BRA)	BENETTON-FORD	1HR 38MIN 51.49SEC
2. MODENA(ITA)	TYRRELL-FORD	1HR 39MIN 23.32SEC
3. PATRESE(ITA)	WILLIAMS-RENAULT	1HR 39MIN 33.71SEC
4. DE CESARIS(ITA)	JORDAN-FORD	1HR 40MIN 11.70SEC
5. GACHOT (BEL)	JORDAN-FORD	1HR 40MIN 13.84SEC
6. MANSELL(GB)	WILLIAMS-RENAULT	68 LAPS

Race: 69 laps of 2.75mile/4.43km (189.75 miles/305.67 kms)
Fastest lap: Mansell, 1min 22min 39sec, 120.28mph/193.65kph
Pole position: Patrese, 1min 19.84sec 26 starters, 10 classified finishers

ROUND 6/MEXICAN GRAND PRIX
MEXICO CITY, 16 JUNE

1.PATRESE(ITA)	WILLIAMS-RENAULT	1HR 29MIN 23.32SEC
2.MANSELL(GB)	WILLIAMS-RENAULT	1HR 29MIN 53.54SEC
3.SENNA(BRA)	MCLAREN-HONDA	1HR 30MIN 49.56SEC
4.DE CESARIS(ITA)	JORDAN-FORD	66 LAPS
5.MORENO(BRA)	BENETTON-FORD	66 LAPS
6.BERNARD(FRA)	LOLA-FORD	66 LAPS

Race: 67 laps of 2.75 mile/4.42 km (184.25 miles/296.14 kms)
Fastest lap: Mansell 1min 16.79sec, 128.79mph/207.35kph
Pole position: Patrese, 1min 16.70sec 26 starters, 12 classified finishers

ROUND 7/FRENCH GRAND PRIX
SILVERSTONE, 14 JULY

1. MANSELL(GB)	WILLIAMS-RENAULT	1HR 38MIN 00.56SEC
2. PROST (FRA)	FERRARI	1HR 38MIN 05.59SEC
3. SENNA(BRA)	MCLAREN-FORD	1HR 38MIN 34.99SEC
4. ALESI(FRA)	FERRARI	1HR 38MIN 35.98SEC
5. PATRESE(ITA)	WILLIAMS-RENAULT	71 LAPS
6. DE CESARIS (ITA)	JORDAN-FORD	71 LAPS

Race: 72 laps of 2.65mile/4.27km (190.8 miles/307.44kms)
Fastest lap: Mansell, 1min 19.17sec,120.68mph/195.10kph
Pole position: Patrese, 1min 14.56sec 26 starters, 12 classified finishers

ROUND 8/BRITISH GRAND PRIX
SILVERSTONE, 14 JULY

1. MANSELL(GB)	WILLIAMS-RENAULT	1HR 27MIN 35.48SEC
2. BERGER(AUT)	MCLAREN-HONDA	1HR 28MIN 17.77SEC
3. PROST(FRA)	FERRARI	1HR 28MIN 35.63SEC
4. SENNA(BRA)	MCLAREN-HONDA	58 LAPS
5. PIQUET(BRA)	BENETTON-FORD	58 LAPS
6. GACHOT(BEL)	JORDAN-FORD	58 LAPS

Race: 59 laps of 3.25 mile/5.23km (191.75 miles/308.57 kms)
Fastest lap: Mansell, 1min 26.38sec,135.25 mph/217.75 kph
Pole position: Mansell, 1min 20.94sec 25 starters, 14 classified finishers

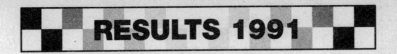

RESULTS 1991

ROUND 9/GERMAN GRAND PRIX
HOCKENHEIM, 28 JULY

1. MANSELL(GB)	WILLIAMS-RENAULT	1HR 19MIN 29.66SEC
2. PATRESE(ITA)	WILLIAMS-RENAULT	1HR 19MIN 43.44SEC
3. ALESI(FRA)	FERRARI	1HR 19MIN 47.28SEC
4. BERGER(AUT)	MCLAREN-HONDA	1HR 20MIN 02.31SEC
5. DE CESARIS(ITA)	JORDAN-FORD	1HR 20MIN 47.20SEC
6. GACHOT (BEL)	JORDAN-FORD	1HR 21MIN 10.23SEC

Race: 45 laps of 4.22 mile/6.8km (189.9 miles/ 306 kms)
Fastest lap: Patrese, 1min 43.57sec, 146.91mph/236.52kph
Pole position: Mansell,1min 37.09sec 26 starters, 13 classified finishers

ROUND 11/HUNGARIAN GRAND PRIX
HUNGARORING, 11 AUGUST

1. SENNA(BRA)	MCLAREN-HONDA	1HR 49MIN 12.80SEC
2. MANSELL(GB)	WILLIAMS-RENAULT	1HR 49MIN 39.50SEC
3. PATRESE(ITA)	WILLIAMS-RENAULT	1HR 49MIN 28.39SEC
4. BERGER(AUT)	MCLAREN-HONDA	1HR 49MIN 34.65SEC
5. ALESI(FRA)	FERRARI	1HR 49MIN 44.19SEC
6. CAPELLI(ITA)	LEYTON HOUSE-ILMOR	76 LAPS

Race: 77 laps of 2.47 mile/3.97 km (190.19 miles/305.69 kms)
Fastest lap: Gachot(BEL), Jordan-Ford, 1min 21.55sec, 108.85mph/174.81kph
Pole position: Senna, 1min 16.15sec 26 starters, 17 classified finishers

ROUND 11/BELGIAN GRAND PRIX
SPA-FRANCORCHAMPS, 25,AUGUST

1. SENNA(BRA)	MCLAREN-HONDA	1HR 27MIN 17.67SEC
2. BERGER(AUT)	MCLAREN-HONDA	1HR 27MIN 19.57SEC
3. PIQUET(BRA)	BENETTON-FORD	1HR 27IN 49.85SEC
4. MORENO(BRA)	BENETTON-FORD	1HR 27MIN 54.99SEC
5. PATRESE(ITA)	WILLIAMS-RENAULT	1HR 28MIN 14.86SEC
6. BLUNDELL(GB)	BRABHAM-YAMAHA	1HR 28MIN 57.70SEC

Race: 44 laps of 4.31 mile/6.94km (189.64 miles/305.36 kms)
Fastest lap: Moreno,1min 55.16sec, 134.81mph/217.08kph
Pole position: Senna, 1min 47.81sec. 26 starters, 13 classified finishers

ROUND 12/ITALIAN GRAND PRIX
MONZA, 8 SEPTEMBER

1. MANSELL(GB)	WILLIAMS-RENAULT	1HR 17MIN 54.32SEC
2. SENNA(BRA)	MCLAREN-HONDA	1HR 18MIN 10.58SEC
3. PROST(FRA)	FERRARI	1HR 18MIN 11.15SEC
4. BERGER(AUT)	MCLAREN-HONDA	1HR 18MIN 22.04SEC
5. M. SCHUMACHER(GER)	BENETTON-FORD	1HR 18MIN 28.78SEC
6. PIQUET(BRA)	BENETTON-FORD	1HR 18MIN 39.92SEC

Race: 52 laps of 3.6 mile/5.8 km (187.2 miles/301.6 kms)
Fastest lap: Senna, 1min 26.06sec, 150.76mph/242.72kph
Pole position: Senna, 1min 21.11sec 26 starters, 16 classified finishers

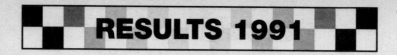

RESULTS 1991

ROUND 13/PORTUGUESE GRAND PRIX

ESTORIL, 22 SEPTEMBER

1. PATRESE(ITA)	WILLIAMS-RENAULT	1HR 35MIN 42.30SEC
2. SENNA(BRA)	MCLAREN-HONDA	1HR 36MIN 03.25SEC
3. ALESI(FRA)	FERRARI	1HR 36MIN 35.86SEC
4. MARTINI(ITA)	MINARDI-FERRARI	1HR 36MIN 45.80SEC
5. PIQUET(BRA)	BENETTON-FORD	1HR 36MIN 52.34SEC
6. M.SCHUMACHER(GER)	BENETTON-FORD	1HR 36MIN 58.89SEC

Race: 71 laps of 2.7 mile/4.35 km (191.7 miles/308.85kms)
Fastest lap: Mansell(GB), Williams-Renault,1min 18.18sec, 124.33mph/200.17kph
Pole position: Patrese, 1min 13.00sec 26 starters, 17 classified finishers

ROUND 14/SPANISH GRAND PRIX

BARCELONA, 29 SEPTEMBER

1. MANSELL(GB)	WILLIAMS-RENAULT	1HR 38MIN 41.54SEC
2. PROST(FRA)	FERRARI	1HR 38MIN 52.87SEC
3. PATRESE(ITA)	WILLIAMS-RENAULT	1HR 38MIN 57.45SEC
4. ALESI(FRA)	FERRARI	1HR 39MIN 04.31SEC
5. SENNA(BRA)	MCLAREN-HONDA	1HR 39MIN 43.94SEC
6. M. SCHUMACHER(GER)	BENETTON-FORD	1HR 40MIN 01.01SEC

Race: 65 laps of 2.95 mile/4.66 km (191.75 miles/302.9 kms)
Fastest lap: Patrese, 1min 22.84sec, 128.19mph/206.39 kph
Pole position: Berger(AUT) McLaren-Honda, 1min 18.75sec 26 starters, 17 class. finishers

ROUND 15/JAPANESE GRAND PRIX

SUZUKA, 20 OCTOBER

1. BERGER(AUT)	MCLAREN-HONDA	1HR 32MIN 10.70SEC
2. SENNA(BRA)	MCLAREN-HONDA	1HR 32MIN 11.04SEC
3. PATRESE(ITA)	WILLIAMS-RENAULT	1HR 33MIN 07.43SEC
4. PROST(FRA)	FERRARI	1HR 33MIN 31.46SEC
5. BRUNDLE(GB)	BRABHAM-YAMAHA	52 LAPS
6. MODENA(ITA)	TYRRELL-HONDA	52 LAPS

Race: 53 laps of 3.64 mile/5.86 km (192.92 miles/310.58kms)
Fastest lap: Senna, 1min 41.53sec, 129.20mph/208.00kph
Pole position: Berger, 1min 34.70sec 26 starters, 11 classified finishers

ROUND 16/AUSTRALIAN GRAND PRIX

ADELAIDE, 3 NOVEMBER

1. SENNA(BRA)	MCLAREN-HONDA	24MIN 34.89SEC
2. MANSELL(GB)	WILLIAMS-RENAULT	24MIN 36.16SEC
3. BERGER(AUT)	MCLAREN-HONDA	24MIN 40.02SEC
4. PIQUET(BRA)	BENETTON-FORD	25MIN 05.00SEC
5. PATRESE(ITA)	WILLIAMS-RENAULT	25MIN 25.44SEC
6. MORBIDELLI(ITA)	FERRARI	25MIN 25.97SEC

Race: 14* laps of 2.35 mile/3.78 km (32.9miles/52.92kms)
Fastest lap: Berger, 1min 41.14sec, 83.60mph/134.55kph
Pole position: Senna, 1min 14.04sec 26 starters, 20 classified finishers
*Race halted due to torrential rain. Half points to top six.

RESULTS 1991/2

DRIVERS' WORLD CHAMPIONSHIP 1991

1. SENNA	96 points	4. BERGER	43 points
2. MANSELL	72 points	5. PROST	34 points
3. PATRESE	53 points	6. PIQUET	26.5 points

CONSTRUCTORS' WORLD CHAMPIONSHIP 1991

1. MCLAREN-HONDA	139 points	4. BENETTON-FORD	38.5 points
2. WILLIAMS-RENAULT	125 points	5. JORDAN-FORD	13 points
3. FERRARI	56.5 points	6. TYRRELL-FORD	12 points

1992 This was the year that the Brummie finally burst the bubble of his detractors' criticism. With nine wins in 16 races, Mansell and Williams ruled the roost. Prost, licking his political wounds, took a sabatical. Schumacher, M. won his first Grand Prix, at Spa and finished third in the Drivers' Championship, ahead of one Senna, A! Some famous names returned to the entry lists. Hill, Damon, son of Graham, struggled to qualify the wieldy Brabham Judd. Fittipaldi, Christian, nephew of Emerson, had better luck with Minardi and claimed a sixth place in Japan. His team-mate was a chap called Zanardi - of whom more later...
Giovanna Amati was an attractive addition to the pit land in her early attempts to qualify a Brabham - but to no avail. The sport lost one of its most colourful former Champions, when Denny Hulme suffered a major heart attack at the wheel during the Bathurst 1000 Kms. The circus returned to South Africa for the first time since 1985 - to a sanitised Kyalami. Mansell won there for Williams in '85 and he did again in '92 to kick-start his year. All rounds counted for the Championships. Points: 10-6-4-3-2-1.

ROUND 1/SOUTH AFRICAN GRAND PRIX
KYALAMI, 1 MARCH

1. MANSELL(GB)	WILLIAMS-RENAULT	1HR 36MIN 45.32SEC
2. PATRESE(ITA)	WILLIAMS-RENAULT	1HR 37MIN 09.68SEC
3. SENNA(BRA)	MCLAREN-HONDA	1HR 37MIN 20.00SEC
4. M.SCHUMACHER(GER)	BENETTON-FORD	1HR 37MIN 33.18SEC
5. BERGER(AUT)	MCLAREN-HONDA	1HR 37MIN 58.95SEC
6. HERBERT(GB)	LOTUS-FORD	71 LAPS

Race: 72 laps of 2.66 mile/4.28 km (191.52 miles/308.16kms)
Fastest lap: Mansell, 1min 17.58sec,123.58mph/198.57kph
Pole position: Mansell, 1min 15.49sec 26 starters, 13 classified finishers

411

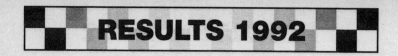

RESULTS 1992

ROUND 2/MEXICAN GRAND PRIX
MEXICO CITY, 22 MARCH

1. MANSELL(GB)	WILLIAMS-RENAULT	1HR 31MIN 53.59SEC
2. PATRESE(ITA)	WILLIAMS-RENAULT	1HR 32MIN 06.56SEC
3. M.SCHUMACHER(GER)	BENETTON-FORD	1HR 32MIN 15.02SEC
4. BERGER(AUT)	MCLAREN-HONDA	1HR 32MIN 26.93SEC
5. DE CESARIS(ITA)	TYRRELL-ILMOR	68 LAPS
6. HAKKINEN(FIN)	LOTUS-FORD	68 LAPS

Race: 69 laps of 2.75 mile/4.42 km (189.75 miles/304.98kms)
Fastest lap: Berger, 1min 17.71sec, 127.26mph/204.76kph
Pole position: Mansell, 1min 16.35sec 26 starters, 13 classified finishers

ROUND 3/BRAZILIAN GRAND PRIX
INTERLAGOS, 5 APRIL

1. MANSELL(GB)	WILLIAMS-RENAULT	1HR 36MIN 51.86SEC
2. PATRESE(ITA)	WILLIAMS-RENAULT	1HR 37MIN 21.19SEC
3. M.SCHUMACHER(GER)	BENETTON-FORD	70 LAPS
4. ALESI(FRA)	FERRARI	70 LAPS
5. CAPELLI(ITA)	FERRARI	70 LAPS
6. ALBORETO(ITA)	FOOTWORK-MUGEN HONDA	70 LAPS

Race: 71 laps of 2.69 mile/4.33km (190.99 miles/307.43 kms)
Fastest lap: Patrese, 1min 19.49sec, 121.71mph/195.83kph
Pole position: Mansell, 1min 15.70sec 26 starters, 10 classified finishers

ROUND 4/SPANISH GRAND PRIX
BARCELONA, 3 MAY

1. MANSELL(GB)	WILLIAMS-RENAULT	1HR 56MIN 10.67SEC
2. M. SCHUMACHER(GER)	BENETTON-FORD	1HR 56MIN 34.59SEC
3. ALESI(FRA)	FERRARI	1HR 56MIN 37.14SEC
4. BERGER(AUT	MCLAREN-HONDA	1HR 57MIN 32.32SEC
5. ALBORETO(ITA)	FOOTWORK-MUGEN HONDA	64 LAPS
6. MARTINI(ITA)	DALLARA-FERRARI	63 LAPS

Race: 65 laps of 2.95 mile/ 4.66 km (191.75 miles/302.9kms)
Fastest lap: Mansell, 1min 42.50sec, 103.59mph/166.68kph
Pole position: Mansell: 1min 20.19sec 26 starters, 12 classified finishers

ROUND 5/SAN MARINO
MOLA,17 MAY

1. MANSELL(GB)	WILLIAMS-RENAULT	1HR 28MIN 40.93SEC
2. PATRESE(ITA)	WILLIAMS-RENAULT	1HR 28MIN 50.38SEC
3. SENNA(BRA)	MCLAREN-HONDA	1HR 29MIN 29.91SEC
4. BRUNDLE(GB)	BENETTON-FORD	1HR 29MIN 33.93SEC
5. ALBORETO(ITA)	FOOTWORK-MUGEN HONDA	59 LAPS
6. MARTINI(ITA)	DALLARA-FERRARI	59 LAPS

Race: 60 laps of 3.13mile/5.04km - 187.8 miles/312.4kms)
Fastest lap: Patrese, 1min 26.1sec, 130.94mph/210.69kph
Pole position: Mansell, 1min 21.84sec 26 starters, 14 classified finishers

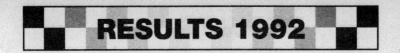
RESULTS 1992

ROUND 6/MONACO GRAND PRIX
MONTE CARLO, 31 MAY

1. SENNA(BRA)	MCLAREN-HONDA	1HR 50MIN 59.37SEC
2. MANSELL(GB)	WILLIAMS-RENAULT	1HR 50MIN 59.59SEC
3. PATRESE(ITA)	WILLIAMS-RENAULT	1HR 51MIN 31.22SEC
4. M.SCHUMACHER(GER)	BENETTON-FORD	1HR 51MIN 38.67SEC
5. BRUNDLE(GB)	BENETTON-FORD	1HR 52MIN 20.72SEC
6. GACHOT(BEL)	LARROUSSE-LAMBORGHINI	77 LAPS

Race: 78 laps of 2.07 mile/3.33km (161.46 miles/259.74kms)
Fastest lap: Mansell, 1min 21.6sec, 91.23mph/146.8kph
Pole position: Mansell, 1min 19.50sec 26 starters, 12 classified finishers

ROUND 7/CANADIAN GRAND PRIX
MONTREAL, 14 JUNE

1. BERGER(AUT)	MCLAREN-HONDA	1HR 37MIN 08.3SEC
2. M.SCHUMACHER(GER)	BENETTON-FORD	1HR 37MIN 20.7SEC
3. ALESI(FRA)	FERRARI	1HR 38MIN 15.63SEC
4. WENDLINGER(AUT)	MARCH-ILMOR	68 LAPS
5. DE CESARIS(ITA)	TYRRELL-ILMOR	68 LAPS
6. COMAS(FRA)	LIGIER-RENAULT	68 LAPS

Race: 69 laps of 2.75 mile/4.43km (189.75 miles/305.67kms)
Fastest lap: Berger, 1min 22.33sec, 120.37mph/193.68kph
Pole position: Senna(BRA) Mclaren-Honda, 1min 19.78sec 26 starters, 14 class. finishers

ROUND 8/FRENCH GRAND PRIX
MAGNY-COURS, 5 JULY

1. MANSELL(GB)	WILLIAMS-RENAULT	1HR 38MIN 08.46SEC
2. PATRESE(ITA)	WILLIAMS-RENAULT	1HR 38MIN 54.91SEC
3. BRUNDLE(GB)	BENETTON-FORD	1HR 39MIN 21.04SEC
4. HAKKINEN(FIN)	LOTUS-FORD	68 LAPS
5. COMAS(FRA)	LIGIER-RENAULT	68 LAPS
6. HERBERT(GB)	LOTUS-FORD	68 LAPS

Race: 69 laps of 2.65 mile/4.27 km (182.85miles/ 294.63 kms)
Fastest lap: Mansell, 1min 17.07sec, 123.36mph/198.49kph
Pole position: Mansell, 1min 13.86sec 26 starters, 11 classified finishers

ROUND 9/BRITISH GRAND PRIX
SILVERSTONE,12 JULY

1. MANSELL(GB)	WILLIAMS-RENAULT	1HR 25MIN 42.99SEC
2. PATRESE(ITA)	WILLIAMS-RENAULT	1HR 26MIN 22.09SEC
3. BRUNDLE(GB)	BENETTON-FORD	1HR 26MIN 32.39SEC
4. M.SCHUMACHER(GER)	BENETTON-FORD	1HR 26MIN 36.26SEC
5. BERGER(AUT)	MCLAREN-HONDA	1HR 26MIN 38.79SEC
6. HAKKINEN(FIN)	LOTUS-FORD	1HR 27MIN 03.13SEC

Race: 59 laps of 3.25 mile/5.23km (191.75 miles/308.57kms)
Fastest lap: Mansell, 1min 22.54sec, 141.63mph/227.88kph
Pole position: Mansell, 1min 18.96sec 26 starters, 17 classified finishers

RESULTS 1992

ROUND 10/GERMAN GRAND PRIX
HOCKENHEIM, 26 JULY

1. MANSELL(GB)	WILLIAMS-RENAULT	1HR 18MIN 22.03SEC
2. SENNA(BRA)	MCLAREN-HONDA	1HR 18MIN 26.53SEC
3. M.SCHUMACHER(GER)	BENETTON-FORD	1HR 18MIN 56.49SEC
4. BRUNDLE(GB)	BENETTON-FORD	1HR 18MIN 58.99SEC
5. ALESI(FRA)	FERRARI	1HR 19MIN 34.64SEC
6. COMAS (FRA)	LIGIER-RENAULT	1HR 19MIN 58.53SEC

Race: 45 laps of 4.24mile/6.82km (190.8miles/306.9kms)
Fastest lap: Patrese(ITA),Williams-Renault, 1min 41.59sec, 150.06mph/241.45kph
Pole position: Mansell, 1min 37.96sec 26 starters, 16 classified finishers

ROUND 11/HUNGARIAN GRAND PRIX
HUNGARORING, 16 AUGUST

1. SENNA(BRA)	MCLAREN-HONDA	1HR 46MIN 19.22SEC
2. MANSELL(GB)	WILLIAMS-RENAULT	1HR 46MIN 59.36SEC
3. BERGER(AUT)	MCLAREN-HONDA	1HR 47MIN 10.00SEC
4. HAKKINEN(FIN)	LOTUS-FORD	1HR 47MIN 13.53SEC
5. BRUNDLE(GB)	BENETTON-FORD	1HR 47MIN 16.71SEC
6. CAPELLI(ITA)	FERRARI	76 LAPS

Race: 77 laps of 2.47 mile/3.97km (190.19miles/305.69kms)
Fastest lap: Mansell, 1min 18.31sec, 113.35mph/182.38kph
Pole position: Patrese(ITA) Williams-Renault,1min 41.59sec 26 starters, 16 class. finishers

ROUND 12/BELGIAN GRAND PRIX
SPA-FRANCORCHAMPS, 30 AUGUST

1. M.SCHUMACHER(GER)	BENETTON-FORD	1HR 36MIN 10.72SEC
2. MANSELL(GB)	WILLIAMS-RENAULT	1HR 36MIN 47.32SEC
3. PATRESE (ITA)	WILLIAMS-RENAULT	1HR 36MIN 54.62SEC
4. BRUNDLE(GB)	BENETTON-FORD	1HR 36MIN 56.78SEC
5. SENNA(GB)	MCLAREN-HONDA	1HR 37MIN 19.09SEC
6. HAKKINEN(FIN)	LOTUS-FORD	1HR 37MIN 20.75SEC

Race: 44 laps of 4.33 mile/6.97km (190.52miles/ 306.68kms)
Fastest lap: Schumacher, 1min 53.79sec, 137.1mph/220.73kph
Pole position: 1min 50.55sec 26 starters, 18 classified finishers

ROUND 13/ITALIAN GRAND PRIX
MONZA, 13 SEPTEMBER

1. SENNA(BRA)	MCLAREN-HONDA	1HR 18MIN 15.35SEC
2. BRUNDLE(GB)	BENETTON-FORD	1HR 18MIN 32.40SEC
3. M. SHUMACHER(GER)	BENETTON-FORD	1HR 18MIN 39.72SEC
4. BERGER(AUT)	MCLAREN-HONDA	1HR 19MIN 40.84SEC
5. PATRESE(ITA)	WILLIAMS-RENAULT	1HR 19MIN 48.51SEC
6. DE CESARIS(ITA)	TYRRELL-ILMOR	52 LAPS

Race: 53 laps of 3.6mile/5.8km (190.8 miles/307.4kms)
*Fastest lap:*Mansell(GB)Williams-Renault, 1min 26.12sec,150.66mph/242.56kph
Pole position: Mansell, 1min 22.22sec 26 starters, 11 classified finishers

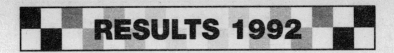

RESULTS 1992

ROUND 14/PORTUGUESE GRAND PRIX
ESTORIL, 27 SEPTEMBER

1. MANSELL(GB)	WILLIAMS-RENAULT	1HR 34MIN 46.66SEC
2. BERGER(AUT)	MCLAREN-HONDA	1HR 35MIN 24.19SEC
3. SENNA(GB)	MCLAREN-HONDA	70 LAPS
4. BRUNDLE(GB)	BENETTON-FORD	70 LAPS
5. HAKKINEN(FIN)	LOTUS-FORD	70 LAPS
6. ALBORETO(ITA)	FOOTWORK-MUGEN HONDA	70 LAPS

Race: 71 laps of 2.7mile/4.35km (191.7 miles/308.85kms)
Fastest lap: Mansell, 1min 18.18sec, 124.33mph/200.17kph
Pole position: Mansell, 1min 13.04sec 26 starters, 14 classified finishers

ROUND 15/JAPANESE GRAND PRIX
SUZUKA, 25 OCTOBER

1. PATRESE(ITA)	WILLIAMS-RENAULT	1HR 33MIN 09.55SEC
2. BERGER(AUT)	MCLAREN-HONDA	1HR 33MIN 23.28SEC
3. BRUNDLE(GB)	BENETTON-FORD	1HR 34MIN 25.06SEC
4. DE CESARIS(ITA)	TYRRELL-ILMOR	52 LAPS
5. ALESI (FRA)	FERRARI	52 LAPS
6. C. FITTIPALDI(BRA)	MINARDI-LAMBORGHINI	52 LAPS

Race: 53 laps of 3.64mile/5.86km (192.92 miles/310.58kms)
Fastest lap: Mansell(GB), Williams-Renault, 1min 40.65sec, 130.33mph/209.83kph
Pole position: Mansell, 1min 37.36sec 26 starters, 15 classified finishers

ROUND 16/AUSTRALIAN GRAND PRIX
ADELAIDE, 8 NOVEMBER

1. BERGER(AUT)	MCLAREN-HONDA	1HR 46MIN 54.79SEC
2. M. SCHUMACHER(GER)	BENETTON-FORD	1HR 46MIN 55.53SEC
3. BRUNDLE(GB)	BENETTON-FORD	1HR 47MIN 48.94SEC
4. ALESI(FRA)	FERRARI	80 LAPS
5. BOUTSEN(BEL)	LIGIER-RENAULT	80 LAPS
6. MODENA(ITA)	JORDAN-YAMAHA	80 LAPS

Race: 81 laps of 2.35mile/3.78km (190.35 miles/306.18kms)
Fastest lap: Schumacher, 1min 16.08sec, 111.14mph/178.83kph
Pole position: Mansell(GB), Williams-Renault, 1min 13.73sec 26 starters, 13 classified finishers

---

 DRIVERS' WORLD CHAMPIONSHIP 1992

1. MANSELL *108 points* 4. SENNA *50 points*
2. PATRESE *56 points* 5. BERGER *49 points*
3. M.SCHUMACHER *53* 6. BRUNDLE *38 points*

RESULTS 1992/3

1993 Mansell headed for more glory in the States and Prost slotted into the vacancy at Williams. The 'Professor' claimed seven victories and his fourth World Drivers' Championship. Damon Hill was elevated from test driver to the second Williams - and won three races. Michael Andretti (son of the legendary, 1978 World Champion, Mario) joined McLaren but had a nightmare season and returned to the USA for keeps before the end of the year. Honda opted out of Formula 1, so McLaren turned to Ford for its power units. Senna wrang the neck of the car to claim five victories and runner-up spot but Williams cruised to yet another Constructors' Championship with ease. The sport was shocked to learn of the sudden death of James Hunt from a massive heart attack at the age of 45. Grand Prix racing returned to Donington Park, Britain's first ever road racing circuit. There were 16 rounds. All results counted. Points: 10-6-4-3-2-1.

ROUND 1/SOUTH AFRICAN GRAND PRIX
KYALAMI, 14 MARCH

1. PROST(FRA)	WILLIAMS-RENAULT	1HR 38MIN 45.08SEC
2. SENNA(BRA)	MCLAREN-FORD	1HR 40MIN 04.91SEC
3. BLUNDELL(GB)	LIGIER-RENAULT	71 LAPS
4. C.FITTIPALDI(BRA)	MINARDI-FORD	71 LAPS
5. LEHTO(FIN)	SAUBER-ILMOR	70 LAPS
6. BERGER(AUT)	FERRARI	69 LAPS

Race: 72 laps of 2.65mile/4.26km (190.8 miles/306.72kms)
Fastest lap: Prost, 1min 19.49sec, 119.91mph/192.97kph
Pole position: Prost, 1min 15.70sec 26 starters, 7 classified finishers

ROUND 2/BRAZILIAN GRAND PRIX
INTERLAGOS, 28 MARCH

1. SENNA(BRA)	MCLAREN-FORD	1HR 51MIN 15.5 SEC
2. D. HILL(GB)	WILLIAMS-RENAULT	1HR 51MIN 32.1SEC
3. M. SCHUMACHER(GER)	BENETTON-FORD	1HR 52MIN 00.9SEC
4. HERBERT(GB)	LOTUS-FORD	1HR 52MIN 02.0SEC
5. BLUNDELL(GB)	LIGIER-RENAULT	1HR 52MIN 07.6SEC
6. ZANARDI(ITA)	LOTUS-FORD	70 LAPS

Race: 71 laps of 2.69 mile/4.33km (190.99 miles/307.43kms)
Fastest lap: Prost(FRA),Williams-Renault, 1min 15.67sec,125.92mph/202.65kph
Pole position: Prost, 1min 15.87sec 25 starters, 12 classified finishers

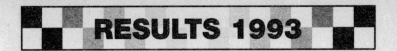
RESULTS 1993

ROUND3/EUROPEAN GRAND PRIX
DONINGTON PARK, 11 APRIL

1. SENNA(BRA)	MCLAREN-FORD	1HR 50MIN 46.6SEC
2. D. HILL(GB)	WILLIAMS-RENAULT	1HR 52MIN 09.8SEC
3. PROST(FRA)	WILLIAMS-RENAULT	75 LAPS
4. HERBERT(GB)	LOTUS-FORD	75 LAPS
5. PATRESE(ITA)	BENETTON-FORD	74 LAPS
6. BARBAZZA(ITA0	MINARDI-FORD	74 LAPS

Race: 76 laps of 2.5 mile/4.02km (190 miles/305.52kms)
Fastest lap: Senna, 1min 18.03sec, 115.33mph/185.61kph
Pole position: Prost 1min 10.46sec 25 starters, 11 classified finishers

ROUND 4/SAN MARINO GRAND PRIX
IMOLA, 25 APRIL

1. PROST(FRA)	WILLIAMS-RENAULT	1HR 33MIN 20.4SEC
2. M.SCHUMACHER(GER)	BENETTON-FORD	1HR 33MIN 52.8SEC
3. BRUNDLE(GB)	LIGIER-RENAULT	60 LAPS
4. LEHTO(FIN)	SAUBER-ILMOR	59 LAPS
5. ALLIOT(FRA)	LAROUSSE-LAMBORGHINI	59 LAPS
6. BARBAZZA(ITA)	MINARDI-FORD	59 LAPS

Race: 61 laps of 3.13mile/5.04km (190.93miles/307.44kms)
Fastest lap: Prost, 1min 26.13sec, 130.9mph/210.1kph
Pole position: Prost, 1min 22.07sec 25 starters, 9 classified finishers

ROUND 5/SPANISH GRAND PRIX
BARCELONA, 9 MAY

1. PROST(FRA)	WILLIAMS-RENAULT	1HR 32MIN 27.7SEC
2. SENNA(BRA)	MCLAREN-FORD	1HR 32MIN 44.6SEC
3. M. SCHUMACHER(GER)	BENETTON-FORD	1HR 32MIN 54.8SEC
4. PATRESE(ITA)	BENETTON-FORD	64 LAPS
5. ANDRETTI(USA)	MCLAREN-FORD	64 LAPS
6. BERGER(AUT)	FERRARI	63 LAPS

Race: 65 laps of 2.95mile/4.75km (191.75miles/302.9kms)
Fastest lap: M.Schumacher, 1min 20.99sec, 131.11mph/211.01kph
Pole position: Prost, 1min 17.81sec 25 starters, 14 classified finishers

ROUND 6/MONACO GRAND PRIX
MONTE CARLO, 23 MAY

1. SENNA(BRA)	MCLAREN-FORD	1HR 52MIN 11.0SEC
2. D.HILL(GB)	WILLIAMS-RENAULT	1HR 53MIN 03.1SEC
3. ALESI(FRA)	FERRARI	1HR 53MIN 14.3SEC
4. PROST(FRA)	WILLIAMS-RENAULT	77 LAPS
5. C.FITTIPALDI(BRA)	MINARDI-FORD	76 LAPS
6. BRUNDLE(GB)	LIGIER-RENAULT	76 LAPS

Race: 78 laps of 2.07mile/3.33km (161.46 miles/259.74kms)
Fastest lap: Prost, 1min 23.6sec, 89.05mph/143.3kph
Pole position: Prost, 1min 20.56sec 25 starters, 14 classified finishers

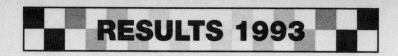

RESULTS 1993

ROUND 7/CANADIAN GRAND PRIX
MONTREAL, 13 JUNE

1. PROST(FRA)	WILLIAMS-RENAULT	1HR 36MIN 41.8SEC
2. M.SCHUMACHER(GER)	BENETTON-FORD	1HR 36MIN 56.4SEC
3. D.HILL(GB)	WILLIAMS-RENAULT	1HR 37MIN 34.5SEC
4. BERGER(AUT)	FERRARI	68 LAPS
5. BRUNDLE(GB)	LIGIER-RENAULT	68 LAPS
6. WENDLINGER(AUT)	SAUBER-ILMOR	68 LAPS

Race: 69 laps of 2.75mile/4.43km (189.75 miles/305.67 kms)
Fastest lap: M.Schumacher, 1min 21.5sec, 121.59mph/195.68kph
Pole position: Prost, 1min 18.99sec 25 starters, 18 classified finishers

ROUND 8/FRENCH GRAND PRIX
MAGNY- COURS, 4 JULY

1. PROST(FRA)	WILLIAMS-RENAULT	1HR 38MIN 35.24SEC
2. D.HILL(GB)	WILLIAMS-RENAULT	1HR 38MIN 35.58SEC
3. M.SCHUMACHER(GER)	BENETTON-FORD	1HR 38MIN 56.5SEC
4. SENNA(BRA)	MCLAREN-FORD	1HR 39MIN 07.7SEC
5. BRUNDLE(GB)	LIGIER-RENAULT	1HR 39MIN 09.0SEC
6. ANDRETTI(USA)	MCLAREN-FORD	71 LAPS

Race: 72 laps of 2.64 mile/4.25km (190.08 miles/306 kms)
Fastest lap: M. Schumacher, 1min 29.26sec, 119.95mph/193.05kph
Pole position: D.Hill, 1min 14.38sec 25 starters, 16 classified finishers

ROUND 9/BRITISH GRAND PRIX
SILVERSTONE, 11 JULY

1. PROST(FRA)	WILLIAMS-RENAULT	1HR 25MIN 38.2SEC
2. M.SCHUMACHER(GER)	BENETTON-FORD	1HR 25MIN 45.9SEC
3. PATRESE(ITA)	BENETTON-FORD	1HR 26MIN 55.7SEC
4. HERBERT(GB)	LOTUS-FORD	1HR 26MIN 56.6SEC
5. SENNA(BRA)	MCLAREN-FORD	58 LAPS
6. WARWICK(GB)	FOOTWORK-MUGEN HONDA	58 LAPS

Race: 59 laps of 3.25 mile/5.23km (191.75miles/308.57kms)
Fastest lap: D. Hill, Williams-Renault, 1min 22.52sec, 141.67mph/228.0kph
Pole position: Prost, 1min 19.00sec 25 starters, 14 classified finishers

ROUND 10/GERMAN GRAND PRIX
HOCKENHEIM, 25 JULY

1. PROST(FRA)	WILLIAMS-RENAULT	1HR 18MIN 40.9SEC
2. M.SCHUMACHER(GER)	BENETTON-FORD	1HR 18MIN 57.6SEC
3. BLUNDELL(GB)	LIGIER-RENAULT	1HR 19MIN 40.2SEC
4. SENNA(BRA)	MCLAREN-FORD	1HR 19MIN 49.1SEC
5. PATRESE(ITA)	BENETTON-FORD	1HR 20MIN 12.4SEC
6. BERGER(AUT)	FERRARI	1HR 20MIN 15.6SEC

Race: 45 laps of 4.24mile/6.82km (190.8 miles/306.9kms)
Fastest lap: M.Schumacher, 1min 41.86sec, 149.67mph/240.86kph
Pole position: Prost,1min 38.75sec 26 starters, 17 classified finishers

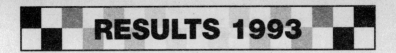

RESULTS 1993

ROUND 11/HUNGARIAN GRAND PRIX
HUNGARORING, 15 AUGUST

1. D.HILL(GB)	WILLIAMS-RENAULT	1HR 47MIN 39.1SEC
2. PATRESE(ITA)	BENETTON-FORD	1HR 48MIN 51.0SEC
3. BERGER(AUT)	FERRARI	1HR 48MIN 57.1SEC
4. WARWICK(GB)	FOOTWORK-MUGEN HONDA	76 LAPS
5. BRUNDLE(GB)	LIGIER-RENAULT	76 LAPS
6. WENDLINGER(AUT)	SAUBER-ILMOR	76 LAPS

Race: 77 laps of 2.47mile/3.97km (190.19 miles/305.69kms)
Fastest lap: Prost(FRA), Williams-Renault, 1min 16.93sec,11.46mph/179.38kph
Pole position: Prost, 1min 14.63sec 26 starters, 12 classified finishers

ROUND 12/BELGIAN GRAND PRIX
SPA-FRANCORCHAMPS, 29 AUGUST

1. D. HILL(GB)	WILLIAMS-RENAULT	1HR 24MIN 32.1SEC
2. M. SCHUMACHER(GER)	BENETTON-FORD	1HR 24MIN 35.8SEC
3. PROST(FRA)	WILLIAMS-RENAULT	1HR 24MIN 47.1SEC
4. SENNA(BRA)	MCLAREN-FORD	1HR 26MIN 11.9SEC
5. HERBERT(GB)	LOTUS-FORD	43 LAPS
6. PATRESE(ITA)	BENETTON-FORD	43 LAPS

Race: 44 laps of 4.33 mile/6.97km (190.52 miles/306.68 kms)
Fastest lap: Prost, 1min 51.1sec, 140.42mph/226.0kph
Pole position: Prost, 1min 47.57sec 25 starters, 15 classified finishers

ROUND 13/ITALIAN GRAND PRIX
MONZA, 12 SEPTEMBER

1. D. HILL(GB)	WILLIAMS-RENAULT	1HR 17MIN 07.5SEC
2. ALESI(FRA)	FERRARI	1HR 17MIN 47.5SEC
3. ANDRETTI(USA)	MCLAREN-FORD	52 LAPS
4. WENDLINGER(AUT)	SAUBER-ILMOR	52 LAPS
5. PATRRESE(ITA)	BENETTON-FORD	52 LAPS
6. COMAS(FRA)	LARROUSSE-LAMBORGHINI	51 LAPS

Race: 53 laps of 3.6 mile/5.8 km (190.8 miles/ 307.4kms)
Fastest lap: Hill, 1min 23.58sec, 159.82mph/257.21kph
Pole position: Prost(FRA) Williams-Renault, 1min 21.18sec 26 starters, 14 classified
finishers

ROUND 14/PORTUGUESE GRAND PRIX
ESTORIL, 26 SEPTEMBER

1. M.SCHUMACHER(GER)	BENETTON-FORD	1HR 32MIN 46.3SEC
2. PROST(FRA)	WILLIAMS-RENAULT	1HR 32MIN 47.3SEC
3. D.HILL(GB)	WILLIAMS-RENAULT	1HR 32MIN 54.5SEC
4. ALESI(FRA)	FERRARI	1HR 33MIN 53.9SEC
5. WENDLINGER(AUT)	SAUBER-ILMOR	70 LAPS
6. BRUNDLE(GB)	LIGIER-RENAULT	70 LAPS

Race: 71 laps of 2.7mile/4.35km (191.7 miles/308.5kms)
Fastest lap: Hill, 1min 14.86sec, 129.99mph/209.19kph
Pole position: Hill, 1min 11.49sec 26 starters, 16 classified finishers

RESULTS 1993/4

ROUND 15/JAPANESE GRAND PRIX
SUZUKA, 24 OCTOBER

1. SENNA(BRA)	MCLAREN-FORD	1HR 40MIN 27.9SEC
2. PROST(FRA)	WILLIAMS-RENAULT	1HR 40MIN 39.4SEC
3. HAKKINEN(FIN)	MCLAREN-FORD	1HR 40MIN 54.0SEC
4. D.HILL(GB)	WILLIAMS-RENAULT	1HR 41MIN 51.5SEC
5. BARRICHELLO(BRA)	JORDAN-HART	1HR 42MIN 0.01SEC
6. IRVINE(GB)	JORDAN-HART	1HR 42MIN 14.3SEC

Race: 53 laps of 3.64 mile/5.86km (192.92 miles/310.58kms)
Fastest lap: Prost, 1min 41,18sec, 129.65mph/208.65kph
Pole position: Prost, 1min 37.15sec 24 starters, 14 classified finishers

ROUND 16/AUSTRALIAN GRAND PRIX
ADELAIDE, 7 NOVEMBER

1. SENNA(BRA)	MCLAREN-FORD	1HR 43MIN 27.5SEC
2. PROST(FRA)	WILLIAMS-RENAULT	1HR 43MIN 36.7SEC
3. D.HILL(GB)	WILLIAMS-RENAULT	1HR 44MIN 01.4SEC
4. ALESI(FRA)	FERRARI	78 LAPS
5. BERGER(AUT)	FERRARI	78 LAPS
6. BRUNDLE(GB)	LIGIER-RENAULT	78 LAPS

Race: 79 laps of 2.35 mile/3.78 km (185.65 miles/298.62kms)
Fastest lap: Hill, 1min 15.38sec, 112.17mph/180.52kph
Pole position: Senna, 1min 13.37sec 24 starters, 15 classified finishers

DRIVERS' WORLD CHAMPIONSHIP 1993

1. PROST	*99 points*	4. M.SCHUMACHER	*52*
2. SENNA	*73 points*	5. PATRESE	*20 points*
3. D. HILL	*69 points*	6. ALESI	*16 points*

CONSTRUCTORS' WORLD CHAMPIONSHIP 1993

1. WILLIAMS-RENAULT	*168 points*	4. FERRARI	*28 points*
2. MCLAREN-FORD	*84 points*	5. LIGIER-RENAULT	*23 points*
3. BENETTON-FORD	*72 points*	6. LOTUS-FORD, SAUBER ILMOR *12*	

1994 Imola. The name will ever recall the tragedy of the 1994 San Marino Grand Prix weekend. It was the weekend in which the great Brazilian, Ayrton Senna, lost his life in the race; the weekend in which young Austrian rookie, Roland Ratzenberger, died instantly in a practice crash; the weekend in which one spectator died when debris flew into the crowd after a start-line accident when Pedro Lamy ploughed into the back of the stalled JJ Lehto: the weekend in which Alboreto's Minardi lost a wheel as it was leaving the pit lane after a refuelling stop, injuring a number of mechanics. It was, quite simply, a weekend of untold horror. Rubens Barrichello was lucky to escape another frightening practice accident.

RESULTS 1994

The year had started on such an upbeat note. Prost had retired (for good) and Senna had taken his place at Williams. There was the mouth-watering prospect of the great Brazilian taking on the young German pretender Michael Schumacher, and of Damon Hill upsetting the odds. Sadly, it was not to be. The eventual battle for the title between Schumacher and Hill degenerated into a bad-tempered tangle of temperaments (both on and off the track) with the German finally taking the title by just one point in controversial circumstances. There were other worrying factors. Karl Wendlinger's life hung in the balance after a practice crash at Monaco, and Jos Verstappen and his pit crew were lucky to escape with their lives when the Benetton went up in flames during one of the newly-introduced refuelling stops at Hockenheim. Young David Coulthard had the unenviable task of taking the vacant Williams seat, and Nigel Mansell was lured back to the team from the States for four races, winning the final round in Australia. McLaren swapped Ford power for Peugeot and Mercedes teamed up with Sauber. There were 16 rounds, two in Japan. All races counted for the Championships.Points: 10-6-4-3-2-1

ROUND 1/BRAZILIAN GRAND PRIX
INTERLAGOS, 27 MARCH

1. M.SCHUMACHER(GER)	BENETTON-FORD	1HR 35MIN 38.8SEC
2. D. HILL(GB)	WILLIAMS-RENAULT	70 LAPS
3. ALESI(FRA)	FERRARI	70 LAPS
4. BARRICHELLO(BRA)	JORDAN-HART	70 LAPS
5. KATAYAMA(JAP)	TYRRELL-YAMAHA	69 LAPS
6. WENDLINGER(AUT)	SAUBER-MERCEDES	69 LAPS

Race: 71 laps of 2.69mile/4.33km (190.99 miles/ 307.43kms)
Fastest lap: M.Schumacher, 1min 18.46sec, 123.32mph/198.46kph
Pole position: Senna(BRA) Williams-Renault, 1min 15.96sec 26 starters, 13 classified finishers

ROUND 2/ PACIFIC GRAND PRIX
AIDA,JAPAN, 17 APRIL

1. M.SCHUMACHER(GER)	BENETTON-FORD	1HR 47MIN 01.7SEC
2. BERGER(AUT)	FERRARI	1HR 47MIN 17.0SEC
3. BARRICHELLO(BRA)	JORDAN-HART	82 LAPS
4. C.FITTIPALDI(BRA)	FOOTWORK-FORD	82 LAPS
5. FRENTZEN(GER)	SAUBER-MERCEDES	82 LAPS
6. COMAS(FRA)	LARROUSSE-FORD	80 LAPS

Race: 83 laps of 2.3mile/3.7km (190.9 miles/307.1 kms)
Fastest lap: M.Schumacher, 1min 14.02sec, 111.9mph/180.09kph
Pole position: Senna(BRA), Williams-Renault,1min 10.22sec 26 starters, 11 classified finishers

RESULTS 1994

ROUND 3/SAN MARINO GRAND PRIX
IMOLA, 1 MAY

1. M.SCHUMACHER(GER)	BENETTON-FORD	1HR 28MIN 28.6SEC
2. LARINI(ITA)	FERRARI	1HR 29MIN 23.6SEC
3. HAKKINEN(FIN)	MCLAREN-PEUGEOT	1HR 29MIN 39.3SEC
4. WENDLINGER(AUT)	SAUBER-MERCEDES	1HR 29MIN 42.3SEC
5. KATAYAMA(JAP)	TYRRELL-YAMAHA	57 LAPS
6. D.HILL(GB)	WILLIAMS-RENAULT	57 LAPS

Race: 58* laps of 3.13 mile/5.04km (181.54 miles/292.32kms)
Fastest lap: Hill, 1min 24.34sec, 133.68mph/215.14kph
Pole position: Senna(BRA),Williams-Renault, 1min 21.55sec 25 starters, 13 class. finishers
*Race restarted after Senna's accident

ROUND 4/MONACO GRAND PRIX
MONTE CARLO, 15 MAY

1. M.SCHUMACHER(GER)	BENETTON-FORD	1HR 49MIN 55.4SEC
2. BRUNDLE(GB)	MCLAREN-PEUGEOT	1HR 50MIN 32.7SEC
3. BERGER(AUT)	FERRARI	1HR 51MIN 12.2SEC
4. DE CESARIS(ITA)	JORDAN-HART	77 LAPS
5. ALESI(FRA)	FERRARI	77 LAPS
6. ALBORETO(ITA)	MINARDI-FORD	77 LAPS

Race: 78 laps of 2.07 mile/3.33km (161.46 miles/259.74kms)
Fastest lap: M.Schumacher, 1min 21.08sec, 91.82mph/147.77kph
Pole position: Schumacher, 1min 18.56sec *24 starters, 11 classified finishers
*Sauber withdrew after Wendlinger's practice accident

ROUND 5/SPANISH GRAND PRIX
BARCELONA, 29 MAY

1.D.HILL(GB)	WILLIAMS-RENAULT	1HR 36MIN 14.4SEC
2.M.SCHUMACHER(GER)	BENETTON-FORD	1HR 36MIN 38.5SEC
3.BLUNDELL(GB)	TYRRELL-YAMAHA	1HR 37MIN 41.3SEC
4.ALESI(FRA)	FERRARI	64 LAPS
5.MARTINI(ITA)	MINARDI-FORD	64 LAPS
6.IRVINE(GB)	JORDAN-HART	64 LAPS

Race: 65 laps of 2.95 mile/4.75km (191.75 miles/302.9kms)
Fastest lap: M.Schumacher, 1min 25.16sec, 124.7mph/200.68kph
*Pole position:*M.Schumacher 1min 21.91sec 26 laps, 11 classified finishers

ROUND 6/CANADIAN GRAND PRIX
MONTREAL, 12 JUNE

1.M.SCHUMACHER(GER)	BENETTON-FORD	1HR 44MIN 31.9SEC
2.D.HILL(GB)	WILLIAMS-RENAULT	1HR 45MIN 11.6SEC
3.ALESI(FRA)	FERRARI	1HR 45MIN 45.3SEC
4.BERGER(AUT)	FERRARI	1HR 45MIN 47.5SEC
5.COULTHARD(GB)	WILLIAMS-RENAULT	68 LAPS
6.*LEHTO(FIN)	BENETTON-FORD	68 LAPS

Race: 69 laps of 2.77 mile/4.45km (191.13 miles/307.05kms)
*Fastest lap:*M.Schumacher, 1min 28.93sec, 111.94mph/180.15kph
Pole position: M.Schumacher, 1min 26.18sec 26 starters, 15 classified finishers
*C. Fittipaldi(BRA),Arrows-Ford, finished 6th but was later disqualified for having an underweight car.

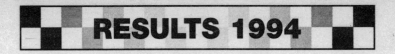

RESULTS 1994

ROUND 7/FRENCH GRAND PRIX
MAGNY-COURS, 3 JULY

1.M.SCHUMACHER(GER)	BENETTON-FORD	1HR 38MIN 35.7SEC
2.D.HILL(GB)	WILLIAMS-RENAULT	1HR 38MIN 48.4SEC
3.BERGER(AUT)	FERRARI	1HR 39MIN 28.5SEC
4.FRENTZEN(GER)	SAUBER-MERCEDES	71 LAPS
5.MARTINI(ITA)	MINARDI-FORD	70 LAPS
6.DE CESARIS(ITA)	SAUBER-MERCEDES	70 LAPS

Race: 72 laps of 2.64-mile/4.25km (190.08 miles/306 kms)
Fastest lap: D.Hill,1min 19.68sec, 119.23mph/192.02kph
Pole position: D.Hill, 1min 16.28sec 26 starters, 11 classified finishers

ROUND 8/BRITISH GRAND PRIX
SILVERSTONE, 10 JULY

1.D. HILL(GB)	WILLIAMS-RENAULT	1HR 30MIN 03.60SEC
2*. ALESI(FRA)	FERRARI	1HR 31MIN 11.77SEC
3. HAKKINEN(FIN)	MCLAREN-PEUGEOT	1HR 31MIN 44.3SEC
4. BARRICHELLO(BRA)	JORDAN-HART	1HR 31MIN 45.4SEC
5. COULTHARD(GB)	WILLIAMS-RENAULT	59 LAPS
6. KATAYAMA(JAP)	TYRRELL-YAMAHA	59 LAPS

Race: 60 laps of 3.14mile/5.06km (188.4 miles/303.4kms)
Fastest lap: D.Hill, 1min 27.1sec, 129.88mph/209.02kph
Pole position: D. Hill 1min 24.96sec 26 starters, 17 classified finishers
* M. Schumacher finished 2nd but disqualified for overtaking on the parade lap.

ROUND 9/GERMAN GRAND PRIX
HOCKENHEIM, 31 JULY

1. BERGER(AUT)	FERRARI	1HR 30MIN 03.60SEC
2. PANIS(FRA)	LIGIER-RENAULT	1HR 31MIN 11.77SEC
3. BERNARD(FRA)	LIGIER-RENAULT	1HR 31MIN 44.30SEC
4. C.FITTIPALDI(BRA)	FOOTWORK-FORD	1HR 31MIN 45.40SEC
5. MORBIDELLI(ITA)	FOOTWORK-FORD	45 LAPS
6. COMAS(FRA)	LARROUSSE-FORD	45 LAPS

Race: 45 laps of 4.24mile/6.82km (190.8 miles/306.9kms)
Fastest lap: Coulthard(GB), Williams-Renault, 1min 46.21sec,143.7mph/231.26kph
Pole position: Berger, 1min 43.58sec 26 starters, 8 classified finishers

ROUND 10/ HUNGARIAN GRAND PRIX
HUNGARORING, 14 AUGUST

1. M.SCHUMACHER(GER)	BENETTON-FORD	1HR 48MIN 00.20SEC
2. D.HILL(GB)	WILLIAMS-RENAULT	1HR 48MIN 21.00SEC
3. VERSTAPPEN(HOL)	BENETTON-FORD	1HR 49MIN 10.50SEC
4. BRUNDLE(GB)	MCLAREN-PEUGEOT	76 LAPS
5. BLUNDELL(GB)	TYRRELL-YAMAHA	76 LAPS
6. PANIS(FRA)	LIGIER-RENAULT	76 LAPS

Race: 77 laps of 2.47 mile/3.97 km (190.19 miles/305.69 kms)
Fastest lap: M.Schumacher, 1min 20.88sec, 109.7mph/176.62kph
Pole position: M.Schumacher, 1min 18.26sec 26 starters, 14 classified finishers

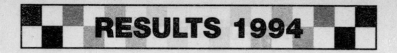

RESULTS 1994

ROUND 11/BELGIAN GRAND PRIX
SPA-FRANCORCHAMPS, 28 AUGUST

1*. D.HILL(GB)	WILLIAMS-RENAULT	1HR 28MIN 47.20SEC
2. HAKKINEN(FIN)	MCLAREN-PEUGEOT	1HR 29MIN 38.60SEC
3. VERSTAPPEN(HOL)	BENETTON-FORD	1HR 29MIN 57.06SEC
4. COULTHARD(GB)	WILLIAMS-RENAULT	1HR 30MIN 33.00SEC
5. BLUNDELL(GB)	TYRRELL-YAMAHA	43 LAPS
6. MORBIDELLI(ITA)	FOOTWORK-FORD	43 LAPS

Race: 44 laps of 4.35mile/7km (191.4 miles/308.0kms)
Fastest lap: D. Hill, 1min 57.12sec, 133.72mph,215.20kph
Pole position: Barrichello(BRA)Jordan-Hart, 2min 21.16sec 26 starters, 13 class. finishers
*M Schumacher finished 1st but was later disqualified for a technical infringement.

ROUND 12/ITALIAN GRAND PRIX
MONZA,11 SEPTEMBER

1. D.HILL(GB)	WILLIAMS-RENAULT	1HR 18MIN 02.8SEC
2. BERGER(AUT)	FERRARI	1HR 18MIN 07.7SEC
3. HAKKINEN(FIN)	MCLAREN-PEUGEOT	1HR 18MIN 28.4SEC
4. BARRICHELLO(BRA)	JORDAN-HART	1HR 18MIN 53.4SEC
5. BRUNDLE(GB)	MCLAREN-PEUGEOT	1HR 19MIN 28.3SEC
6. COULTHARD(GB)	WILLIAMS-RENAULT	52 LAPS

Race: 53 laps of 3.6mile/5.8km (190.8 miles/307.4kms)
Fastest lap: D.Hill, 1min 25.93sec, 150.99mph/242.99kph
Pole position: Alesi(FRA),Ferrari,1min 23.84sec 26 starters, 10 classified finishers

ROUND 13/PORTUGUESE GRAND PRIX
ESTORIL, 25 SEPTEMBER

1.D.HILL(GB)	WILLIAMS-RENAULT	1HR 41MIN 10.2SEC
2.COULTHARD(GB)	WILLIAMS-RENAULT	1HR 41MIN 10.8SEC
3.HAKKINEN(FIN)	MCLAREN-PEUGEOT	1HR 41MIN 30.4SEC
4.BARRICHELLO(BRA)	JORDAN-HART	1HR 41MIN 38.2SEC
5.VERSTAPPEN(HOL)	BENETTON-FORD	1HR 41MIN 39.6SEC
6. BRUNDLE(GB)	MCLAREN-PEUGEOT	1HR 42MIN 02.9SEC

Race: 71 laps of 2.71 mile/4.36 km (192.41 miles/309.56kms)
Fastest lap: Coulthard, 1min 22.45sec, 118.29mph/190.38kph
Pole position: Berger(AUT),Ferrari, 1min 20.61sec 26 starters,16 classified finishers

ROUND 14/EUROPEAN GRAND PRIX
JEREZ, 16 OCTOBER

1.M.SCHUMACHER(GER)	BENETTON-FORD	1HR 40MIN 26.70SEC
2.D.HILL(GB)	WILLIAMS-RENAULT	1HR 40MIN 51.40SEC
3.HAKKINEN(FIN)	MCLAREN-PEUGEOT	1HR 41MIN 36.30SEC
4.IRVINE(GB)	JORDAN-HART	1HR 41MIN 45.10SEC
5.BERGER(AUT)	FERRARI	68 LAPS
6.FRENTZEN(GER)	SAUBER-MERCEDES	68 LAPS

Race: 69 laps of 2.75 mile/4.43km (189.75 miles/305.67kms)
Fastest lap: M.Schumacher, 1min 25.04sec, 116.48mph/187.45kph
Pole position: M.Schumacher, 1min 22.76sec 26 starters, 19 classified finishers

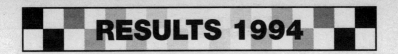

RESULTS 1994

ROUND 15/JAPANESE GRAND PRIX
SUZUKA, 6 NOVEMBER

1. D.HILL(GB)	WILLIAMS-RENAULT	1HR 55MIN 53.50SEC
2. M.SCHUMACHER(GER)	BENETTON-FORD	1HR 55MIN 56.90SEC
3. ALESI(FRA)	FERRARI	1HR 56MIN 45.60SEC
4. MANSELL(GB)	WILLIAMS-RENAULT	1HR 56MIN 49.60SEC
5. IRVINE(GB)	JORDAN-HART	1HR 57MIN 35.60SEC
6. FRENTZEN(GER)	SAUBER-MERCEDES	1HR 57MIN 53.40SEC

Race: 50 laps of 3.64 mile/5.86 km (182.0 miles/293.0kms)*
Fastest lap: D.Hill, 1min 56.6sec, 112.50mph/181.05kph
Pole position: M. Schumacher, 1min 37.21sec 26 starters, 13 classified finishers
*Rain interrupted race

ROUND 16/AUSTRALIAN GRAND PRIX
ADELAIDE,13 NOVEMBER

1. MANSELL(GB)	WILLIAMS-RENAULT	1HR 47MIN 51.50SEC
2. BERGER(AUT)	FERRARI	1HR 47MIN 54.00SEC
3. BRUNDEL(GB)	MCLAREN-PEUGEOT	1HR 48MIN 44.00SEC
4. BARRICHELLO(BRA)	JORDAN-HART	1HR 49MIN 02.00SEC
5. PANIS(FRA)	LIGIER-RENAULT	80 LAPS
6. ALESI(FRA)	FERRARI	80 LAPS

Race: 81 laps of 2.35 mile/ 3.78 km (190.35 miles/306.18 kms)
Fastest lap: M. Schumacher(GER),Benetton-Ford, 1min 17.14sec, 109.61mph/176.41kph
Pole position: Mansell, 1min 16.18sec 26 starters, 12 classified finishers

DRIVERS' WORLD CHAMPIONSHIP 1994
1. M.SCHUMACHER 92	4. HAKKINEN 26 points
2. D.HILL 91 points	5. ALESI 24 points
3. BERGER 41 points	6. BARRICHELLO 19

CONSTRUCTORS' WORLD CHAMPIONSHIP 1994
1. WILLIAMS-RENAULT 118 points	4. MCLAREN-PEUGEOT 42 points
2. BENETTON-FORD 103 points	5. JORDAN-HART 28 points
3. FERRARI 71 points	6. LIGIER-RENAULT, TYRRELL-YAMAHA 13

RESULTS 1995

1995 Schumacher won his second successive Drivers' title with nine victories. His bad tempered battles with Hill continued, although never reaching the magnitude of the infamous Prost/Senna 'war'. Britain's Johnny Herbert partnered the German at Benetton and claimed his first Grand Prix victory in front of ecstatic fans at Silverstone. Jean Alesi - after 91 attempts - took his first ever emotion-charged win for Ferrari, appropriately, at the Gilles Villeneuve circuit in Canada. And Scotland's new young hero, David Coulthard, tasted the champagne in only his 21st Grand Prix, in Portugal. Brilliant work by the paramedics saved Hakkinen's life after a high-speed accident in practice in Adelaide. The sport mourned when one of its greatest - if not *the* greatest driver of all time- Juan-Manuel Fangio, died at the age of 84. The once mighty Team Lotus joined Brabham on the Grand Prix scrap heap. And Nigel Mansell became a figure of fun when he proved to be too broad in the beam to fit into the McLaren cockpit! His season would last just one and one third races...Benetton had Renault power and McLaren embarked upon their relationship with Mercedes. Benetton won the Constructors' Championship for the first time. There were 17 rounds in a crowded calendar. All races counted for both Championships. Points: 10-6-4-3-2-1.

ROUND 1/BRAZILIAN GRAND PRIX
INTERLAGOS, 26 MARCH

1. M.SCHUMACHER(GER)	BENETTON-RENAULT	1HR 38MIN 34.2SEC
2. COULTHARD(GB)	WILLIAMS-RENAULT	1HR 38MIN 42.2SEC
3. BERGER(AUT)	FERRARI	70 LAPS
4. HAKKINEN(FIN)	MCLAREN-MERCEDES	70 LAPS
5. ALESI(FRA)	FERRARI	70 LAPS
6. BLUNDELL(GB)	MCLAREN-MERCEDES	70 LAPS

Race: 71 laps of 2.69 mile/4.33km (190.99 miles/307.43kms)
Fastest lap: M. Schumacher, 1min 20.92sec, 119.56mph/192.41kph
Pole position: D. Hill(GB) Williams-Renault, 1min 20.08sec 26 starters, 10 classified finishers

ROUND 2/ARGENTINE GRAND PRIX
BUENOS AIRES, 9 APRIL

1. D.HILL(GB)	WILLIAMS-RENAULT	1HR 53MIN 14.5SEC
2. ALESI(FRA)	FERRARI	1HR 53MIN 20.9SEC
3. M.SCHUMACHER(GER)	BENETTON-RENAULT	1HR 53MIN 47.9SEC
4. HERBERT(GB)	BENETTON-RENAULT	71 LAPS
5. FRENTZEN(GER)	SAUBER-FORD	70 LAPS
6. BERGER(AUT)	FERRARI	70 LAPS

Race: 72 laps of 2.65miles/4.26km (190.8miles/306.72kms)
Fastest lap: M.Schumacher, 1min 30.52sec, 105.25mph/169.38kph
Pole position: Coulthard(GB) Williams-Renault, 1min 53.24sec 26 starters, 9 classified finishers

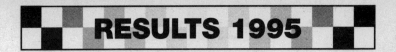
RESULTS 1995

ROUND 3/SAN MARINO
IMOLA, 30 APRIL

1. D. HILL(GB)	WILLIAMS-RENAULT	1HR 41MIN 42.6SEC
2. ALESI(FRA)	FERRARI	1HR 42MIN 01.1SEC
3. BERGER(AUT)	FERRARI	1HR 42MIN 25.7SEC
4. COULTHARD(GB)	WILLIAMS-RENAULT	1HR 42MIN 34.4SEC
5. HAKKINEN(FIN)	MCLAREN-MERCEDES	62 LAPS
6. FRENTZEN(GER)	SAUBER-FORD	62 LAPS

Race: 63 laps of 3.04mile/4.9km (191.52 miles/308.7kms)
Fastest lap: Berger, 1min 29.57sec, 122.25mph/196.74kph
Pole position: M.Schumacher(GER) Benetton-Renault, 1min 27.27sec 26 starters, 16 classified finishers

ROUND 4/SPANISH GRAND PRIX
BARCELONA, 14 MAY

1. M.SCHUMACHER(GER)	BENETTON-RENAULT	1HR 34MIN 20.5SEC
2. HERBERT(GB)	BENETTON-RENAULT	1HR 35MIN 12.5SEC
3. BERGER(AUT)	FERRARI	1HR 35MIN 25.7SEC
4. D.HILL(GB)	WILLIAMS-RENAULT	1HR 36MIN 22.3SEC
5. IRVINE(GB)	JORDAN-PEUGEOT	64 LAPS
6. PANIS(FRA)	LIGIER-MUGEN HONDA	64 LAPS

Race: 65 laps of 2.94mile/4.73km (191.10miles/307.45kms)
Fastest lap: D. Hill, 1min 24.53sec, 125.09mph/201.31kph
Pole position: M. Schumacher, 1min 21.45sec 26 starters, 15 classified finishers

ROUND 5/MONACO GRAND PRIX
MONTE CARLO, 28 MAY

1. M.SCHUMACHER(GER)	BENETTON-RENAULT	1HR 53MIN 11.3SEC
2. D.HILL(GB)	WILLIAMS-RENAULT	1HR 53MIN 46.1SEC
3. BERGER(AUT)	FERRARI	1HR 54MIN 22.7SEC
4. HERBERT(GB)	BENETTON-RENAULT	77 LAPS
5. BLUNDELL(GB)	MCLAREN-MERCEDES	77 LAPS
6. FRENTZEN(GER)	SAUBER-FORD	76 LAPS

Race: 78 laps of 2.07mile/3.33km (161.46 miles/ 259.74kms)
Fastest lap: Alesi(FRA) Ferrari, 1min 24.62sec, 87.98mph/141.58kph
Pole position: D. Hill, 1min 21.95sec 26 starters, 10 classified finishers

ROUND 6/CANADIAN GRAND PRIX
MONTREAL, 11 JUNE

1. ALESI(FRA)	FERRARI	1HR 46MIN 31.03SEC
2. BARRICHELLO(BRA)	JORDAN-PEUGEOT	1HR 47MIN 00.03SEC
3. IRVINE(GB)	JORDAN-PEUGEOT	1HR 47MIN 04.06SEC
4. PANIS(FRA)	LIGIER-MUGEN HONDA	1HR 47MIN 07.08SEC
5. M.SCHUMACHER(GER)	BENETTON-RENAULT	1HR 47MIN 08.04SEC
6. MORBIDELLI(ITA)	FOOTWORK-HART	67 LAPS

Race: 68 laps of 2.75mile/4.43km (187.0 miles/301.24kms)
Fastest lap: M.Schumacher, 1min 29.17sec, 111.13mph/178.84kph
*Pole position:*M.Schumacher, 1min 27.66sec 24 starters, 11 classified finishers

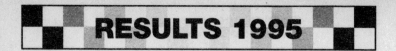

RESULTS 1995

ROUND 7/FRENCH GRAND PRIX
MAGNY-COURS, 2 JULY

1. M. SCHUMACHER(GER)	BENETTON-RENAULT	1HR 38MIN 28.04SEC
2. D. HILL(GB)	WILLIAMS-RENAULT	1HR 38MIN 59.07SEC
3. COULTHARD(GB)	WILLIAMS-RENAULT	1HR 39MIN 31.25SEC
4. BRUNDLE(GB)	LIGIER-MUGEN HONDA	1HR 39MIN 31.72SEC
5. ALESI(FRA)	FERRARI	1HR 39MIN 46.03SEC
6. BARRICHELLO(BRA)	JORDAN-PEUGEOT	71 LAPS

Race: 72 laps of 2.64mile/4.25 km (190.08 miles/306.0kms)
Fastest lap: M.Schumacher, 1min 20.22sec, 118.51mph/190.73kph
Pole position: D.Hill, 1min 17.23sec 24 starters, 16 classified finishers

ROUND 8/BRITISH GRAND PRIX
SILVERSTONE, 16 JULY

1. HERBERT(GB)	BENETTON-RENAULT	1HR 34MIN 35.01SEC
2. ALESI(FRA)	FERRARI	1HR 34MIN 51.06SEC
3. COULTHARD(GB)	WILLIAMS-RENAULT	1HR 34MIN 59.00SEC
4. PANIS(FRA)	LIGIER-MUGEN HONDA	1HR 36MIN 08.03SEC
5. BLUNDELL(GB)	MCLAREN-MERCEDES	1HR 39MIN 23.03SEC
6. FRENTZEN(GER)	SAUBER-FORD	60 LAPS

Race: 61 laps of 3.14mile/5.06km (191.54 miles / 308.66kms)
Fastest lap: D.Hill(GB) Williams-Renault, 1min 29.75sec, 126.04mph/202.84kph
Pole position: D.Hill 1min 28.12sec 24 starters, 12 class. finishers

ROUND 9/GERMAN GRAND PRIX
HOCKENHEIM, 30 JULY

1. M.SCHUMACHER(GER)	BENETTON-RENAULT	1HR 22MIN 56.00SEC
2. COULTHARD(GB)	WILLIAMS-RENAULT	1HR 23MIN 00.02SEC
3. BERGER(AUT)	FERRARI	1HR 24MIN 04.01SEC
4. HERBERT(GB)	BENETTON-RENAULT	1HR 24MIN 19.05SEC
5. BOUILLON(FRA)	SAUBER-FORD	44 LAPS
6. A. SUZUKI(JAP)	LIGIER-MUGEN HONDA	44 LAPS

Race: 45 laps of 4.24mile/6.82km (190.8 miles/306.9 kms)
Fastest lap: M.Schumacher, 1min 48.82sec, 140.25mph/225.71kph
Pole position: D. Hill(GB), Williams-Renault, 1min 44.39sec 24 starters, 9 class. finishers

ROUND 10/HUNGARIAN GRAND PRIX
HUNGARORING, 13 AUGUST

1. D.HILL(GB)	WILLIAMS-RENAULT	1HR 46MIN 25.07SEC
2. COULTHARD(GB)	WILLIAMS-RENAULT	1HR 46MIN 59.01SEC
3. BERGER(AUT)	FERRARI	76 LAPS
4. HERBERT(GB)	BENETTON-RENAULT	76 LAPS
5. FRENTZEN(GER)	SAUBER-FORD	76 LAPS
6. PANIS(FRA)	LIGIER-MUGEN HONDA	76 LAPS

Race: 77 laps of 2.47mile/3.97km (190.19 miles/305.69kms)
Fastest lap: D.Hill, 1min 20.43sec, 110.61mph/178.01kph
Pole position: D. Hill, 1min 16.98sec 24 starters, 13 classified finishers

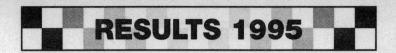

RESULTS 1995

ROUND 11/BELGIAN GRAND PRIX
SPA-FRANCORCHAMPS, 27 AUGUST

1. M.SCHUMACHER(GER)	BENETTON-RENAULT	1HR 36MIN 47.09SEC
2. D.HILL(GB)	WILLIAMS-RENAULT	1HR 37MIN 07.04SEC
3. BRUNDLE(GB)	LIGIER-MUGEN HONDA	1HR 37MIN 12.09SEC
4. FRENTZEN(GER)	SAUBER-FORD	1HR 37MIN 14.09SEC
5. BLUNDELL(GB)	MCLAREN-MERCEDES	1HR 37MIN 21.07SEC
6. BARRICHELLO(BRA)	JORDAN-PEUGEOT	1HR 37MIN 27.06SEC

Race: 44 laps of 4.33mile/6.97km (190.52 miles/ 306.68 kms)
Fastest lap: Coulthard(GB) Williams-Renault, 1min 53.41sec, 137.56mph/221.37kph
Pole position: Berger(AUT) Ferrari, 1min 54.39 sec 24 starters, 14 classified finishers

ROUND 12/ITALIAN GRAND PRIX
MONZA, 10 SEPTEMBER

1. HERBERT(GB)	BENETTON-RENAULT	1HR 16MIN 27.09SEC
2. HAKKINEN(FIN)	MCLAREN-MERCEDES	1HR 18MIN 45.07SEC
3. FRENTZEN(GER)	SAUBER-FORD	1HR 18MIN 52.02SEC
4. BLUNDELL(GB)	MCLAREN-MERCEDES	1HR 18MIN 56.01SEC
5. SALO(FIN)	TYRRELL-YAMAHA	52 LAPS
6. BOUILLON(FRA)	SAUBER-FORD	52 LAPS

Race: 53 laps of 3.6 mile/5.8km (190.8 miles/307.4kms)
Fastest lap: Berger(AUT) Ferrari, 1min 26.42sec, 149.36mph/240.36kph
Pole position: Coulthard, 1min 24.46sec 24 starters, 10 classified finishers

ROUND 13/PORTUGUESE GRAND PRIX
ESTORIL, 24 SEPTEMBER

1. COULTHARD(GB)	WILLIAMS-RENAULT	1HR 41MIN 52.02SEC
2. M.SCHUMACHER(GER)	BENETTON-RENAULT	1HR 41MIN 59.04SEC
3. D.HILL(GB)	WILLIAMS-RENAULT	1HR 42MIN 14.03SEC
4. BERGER(AUT)	FERRARI	1HR 43MIN 17.00SEC
5. ALESI(FRA)	FERRARI	1HR 43MIN 17.06SEC
6. FRENTZEN(GER)	SAUBER-FORD	70 LAPS

Race: 71 laps of 2.71 mile/4.36 km (192.41 miles/309.56kms)
Fastest lap: Coulthard, 1min 23.22sec, 117.20mph/188.61kph
Pole position: Coulthard, 1min 20.54sec 24 starters, 17 classified finishers

ROUND 14/EUROPEAN GRAND PRIX
NURBURGRING, 1 OCTOBER

1. M.SCHUMACHER(GER)	BENETTON-RENAULT	1HR 39MIN 59.04SEC
2. ALESI(FRA)	FERRARI	1HR 40MIN 01.73SEC
3. COULTHARD(GB)	WILLIAMS-RENAULT	1HR 40MIN 34.40SEC
4. BARRICHELLO(BRA)	JORDAN-PEUGEOT	66 LAPS
5. HERBERT(GB)	BENETTON-RENAULT	66 LAPS
6. IRVINE(GB)	JORDAN-PEUGEOT	66 LAPS

Race: 67 laps of 2.83 mile/4.56km (189.61 miles/ 305.52kms)
Fastest lap: M.Schumacher, 1min 21.18sec, 125.42mph/202.04kph
Pole position: Coulthard, 1min 18.74sec 24 starters, 15 classified finishers

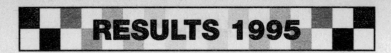

RESULTS 1995

ROUND 15/PACIFIC GRAND PRIX
AIDA, 22 OCTOBER

1. M.SCHUMACHER(GER)	BENETTON-RENAULT	1HR 48MIN 50.0SEC
2. COULTHARD(GB)	WILLIAMS-RENAULT	1HR 49MIN 04.9SEC
3. D. HILL(GB)	WILLIAMS-RENAULT	1HR 49MIN 38.3SEC
4. BERGER(AUT)	FERRARI	82 LAPS
5. ALESI(FRA)	FERRARI	82 LAPS
6. HERBERT(GB)	BENETTON-RENAULT	82 LAPS

Race: 83 laps of 2.3mile/3.7km (190.9miles/307.1kms)
Fastest lap: M.Schumacher, 1min 16.37sec,108.46mph/174.55kph
Pole position: Coulthard, 1min 14.01sec 24 starters, 17 classified finishers

ROUND 16/JAPANESE GRAND PRIX
SUZUKA, 29 OCTOBER

1. M.SCHUMACHER(GER)	BENETTON-RENAULT	1HR 36MIN 52.9SEC
2. HAKKINEN(FIN)	MCLAREN-MERCEDES	1HR 37MIN 12.3SEC
3. HERBERT(GB)	BENETTON-RENAULT	1HR 38MIN 16.7SEC
4. IRVINE(GB)	JORDAN-PEUGEOT	1HR 38MIN 35.1SEC
5. PANIS(FRA)	LIGIER-MUGEN HONDA	52 LAPS
6. SALO(FIN)	TYRRELL-YAMAHA	52 LAPS

Race: 53 laps of 3.64 mile/5.86 km (192.92 miles/310.58kms)
Fastest lap: M.Schumacher, 1min 43.0sec,127.38mph/205.0kph
Pole position: M.Schumacher, 1min 38.02sec 23 starters, 12 classified finishers

ROUND 17/AUSTRALIAN GRAND PRIX
ADELAIDE, 12 NOVEMBER

1. D.HILL(GB)	WILLIAMS-RENAULT	1HR 49MIN 16.0SEC
2. PANIS(FRA)	LIGIER-MUGEN HONDA	79 LAPS
3. MORBIDELLI(ITA)	FOOTWORK-HART	79 LAPS
4. BLUNDELL(GB)	MCLAREN-MERCEDES	79 LAPS
5. SALO(FIN)	TYRRELL-YAMAHA	78 LAPS
6. LAMY(POR)	MINARDI-FORD	78 LAPS

Race: 81 laps of 2.35mile/3.78 km (190.35 miles/306.18 kms)
Fastest lap: D. Hill, 1min 17.94sec, 108.49mph/174.59kph
Pole position: D. Hill, 1min 15.50sec 23 starters, 8 classified finishers

---

DRIVERS' WORLD CHAMPIONSHIP 1995

1. M.SCHUMACHER *102*	4. HERBERT	45 *points*
2. D.HILL *69 points*	5. ALESI	42 *points*
3. COULTHARD *49 points*	6. BERGER	31 *points*

CONSTRUCTORS' WORLD CHAMPIONSHIP 1995

1. BENETTON-RENAULT *137 points*	4. MCLAREN-MERCEDES *30 points*
2. WILLIAMS-RENAULT *112 points*	5. LIGIER-MUGEN HONDA *24 points*
3. FERRARI *73 points*	6. JORDAN-PEUGEOT *21 points*

RESULTS 1996

1996 What a difference a year makes! After one of the biggest driver shake-ups in the history of the sport, Damon (son of Graham) Hill won the Drivers' Championship from team-mate Jacques (son of Gilles) Villeneuve. The Williams team simply pulverised the opposition, thanks to Damon's eight wins and Jacques' four. The little French Canadian had arrived hot foot from dominating the Indycar series and took to Formula 1 like a duck to water. Schumacher joined Ferrari for a king's (or should it be a double-Champion's?) ransom and found himself sharing his pit with Irishman Eddie Irvine, who left Jordan in one of the shock moves of the closed season. Ferrari refugees, Alesi and Berger both moved to Benetton and David Coulthard confirmed one of the worst kept secrets of the sport by joining Hakkinen, who had made a brave recovery from his Adelaide accident, at McLaren...watch this space! Britain's Johnny Herbert found refuge alongside Frentzen at Sauber and Martin Brundle returned to the bosom of the Jordan team. Shock result of the year came in the wet at Monaco, when Panis gave Ligier its first win in 15 years. The season kicked off in Australia, where it had finished in '95, but at a new venue, Albert Park, Melbourne. There were 16 rounds. All races counted for both Championships. Points: 10-6-4-3-2-1.

ROUND 1/AUSTRALIAN GRAND PRIX

MELBOURNE, 10 MARCH

1. D.HILL(GB)	WILLIAMS-RENAULT	1HR 32MIN 50.5SEC
2. J.VILLENEUVE(CAN)	WILLIAMS-RENAULT	1HR 33MIN 28.5SEC
3. IRVINE(GB)	FERRARI	1HR 33MIN 53.1SEC
4. BERGER(AUT)	BENETTON-RENAULT	1HR 34MIN 07.5SEC
5. HAKKINEN(FIN)	MCLAREN-MERCEDES	1HR 34MIN 25.6SEC
6. SALO(FIN)	TYRRELL-YAMAHA	57 LAPS

Race: 58 laps of 3.3mile/5.3km (191.4 miles/307.4kms)
Fastest lap: J.Villeneuve, 1min 33.42sec, 129.96mph/204.31kph
Pole position: J.Villeneuve,1min 32.37sec 20 starters, 11 classified finishers

ROUND 2/BRAZILIAN GRAND PRIX

INTERLAGOS, 31 MARCH

1.D.HILL(GB)	WILLIAMS-RENAULT	1HR 49MIN 53.0SEC
2.ALESI(FRA)	BENETTON-RENAULT	1HR 50MIN 01.0SEC
3.M.SCHUMACHER(GER)	FERRARI	70 LAPS
4.HAKKINEN(FIN)	MCLAREN-MERCEDES	70 LAPS
5.SALO(FIN)	TYRRELL-YAMAHA	70 LAPS
6.PANIS(FRA)	LIGIER-MUGEN HONDA	70 LAPS

Race: 71 laps of 2.69 mile/4.33km (190.99 miles/ 307.43 kms)
Fastest lap: D.Hill, 1min 21.55sec, 118.64mph/190.93kph
Pole position: D. Hill, 1min 18.11sec 22 starters, 12 classified finishers

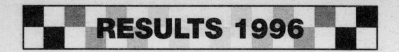

RESULTS 1996

ROUND 3/ARGENTINE GRAND PRIX
BUENOS AIRES, 7 APRIL

1. D.HILL(GB)	WILLIAMS-RENAULT	1HR 54MIN 55.03SEC
2. J.VILLENEUVE(CAN)	WILLIAMS-RENAULT	1HR 55MIN 07.49SEC
3. ALESI(FRA)	BENETTON-RENAULT	1HR 55MIN 10.08SEC
4. BARRICHELLO(BRA)	JORDAN-PEUGEOT	1HR 55MIN 50.05SEC
5. IRIVINE(GB)	FERRARI	1HR 56MIN 00.31SEC
6. VERSTAPPEN(HOL)	FOOTWORK-HART	1HR 56MIN 04.24SEC

Race: 72 laps of 2.65 mile/4.26km (190.8 miles/306.72kms)
Fastest lap: Alesi, 1min 29.41sec, 106.45mph/171.48 kph
Pole position: D. Hill, 1min 30.35sec 22 starters, 10 classified finishers

ROUND 4/EUROPEAN GRAND PRIX
NURBURGRING, 28 APRIL

1. J.VILLENEUVE(CAN)	WILLIAMS-RENAULT	1HR 33MIN 26.47SEC
2. M.SCHUMACHER(GER)	FERRARI	1HR 33MIN 27.24SEC
3. COULTHARD(GB)	MCLAREN-MERCEDES	1HR 33MIN 59.31SEC
4. D.HILL(GB)	WILLIAMS-RENAULT	1HR 33MIN 59.98SEC
5. BARRICHELLO(BRA)	JORDAN-PEUGEOT	1HR 34MIN 00.19SEC
6. BRUNDLE(GB)	JORDAN-PEUGEOT	1HR 34MIN 22.04SEC

Race: 67 laps of 2.83mile/4.56 km (189.61 miles/305.52 kms)
Fastest lap: D.Hill, 1min 21.36sec, 125.26mph/201.59kph
Pole position: D.Hill, 1min 18.94sec 20 starters, 13 classified finishers

ROUND 5/SAN MARINO GRAND PRIX
IMOLA, 5 MAY

1. D.HILL(GB)	WILLIAMS-RENAULT	1HR 35MIN 26.2SEC
2. M.SCHUMACHER(GER)	FERRARI	1HR 35MIN 42.6SEC
3. BERGER(AUT)	BENETTON-RENAULT	1HR 36MIN 13.1SEC
4. IRVINE(GB)	FERRARI	1HR 36MIN 27.7SEC
5. BARRICHELLO(BRA)	JORDAN-PEUGEOT	1HR 36MIN 44.7SEC
6. ALESI(FRA)	BENETTON-RENAULT	62 LAPS

Race: 63 laps of 3.04 mile/4.89km (191.52 miles/ 308.7kms)
Fastest lap: D. Hill,1min 28.93sec, 123.05mph/198.03kph
Pole position: M.Schumacher, 1min 26.90sec 21 starters, 11 classified finishers

ROUND 6/MONACO GRAND PRIX
MONTE CARLO, 19 MAY

1. PANIS(FRA)	LIGIER-MUGEN HONDA	2HR 00MIN 45.63SEC
2. COULTHARD(GB)	MCLAREN-MERCEDES	2HR 00MIN 50.46SEC
3. HERBERT(GB)	SAUBER-FORD	2HR 01MIN 23.01SEC
4. FRENTZEN(GER)	SAUBER-FORD	74 LAPS
5. SALO(FIN)	TYRRELL-YAMAHA	70 LAPS
6. HAKKINEN(FIN)	MCLAREN-MERCEDES	70 LAPS

Race: 75* laps of 2.07 mile/3.33km (155.25 miles/ 249.75kms)
Fastest lap: Alesi(FRA)Benetton-Renault,1min 25.21sec, 87.37mph/140.61kph
Pole position: M.Schumacher, 1min 20.36sec 21 starters, 7 classified finishers
*Race stopped after 2hrs (75 of 78 scheduled laps) due to rain

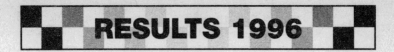

RESULTS 1996

ROUND 7/SPANISH GRAND PRIX
BARCELONA, 2 JUNE

1. M.SCHUMACHER(GER)	FERRARI	1HR 59MIN 49.3SEC
2. ALESI(FRA)	BENETTON-RENAULT	2HR 00MIN 34.6SEC
3. J.VILLENEUVE(CAN)	WILLIAMS-RENAULT	2HR 00MIN 37.7SEC
4. FRENTZEN(GER)	SAUBER-FORD	64 LAPS
5. HAKKINEN(FIN)	MCLAREN-MERCEDES	64 LAPS
6. DINIZ(BRA)	LIGIER-MUGEN-HONDA	63 LAPS

Race: 65 laps of 2.94 mile/4.73km (191.10 miles/307.45 kms)
Fastest lap: M.Schumacher,1min 45.52sec, 100.21mph/161.27kph
Pole position: D.Hill, 1min 20.65sec 20 starters, 6 classified finishers

ROUND 8/CANADIAN GRAND PRIX
MONTREAL, 16 JUNE

1. D.HILL(GB)	WILLIAMS-RENAULT	1HR 36MIN 03.47SEC
2. J.VILLENEUVE(CAN)	WILLIAMS-RENAULT	1HR 36MIN 07.65SEC
3. ALESI(FRA)	BENETTON-RENAULT	1HR 36MIN 58.01SEC
4. COULTHARD(GB)	MCLAREN-MERCEDES	1HR 37MIN 07.01SEC
5. HAKKINEN(FIN)	MCLAREN-MERCEDES	68 LAPS
6. BRUNDLE(GB)	JORDAN-PEUGEOT	68 LAPS

Race: 69 laps of 2.75 mile/4.42 km (189.75 miles/ 304.98kms)
Fastest lap: J.Villeneuve, 1min 21.92sec, 120.73mph/194.29kph
Pole position: D. Hill, 1min 21.06sec 22 starters, 8 classified finishers

ROUND 9/FRENCH GRAND PRIX
MAGNY-COURS, 30 JUNE

1. D.HILL(GB)	WILLIAMS-RENAULT	1HR 36MIN 28.08SEC
2. J.VILLENEUVE(CAN)	WILLIAMS-RENAULT	1HR 36MIN 36.09SEC
3. ALESI(FRA)	BENETTON-RENAULT	1HR 37MIN 15.24SEC
4. BERGER(AUT)	BENETTON-RENAULT	1HR 37MIN 15.65SEC
5. HAKKINEN(FIN)	MCLAREN-MERCEDES	1HR 37MIN 31.06SEC
6. COULTHARD(GB)	MCLAREN-MERCEDES	71 LAPS

Race: 72 laps of 2.64 mile/4.25km (190.08 miles/ 306.0kms)
*Fastest lap:*Villeneuve, 1min 18.61sec, 120.94mph/194.63kph
Pole position: M.Schumacher, 1min 15.99sec 21* starters, 12 classified finishers
*M.Schumacher's Ferrari expired on the warm-up lap!

ROUND 10/BRITISH GRAND PRIX
SILVERSTONE, 14 JULY

1. J.VILLENEUVE(CAN)	WILLIAMS-RENAULT	1HR 33MIN 00.09SEC
2. BERGER(AUT)	BENETTON-RENAULT	1HR 33MIN 19.09SEC
3. HAKKINEN(FIN)	MCLAREN-MERCEDES	1HR 33MIN 51.07SEC
4. BARRICHELLO(BRA)	JORDAN-PEUGEOT	1HR 34MIN 07.06SEC
5. COULTHARD(GB)	MCLAREN-MERCEDES	1HR 34MIN 23.04SEC
6. BRUNDLE(GB)	JORDAN-PEUGEOT	60 LAPS

Race: 61 laps of 3.15 mile/5.07 km (192.15 miles/309.27 kms)
*Fastest lap:*J.Villeneuve,1min 29.28sec, 127.07mph/204.5kph
Pole position: D.Hill(GB)Williams-Renault, 1min 26.88sec 20 starters, 11 class. finishers

433

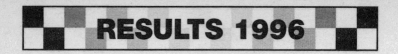

RESULTS 1996

ROUND 11/GERMAN GRAND PRIX
HOCKENHEIM,28 JULY

1. D. HILL(GB)	WILLIAMS-RENAULT	1HR 21MIN 43.4SEC
2. ALESI(FRA)	BENETTON-RENAULT	1HR 21MIN 54.9SEC
3. J.VILLENEUVE(CAN)	WILLIAMS-RENAULT	1HR 22MIN 17.3SEC
4. M.SCHUMACHER(GER)	FERRARI	1HR 22MIN 24.9SEC
5. COULTHARD(GB)	MCLAREN-MERCEDES	1HR 22MIN 25.6SEC
6. BARRICHELLO(BRA)	JORDAN-PEUGOT	1HR 23MIN 25.5SEC

Race: 45 laps of 4.24 mile/ 6.82 km (190.8 miles/306.9 kms)
Fastest lap: D.Hill,1min 46.5sec, 143.31mph/230.63kph
Pole position: D. Hill, 1min 43.91sec 19 starters, 13 classified finishers

ROUND 12/HUNGARIAN GRAND PRIX
HUNGARORING, 11 AUGUST

1. J.VILLENEUVE(CAN)	WILLIAMS-RENAULT	1HR 46MIN 21.13SEC
2. D.HILL(GB)	WILLIAMS-RENAULT	1HR 46MIN 21.91SEC
3. ALESI(FRA)	BENETTON-RENAULT	1HR 47MIN 45.04SEC
4. HAKKINEN(FIN)	MCLAREN-MERCEDES	76 LAPS
5. PANIS(FRA)	LIGIER-MUGEN HONDA	76 LAPS
6. BARRICHELLO(BRA)	JORDAN-PEUGEOT	75 LAPS

Race: 77 laps of 2.47 mile/3.97 km (190.19 miles/305.69 kms)
Fastest lap: D.Hill, 1min 20.09sec,110.82mph/178.35kph
Pole position: M. Schumacher(GER), Ferrari 20 starters, 10 classified finishers

ROUND 13/BELGIAN GRAND PRIX
SPA-FRANCORCHAMPS, 25 AUGUST

1.M.SCHUMACHER(GER)	FERRARI	1HR 28MIN 15.1SEC
2.J.VILLENEUVE(CAN)	WILLIAMS-RENAULT	1HR 28MIN 20.7SEC
3.HAKKINEN(FIN)	MCLAREN-MERCEDES	1HR 28MIN 30.8SEC
4.ALESI(FRA)	BENETTON-RENAULT	1HR 28MIN 34.3SEC
5.D.HILL(GB)	WILLIAMS-RENAULT	1HR 28MIN 44.3SEC
6.BERGER(AUT)	BENETTON-RENAULT	1HR 28MIN 45.0SEC

Race: 44 laps of 4.33mile/6.97 km (190.52 miles/306.68 kms)
Fastest lap: Berger, 1min 53.07sec, 137.86mph/221.86kph
Pole position: J.Villeneuve, 1min 59.57sec 19 starters, 10 classified finishers

ROUND 14/ITALIAN GRAND PRIX
MONZA, 8 SEPTEMBER

1. M.SCHUMACHER(GER)	FERRARI	1HR 17MIN 43.06SEC
2. ALESI(FRA)	BENETTON-RENAULT	1HR 18MIN 01.09SEC
3. HAKKINEN(FIN)	MCLAREN-MERCEDES	1HR 18MIN 50.03SEC
4. BRUNDLE(GB)	JORDAN-PEUGOT	1HR 19MIN 08.85SEC
5. BARRICHELLO(BRA)	JORDAN-PEUGOT	1HR 19MIN 09.11SEC
6. DINIZ(BRA)	LIGIER-MUGEN HONDA	52 LAPS

Race: 53 laps of 3.59 mile/5.77 km (190.27 miles/305.81 kms)
Fastest lap: M. Schumacher, 1min 26sec, 149.89mph/241.23kph
Pole position: D. Hill(GB) Williams-Renault, 1min 24.20sec 20 starters, 10 class. finishers

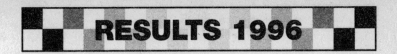

RESULTS 1996

ROUND 15/PORTUGUESE GRAND PRIX

ESTORIL, 22 SEPTEMBER

1. J.VILLENEUVE(CAN)	WILLIAMS-RENAULT	1HR 40MIN 22.09SEC
2. D.HILL(GB)	WILLIAMS-RENAULT	1HR 40MIN 42.09SEC
3. M.SCHUMACHER(GER)	FERRARI	1HR 41MIN 16.68SEC
4. ALESI(FRA)	BENETTON-RENAULT	1HR 41MIN 18.02SEC
5. IRVINE(GB)	FERRARI	1HR 41MIN 50.03SEC
6. BERGER(AUT)	BENETTON-RENAULT	1HR 41MIN 56.01SEC

Race: 70 laps of 2.71 mile/4.36 km (189.7 miles/ 305.2kms)
Fastest lap: J.Villeneuve, 1min 22.87sec, 117.69mph/189.40 kph
Pole position: D. Hill, 1min 20,33sec 20 starters, 16 classified finishers

ROUND 16 JAPANESE GRAND PRIX

SUZUKA, 13 OCTOBER

1. D.HILL(GB)	WILLIAMS-RENAULT	1HR 32MIN 33.79SEC
2. M.SCHUMACHER(GER)	FERRARI	1HR 32MIN 35.67SEC
3. HAKKINEN(FIN)	MCLAREN-MERCEDES	1HR 32MIN 37.00SEC
4. BERGER(AUT)	BENETTON-RENAULT	1HR 33MIN 00.03SEC
5. BRUNDLE(GB)	JORDAN-PEUGEOT	1HR 33MIN 40.09SEC
6. FRENTZEN(GER)	SAUBER-FORD	1HR 33MIN 55.00SEC

Race: 52 laps of 3.64 mile/5.86km (192.92 miles/310.85kms)
Fastest lap: J.Villeneuve(CAN) Williams-Renault, 1min 44.04sec, 126.08mph/202.90kph
Pole position: J.Villeneuve, 1min 38.91sec 19 starters, 13 classified finishers

DRIVERS' WORLD CHAMPIONSHIP 1996

1. D.HILL	97 points	4.	ALESI	47 points
2. J. VILLENEUVE	78	5.	HAKKINEN	31 points
3. M.SCHUMACHER	59	6.	BERGER	21 points

CONSTRUCTORS' WORLD CHAMPIONSHIP 1996

1. WILLIAMS-RENAULT	175 points	4. MCLAREN-MERCEDES	49 points
2. FERRARI	70 points	5. JORDAN-PEUGEOT	22 points
3. BENETTON-RENAULT	68 points	6. LIGIER–MUGEN HONDA	15 points

RESULTS 1997

1997 Villeneuve refused to be bullied by Schumacher and won the Drivers' title in only his second Formula One season with seven wins in total. Controversy dogged the German throughout a see-saw season in which he rose to brilliant heights and sank to ignominious depths. The FIA took away his overall second place in the Championship as punishment for his petulant move on Villeneuve in Jerez. Yet again, Williams ditched their World Champion and D.Hill bit the bullet and signed for Arrows, a team yet to score a Grand Prix victory. He nearly rectified matters in Hungary! Stewart Racing joined the circus and Barrichello finished an outstanding second for the fledgling team in Monaco. Four-times World Champion Alain Prost bought out Ligier but poor Panis broke both legs in an accident in Canada. Frentzen, Hill's replacement at Williams, won his first Grand Prix at Imola and a Finn called Hakkinen finally won, at his 96th attempt, in Jerez for McLaren-Mercedes. Berger, struggling with ill-health, took the most popular win of the year after a very brave drive for Benetton at Hockenheim, then retired at the end of the season. He would later take up the motorsport reins at BMW. Another Schumacher, Ralf, joined another young charger, Fisichella, at Jordan. There were 17 rounds. All counted towards the Championships Points: 10.6-4-3-2-1.

ROUND 1/AUSTRALIAN GRAND PRIX
MELBOURNE, 9 MARCH

1. COULTHARD(GB)	MCLAREN-MERCEDES	1HR 30MIN 28.7SEC
2. SCHUMACHER(GER)	FERRARI	1HR 30MIN 48.8SEC
3. HAKKINEN(FIN)	MCLAREN-MERCEDES	1HR 30MIN 50.9SEC
4. BERGER(AUT)	BENETTON-RENAULT	1HR 31MIN 29.0SEC
5. PANIS(FRA)	PROST-MUGEN HONDA	1HR 32MIN 04.8SEC
6. LARINI(ITA)	SAUBER-PETRONAS	1HR 32MIN 11.6SEC

Race: 58 laps of 3.3mile/5.3km (191.4 miles/307.4kms)
Fastest lap: Frentzen(GER) Williams-Renault,1min 30.59sec, 130.94mph/209.5kph
Pole position: J.Villeneuve(CAN), Williams-Renault 1min 29.37sec 21 starters, 10 classified finishers

ROUND 2/BRAZILIAN GRAND PRIX
INTERLAGOS, 30 MARCH

1. J.VILLENEUVE(CAN)	WILLIAMS-RENAULT	1HR 36MIN 06.9SEC
2. BERGER(AUT)	BENETTON-RENAULT	1HR 36MIN 11.2SEC
3. PANIS(FRA)	PROST-MUGEN HONDA	1HR 36MIN 22.9SEC
4. HAKKINEN(FIN)	MCLAREN-MERCEDES	1HR 36MIN 40.02SEC
5. M.SCHUMACHER(GER)	FERRARI	1HR 36MIN 40.72SEC
6. ALESI(FRA)	BENETTON-RENAULT	1HR 36MIN 41.01SEC

Race: 72 laps of 2.66 mile/4.26km (191.52 miles/306.72 kms)
Fastest lap: J.Villeneuve, 1min 18.4sec,122.47mph/195.95kph
Pole position: J.Villeneuve, 1min 16.00sec 22 starters, 18 classified finishers.

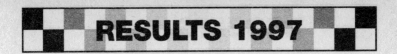
RESULTS 1997

ROUND 3/ARGENTINE GRAND PRIX
BUNEOS AIRES, 7 APRIL

1. J.VILLENEUVE(CAN)	WILLIAMS-RENAULT	1HR 52MIN 01.72SEC
2. IRVINE(GB)	FERRARI	1HR 52MIN 02.69SEC
3. R. SCHUMACHER(GER)	JORDAN-PEUGEOT	1HR 52MIN 13.08SEC
4. HERBERT(GB)	SAUBER-PETRONAS	1HR 52MIN 32.07SEC
5. HAKKINEN(FIN)	MCLAREN-MERCEDES	1HR 52MIN 33.11SEC
6. BERGER(AUT)	BENETTON-RENAULT	1HR 52MIN 48.01SEC

Race: 72 laps of 2.65 mile/4.26km (190.8 miles/306.72kms)
Fastest lap: Berger, 1min 27.98sec, 108.29mph/173.26kph
Pole position: J.Villeneuve, 1min 24.47sec 22 starters, 10 classified finishers

ROUND 4/ SAN MARINO GRAND PRIX
IMOLA, 27 APRIL

1. FRENTZEN(GER)	WILLIAMS-RENAULT	1HR 31MIN 00.67SEC
2. M.SCHUMACHER(GER)	FERRARI	1HR 31MIN 01.91SEC
3. IRVINE(GB)	FERRARI	1HR 32MIN 19.00SEC
4. FISICHELLA(ITA)	JORDAN-PEUGEOT	1HR 32MIN 24.01SEC
5. ALESI(FRA)	BENETTON-RENAULT	61 LAPS
6. HAKKINEN(FIN)	MCLAREN-MERCEDES	61 LAPS

Race: 62 laps of 3.04 mile/4.89 km (188.48 miles/303.18kms)
Fastest lap: Frentzen, 1min 25.53sec, 128.94mph/206.30kph
Pole position: J.Villeneuve(CAN),Williams-Renault, 1min 23.30sec 21 starters, 11 class. finishers

ROUND 5/MONACO GRAND PRIX
MONTE CARLO, 11 MAY

1. M.SCHUMACHER(GER)	FERRARI	2HR 00MIN 05.7SEC
2. BARRICHELLO(BRA)	STEWART-FORD	2HR 00MIN 59.0SEC
3. IRVINE(GB)	FERRARI	2HR 01MIN 27.8SEC
4. PANIS(FRA)	PROST-MUGEN-HONDA	2HR 01MIN 50.1SEC
5. SALO(FIN)	TYRRELL-FORD	61 LAPS
6. FISICHELLA(FRA)	JORDAN-PEUGEOT	61 LAPS

Race: 62 laps of 2.09 mile/3.34km (129.58 miles/ 207.08 kms)
Fastest lap: M.Schumacher, 1min 53.32sec, 66.45mph/106.32kph
Pole position: Frentzen(GER) Williams-Renault, 1min 18.22sec 22 starters,10 class. finishers.

ROUND 6/SPANISH GRAND PRIX
BARCELONA, 25 MAY

1. J.VILLENEUVE(CAN)	WILLIAMS-RENAULT	1HR 30MIN 35.09SEC
2. PANIS(FRA)	PROST-MUGEN HONDA	1HR 30MIN 41.07SEC
3. ALESI(FRA)	BENETTON-RENAULT	1HR 30MIN 48.04SEC
4. M.SCHUMACHER(GER)	FERRARI	1HR 30MIN 54.00SEC
5. HERBERT(GB)	SAUBER-PETRONAS	1HR 31MIN 03.88SEC
6. COULTHARD(GB)	MCLAREN-MERCEDES	1HR 31MIN 05.64SEC

Race: 64 laps of 2.94mile/4.73 km (188.16 miles/ 302.72kms)
Fastest lap: Fisichella (ITA),Jordan-Peugeot, 1min 22.24sec, 128.60mph/205.76 kph
Pole position: J.Villeneuve,1min 16.53sec 22 starters, 15 classified finishers.

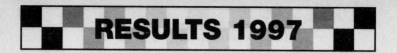

RESULTS 1997

ROUND7/CANADIAN GRAND PRIX

MONTREAL, 15 JUNE 1997

1. M.SCHUMACHER(GER)	FERRARI	1HR 17MIN 40.07SEC
2. ALESI(FRA)	BENETTON-RENAULT	1HR 17MIN 43.21SEC
3. FISICHELLA(ITA)	JORDAN-PEUGEOT	1HR 17MIN 43.87SEC
4. FRENTZEN(GER)	WILLIAMS-RENAULT	1HR 17MIN 44.41SEC
5. HERBERT(GB)	SAUBER-PETRONAS	1HR 17MIN 45.36SEC
6. NAKANO(JAP)	PROST-MUGEN HONDA	1HR 18MIN 17.03SEC

Race: 54 laps of 2.75 mile/4.42 km (148.50 miles/238.68kms)
Fastest lap: Coulthard(GB) McLaren-Mercedes, 1min 19.64sec, 124.19 mph/ 198.70 kph
Pole position: M.Schumacher,1 min 18.10sec 22 starters,11 classified finishers

ROUND 8/FRENCH GRAND PRIX

MAGNY-COURS, 29 JUNE

1. M.SCHUMACHER(GER)	FERRARI	1HR 38MIN 50.05SEC
2. FRENTZEN(GER)	WILLIAMS-RENAULT	1HR 39MIN 00.14SEC
3. IRVINE(GB)	FERRARI	1HR 40MIN 05.03SEC
4. J.VILLENEUVE(CAN)	WILLIAMS-RENAULT	1HR 40MIN 12.03SEC
5. ALESI(FRA)	BENETTON-RENAULT	1HR 40MIN 13.02SEC
6. R. SCHUMACHER(GER)	JORDAN-PEUGEOT	1HR 40MIN 20.04SEC

Race: 72 laps of 2.64 mile/4.25 km (190.08miles3306.0kms)
Fastest lap: M. Schumacher, 1min 17.91sec, 122.03mph/195.25kph
Pole position: M. Schumacher, 1min 14.55sec 22 starters,12 classified finishers

ROUND 9/BRITISH GRAND PRIX

SILVERSTONE, 13 JULY

1. J.VILLENEUVE(CAN)	WILLIAMS-RENAULT	1HR 28MIN 01.07SEC
2. ALESI(FRA)	BENETTON-RENAULT	1HR 28MIN 11.87SEC
3. WURZ(AUT)	BENETTON-RENAULT	1HR 28MIN 12.96SEC
4. COULTHARD(GB)	MCLAREN-MERCEDES	1HR 28MIN 32.89SEC
5. R. SCHUMACHER(GER)	JORDAN-PEUGEOT	1HR 28MIN 33.55SEC
6. D. HILL(GB)	ARROWS-YAMAHA	1HR 29MIN 15.02SEC

Race: 59 laps of 3.19 mile/5.1 km (188.21 miles/300.9kms)
Fastest lap: M.Schumacher(GER) Ferrari, 1min 24.48sec, 136.12mph/217.79kph
*Pole position:*J. Villeneuve, 1min 21.60sec 22 starters, 11 classified finishers

ROUND 10/GERMAN GRAND PRIX

HOCKENEHEIM, 27 JULY

1. BERGER(AUT)	BENETTON-RENAULT	1HR 20MIN 59.01SEC
2. M.SCHUMACHER(GER)	FERRARI	1HR 21MIN 16.06SEC
3. HAKKINEN(FIN)	MCLAREN-MERCEDES	1HR 21MIN 23.08SEC
4. TRULLI(ITA)	PROST-MUGEN HONDA	1HR 21MIN 26.02SEC
5. R. SCHUMACHER(GER)	JORDAN-PEUGEOT	1HR 21MIN 29.00SEC
6. ALESI(FRA)	BENETTON-RENAULT	1HR 21MIN 33.08SEC

Race: 45 laps of 4.24mile/6.82km (190.8 miles/306.9kms)
Fastest lap: Berger, 1min 45.75sec, 144.34mph/ 230.94kph
Pole position: Berger, 1min 41.87sec 22 starters, 11 classified finishers

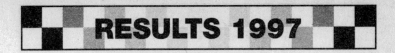

RESULTS 1997

ROUND 11/HUNGARIAN GRAND PRIX
HUNGARORING, 10 AUGUST

1. J.VILLENEUVE(CAN)	WILLIAMS-RENAULT	1HR 45MIN 47.02SEC
2. D.HILL(GB)	ARROWS-YAMAHA	1HR 45MIN 56.03SEC
3. HERBERT(GB)	SAUBER-PETRONAS	1HR 46MIN 07.06SEC
4. M.SCHUMACHER(GER)	FERRARI	1HR 46MIN 17.65SEC
5. R.SCHUMACHER(GER)	JORDAN-PEUGEOT	1HR 46MIN 17.86SEC
6. NAKANO(JAP)	PROST-MUGEN HONDA	1HR 46MIN 28.07SEC

Race: 77 laps of 2.47 mile/3.97 km (190.19miles/305.69 kms)
Fastest lap: Frentzen(GER)Williams-Renault, 1min 18.37sec, 113.26mph/181.22kph
Pole position: M.Schumacher, 1min 14.67sec 22 starters,13 classified finishers

ROUND 12/BELGIAN GRAND PRIX
SPA-FRANCORCHAMPS, 24 AUGUST

1. M.SCHUMACHER(GER)	FERRARI	1HR 33MIN 46.07SEC
2. FISICHELLA(ITA)	JORDAN-PEUGEOT	1HR 34MIN 13 05SEC
3*. FRENTZEN(GER)	WILLIAMS-RENAULT	1HR 34MIN 18.09SEC
4. HERBERT(GB)	SAUBER-PETRONAS	1HR 34MIN 25.07SEC
5. J.VILLENEUVE(CAN)	WILLIAMS-RENAULT	1HR 34MIN 28.08SEC
6. BERGER(AUT)	BENETTON-RENAULT	1HR 34MIN 50.05SEC

Race: 44 laps of 4.33 mile/6.97 km (190.52 miles/306.68 kms)
Fastest lap: J.Villeneuve, 1min 52.69sec, 138.32mph/221.31kph
Pole position: J.Villeneuve, 1min 49.45sec 22 starters, 16* classified finishers
Hakkinen(FIN)McLaren-Mercedes, finished 3rd but disqualified for fuel irregularities

ROUND 13 ITALIAN GRAND PRIX
MONZA, 7 SEPTEMBER

1. COULTHARD(GB)	MCLAREN-MERCEDES	1HR 17MIN 04.06SEC
2. ALESI(FRA)	BENETTON-RENAULT	1HR 17MIN 06.06SEC
3. FRENTZEN(GER)	WILLIAMS-RENAULT	1HR 17MIN 09.00SEC
4. FISICHELLA(ITA)	JORDAN-PEUGEOT	1HR 17MIN 10.05SEC
5. J.VILLENEUVE(CAN)	WILLIAMS-RENAULT	1HR 17MIN 11.00SEC
6. M.SCHUMACHER(GER)	FERRARI	1HR 17MIN 16.01SEC

Race: 53 laps of 3.59 mile/5.77 km (190.27 miles/305.81kms)
Fastest lap: Hakkinen(FIN)McLaren-Mercedes, 1min 24.81sec, 152.02mph/243.52kph
Pole position: Alesi,1min 22.99sec 22 starters, 14 classified finishers

ROUND 14/AUSTRIAN GRAND PRIX
A-1 RING, 21 SEPTEMBER

1. J.VILLENEUVE(CAN)	WILLIAMS-RENAULT	1HR 27MIN 36.00SEC
2. COULTHARD(GB)	MCLAREN-MERCEDES	1HR 27MIN 38.91SEC
3. FRENTZEN(GER)	WILLIAMS-RENAULT	1HR 27MIN 39.96SEC
4. FISICHELLA(ITA)	JORDAN-PEUGEOT	1HR 27MIN 48.01SEC
5. R.SCHUMACHER(GER)	JORDAN-PEUGEOT	1HR 28MIN 07.09SEC
6. M.SCHUMACHER(GER)	FERRARI	1HR 28MIN 09.04SEC

Race: 71 laps of 2.67 mile/4.27 km (189.57 miles/303.17 kms)
Fastest lap: J.Villeneuve, 1min 11.81sec, 135.44mph/216.7kph
Pole position: J. Villeneuve, 1min 10.30sec 21 starters, 14 classified finishers

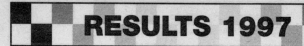

RESULTS 1997

ROUND 15/LUXEMBOURG GRAND PRIX
NURBURGRING, 28 SEPTEMBER

1. J.VILLENEUVE(CAN)	WILLIAMS-RENAULT	1HR 31MIN 27.08SEC
2. ALESI(FRA)	BENETTON-RENAULT	1HR 31MIN 39.06SEC
3. FRENTZEN(GER)	WILLIAMS-RENAULT	1HR 31MIN 41.03SEC
4. BERGER(AUT)	BENETTON-RENAULT	1HR 31MIN 44.03SEC
5. DINIZ(BRA)	ARROWS-YAMAHA	1HR 32MIN 10.99SEC
6. PANIS(FRA)	PROST-MUGEN HONDA	1HR 32MIN 11.59SEC

Race: 67 laps of 2.83 mile/4.56 km (189.61 miles/305.52kms)
Fastest lap: Frentzen, 1min 18.81sec, 129.31mph/206.89kph
*Pole position:*Hakkinen(FIN)McLaren-Mercedes, 1min 16.60sec 22 starters, 10
classified finishers

ROUND 16/JAPANESE GRAND PRIX
SUZUKA, 12 OCTOBER

1. M.SCHUMACHER(GER)	FERRARI	1HR 29MIN 48.45SEC
2. FRENTZEN(GER)	WILLIAMS-RENAULT	1HR 29MIN 49.82SEC
3. IRVINE(GB)	FERRARI	1HR 30MIN 14.83SEC
4. HAKKINEN(FIN)	MCLAREN-MERCEDES	1HR 30MIN 15.58SEC
5.* ALESI(FRA)	BENETTON-RENAULT	1HR 30MIN 28.85SEC
6. HERBERT(GB)	SAUBER-PETRONAS	1HR 30MIN 30.01SEC

Race: 53 laps of 3.64 mile/5.96km (192.92 miles/ 310.58 kms)
Fastest lap: Frentzen, 1min 38.94sec, 130.66mph/209.06kph
Pole position: J.Villeneuve(CAN)Williams-Renault, 1min 36.07sec 20 starters, 13*
classified finishers
*J.Villeneuve raced under appeal after practice infringement. He finished fifth but was
disqualified by FIA.

ROUND 17/EUROPEAN GRAND PRIX
JEREZ, 26 OCTOBER

1. HAKKINEN(FIN)	MCLAREN-MERCEDES	1HR 38MIN 57.77SEC
2. COULTHARD(GB)	MCLAREN-MERCEDES	1HR 38MIN 59.43SEC
3. J.VILLENEUVE(CAN)	WILLIAMS-RENAULT	1HR 38MIN 59.54SEC
4. BERGER(AUT)	BENETTON-RENAULT	1HR 38MIN 59.69SEC
5. IRVINE(GB)	FERRARI	1HR 39MIN 01.56SEC
6. FRENTZEN(GER)	WILLIAMS-RENAULT	1HR 39MIN 02.31SEC

Race: 69 laps of 2.75 mile/4.4km (189.75 miles/303.6kms)
Fastest lap: Frentzen, 1min 25.14sec, 119.15mph/191.75kph
Pole position: J.Villeneuve, 1min 20.07sec 22 starters, 17 classified finishers

DRIVERS' WORLD CHAMPIONSHIP 1997
1. VILLENEUVE *81 points*   3. COULTHARD *36 points*
2* FRENTZEN *42 points*   5. BERGER   *26 points*
3. ALESI   *36 points*   5. HAKKINEN *26 points*
*M. SCHUMACHER FINISHED SECOND WITH 78 POINTS BUT
WAS DISQUALIFIED BY THE FIA AT THE END OF THE SEASON.

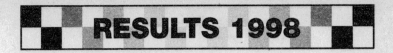

RESULTS 1998

1998 Hakkinen's miracle year ended in eight victories and narry a cross word between himself and second-placed Schumacher, M. The season went down to the wire again. There was controversy aplenty throughout the season but plenty of respect between the two main protagonists. McLaren-Mercedes were a class act and Bridgestone emerged victorious at their first attempt. Goodyear pulled out at the end of the year with 368 wins to their credit since 1965. Damon Hill moved to Jordan and scored the team's first-ever Grand Prix victory in Belgium. Reigning Champion, Villeneuve discovered that the Williams team had been caught napping during the closed season and could finish no higher than fifth overall. Renault had withdrawn their factory support. Benetton signed two young lions in Fisichella and Wurz but new team-manager David Richards didn't last the pace. Jordan finished fourth ahead of them in the Constructors' table for the first time. Stewart had a nightmare season, as did Arrows and Prost. And 'Uncle Ken' Tyrrell found the precocious new BAR management too much to bear and left them to it - nulle points...There were 16 rounds. All results counted for both Championships. Points: 10-6-4-3-2-1.

ROUND 1 AUSTRALIAN GRAND PRIX
MELBOURNE, 8 MARCH

1. HAKKINEN(FIN)	MCLAREN-MERCEDES	1HR 31MIN 46.00SEC
2. COULTHARD(GB)	MCLAREN-MERCEDES	1HR 31MIN 47.12SEC
3. FRENTZEN(GER)	WILLIAMS-MECACHROME	57 LAPS
4. IRVINE(GB)	FERRARI	57 LAPS
5. J.VILLENEUVE(CAN)	WILLIAMS-MECACHROME	57 LAPS
6. HERBERT(GB)	SAUBER-PETRONAS	57 LAPS

Race: 58 laps of 3.3 mile/5.3km circuit 6 191.4 miles/307.4 kms)
Fastest lap: Hakkinen, 1min 31.65sec, 129.43mph/208.30kph
Pole position: Hakkinen, 1min 30.01sec 22 starters, 9 classified finishers

RESULTS 1998

ROUND 2/ BRAZILIAN GRAND PRIX
INTERLAGOS, 29 MARCH

1. HAKKINEN(FIN)	MCLAREN-MERCEDES	1HR 37MIN 11.75SEC
2. COULTHARD(GB)	MCLAREN-MERCEDES	1HR 37MIN 12.85SEC
3. M. SCHUMACHER(GER)	FERRARI	1HR 38MIN 12.20SEC
4. WURZ(AUT)	BENETTON-PLAYLIFE	1HR 38MIN 19.65SEC
5. FRENTZEN(GER)	WILLIAMS-MECACHROME	71 LAPS
6. FISICHELLA(ITA)	BENETTON-PLAYLIFE	71 LAPS

Race: 72 laps of 2.66 mile/4.26km (191.52 miles/306.72 kms)
Fastest lap: Hakkinen, 1min 19.34sec, 121.01mph/194.75kph
Pole position: Hakkinen, 1min 17.09sec 22 starters, 11 classified finishers

ROUND 3/ARGENTINE GRAND PRIX
BUENOS AIRES, 7 APRIL

1. M.SCHUMACHER(GER)	FERRARI	1HR 48MIN 36.18SEC
2. HAKKINEN(FIN)	MCLAREN-MERCEDES	1HR 48MIN 59.08SEC
3. IRVINE(GB)	FERRARI	1HR 49MIN 33.93SEC
4. WURZ(AUT)	BENETTON-PLAYLIFE	1HR 49MIN 44.31SEC
5. ALESI(FRA)	SAUBER-PETRONAS	1HR 49MIN 54.47SEC
6. COULTHARD(GB)	MCLAREN-MERCEDES	1HR 49MIN 55.93SEC

Race: 72 laps of 2.65 mile/4.26 km (190.8miles/306.72 kms)
Fastest lap: Wurz, 1min 28.19sec, 108.04mph/173.88kph
Pole position: Coulthard, 1min 25.85sec 22 starters, 15 classified finishers

ROUND 4/SAN MARINO GRAND PRIX
IMOLA, 27 APRIL

1. COULTHARD(GB)	MCLAREN-MERCEDES	1HR 34MIN 24.59SEC
2. M.SCHUMACHER(GER)	FERRARI	1HR 34MIN 29.14SEC
3. IRVINE(GB)	FERRARI	1HR 35MIN 16.37SEC
4. J. VILLENEUVE(CAN)	WILLIAMS-MECACHROME	1HR 35MIN 19.18SEC
5. FRENTZEN(GER)	WILLIAMS-MECACHROME	1HR 35MIN 42.07SEC
6. ALESI(FRA)	SAUBER-PETRONAS	61 LAPS

Race: 62 laps of 3.06 mile/4.93km (189.72 miles/305.66kms)
Fastest lap: M. Schumacher, 1min 29.35sec, 123.43mph/ 198.65kph
Pole position: Coulthard, 1min 25.97sec 22 starters, 11 classified finishers

ROUND 5/SPANISH GRAND PRIX
BARCELONA, 10 MAY 1998

1. HAKKINEN(FIN)	MCLAREN-MERCEDES	1HR 33MIN 37.62SEC
2. COULTHARD(GB)	MCLAREN-MERCEDES	1HR 33MIN 47.06SEC
3. M. SCHUMACHER(GER)	FERRARI	1HR 34MIN 24.71SEC
4. WURZ(AUT)	BENETTON-PLAYLIFE	1HR 34MIN 40.16SEC
5. BARICHELLO(BRA)	STEWART-FORD	64 LAPS
6. J.VILLENEUVE(CAN)	WILLIAMS-MECACHROME 64 LAPS	

Race: 65 laps of 2.94 mile/4.73km (191.10 miles/307.45 kms)
Fastest lap: Hakkinen, 1min 24.28sec, 125.50 mph/ 201.97kph
Pole position: Hakkinen, 1min 20.62sec 21 starters, 16 classified finishers

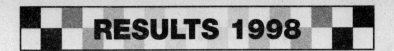

RESULTS 1998

ROUND 6/MONACO GRAND PRIX
MONTE CARLO, 24 MAY

1. HAKKINEN(FIN)	MCLAREN-MERCEDES	1HR 51 MIN 23.60SEC
2. FISICHELLA(ITA)	BENETTON-PLAYLIFE	1HR 51 MIN 35.08SEC
3. IRVINE(GB)	FERRARI	1HR 52MIN 05.00SEC
4. SALO(FIN)	ARROWS	1HR 52MIN 23.96SEC
5. J.VILLENEUVE(CAN)	WILLIAMS-MECACHROME	77 LAPS
6. DINIZ(BRA)	ARROWS	77 LAPS

Race: 78 laps of 2.09 mile/ 3.34km (163.02 miles/ 260.52kms)
Fastest lap: Hakkinen,1 min 22,95sec,90.80mph/146.13kph
Pole position: Hakkinen, 1min 19.80sec 21 starters, 12 classified finishers

ROUND 7 CANADIAN GRAND PRIX
MONTREAL, 7 JUNE

1. M. SCHUMACHER(GER)	FERRARI	1HR 40MIN 57.36SEC
2. FISICHELLA (ITA)	BENETTON-PLAYLIFE	1HR 41MIN 14.02SEC
3. IRVINE (GB)	FERRARI	1HR 41MIN 57.72SEC
4. WURZ (AUT)	BENETTON-PLAYLIFE	1HR 42MIN 00.59SEC
5. BARRICHELLO(BRA)	STEWART-FORD	1HR 43MIN 18.87SEC
6. MAGNUSSEN(DEN)	STEWART-FORD	68 LAPS

Race: 69 laps of 2.75 mile/4.42 km (189.75 miles / 304.98kms)
Fastest lap: M. Schumacher, 1min 19.38sec
Pole position: Coulthard(GB) Mclaren-Mercedes, 1min 18.21sec 22 starters, 10 class. finishers

ROUND 8/ FRENCH GRAND PRIX
MAGNY-COURS, 28 JUNE

1. M.SCHUMACHER(GER)	FERRARI	1HR 34MIN 45.03SEC
2. IRIVINE(GB)	FERRARI	1HR 35MIN 04.61SEC
3. HAKKINEN(FIN)	MCLAREN-MERCEDES	1HR 35MIN 04.78SEC
4. J.VILLENEUVE(CAN)	WILLIAMS-MECACHROME	1HR 35MIN 52.00SEC
5. WURZ(AUT)	BENETTON-PLAYLIFE	70 LAPS
6. COULTHARD(GB)	MCLAREN-MERCEDES	70 LAPS

Race: 71 laps of 2.64 mile/4.25 km (187.44 miles/301.75kms)
Fastest lap: Coulthard, 1min 17.52sec, 122.63mph/197.36kph
Pole position: Hakkinen, 1min 14.93sec 22 starters, 17 classified finishers

ROUND 9 /BRITISH GRAND PRIX
SIVERSTONE/12 JULY

1. M.SCHUMACHER(GER)	FERRARI	1HR 47MIN 12.45SEC
2. HAKKINEN(FIN)	MCLAREN-MERCEDES	1HR 47MIN 24.92SEC
3. IRVINE(GB)	FERRARI	1HR 47MIN 31.65SEC
4. WURZ(AUT)	BENETTON-PLAYLIFE	59 LAPS
5. FISICHELLA(ITA)	BENETTON-PLAYLIFE	59 LAPS
6. R. SCHUMACHER(GER)	JORDAN-MUGEN HONDA	59 LAPS

Race: 60 laps of 3.19mile/5.1km (191.4 miles/306.0kms)
Fastest lap: M. Schumacher, 1min 35.70sec, 120.14mph/193.35kph
Pole position: Hakkinen, 1min 23.27sec 22 starters, 9 classified finishers

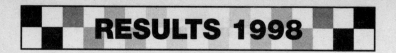
RESULTS 1998

ROUND 10/AUSTRIAN GRAND PRIX
A-1 RING

1. HAKKINEN(FIN)	MCLAREN-MERCEDES	1HR 30MIN 44.09SEC
2. COULTHARD(GB)	MCLAREN-MERCEDES	1HR 30MIN 49.38SEC
3. M. SCHUMACHER(GER)	FERRARI	1HR 31MIN 23.18SEC
4. IRVINE(GB)	FERRARI	1HR 31MIN 28.07SEC
5. R. SCHUMACHER(GER)	JORDAN-MUGEN HONDA	1HR 31MIN 34.74SEC
6. J. VILLENEUVE(CAN)	WILLIAMS-MECACHROME	1HR 31MIN 37.29SEC

Race: 71 laps of 2.68 mile/4.32km (190.28 miles/306.72 kms)
Fastest lap: Coulthard, 1min 12.88sec, 132.57mph/213.35kph
Pole position: Fisichella(ITA) Benetton Mecachrome, 1min 29.60sec 22 starters, 12 class. finishers

ROUND 11/GERMAN GRAND PRIX
HOCKENHEIM, 2 AUGUST

1. HAKKINEN(FIN)	MCLAREN-MERCEDES	1HR 20MIN 47.98SEC
2. COULTHARD(GB)	MCLAREN-MERCEDES	1HR 20MIN 48.41SEC
3. J.VILLENEUVE(CAN)	WILLIAMS-MECACHROME	1HR 20MIN 50.56SEC
4. D. HILL(GB)	JORDAN-MUGEN HONDA	1HR 20MIN 55.17SEC
5. M. SCHUMACHER(GER)	FERRARI	1HR 21MIN 00.59SEC
6. R. SCHUMACHER(GER)	JORDAN-MUGEN HONDA	1HR 21MIN 17.72SEC

Race: 45 laps of 4.24mile/ 6.82km (190.8miles/306.9kms)
Fastest lap: Coulthard, 1min 46.12sec, 143.83mph/231.47kph
Pole position: Hakkinen, 1min 41.84sec 21 starters, 16 classified finishers

ROUND 12/HUNGARIAN GRAND PRIX
HUNGARORING, 16 AUGUST

1. M. SCHUMACHER(GER)	FERRARI	1HR 45MIN 25.55SEC
2. COULTHARD(GB)	MCLAREN-MERCEDES	1HR 45MIN 34.98SEC
3. J.VILLENEUVE(CAN)	WILLIAMS-MECACHROME	1HR 46MIN 09.99SEC
4. D. HILL(GB)	JORDAN-MUGEN HONDA	1HR 46MIN 20.63SEC
5. FRENTZEN(GER)	WILLIAMS-MECACHROME	1HR 46MIN 22.06SEC
6. HAKKINEN(FIN)	MCLAREN-MERCEDES	76 LAPS

Race: 77 laps of 2.47 mile/3.97km (190.19 miles/ 305.69 kms)
Fastest lap: M.Schumacher, 1min 19.29sec, 112.06mph/180.35kph
Pole position: Hakkinen, 1min 16.97sec 21 starters, 16 classified finishers

ROUND 13/BELGIAN GRAND PRIX
SPA-FRANCORCHAMPS, 30 AUGUST

1. D. HILL(GB)	JORDAN-MUGEN HONDA	1HR 43MIN 47.41SEC
2. R. SCHUMACHER(GER)	JORDAN-MUGEN HONDA	1HR 43MIN 48.34SEC
3. ALESI(FRA)	SAUBER-PETRONAS	1HR 43MIN 54.65SEC
4. FRENTZEN(GER)	WILLIAMS-MECACHROME	1HR 44MIN 19.65SEC
5. DINIZ(BRA)	ARROWS	1HR 44MIN 39.09SEC
6. TRULLI(ITA)	PROST-PEUGEOT	42 LAPS

Race: 44 laps of 4.33mile/6.96km (190.52 miles/306.68 kms)
Fastest lap: M.Schumacher(GER) Ferrari, 2min 03.77sec, 125.94mph/202.68kph
Pole position: Hakkinen(FIN), McLaren-Mercedes, 1min 48.68sec 22 starters, 8 class. finishers

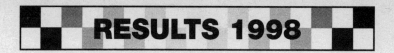
RESULTS 1998

ROUND 14/ITALIAN GRAND PRIX
MONZA, 13 SEPTEMBER

1. M.SCHUMACHER(GER)	FERRARI	1HR 17MIN 09.67SEC
2. IRVINE(GB)	FERRARI	1HR 17MIN 47.65SEC
3. R.SCHUMACHER(GER)	JORDAN-MUGEN HONDA	1HR 17MIN 50.82SEC
4. HAKKINEN(FIN)	MCLAREN-MERCEDES	1HR 18MIN 05.34SEC
5. ALESI(FRA)	SAUBER-PETRONAS	1HR 18MIN 11.54SEC
6. D. HILL(GB)	JORDAN-MUGEN HONDA	1HR 18MIN 16.56SEC

Race: 53 laps of 3.59 mile/5.77 km (190.27 miles/ 305.81kms)
Fastest lap: Hakkinen, 1min 25.14sec, 151.60mph/243.98kph
Pole position: M. Schumacher, 1min 25.29sec 22 starters, 13 classified finishers

ROUND 15/LUXEMBOURG GRAND PRIX
NURBURGRING, 28 SEPTEMBER

1. HAKKINEN(FIN)	MCLAREN-MERCEDES	1HR 32MIN 14.79SEC
2. M.SCHUMACHER(GER)	FERRARI	1HR 32MIN 17.00SEC
3. COULTHARD(GB)	MCLAREN-MERCEDES	1HR 32MIN 48.95SEC
4. IRVINE(GB)	FERRARI	1HR 33MIN 12.97SEC
5. FRENTZEN(GER)	WILLIAMS-MECACHROME	1HR 33MIN 14.80SEC
6. FISICHELLA(ITA)	BENETTON-PLAYLIFE	1HR 33MIN 16.15SEC

Race: 67 laps of 2.83 mile/4.56km (189.61 miles/ 305.52kms)
Fastest lap: Hakkinen, 1min 20.45sec, 126.69mph/203.87kph
Pole position: M.Schumacher, 1min 18.56sec 22 starters, 16 classified finishers

ROUND 16/JAPANESE GRAND PRIX
SUZUKA, 1 NOVEMBER

1. HAKKINEN(FIN)	MCLAREN-MERCEDES	1HR 27MIN 22.54SEC
2. IRVINE(GB)	FERRARI	1HR 27MIN 29.03SEC
3. COULTHARD(GB)	MCLAREN-MERCEDES	1HR 27MIN 50.20SEC
4. D.HILL(GB)	JORDAN-MUGEN HONDA	1HR 28MIN 36.03SEC
5. FRENTZEN(GER)	WILLIAMS-MECACHROME	1HR 28MIN 36.40SEC
6. J.VILLENEUVE(CAN)	WILLAIMS-MECACHROME	1HR 28MIN 38.40SEC

Race: 51 laps of 3.64 mile/ 5.86 km (185.64 miles/298.86 kms)
Fastest lap: M.Schumacher(GER), Ferrari, 1min 40.19sec, 130.93mph/210.70kph
Pole position: M.Schumacher, 1min 36.29sec 21 starters, 12 classified finishers

---

DRIVERS' WORLD CHAMPIONSHIP 1998

1. HAKKINEN *100 points*	4. IRVINE *47 points*
2. M.SCHUMACHER *86 points*	5. J. VILLENEUVE *21*
3. COULTHARD *56 points*	6. D.HILL *20 points*

CONSTRUCTORS' WORLD CHAMPIONSHIP 1998

1. MCLAREN-MERCEDES *156 points*	4. JORDAN MUGEN-HONDA *34*
2. FERRARI *133 points*	5. BENETTON-PLAYLIFE *33 points*
3. WILLIAMS-MECACHROME *38*	6. SAUBER-PETRONAS *10 points*

GENERAL

RESULTS

ROLL OF HONOUR

THE WORLD DRIVERS' CHAMPIONS 1950 - 1998

Drivers from 13 different nations have won the World Drivers' Championship since its inception in 1950. Here, we present the roll of honour:-

1950	GUISEPPE FARINA (ITALY)	**1975**	NIKI LAUDA (AUSTRIA)
1951	JUAN-MANUEL FANGIO (ARGENTINA)	**1976**	JAMES HUNT (GREAT BRITAIN)
1952	ALBERTO ASCARI (ITALY)	**1977**	NIKI LAUDA (AUSTRIA)
1953	ALBERTO ASCARI (ITALY)	**1978**	MARIO ANDRETTI (USA)
1954	JUAN-MANUEL FANGIO (ARGENTINA)	**1979**	JODY SCHECKTER (SOUTH AFRICA)
1955	JUAN-MANUEL FANGIO (ARGENTINA)	**1980**	ALAN JONES (AUSTRALIA)
1956	JUAN-MANUEL FANGIO (ARGENTINA)	**1981**	NELSON PIQUET (BRAZIL)
1957	JUAN-MANUEL FANGIO (ARGENTINA)	**1982**	KEKE ROSBERG (FINLAND)
1958	MIKE HAWTHORN (GREAT BRITAIN)	**1983**	NELSON PIQUET (BRAZIL)
1959	JACK BRABHAM (AUSTRALIA)	**1984**	NIKI LAUDA (AUSTRIA)
1960	JACK BRABHAM (AUSTRALIA)	**1985**	ALAIN PROST (FRANCE)
1961	PHIL HILL (USA)	**1986**	ALAIN PROST (FRANCE)
1962	GRAHAM HILL (GREAT BRITAIN)	**1987**	NELSON PIQUET (BRAZIL)
1963	JIM CLARK (GREAT BRITAIN)	**1988**	AYRTON SENNA (BRAZIL)
1964	JOHN SURTEES (GREAT BRITAIN)	**1989**	ALAIN PROST (FRANCE)
1965	JIM CLARK (GREAT BRITAIN)	**1990**	AYRTON SENNA (BRAZIL)
1966	JACK BRABHAM (AUSTRALIA)	**1991**	AYRTON SENNA (BRAZIL)
1967	DENNY HULME (NEW ZEALAND)	**1992**	NIGEL MANSELL (GREAT BRITAIN)
1968	GRAHAM HILL (GREAT BRITAIN)	**1993**	ALAIN PROST (FRANCE)
1969	JACKIE STEWART (GREAT BRITAIN)	**1994**	MICHAEL SCHUMACHER (GER)
1970	JOCHEN RINDT (AUSTRIA)	**1995**	MICHAEL SCHUMACHER (GER)
1971	JACKIE STEWART (GREAT BRITAIN)	**1996**	DAMON HILL (GREAT BRITAIN)
1972	EMERSON FITTIPALDI (BRAZIL)	**1997**	JACQUES VILLENEUVE (CANADA)
1973	JACKIE STEWART (GREAT BRITAIN)	**1998**	MIKA HAKKINEN (FINLAND)
1974	EMERSON FITTIPALDI (BRAZIL)		

ROLL OF HONOUR

THE WORLD CONSTRUCTORS' CHAMPIONSHIP 1958 - 1998

Eleven different constructors have won the title in the 40 years since its inception in 1958, with a variety of power units. Here is their roll of honour:

1958	VANWALL	**1979**	FERRARI
1959	COOPER-CLIMAX	**1980**	WILLIAMS-FORD
1960	COOPER-CLIMAX	**1981**	WILLIAMS-FORD
1961	FERRARI	**1982**	FERRARI
1962	BRM	**1983**	FERRARI
1963	LOTUS-CLIMAX	**1984**	MCLAREN-TAG
1964	FERRARI	**1985**	MCLAREN-TAG
1965	LOTUS-CLIMAX	**1986**	WILLIAMS-HONDA
1966	BRABHAM-REPCO	**1987**	WILLIAMS-HONDA
1967	BRABHAM-REPCO	**1988**	MCLAREN-HONDA
1968	LOTUS-FORD	**1989**	MCLAREN-HONDA
1969	MATRA-FORD	**1990**	MCLAREN-HONDA
1970	LOTUS-FORD	**1991**	MCLAREN-HONDA
1971	TYRRELL-FORD	**1992**	WILLIAMS-RENAULT
1972	LOTUS-FORD	**1993**	WILLIAMS-RENAULT
1973	LOTUS-FORD	**1994**	WILLIAMS-RENAULT
1974	MCLAREN-FORD	**1995**	BENETTON-RENAULT
1975	FERRARI	**1996**	WILLIAMS-RENAULT
1976	FERRARI	**1997**	WILLIAMS-RENAULT
1977	FERRARI	**1998**	MCLAREN-MERCEDES
1978	LOTUS-FORD		

ROLL OF HONOUR

WORLD CHAMPIONSHIP WINS PER DRIVER 1950 - 1998

Some 87 drivers have tasted the victory champagne in a World Championship round between 1950 and 1998 (including Indianapolis from 1950 to 1960). Here, we salute their achievements:

ALAIN PROST (FRANCE)	51
AYRTON SENNA (BRAZIL)	41
MICHAEL SCHUMACHER (GERMANY)	33
NIGEL MANSELL (GREAT BRITAIN)	31
JACKIE STEWART (GREAT BRITAIN)	27
JIM CLARK (GREAT BRITAIN)	25
NIKI LAUDA (AUSTRIA)	25
JUAN- MANUEL FANGIO (ARGENTINA)	24
NELSON PIQUET (BRAZIL)	23
DAMON HILL (GREAT BRITAIN)	22
STIRLING MOSS (GREAT BRITAIN)	16
JACK BRABHAM (AUSTRALIA)	14
EMERSON FITTIPALDI (BRAZIL)	14
GRAHAM HILL (GREAT BRITAIN)	14
ALBERTO ASCARI (ITALY)	13
MARIO ANDRETTI (USA)	12
ALAN JONES (AUSTRALIA)	12
CARLOS REUTEMANN (ARGENTINA)	12
JACQUES VILLENEUVE (CANADA)	11
GERHARD BERGER (AUSTRIA)	10
JAMES HUNT (GREAT BRITAIN)	10
RONNIE PETERSON (SWEDEN)	10
JODY SCHECKTER (SOUTH AFRICA)	10
MIKA HAKKINEN (FINLAND)	9
DENNY HULME (NEW ZEALAND)	8
JACKY ICKX (BELGIUM)	8
RENE ARNOUX (FRANCE)	7
TONY BROOKS (GREAT BRITAIN)	6
JACQUES LAFFITE (FRANCE)	6
RICCARDO PATRESE (ITALY)	6
JOCHEN RINDT (AUSTRIA)	6
JOHN SURTEES (GREAT BRITAIN)	6
GILLES VILLENEUVE (CANADA)	6
MICHELE ALBORETO (ITALY)	5
GUISEPPE FARINA (ITALY)	5
CLAY REGAZZONI (SWITZERLAND)	5
KEKE ROSBERG (FINLAND)	5
JOHN WATSON (GREAT BRITAIN)	5
DAVID COULTHARD (GREAT BRITAIN)	4
DAN GURNEY (USA)	4
BRUCE MCLAREN (NEW ZEALAND)	4

ROLL OF HONOUR

THIERRY BOUTSEN (BELGIUM)	3
PETER COLLINS (GREAT BRITAIN)	3
PHIL HILL (USA)	3
MIKE HAWTHORN (GREAT BRITAIN)	3
DIDIER PIRONI (FRANCE)	3
ELIO DE ANGELIS (ITALY)	2
PATRICK DEPAILLER (FRANCE)	2
FROILAN GONZALEZ (ARGENTINA)	2
JOHNNY HERBERT (GREAT BRITAIN)	2
JEAN-PIERRE JABOUILLE (FRANCE)	2
PETER REVSON (USA)	2
PEDRO RODRIGUEZ (MEXICO)	2
JO SIFFERT (SWITZERLAND)	2
PATRICK TAMBAY (FRANCE)	2
MAURICE TRINTIGNANT (FRANCE)	2
WOLFGANG VON TRIPS (GERMANY)	2
BILL VUKOVICH (USA)	2
JEAN ALESI (FRANCE)	1
GIANCARLO BAGHETTI (ITALY)	1
LORENZO BANDINI (ITALY)	1
JEAN-PIERRE BELTOISE (FRANCE)	1
JO BONNIER (SWEDEN)	1
VITTORIO BRAMBILLA (ITALY)	1
JIMMY BRYAN (USA)	1
FRANCOIS CEVERT (FRANCE)	1
LUIGI FAGIOLI (ITALY)	1
PAT FLAHERTY (USA)	1
HEINZ-HARALD FRENTZEN (GERMANY)	1
PETER GETHIN (GREAT BRITAIN)	1
RICHIE GINTHER (USA)	1
SAM HANKS (USA)	1
INNES IRELAND (GREAT BRITAIN)	1
JOCHEN MASS (GERMANY)	1
LUIGI MUSSO (ITALY)	1
ALESSANDRO NANNINI (ITALY)	1
GUNNAR NILSSON (SWEDEN)	1
CARLOS PACE (BRAZIL)	1
OLIVIER PANIS (FRANCE)	1
JOHNNIE PARSONS (USA)	1
JIM RATHMANN (USA)	1
TROY RUTTMAN (USA)	1
LUDOVICO SCARFIOTTI	1
BOB SWEIKERT (USA)	1
PIERO TARUFFI (ITALY)	1
LEE WALLARD (USA)	1
RODGER WARD (USA)	1

ROLL OF HONOUR

CONSTRUCTORS' RACE WINS 1958 - 1998

Some 25 Constructors have scored victories in World Championship Grands Prix since 1958. The latest to join the honour roll is Jordan in 1998. Ferrari and McLaren are neck-a-neck but watch out for Williams in 1999!

FERRARI	119	MATRA	9
MCLAREN	116	MERCEDES	9
WILLIAMS	103	VANWALL	9
LOTUS	79	MARCH	3
BRABHAM	35	WOLF	3
BENETTON	27	HONDA	2
TYRRELL	23	EAGLE	1
BRM	17	HESKETH	1
COOPER	16	JORDAN	1
RENAULT	15	PENSKE	1
ALFA ROMEO	10	PORSCHE	1
LIGIER	9	SHADOW	1
MASERATI	9		

1999

CHALLENGERS

CAR NO.1

THE CHAMPIONSHIP CHALLENGERS 1999

There are 21 drivers in Mika Hakkinen's mirrors in the 1999 World Championship.

Here we take a brief look at their pedigree, as of the end of the 1998 season, starting with the 1998 Champion himself: MIKA HAKKINEN:

CAR. NO.1 MCLAREN-MERCEDES

MIKA HAKKINEN

Age: 30 (28.09.68)   *Grands Prix:* 112

Born: Helsinki, Finland   *Wins:* 9

Status: Married   *Pole positions:* 10

     Fastest laps: 7

Mika won the inaugural GM Lotus Euroseries in 1988, egged on by former World Champion James Hunt.

The Finn then took the British Formula Three Championship in 1990 with the West Surrey Racing Team.

Team Lotus snapped him up or his first full Formula One season in 1991 and Mika filed a fifth position in only his second race at Imola.

McLaren and Williams fought over him in 1993. The matter went before the contracts recognition board and Ron Dennis secured his signature. But Mika was relegated to the ranks of test driver (not that that did him any harm!) for most of the season, whilst Ayrton Senna and Michael Andretti got to race.

Dennis dispensed with Andretti's services for the last three rounds of 1993 and Mika got his big chance in Portugal, where he qualified third on the grid - ahead of Senna!

Sadly, he crashed out of the race but claimed his first ever podium finish in the following race at Suzuka.

Promoted to team-leader in 1994 after Senna's departure for Williams, Mika's best result was second place in the Belgian Grand Prix.

An emergency apendectomy forced him to miss the Aida Grand Prix in 1995 but he bounced back one week later to take a brilliant second place in Suzuka.

He suffered potentially fatal head injuries in a high speed practice accident in the final round of the series in Adelaide,when his head hit the steering wheel (McLaren would later introduce a padded steering wheel as a result). Only

454

prompt, professional trackside medical aid saved his life and many feared that he would never drive in Formula One again.

But he made a miraculous recovery and finished third four times in 1996.

He took his first pole position at the Nurburgring in 1997 and his first Grand Prix victory at Jerez at the end of the season.

His dominating displays in the 1998 season are well-chronicled and he was a popular and deserving World Drivers' Champion at the end of the year, with nine pole positions and eight wins to his credit.

CAR NO.2

CAR NO.2 MCLAREN-MERCEDES

DAVID COULTHARD

Age: 28 (27.3.71)	**Grands Prix:** 74
Born: Twynholm, Scotland	**Wins:** 4
Status: Single	**Pole positions:** 8
(but very mch in love according to Jacques Villeneuve)	**Fastest laps:** 8

Winner of the inaugural McLaren/Autosport Young Driver of the year award in 1989, Coulthard joined Paul Stewart Racing in 1990 to compete in Formula Vauxhall.

A broken leg, sustained in an accident at Spa saw him finish a disappointed fourth in the British series.

Moved up to Formula 3 and finished runner-up to Rubens Barrichello. But won the prestigious European Masters race at Zandvoort and the Macau Formula 3 classic at the end of 1991.

Moved up to Formula 3000 and took his first win in the category at Enna in Italy.

Undertook a number of test sessions for Williams during the year and was appointed official test driver for 1994.

Then came the awful news of Senna's death at Imola.

David faced the impossible task of replacing the brilliant Brazilian in the Grand Prix team.

He qualified a respectable ninth in his first race in Spain and scored points in the very next round in Canada, where he finished fifth.

He faced a difficult season, as Williams invited Nigel Mansell to drive the car in France and invited their former employee back to replaced David in the last three round of 1994.

But undeterred, young Coulthard qualified third for his final race in Portugal and finished a fine second behind team-leader Damon Hill.

Frank Williams signed him for a full season in 1995. Plagued by persistent tonsillitis during the first half of the season, he was seen to be underperforming by the demanding Williams mafia.

But once the offending tonsils had been removed he returned to form and underlined his liking for the Estoril circuit by taking his first Grand Prix victory there.

CAR NO.2

Aware of the rumours about Jacques Villeneuve's imminent arrival in the team, David signed with McLaren for 1996.

Second place at Monaco in the rain was his best result in '96 but he kicked off the 1997 season with a win in Melbourne and had the satisfaction of winning at Monza too.

1998 could have been his year. But the controversial pact with Hakkinen in Melbourne saw him playing catch-up to his team-mate from day one. And team orders later in the year, meant only one victory, at Imola, and third place overall in the Drivers' Championship.

457

CAR NO.3

CAR NO.3 FERRARI

MICHAEL SCHUMACHER

Age: 30 (3.1.69)

Born: Kerpen, Germany

Status: Married

Grands Prix: 118

Wins: 33

Pole positions: 20

Fastest laps: 35

Yet another former karting star, Michael was signed to drive alongside Heinz-Harald Frenzen in the German Formula 3 Championship in 1989.

The pair finished just one points behind Karl Wendlinger and Jochen Neerpasch signed the three young flyers for his junior sports car team in 1990.

Under the watchful eye of former Grand Prix star and sports car supremo, Jochen Mass, the lads learned the art of controlling the powerful Sauber Mercedes Group C machines.

Michael won the 1990 German Formula 3 Championship with ease and won the end of year showcase Formula 3 races at Fuji and Macau.

Eagle-eyed Eddie Jordan, talent spotter extraordinaire, put him into his first Grand Prix at Spa, in place of the imprisoned Bertrand Gachot.

Michael qualified a startling seventh but his clutch failed on the start-line. Benetton homed in on this 'hot property' and, after much wrangling, Flavio Briatore got his man in time for the 1991 Italian Grand Prix at Monza, where he scored his first points, with a fifth place finish.

He took his first podium finish, third, in he second round of 1992 in Mexico and won his first Grand Prix at Spa later in the season. Third overall in the 1992 Drivers' table, he slipped to fourth in 1993, but added another win to his tally in Portugal.

Eight wins in 1994 saw him take his first World Championship for Benetton (albeit after the contentious coming-together with Damon Hill) and he notched up nine victories in 1995 to secure back-to-back titles.

His move to Ferrari for 25 million dollars in 1996 made the headlines. But he has yet to deliver the goods to the men from Maranello, despite winning 14 races in the last three seasons (and becoming embroiled in still more controversy with Jacques Villeneuve in Estoril in 1997)

CAR NO.4

CAR NO.4 FERRARI

EDDIE IRVINE

Age: 33 (10.11.65)
Born: Newtownards, Northern Ireland
Status: Single

Grands Prix: 81
Wins: 0
Pole positions: 0
Fastest laps: 0

Winner of the 1987 Formula Ford Festival, Eddie found Formula 3 tough in 1988, having to give best to JJ Lehto and Gary Brabham.

Moved up to Formula 3000 and finished third in the 1990 Championship with Eddie Jordan.

Moved on the contest the Japanese Formula 3000 series and drove for Toyota in sports car races in Japan and at Le Mans, where he finished second in 1994.

Drafted into the Jordan Grand Prix team at Suzuka in 1993, he picked up a point in his very first race and signed up for a full season with his compatriot's team for 1994.

Blamed for causing a pile-up in Brazil, poor Eddie collected a three-race ban at the start of the year. Gained his only podium finish for Jordan in the 1995 Canadian Grand Prix.

A surprise selection to partner Schumacher at Ferrari, Eddie struggled through 1996 with just one podium finish to his name in Melbourne. 1997 was a little better, and he finished second in Argentina. 1998 was a whole lot better, with three second place finishes, including an unforgettable one-two behind Schumacher in front of the Ferrari faithful at Monza and five thirds.

CAR NO.5

CAR NO.5 WILLIAMS-MECACHROME

ALESSANDRO ZANARDI

Age: 32 (23.10.66)

Born: Rome

Status: Married

Grands Prix: 25

Wins: 0

Pole positions: 0

Fastest laps: 0

Second in the 1990 Italian Formula 3 Championship, Zanardi stepped up to Formula 3000 for 1991 and narrowly lost out on the title to Christian Fittipaldi. But Eddie Jordan still drafted him into his Formula One team for the last three races of the year to replace the departed Schumacher.

He did not cover himself in glory and had three miserable races for Minardi in 1992, although he did secure a Benetton test contract for the year.

Took the seat vacated by Hakkinen at Lotus in 1993 and scored only Grand Prix point to date in Brazil. Showed plenty of spirit until a massive shunt at Spa landed him in hospital with severe concussion. Saw his seat taken by Pedro Lamy for 1994, but ironically returned to the team when Lamy was injured in a test accident. Headed across the Pond in 1996 and won back-to-back Indy Car titles in 1997 and 1998 in style, which prompted Frank Williams to invite him to lead his team in 1999.

CAR NO.6

CAR NO.6 WILLIAMS-MECACHROME

RALF SCHUMACHER

Age: 23 (30.6.75)

Born: Huerth, Germany

Status: Single

Grands Prix: 33

Wins: 0

Pole positions: 0

Fastest laps: 0

Another karting kid, like big brother Michael, Ralf stepped into a Formula One seat at Jordan after winning the German Formula 3 Championship in 1996.

A podium third place finish in only his third Grand Prix in Argentina in 1997 silenced some of the doubters but he tended to be accident prone. His biggest error came at the first corner at the Nurburgring in '97 when he contrived to crash out over the head of his brother, eliminating himself and Michael.

The arrival of Damon Hill at Jordan in 1998 helped him calm down a little and he scored a memorable second behind Hill at Spa, in Jordan's first ever one-two finish. His third place at Monza saw him climb onto the podium with his brother, another famous first for the history books.

A surprise signing for Williams for 1999, many wonder how the seemingly brash (but innately) shy Schumacher Junior will fare in the chilly environs of the Grove team.

461

CAR NO.7

CAR NO.7 JORDAN MUGEN-HONDA

DAMON HILL

Age: 38 (19.9.60)
Born: London, GB
Status: Married

Grands Prix: 99
Wins: 22
Pole positions: 20
Fastest laps: 19

The 'old man' of Formula One, Damon Hill started his racing career on two wheels before moving into Formula Ford, thence Formula 3 in 1986. Results were not outstanding but he did win the prestigious Grand Prix support race at Silverstone in 1988.

His Formula 3000 career was bereft of a victory but he secured a Williams test contract for 1992. His work-rate and intelligent feed-back led Patrick Head to persuade Frank Williams to sign him as number two to the great Alain Prost for the 1993 Grand Prix season, despite Damon's disastrous half-season with the uncompetitive Brabham in '92.

He took his first podium in the second race of '93 in Brazil and thrilled the fans at Donington by finishing second there. He qualified on pole position for the first time in France, won his very first Grand Prix later in the year in Hungary and finished third in the Drivers' Championship.
Senna's death set a heavy burden on Damon's shoulders in 1994 but he rose to the challenge. He won six races and, thanks to Schumacher's indiscretions, was in with a shout for the Championship at Suzuka. What happened next is well chronicled.

The 1995 season saw Schumacher excel but Hill still finished second in the drivers' title chase. But 1996 was HIS year. Eight wins and nine pole positions gave him the coveted World title, the only son of a former Champion to lift the crown to date.

Booted out by Williams in favour of Frentzen (now ironically his team-mate for 1999), Damon had a lack-lustre season at Arrows, although he nearly won in Hungary.

Much happier in the Jordan team in 1998, he was elated to score the Silverstone-based team's first ever Grand Prix victory at Spa and his determined fourth-place finish in Japan lifted EJ's team into the prized fourth position in the Constructors' table.

CAR NO.8

CAR NO.8 JORDAN MUGEN-HONDA

HEINZ-HARALD FRENTZEN

Age: *31 (18.5.67)*	**Grands Prix:** *81*
Born: *Monchengladbach, Germany*	**Wins:** *1*
Status: *Single*	**Pole positions:** *1*
	Fastest laps: *6*

Although suffering from comparisons with his former Formula 3 and Mercedes team-mate, Michael Schumacher, Heinz-Harald seems much happier now that he has signed for the genial Jordan team for 1999. Winner of the German Opel Lotus series in 1988, this former karting Champion, found himself teamed with Schumacher M. in Formula 3 in 1989 and then in sports cars with Mercedes the following year. Joined Jordan's Formula 3000 effort too in 1990 but struggled throughout the year and did not fare any better in 1991. Out of a drive in 1992, he restored his confidence in Japan, enjoying life in the Japanese Formula 3000 series.

Signed up by Sauber for 1994, Frentzen found himself team-leader after Wendlinger's horrific accident at Monaco.

Frank Williams had approached him after Senna's death but he preferred to remain loyal to Sauber, although there would be only one podium finish to show for his integrity, third at Monza in 1995.

His eventual move to Williams in 1997 was at the expense of Damon Hill and he found himself under pressure to match the mercurial talents of Jacques Villeneuve. He claimed his first and to date his only pole position in Monaco in 1997, hard on the heels of his sole Grand Prix victory in the San Marino Grand Prix.

Like Villeneuve, he fell victim to the Williams' team's inadequacies in 1998 and, his confidence severely undermined returned to the comfort of EJ's team for 1999.

CAR NO.9

CAR NO.9 BENETTON-PLAYLIFE

GIANCARLO FISICHELLA

Age: 26 (14.1.73)
Born: Roma, Italy
Status: Married

Grands Prix: 41
Wins: 0
Pole positions: 1
Fastest laps: 1

A former Italian Formula 3 Champion, Giancarlo came into Formula One in 1996 with the little Minardi team struggling at the back of the grid. Eighth place in Canada was his best result of the season but , once again, Eddie Jordan pounced and lined him alongside another up-and-coming young hopeful, Ralf Schumacher, for the 1997 season.

The two young chargers were bound to clash and they actually did in Argentina, so EJ had to remind them of their responsibilities in no uncertain terms!

Fisichella lined up on the front row alongside Gerhard Berger at Hockenheim and finished an excellent second behind Michael Schumacher at Spa. Contractual obligations saw EJ again forced to relinquish one of his proteges to Benetton for 1998, and he had to watch the young Italian finish second in Monte Carlo and Montreal, where he lead for 24 laps, and take his first ever pole position in Austria.

CAR NO.10

CAR NO.10 BENETTON-PLAYLIFE

ALEXANDER WURZ

Age: 25 (15.2.74)	*Grands Prix:* 19
Born: Waithofen, Austria	*Wins:* 0
Status: Single	*Pole positions:* 0
	Fastest laps: 1

The son of multiple rallycross Champion, Franz Wurz, Alexander established his credentials in sports car racing, including victory in the Le Mans 24 Hours in 1996.

He seized his Formula One chance in 1997, when he replaced the unfit Gerhard Berger, and took a superb third place at Silverstone in only his third Grand Prix.

Teamed with Fisichella at Benetton for 1998, the duo are one of the most exciting young pairings around. Wurz is certainly no respecter of reputations viz his wheel-banging exploits with Schumacher in Monaco in 1998. And he has a very cool head on young shoulders, as he proved when he climbed into the spare car minutes after cartwheeling into the gravel trap at the start of the Canadian Grand Prix.

CAR NO.11

JEAN ALESI

Age: 34 (11.6.64)

Born: Avignon, France

Status: Married

Grands Prix: 151

Wins: 1

Pole positions: 2

Fastest laps: 4

The enigma that is Jean Alesi is often attributed to his Sicilian roots. The 1987 French Formula 3 Champion, took the Formula 3000 title with Eddie Jordan's team in 1989. At the same time, he made a sensational debut in Formula 1 for Tyrrell finishing fourth in the French Grand Prix in his first outing.

Second places in Phoenix and Monaco were enough to convince Ferrari that he was their man and he joined the Maranello team in 1991. It was a relationship which would last five years. But, to everybody's astonishment, Alesi only managed to score one victory in all that time, in Canada in 1995. He delighted the tifosi by claiming his first pole for the Prancing Horse at Monza in 1994.

But Ferrari dispensed with his services in 1996, when Michael Schumacher arrived on the doorstep, and a bewildered Jean found himself 'transferred' to Benetton, together with team-mate Gerhard Berger.

Four second place finishes in 1996 and four more in 1997 were as close as Alesi came to taking the chequered flag for Enstone team and 1998 found him putting the pressure on Johnny Herbert at Sauber. An acknowledged 'Rain master', third place at a rain-soaked Spa was his only podium finish of the year.

CAR NO.12 SAUBER PETRONAS

PEDRO DINIZ

Age: 28 (22.5.70)

Born: Sao Paulo, Brazil

Status: Single

Grands Prix: 66

Wins: 0

Pole positions: 0

Fastest laps: 0

The 'richest man in the Paddock' (next to Bernie Ecclestone that is.), Diniz bought himself a drive in the British Formula 3 Championship in 1991 and found himself suffering by comparison to his team-mates, Rubens Barrichello and Jordi Gene. He soldiered on in 1992 and improved sufficiently to sign up with Forti Corse for Formula 3000. Results were unimpressive but he moved up into Formula One with the Forti team in 1995 - and has been trying to live it down ever since!

He snapped up a chance to drive for Ligier in 1996 and scored his first World Championship point in Spain. He took his millions to Arrows in 1997 and caused something of a stir when he outqualified his team-mate, the reigning World Champion, Damon Hill at Spa and Suzuka. Fifth place at the Nurburgring was his season's best - and he finished fifth in the rain-soaked round at Spa in 1998, again for Arrows, where he again got the better of the much-vaunted Mika Salo on occasion. Has transferred his fortune to Sauber for 1999, much to Tom Walkinshaw's displeasure.

CAR NO.14

CAR NO: 14: ARROWS ARROWS V10

PEDRO DE LA ROSA

Age: 28 (24.2.71)	*Grands Prix:* 0
Born: Barcelona, Spain	*Wins:* 0
Status: Married	*Pole positions:* 0
	Fastest laps: 0

Winner of the Spanish Formula Fiat Championship in 1992, Pedro competed in the British Formula 3 Championship in 1993 and 1994.

A move out to the Orient with the TOM's team, brought him the all-Japan Formula 3 title in 1995, with a total of eight victories. Finished third at Macau the same year, behind Ralf Schumacher and Jarno Trulli. Won the 1997 Formula Nippon title and the Japanese GT Championship and was contracted as test and reserve driver for Jordan. Brings substantial backing from the Spanish fuel giant, Repsol, to the Arrows team.

CAR NO.15

CAR NO: 15 ARROWS ARROWS V10

TARNOSUKE 'TORA' TAKAGI

Age: 25 (12.2.74)
Born: Japan
Status: Single

Grands Prix: **16**
Wins: **0**
Pole positions: 0
Fastest laps: 0

Takagi made his Grand Prix debut for Tyrrell in 1998. He qualified for all 16 races but spent a lot of time exploring the gravel traps of the world. His nickname 'Tora' means tiger in Japanese and he is reputedly very quick (?) if lacking in race-craft. Got the nod from Arrows over the experienced Mika Salo in the week before Melbourne. His new team-mate, Pedro de la Rosa beat him in the 1997 Formula Nippon Championship.

CAR NO.16

CAR NO: 16 STEWART FORD

RUBENS BARRICHELLO

Age: 26 (23.5.72)

Born: Sao Paulo, Brazil

Status: Married

Grands Prix: 96

Wins: 0

Pole positions: 1

Fastest laps: 0

Five times Brazilian karting Champion, Barrichello came to Europe as a 17-year-old and promptly won the Lotus Euroseries in 1990. In 1991 he won the British Formula 3 Championship at his first attempt. Moved into Formula 3000 and was signed up by Eddie Jordan for Formula One in 1993 at the age of 20. Captured the only pole of his career (and the only one for Jordan to date) at Spa in 1994 and claimed his best finish for Jordan in Canada the same year, second in Montreal.

Hankered after the second Ferrari seat for 1996 but was beaten to it by his Jordan team-mate, Eddie Irvine. Signed for Stewart for 1997 and gave the team a fairy-tale second place finish at Monaco in only his fifth outing for the team. Two fifth place finishes were all he had to show for a troubled season in 1998 but has high hopes for 1999 now that Gary Anderson has joined the team.

CAR NO.17

JOHNNY HERBERT

Age: 34 (27.6.64)

Born: Romford, Essex, 129 Grands Prix

Status: Married

Grands Prix:

Wins: 2

Pole positions: 0

Fastest laps: 0

The second most experienced driver in the field, Johnny was one of THE prospects of the 1980s. Winner of the 1985 Formula Ford Festival, Johnny won the 1987 British Formula 3 title for Eddie Jordan. A Benetton test drive was the prize and an option to step up to Formula One with the team in 1989. Herbert decided on an interim season in Formula 3000 but it was cruelly curtailed by an horrific crash at Brands Hatch which smashed his legs and feet and left him with a limp for life.

Benetton honoured their promise and Johnny finished a very brave fourth indeed in his first Grand Prix in Brazil. But the injuries still hindered his performance and he was replaced after failing to qualify in both Canada and Portugal. Three and a half seasons trying to boost the dwindling fortunes at Lotus followed, highlight of which was probably fourth at Silverstone in 1993. In 1995, he found himself back at Benetton, faced with the thankless task of playing back-up to one M. Schumacher. But, luck was on his side. Whilst Messrs Hill and Schumacher were busy eliminating each other at Silverstone and Monza, Johnny slipped through to take the first two Grand Prix victories of his career. And the British crowds gave him a rousing ovation.

Three years at Sauber followed with just two third-place podium finishes, in Monaco in 1996 and Hungary 1997. May be hard-pressed to match Barrichello for speed at Stewart in 1999.

CAR NO.18

OLIVIER PANIS

Age: 32 (2.9.66)

Born: Lyons, France

Status: Married

Grands Prix: 74

Wins: 1

Pole positions: 0

Fastest laps: 0

The 1989 Formula Renault Champion, Panis moved into the French Formula 3 Championship in 1990 Despite five wins in 1992, he lost out on the title to Christophe Bouchut. Came out on top the following year in the International Formula 3000 Championship (heading one David Coulthard in the process).

Given his Formula One chance by Ligier in 1994, he finished in a fine second place in the accident-strewn German Grand Prix. In 1995, he took second place in the final round of the year in Adelaide. His sole Grand Prix victory to date came in the wet at Monaco in 1996 - what a race to take your first win! But he suffered severed leg injuries in Montreal the following season which had started so well for him, with third place in Brazil and second in Spain for his new boss Alain Prost. In 1998, the Prost proved frustratingly unreliable - and Panis still had pins in his legs from his Canadian accident. Is hoping for better luck in 1999.

CAR NO: 19 PROST PEUGEOT

JARNO TRULLI

Age: 24 (13.7.74)

Born: Pescara, Italy

Status: Single

Grands Prix: 30

Wins: 0

Pole positions: 0

Fastest laps: 0

Yet another karting superstar, Trulli won the 1995 German Formula 3 Championship and finished second in the showcase Macau Grand Prix behind Ralf Schumacher.

Flavio Briatore installed him at Minardi at the start of 1997 before he was drafted into the Prost team in place of the injured Panis. Picked up his first Grand Prix points with fourth place in Germany and sensationally led the 1997 Austrian Grand Prix before having to give best to Villeneuve. Sixth place in Belgium was the best he could manage, through no fault of his own, in a 1998 which will probably live in memory as the year he landed on top of Jean Alesi's Sauber in a massive first corner accident in Canada.

CAR NO.20

LUCA BADOER

Age: 28 (25.1.71)	**Grands Prix:** 34
Born: Montebelluna, Treviso, Italy	**Wins:** 0
Status: Single	**Pole positions:** 0
	Fastest laps: 0

Regarded as something of a prodigy in his early days in Italian Formula 3, Badoer won the 1992 Formula 3000 Championship.

Drove for the disastrous new Lola Scuderia Italia team until it folded in 1993 but somehow managed to finish seventh at Imola that year. Luca tested for Benetton in the closed season but was unimpressive and he was left without a drive for the 1994 season. Minardi offered him another chance in 1995 but there were no improvements in results, as the team struggled at the back of the grid. And 1996 was an even bigger nightmare, as he battled to keep out of everybody's way in the ponderous Forti - when he qualified. Now back on the Grand Prix scene after his enforced two-year absence, Badoer will find the going as tough as ever at the back of the grid with Minardi.

CAR NO.21

CAR NO. 21 MINARDI FORD

MARC GENE

Age: 24 (29.3.74)

Born: Sabadell,Spain

Status: Single

Grands Prix: 0

Wins: 0

Pole positions: 0

Fastest laps: 0

Runner up in the 1994 Formula Ford Festival, Marc Gene is the younger brother of former Benetton test driver, Jordi. Drove in British Formula 3 Championship in 1995 and 1996 before moving up to Formula 3000 in 1997. Won Spain's Opel Fortuna series in 1997 with six wins and three poles. Has hefty backing from Spanish telecommunications giant Telefonica. Main claim to fame seems to be that he is the only current Grand Prix driver with a degree, in economics, presented to him by Margaret Thatcher, no less!

CAR NO.22

CAR NO: 22 BAR SUPERTEC

JACQUES VILLENEUVE

Age: 28 (9.4.71)
Born: St. Jean sur Richelieu, Canada
Status: Single

Grands Prix: 49
Wins: 11
Pole positions: 13
Fastest laps: 9

Son of the late, great Gilles, it seems hard to believe that Jacques Villeneuve has only been around the Grand Prix scene for three seasons. Schooled in Switzerland, with homes in Monaco and Canada, 'Happy' Jacques and his multi-colour hair dyes made an immediate impact on Formula One in his debut year 1996.

A former Formula Atlantic Champion back home, he arrived in Europe as the reigning Indy Car Champion and 1996 Indy 500 race winner. He put his Williams on pole at his first race in Melbourne and was leading five laps from the flag, until forced to give best to team-leader Hill because of an oil leak. Four wins in his first Formula One season ensured his place in the motor sport history books and he finished the year runner-up to Hill in the Drivers' table. In 1997, he went one better. Seven wins, 10 pole positions and the World Drivers' Championship in only his second year in Grand Prix Racing (despite the efforts of Michael Schumacher to barge him off the road in Jerez!).

But 1998 was not much fun for the French-Canadian, as he struggled with the uncompetitive Williams. There were just two third place finishes in Germany and Hungary.

No-one was surprised when the worst kept secret in Formula One was revealed towards the end of the year as Jacques announced his intentions of joining up with his former sports teacher, mentor and good friend, Craig Pollock in the brand new, all-singing, all dancing BAR team in 1999.

CAR NO.23

RICARDO ZONTA

Age: 22 (23.3.76)

Born: Curitiba, Brazil

Status: Single

Grands Prix: 0

Wins: 0

Pole positions: 0

Fastest laps: 0

The 'baby' of the Grand Prix scene, now that Esteban Tuero has withdrawn from the fray, Ricardo Zonta won the FIA Formula 3000 Championship in 1997. In 1998, he drove superbly for Mercedes and is currently the reigning GT Champion. McLaren have also been much impressed with his testing ability and he is tipped as a star of the future.

SLOWING DOWN LAP

SLOWING DOWN LAP

Did you know that Jody Scheckter's nickname in his early years in Formula One was 'Fletcher'?

His peers called him that after the young seagull in the cult book 'Jonathan Livingstone Seagull' who kept crash-landing when he was learning how to fly...

The Scheckter brothers,Jody and Ian, and the Fittipaldis, Emerson and Wilson were the last sets of brothers to race against each other in Formula One before the advent of the Schumachers.

Italy's Andrea de Cesaris was known throughout the Paddock as 'de Crasheris' in the eighties (answers on the back of a post-card please)

A young Italian named Mantovani raced for Maserati in the 'fifties. We are unsure of his musical connections in the Moutains, but he was a talented driver who shared a two-litre sports car with Fangio in the 1953 Mille Miglia.

He finished fifth in the Grands Prix at the Nurburgring and in Switzerland in 1954. Sadly, an accident in the non-Championship Valentino Grand Prix in Turin in 1955 caused him the loss of a lower leg, but he returned to take his place as a member of the Italian Sporting Commission.

And on another musical note, one Jesus Iglesias took part in the 1955 Argentine Grand Prix..

An American named Fred Wacker escaped with a 'lightly fractured skull' after crashing in practice for the 1953 Swiss Grand Prix.

He finished sixth in the 1954 Italian Grand Prix at Monza for Gordini...

Did you know that: eight different British drivers have won the World Championship to date.

Only one Argentinian driver has secured the Crown (five times in all) - Juan-Manuel Fangio.

And only one French driver has won the World Drivers' Championship to date (four times in all) Alain Prost.

Only one German driver has won the title (twice) M. Schumacher

And, amazingly, the last Italian driver to lift the laurels was Alberto Ascari, way back in 1953!

Two Finnish drivers have taken the coveted crown to date.

1999 CALENDAR

1999 GRAND PRIX CALENDAR

ROUND 1 AUSTRALIAN GRAND PRIX/MELBOURNE	**7 MARCH**
ROUND 2 BRAZILIAN GRANDPRIX/INTERLAGOS	11APRIL
ROUND 3 SAN MARINO GRAND PRIX, IMOLA	**2 MAY**
ROUND 4 MONACO GRAND PRIX, MONTE CARLO	16 MAY
ROUND 5 SPANISH GRAND PRIX, BARCELONA	**30 MAY**
ROUND 6 CANADIAN GRAND PRIX, MONTREAL	13 JUNE
ROUND 7 FRENCH GRAND PRIX, MAGNY-COURS	**27 JUNE**
ROUND 8 BRITISH GRAND PRIX, SILVERSTONE	11 JULY
ROUND 9 AUSTRIAN GRAND PRIX, A-1 RING	**25 JULY**
ROUND 10 GERMAN GRAND PRIX, HOCKENHEIM	1 AUGUST
ROUND 11 HUNGARIAN GRAND PRIX, HUNGARORING	**15 AUGUST**
ROUND 12 BELGIAN GRAND PRIX, SPA-FRANCORCHAMPS	29 AUGUST
ROUND 13 ITALIAN GRAND PRIX, MONZA	**12 SEPTEMBER**
ROUND 14 LUXEMBOURG GRAND PRIX, NURBURGRING	26 SEPTEMBER
ROUND 15 MALAYSIAN GRAND PRIX, SEPANG	**17 OCTOBER**
ROUND 16 JAPANESE GRAND PRIX, SUZUKA	31 OCTOBER